THE PACIFIC BASIN
A History of Its Geographical Exploration

AMERICAN GEOGRAPHICAL SOCIETY
Special Publication No. 38

CONTRIBUTORS TO THIS PUBLICATION

Kenneth J. Bertrand

Donald D. Brand

Jan O. M. Broek

Robert J. Garry

Chiao-min Hsieh

H. Arnold Karo

Dimitri M. Lebedev and Vadim I. Grekov

Gordon R. Lewthwaite

Nobuo Muroga

Richard I. Ruggles

Raleigh A. Skelton

William L. Thomas, Jr.

Norman J. W. Thrower

Wilcomb E. Washburn

AMERICAN GEOGRAPHICAL SOCIETY · SPECIAL PUBLICATION NO. 38

WILFRID WEBSTER, *Editor of Special Publications*

THE PACIFIC BASIN

A History of Its Geographical Exploration

Edited by

HERMAN R. FRIIS

Senior Specialist in Cartographic Archives
The National Archives and Records Service

Published under the support of the
NATIONAL SCIENCE FOUNDATION

AMERICAN GEOGRAPHICAL SOCIETY

BROADWAY AT 156TH STREET · NEW YORK

1967

COPYRIGHT 1967

BY THE AMERICAN GEOGRAPHICAL SOCIETY

LIBRARY OF CONGRESS CATALOG CARD NUMBER 67–12957

PRINTED IN THE UNITED STATES OF AMERICA

THE LANE PRESS, BURLINGTON, VERMONT

FOREWORD

Geographical exploration has been a major interest of the American Geographical Society since its inception more than a hundred years ago. The story of the Society's wide-ranging participation in exploration and of its extensive research and publication program has been interestingly told by Dr. John K. Wright, a former Director, in his *Geography in The Making: The American Geographical Society, 1851–1951*. To borrow Dr. Wright's apt title, this newest addition to the Society's Special Publication Series is also a book about geography in the making.

The documents cited in the Notes section of this volume make it clear that there is a wealth of source material covering the long and fascinating history of the exploration of the Pacific Basin. What has been lacking is an authoritative recounting of the diverse contributions to this history, from the pre-European "Vikings of the Sunrise" down to the present time. The Society welcomes the opportunity to publish this cooperative effort of fifteen geographers, each a specialist in his phase of the subject. Publication has been made possible by a generous grant from the National Science Foundation.

To Herman R. Friis must go our thanks for his success in enlisting the participation of his authors, for his accomplishment as an Editor—always a difficult task—and for his share in the development and enrichment of the Notes section. Also, it seems particularly appropriate that he has dedicated the book to W. L. G. Joerg. During Mr. Joerg's many years as editor and author on the Society's staff, and later as Chief of the Cartographic Records Division in the National Archives, his abiding interest was the history of discovery and exploration.

Charles B. Hitchcock
American Geographical Society

PREFACE

This book is an outgrowth of a symposium on "Highlights of the History of Scientific Geographical Exploration in Relation to the Development of the Pacific Map," held as part of the Tenth Pacific Science Congress meeting at the University of Hawaii in Honolulu, August 21 to September 6, 1961. Dr. William L. Thomas, Jr., organizer of the Section of Geography of the Congress, invited me to convene and to chair the symposium. Papers were presented by Professors Kenneth J. Bertrand, Donald D. Brand, Robert J. Garry, Chiao-min Hsieh, Gordon R. Lewthwaite, and Richard I. Ruggles, and by Robert H. Randall. I was encouraged by the excellent response to the session to undertake an expansion of the subject of the symposium into a book which would be a history of the principal geographical explorations of the Pacific Basin. Dr. Charles B. Hitchcock, Director of the American Geographical Society of New York, expressed an interest in publishing the final manuscript and the National Science Foundation generously granted funds for publication.

Six of the participants in the symposium have considerably revised and expanded the text and documentation of their papers, and to their chapters have been added the others that round out the book. Final publication of the book has been somewhat delayed because the magnitude of the task was far greater than originally envisioned.

This book has two purposes: to describe and discuss the highlights of the history of significant geographical exploration of the Pacific Basin, and to document the presentation as fully as possible. It is essentially a collection of closely related essays, rather than an organized encyclopedic recitation of the chronology of historical events. The first three chapters are intended to serve as background information for the eleven chapters that follow, and the final chapter summarizes the history of the impact of exploration on the cultures of the West and of the East. Obviously, this book cannot cover all of this history, but I believe it discusses the most significant contributions to our increasingly accurate geographical knowledge of the Pacific Basin.

The text and the Notes which follow it have been edited as nearly as possible in terms of the general practices of the American Geographical Society. However, because the chapters have been prepared by knowledgeable specialists, a certain amount of deference has been given to the wishes of each author in the matter of spelling of geographical and personal names. In a symposium such as this, the problem of current as well as historical spelling of names is acute. An attempt has been made throughout the chapters to identify historical geographical names with their present-day equivalents, which appear within parentheses. All current geographical names in the text have been reviewed by William H. Lloyd, geographer-editor in the Office of Geography, United States Department of the Interior in Washington. This valuable service and careful work by Mr. Lloyd has made it possible to achieve a standard form of spelling for current geographical features and places, a consistent name usage that is official for the United States government. His source has been the more than 3,000,000 names approved by the United States Board on Geographic Names and related supporting evidence on file in the Office of Geography. Most of the gazetteers of areas in and peripheral to the Pacific Basin prepared by the Board and published by the Government Printing Office are out of print, but can be consulted in depository libraries throughout the United States and in libraries in other countries.

The Notes include entries to some 4000 different sources which have been referenced or cited in the text. I felt it incumbent upon me, as Editor, to have the Notes make full use of the rich documentary resources available in Washington. This section, in itself, is a contribution to the bibliography of the history of geographical exploration. Each author has made it a point to include references to the official or most authentic publications about each expedition. All but a few of the entries have been checked against the reference in the Library of Congress and/or in the Smithsonian Institution Library. Whenever possible the Library of Congress (General Reference and National Union) catalog entry has been used, though even here there are inconsistencies because the Library has from time to time modified its procedures, especially as concerns capitalization of foreign words in the main entry.

A large number of persons, especially in libraries, archives, and historical societies, have been helpful in the development of this book. To them the contributors and I owe our thanks. In the National Archives I am indebted to Dr. Wayne C. Grover, former Archivist of the United States (1948–1965), and to Dr. Robert H. Bahmer, Archivist of the United States, for their generosity in permitting me to do so much of the work on this book as time permitted during the course of my duties in the National Archives. Without the continuous cooperation, encouragement, and unfailing support of Dr. Grover and Dr. Bahmer I could not have undertaken and completed this exciting and exacting task. I am also indebted to Dr. G. Philip Bauer, Mr. Herman Kahn, Dr. J. Berton Rhoads, Mr. Sherrod E. East, Miss Grace Quimby, and Miss Camille Hannon in the National Archives, who have helped in many ways.

To Dr. Harold J. Coolidge, Executive Director of the Pacific Science Board in the National Academy of Sciences—National Research Council in Washington and to Mrs. Lenore Smith, his administrative assistant, go my thanks for their unfailing assistance during the Tenth Pacific Science Congress, of which Dr. Coolidge was the Secretary-General. Dr. Coolidge's encouragement of and cooperation in the development of this volume have been steadfast from the beginning.

In the National Science Foundation, Mr. Randall Worthington's patience and cooperation throughout the project have been deeply appreciated. Thanks are also due to Dr. Burton W. Adkinson for his assistance.

It is a pleasure to record my appreciation of the unstinting assistance given by Mrs. Mary H. Huffer, Miss Jean C. Smith, Miss Ruth E. Blanchard, Mr. Jack F. Marquardt, Miss Mary L. Horgan, Mr. A. James Spohn, Mrs. Sue Y. Chen, Mr. Jack Goodwin, and Mr. Charles G. Berger of the Smithsonian Institution Library; by Mr. Mark W. Pangborn, Jr., and Mr. William H. Heers in the United States Geological Library; by Dr. Arch C. Gerlach, Dr. Walter W. Ristow, Mr. Richard M. Stephenson, Mrs. Dorothy W. Bartlett, Mr. Richard S. Ladd, and Mr. Andrew Modelski, in the Division of Geography and Maps in the Library of Congress; by Mrs. Constance Olsen and Mrs. Aleita A. Hogenson in the Freer Gallery of Art; and by Mr. Paul Alexander, Mr. Edward Vogel, Mr. Norman Granims, Mr. Eugene Hall, and Mr. Frank Nicoletti in the Army Map Service, all in Washington.

Dr. Meredith F. Burrill, Director, Mr. Allen Belden, Chief of the Regional Branch, Mr. Ole C. Schelsnes, Chief of the Editing and Processing Section, and Mr. Edwin Bonsack, linguist, of the Office of Geography in the United States Department of the Interior, assisted in determining the spelling of names.

Professor William L. Thomas, Jr., kindly gave permission for the use of his outline map of the Pacific Basin as the base for work-map plotting by the authors and for the preparation of most of the final maps that appear in these pages. Mr. Neal Benfer, oceanographer-editor in the United States Environmental Sciences Administration in Rockville, Maryland, has contributed both information and text that appear in several portions of the book and has offered helpful suggestions on the use of subject matter.

This book has profited greatly from the professional competence of the staff of the American Geographical Society. The maps bear witness to the cartographic skill and sense of design possessed by Mr. Miklos Pinther, of the cartographic department. Most important has been the professional touch of Mr. Wilfrid Webster, Editor of Special Publications of the American Geographical Society. His patience, advice, and know-how have been invaluable, his guidance has been thorough, and his constructive editorial criticism has improved the quality and the content of the book. Mrs. Betty Chagaris capably assisted Mr. Webster in proofreading, and in other facets of the work.

I have been fortunate in having several capable and patient secretaries who, during the past several years, have given time and effort to one or several aspects of the preparation of the manuscript. Mrs. Jean S. Lansche and Mrs. Caroline Receveur assisted in the early phases of work on the book, and Mrs. Suzanne P. Rice assisted in some of the research and in the typing and proofreading of several chapters. During the last year and a half Miss Barbara Jones faithfully and accurately typed several versions of the text, the Notes, and the Index, and assisted in the proofreading. This is indeed an accomplishment when one considers the magnitude of the task and the large number of technical, scientific, and foreign names.

Finally, this book could not have been possible without the contributions by the authors, each of whom has had to take considerable time from other duties and responsibilities. I have the deepest respect for their scholarship, for their cooperation, and for their patience. They are the architects and the builders!

HERMAN R. FRIIS

The National Archives
Washington, D. C.
December, 1966

CONTENTS

1

THE PACIFIC BASIN
AN INTRODUCTION

WILLIAM L. THOMAS, JR.*

The ocean comprising the Pacific Basin is the largest single earth feature. It occupies one third of the earth's surface, an area greater than all the land above sea level on the face of the globe. In no other ocean has it been as difficult for a piece of the earth's crust to raise its head above the great volume of overlying water to become an island. Yet the Pacific Ocean contains about 25,000 islands, more than in all the rest of the world's oceans combined,[1] and totaling more than 1,000,000 square miles of land area. The wonder is not that most islands are small and scattered, but that there are so many of them.

More amazing still, almost all the islands and the continental shores of the Pacific Ocean were discovered and settled in prehistoric time. The European explorers were preceded by Australoids in Australia and Tasmania; by Negroids in southeast Asia, Indonesia, New Guinea, and adjacent islands; by southern Mongoloids in southeast Asia and almost all of the Pacific islands; and by northern Mongoloids in China, Japan, Korea, Siberia, including Aleuts and Eskimos in western and northern Alaska, and Amerindians from Alaska to Tierra del Fuego, the whole length of the Pacific coast of the Americas.[2]

The story of scientific geographical exploration in the Pacific Basin is essentially a record of investigations by the late-comers, the Caucasoids from Europe and North America, after economic and religious interests had stimulated the age of European discovery in the Pacific Ocean.[3] Science was most fully developed in Europe; organized, cumulative, and continually corrected knowledge had and continues to have great economic and strategic value.[4] The uniqueness of the Pacific Basin still remains a challenge to man's understanding of the planet he calls home. But in terms of the total human story one should remember that the "Age of European Discovery" came late, and that it was mostly a *re*-discovery, albeit using advanced techniques for analysis and recording most information so that it has now become part of public knowledge.[5]

The sheer magnitude of the Pacific Basin, the extreme ranges of latitudes of its continental margins, and the widespread distribution of its islands are among the factors contributing to the great variety of physical-biotic environments and human habitats.[6] The purpose of this chapter is to introduce the Pacific Basin as we know it today, by surveying the physical differences in location, size, origin, composition, and shapes of the major landform features; by portraying the distribution of climatic types, vegetation associations, and life zones; and by outlining in broad terms the regional patterns of habitats suitable for occupance by man.

---

*DR. THOMAS is professor of anthropology and geography and chairman of the department, California State College at Hayward.

There is no shortage of general works describing the Pacific Basin.[7] Some writings focus on the vast ocean, its physical and biotic qualities and/or problems in navigation.[8] Others consider the island world,[9] or enlarge Oceania to include Australia and New Zealand.[10] Still others are concerned with peoples and customs and politics. The best over-all synthesis on the Pacific and its human occupance and utilization is Freeman.[11]

ARRANGEMENT OF LAND

The Pacific Rim

Any consideration of the Pacific Basin must begin with its immensity and great distances. It is 9200 statute miles from Bering Strait on the north to the Antarctic Circle. The Pacific is 10,400 statute miles wide at the equator from Ecuador to Indonesia, and it is 12,300 miles, almost half the distance around the earth, from Singapore to Panama.

The Pacific Basin is ringed by mountain barriers thrown up along one of the earth's great zones of crustal instability and marked by more than four hundred active volcanoes.[12] On the east the Andes and Rocky Mountains, comprised of thickly folded sediments and abundant volcanic material all strongly faulted, parallel a coastline that is generally regular, except for the fiord coasts of southern Chile and of North America from Seattle northward, with their numerous near-coastal islands and sheltered inlets.[13] The arc of the Aleutian Islands is the northernmost of a series of island chains that convexly face the western Pacific along the Asian continent. The Aleutians extend nearly to the peninsula of Kamchatka. Southward follow the arcuate structures of the Kurils, Japan, the Ryukyus, the Philippines, Indonesia (the zone of intersection with the Asian arcs from the Himalayas through mainland Southeast Asia), and New Guinea, north of Australia. Between these curving festoons of islands and their adjacent mainlands and comprising the several arms of the western Pacific, are a series of marginal seas: Bering, East China, South China (the Asian equivalent of the Mediterranean), Coral, and Tasman seas, Sea of Okhotsk, Sea of Japan, and eight smaller seas among the Philippines and Indonesia. Vening-Meinesz[14] considered the earth's mantle to be drifting westward, away from the island arcs off Asia, and toward the great oceanic trenches which, over long distances, are situated at the foot of the western continental slope of the Americas.

The Empty Areas

The most characteristic feature of the Pacific Basin is its emptiness of land. The greatest of the empty areas has the shape of a huge horseshoe open to the west. One arm extends across the North Pacific from Japan to North America, swings south through the eastern Pacific, and thence westward from southern South America to New Zealand north of Antarctica.

Another way to visualize the emptiness of the Pacific is to draw on a map the great circle or shortest distance route diagonally from Tokyo, Japan (about latitude 36° N.) to central Chile (about latitude 30° S.). Only the Galapagos Islands and a few small islands near the American coast lie northeast of such a line. Further, in the

South Pacific, between latitude 30° S. and Antarctica, there is a great void of islands across 90 degrees of longitude between New Zealand and Chilean territories.

THE ISLANDS: ARCS, CLUSTERS, AND ISOLATES

All of the larger island masses are situated in the western or southern Pacific, usually as parts of island chains relatively close to the Asian or Australian continents and generally forming arcs curved convexly toward the open Pacific. Deep-sea furrows are situated along their outer, or convex, sides. The island arcs may be single arcs (such as the Bonins or the Marianas), pseudo-single (such as the Aleutians and Kurils, which have double parallel arcs for short distances), or double arcs (such as the Ryukyus or in Indonesia, where the inner arc is always volcanic). Japan and the Philippines are exceptional insofar as several arcs meet to form an intricate pattern.[15]

Though the many islands in the huge ocean represent a tremendous fragmentation, their arrangement is not just a random scatter. Almost all of the islands of the Pacific lie between latitudes 30° N. and 30° S., extending east-southeastward from mainland southeast Asia in the form of an elongated v, which tapers to a point at Easter Island (latitude 27° S.). Most islands are close enough to others that man tends to group them into island clusters or archipelagos and give them names which distinguish one group from another. From west to east across the Pacific are such island groups as the Philippines, Indonesia, New Guinea (and adjacent islands), Palau Islands, Yap Islands, Volcano Islands, Bonin Islands, Mariana Islands, Caroline Islands, Bismarck Archipelago, Solomon Islands, Santa Cruz Islands, New Caledonia and the Loyalty Islands, New Hebrides, Marshall Islands, Gilbert Islands, New Zealand, Fiji Islands, Ellice Islands, Tonga Islands, Samoa Islands, Phoenix Islands, Tokelau Islands, Hawaiian Islands, Line Islands, Cook Islands, Îles Tubuai (or Austral Islands), Society Islands, Tuamotu Archipelago, Marquesas Islands, and the Galapagos Islands. Wholly isolated islands, more than 400 statute miles from any other, are much fewer. Outstanding examples are, from east to west, Clipperton Island, Easter Island, and Isla Sala y Gomez, Johnston Island, Norfolk Island, Marcus Island, and Parece Vela.

ISLAND ORIGINS AND SIZES

THE "ANDESITE LINE"

The most significant regional distinction in the Pacific Basin is that established by the so-called "Andesite Line" which separates the deeper Pacific from the partially submerged continental areas on its margins. The andesite line follows the eastern edge of New Zealand, Tonga, Fiji, the Solomons, Bismarck Archipelago, New Guinea, Yap, Mariana Islands, Japan, the Kurils, and Kamchatka.[16] Similarly, the andesite line passes south of the Aleutian arc and across the Gulf of Alaska, thence westward of the islands off the California coast and along the western edge of the Albatross Cordillera, a sickle-shaped curve extending 8000 miles from the coast of Mexico nearly to New Zealand.[17]

Within the closed loop of the andesite line lies the real Pacific Basin with its deep troughs, submerged volcanic mountains, and oceanic volcanic islands predominantly composed of heavy dark basalt, which also comprises the platforms capped by reef corals and atolls. Outside the line, including all of New Zealand, New Guinea, Indonesia, the Philippines, and Japan (which represent the far eastward extension of the continental blocks of Australia and Asia), the islands are composed of mixed rock types characteristic of continental masses and markedly deformed by folding and faulting. They contain such ancient metamorphic rocks as slate, gneiss, and schist; such sediments as coal and clay; and such intrusive and volcanic rocks as andesite, high in silica and alumina.

VOLCANOES AND EARTHQUAKES

The distinction between basaltic and andesitic lavas is chemically small, but the types of volcanic activity associated with them are very different.[18] Floods of quietly flowing basaltic lavas have poured out of rifts to build up huge domical volcanic mountains, whose eroded summits comprise such island chains or clusters as the Samoa, Hawaiian, Society, and Marquesas islands. The vast bulk of these mountain masses are below sea level; for example, Mauna Kea (13,784 feet altitude) and Mauna Loa (13,680 feet) on the island of Hawaii rise from ocean depths of 18,000 feet. Volcanism along the rim outside of the andesite line is largely explosive. The more viscid siliceous lava explodes under gas pressure, and the considerable fragmentary debris builds steep-sided ash cones. Examples of the violence of explosive volcanoes are the famed eruptions of Tamboro (Gunung Tambora), on Sumbawa Island east of Java, and Krakatau (Pulau Rakata) in the Sunda Strait between Sumatra and Java. When Tamboro erupted in 1815 it blew between 28 and 50 cubic miles of lava, ash, and dust into the air. When Krakatau exploded in 1883, the noise was heard in Australia, 1500 miles away, and its dust, thrust into the upper atmosphere, extended around the world.

The andesite line is defined on the basis of underlying magmas and their volcanic products, but the distinction is fundamental. Within the line is the largest homogeneous unit of strong individuality on the earth's surface, a region which is so peacefully at rest that no tectonic earthquakes originate within it, save for the moderate activity associated with the rift structures of the Hawaiian Islands. In direct contrast to this passivity, the Pacific rim outside of the line is not only the world's greatest belt of explosive volcanic activity, but also the most prevalent zone of seismic disturbance. This circum-Pacific zone includes about 80 percent of the shallow shocks, 90 percent of the intermediate shocks, and all of the deep shocks ever recorded. The annual number of true earthquakes around the Pacific is about one million; the annual average includes two great shallow shocks and seventeen other major earthquakes, of which about five are intermediate and one is deep.[19]

Neither volcanic nor seismic activity is evenly distributed, nor are the areas of these activities everywhere the same. Shallow seismicity is highest in Japan, western Mexico, Melanesia, and the Philippines; South America has an exceptionally high proportion of great shocks. The island arcs of the western Pacific and the mountainous fringe of the American continents are the results of Tertiary to Recent crustal upheavals; earthquakes and much volcanic activity are secondary features which accompany active folding and faulting.[20] Pacific earthquakes have caused even more damage than volcanic eruptions. Probably the most devastating earthquake was that in Japan in 1703, which killed about 200,000 people. The Tokyo earthquake of 1923 killed half this number. Submarine earthquakes are the cause of tsunamis, or seismic waves in the ocean. A series of these waves, perhaps as much as 100 feet high, followed the Krakatau explosion in 1883 and swept over the shores of nearby Java and Sumatra, destroying villages and drowning more than 30,000 people. The tsunami of April 1, 1946, which struck the north and east coasts of the Hawaiian Islands, killed more than 150 persons and resulted in $25,000,000 in property damage.

THE OCEAN FLOOR

The last great frontier of the earth's physical geography is the vast, almost unknown floor of the oceans, about which we know much less than we do about the face of the moon. Fifteen elongated trenches in the Pacific mark the seaward extent of the island arcs and the centers of most intensive earthquake activity. The deepest trenches all have about the same maximum depth, as the foundering sea floor being dragged down into the earth stabilizes at about 35,000 feet below sea level. The Albatross Cordillera is another gigantic feature whose crest lies an average of two miles above the floor of the Pacific, yet remains 1.5 miles beneath the ocean's surface, except where volcanic islands such as Easter Island, Isla Sala y Gomez, and the Galapagos Islands thrust upward atop the bulge of the rise.[21]

Nearly 200 flat-topped submarine peaks, termed tablemounts or guyots, have been discovered beneath the North Pacific.[22] These were chains of basaltic islands in Cretaceous time whose tops were wave-eroded to relatively flat banks on which reef fauna found lodgement. The tops of these truncated volcanoes now lie at depths of 700 to 900 fathoms as a result of large-scale subsidence of the sea bottom. Due to submergence these fossil landforms are preserved as the oldest uneroded mountains on earth, disturbed only by gentle currents and the slow rain of shallow water debris from above.[23]

CALCAREOUS REEFS

The most distinctive feature of the tropical Pacific is the presence of numerous calcareous reefs, built by coral and calcareous algae which require warm, relatively shallow, clear saline water. The principal development of coral reefs in the world is in the Pacific Ocean and its connecting Asian seas. Reef formations are more numerous in the central and western parts of oceans because of the movements of warm ocean currents, and weakly developed in the eastern parts of oceans because of lower water temperatures due to the equatorward movement of cool ocean currents and the upwelling of colder water from oceanic depths. This is the reason why the volcanic Galapagos Islands are not fringed by coral reefs.

Coral is the skeleton of a fleshy polyp, a marine animal which secretes lime from sea water. Most such polyps live in large colonies with their skeletons connected to one another and overlying the calcareous remains of their predecessors. But corals are not the only reef-building organisms. Mixed among them are calcareous algae, principally of the genera *Porolithon* and *Halimeda*, which encrust and fill up the pores and crevices of the coral, converting the whole mass into more solid limestone.

Vigorous reef-forming corals may endure surface water temperatures as low as 18.2° C. (64.7° F.), but generally a temperature of 22.8° C. (73° F.) or above is considered necessary. Most corals thrive at depths of less than 15 fathoms (90 feet), while maximum depths of living reef corals are generally between 20 and 25 fathoms (120 to 150 feet), since sunlight penetration and temperatures decrease with depth. Corals cannot gain a foothold on a muddy sea floor because either the sediments smother the coral polyps or the turbidity cuts down the amount of light necessary for photosynthesis of the symbiotic algae. Corals also require a salinity at least 80 percent that of sea water; hence, reefs are also absent near river mouths where the sea is diluted by fresh water.

During 1951, two deep holes were drilled through the calcareous reef of Eniwetok to the incredible depths of 4222 and 4610 feet before encountering volcanic bedrock. This scoriaceous olivine basalt, associated with tuff and volcanic glass, was the first proof that volcanoes form the bases of the oceanic islands of the Pacific within the andesite line. The hundreds of calcareous reefs were formed in Tertiary time, not upon wave-eroded platforms (which became submerged tablemounts) but atop volcanic mountains, whose higher elevations delayed their subsidence beneath the sea and allowed more time for the calcareous reef organisms to gain a foothold and grow upward as rapidly as the rate of subsidence of the volcanic basement. The upper seaward slopes of calcareous reef islands are generally steeper than the repose angle of loose sediments. This is a consequence of upward growth by the reef-building organisms from a subsiding base now too deep for such growth to take place. Thus, the present existence of calcareous reef islands depends primarily, for their volcanic platforms, upon pre-Pleistocene geologic history and the character of the ocean floor, and secondarily, for their surface form, upon late Pleistocene to Recent geologic history and the existence of reef-building organisms.[24]

THE PLEISTOCENE HERITAGE

The distribution and extent of land in an ocean area depends in great part upon the "accident" of sea level. The height of the sea with respect to that of rock masses comprising islands is related not solely to localized tectonic activity but also to the fluctuations of continental glaciers which "lock up" water elsewhere on the earth. Thus, the numbers, sizes, and distribution of islands have varied with the successive falls and rises of the sea during Pleistocene glacial and interglacial stages.[25] At low sea stands during glacial periods, New Guinea was reunited with Australia; Java, Sumatra, and Borneo again became part of the Asian mainland; and Bering Strait became an isthmus. Concurrently, there were many more oceanic islands—hilly, reef-fringed, or barrier-encircled. Sub-aerial erosion, principally chemical solution by sea water, lowered the exposed calcareous reefs down to or near to the Pleistocene sea surface. Then the last great rise of sea level permitted the upbuilding of calcareous reef rims around enclosed central lagoons.[26]

ISLAND TYPES

Islands in the Pacific range in size from New Guinea and Borneo (the world's second and third largest, respectively, after Greenland) to the smallest of rocks visible above the high-tide line. In the whole of the North Pacific, between the Hawaiian Islands and the island arcs from Japan to Indonesia, there are only three islands larger than 100 square miles: Guam (215 square miles); Babelthuap in the Palaus (153 square miles), and Ponape in the eastern Carolines (127 square miles). By contrast, the 1156 islets of the Marshall Islands have a combined land area of less than 70 square miles, or 38 acres each on the average. South of the equator and east of New Guinea and Australia, the largest islands are North Island and South Island of New Zealand. There are, in addition, a number of islands more than 3000 square miles in extent, among them New Britain, New Ireland, Bougainville, New Caledonia, and Viti Levu, all outside of the andesite line. Again, by contrast, the oceanic Tuamotu Archipelago, farther east, consists of some 75 main groups of islets; but the total land area adds up to only 330 square miles.

Throughout the Pacific are four distinct types of islands, each with some variations that give rise to minor types:

Low islands of carbonate rock: These islands are generally very small in land area, but are the most distinctive, numerous, and widespread in the tropical Pacific. Examples are found in the Tuamotu Archipelago and Society, Cook, Line, Tokelau, Phoenix, Ellice, Gilbert, Marshall, and Caroline islands.

Islands of elevated reef rock: These are usually only slightly larger than the low islands. Examples are found in the Fijis, Loyalty Islands, central and northern Palaus, Fais, Ocean Island, Nauru, Niue, and Makatea in the Tuamotus.

Volcanic islands: These are generally small to intermediate size, such as Galapagos Islands, Hawaii, Samoa Islands, the Marquesas, Kusaie, Ponape, and the northern Mariana Islands.

Islands containing ancient "continental" rocks: These include the largest of the Pacific islands, all outside of the andesite line, from Fiji to Japan, including Babelthuap and Yap islands in the western Carolines.

ISLAND LANDFORMS

The landforms of the Pacific islands outside of the andesite line are as varied as those of any other great expanse of the earth's surface. Some are low-lying plains; others are plateaus or cuestas; still others are mountains, flat-topped, serrate, peneplained, or conical. Some present, on a small scale, the complex structures of great mountain ranges. Likewise, in degree and manner of erosion, the islands range from newly made masses through remnants in all stages of dissection to submarine banks from which all land has been stripped away and on which corals have established themselves. The classic distinction among Pacific islands landforms is between "high" islands of continental or volcanic type and "low" islands of carbonate rock. On the former almost any type of landform may somewhere be found: deep canyons, broadly sloping valleys, and flat floodplains. The sea is bordered by extensive coastal plains or narrow shelves or it meets the land in cliffs of impressive height.[27]

"High" Islands: "Continental" and Volcanic

New Guinea comprises the best example of a large continental island.[28] It has an area of about 312,000 square miles and is approximately 1300 miles long by nearly

500 miles wide at its central portion. The most distinctive major landform feature is the towering snow-capped cordillera that dominates almost the whole length of the island's interior, together with the dissected high central plateaus. To the north and south are vast, swampy lowlands covered with dense swamp forests. The coastal pattern is that of alternating small coastal plains, low river terraces, high marine benches, coastal hills, and steep mountain slopes plunging into the sea.

Viti Levu, the largest of the Fiji Islands, is another example of a continental island.[29] Its area of 4053 square miles is smaller than New Caledonia[30] or New Zealand,[31] yet it forms more than half of the surface area of the Fiji group and is one of the larger islands in the Pacific. Viti Levu has four types of landforms: the high central plateau, the mountain ranges, large areas of hilly uplands, and coastal areas of low-lying plains and river deltas.

All of the large islands of the Pacific lie west of, and outside, the andesite line and are continental in type. The islands between New Zealand and the Philippines thus include a far greater range of landforms, climates, soils, and natural minerals than do the clusters of small oceanic "low" islands of the central Pacific. This major difference in geologic structure is important, for it explains why the islands of the western Pacific have much greater natural resources than those of the east.

Of the volcanic islands, the Hawaiian chain is probably the best known, but there are many more scattered through the southern and western Pacific. On these high islands, precipitous cliffs rise from exposed windward shores where wave erosion has cut into lava slopes which once descended gradually to the sea. Among the remarkable landform features are the large deep valleys with amphitheater heads that rise steeply from a nearly flat floor. Cliffs of such valleys on Tahiti and Molokai tower above 3000 feet. Occasionally, amphitheaters may coalesce to form low passes. Other examples of volcanic high islands are five island groups in the Carolines: from east to west, Kusaie, Ponape, Truk, Yap, and Palau. Each consists of more than a single island, but with varying degrees of complexity. The western two (Yap and Palau) are composed of old volcanic lavas and ancient metamorphic rock that testify to their continental nature; the others are composed chiefly of basaltic lava in keeping with their location inside of the andesite line. Most volcanic islands in the Pacific realm are ringed by coral reefs, either as fringing reefs adjacent to the shore, or, less frequently, as barrier reefs lying offshore.

"Low" Islands: Elevated and Sea-Level Reefs

Tayama has provided the most thorough morphological classification of coral reefs, which comprise the low islands of the Pacific.[32] He distinguishes among eight forms (Fig. 1) which intergrade from one to the other:

Apron reef: The initial stage of a fringing reef, attached to part of an island but occupying discontinuous small areas.

Fringing or shore reef: A coral reef in contact with a coast, continuous or almost continuous, and covering a substantial area.

Almost barrier reef: A coral reef separated from the island it surrounds by a shallow, narrow lagoon, generally 15 to 60 feet deep, which forms the so-called "boat channel."

Barrier reef: A coral reef surrounding an island or islands like a breakwater, and including a lagoon between the island and the reef.

Almost atoll: A barrier reef around a central island or islands that occupy a much smaller area than the lagoon.

Atoll: A coral reef rim embracing a lagoon but lacking any central island; instead, volcanic material forms the foundation of the reef.

Almost table reef: Like the atoll, it encircles a lagoon, but the ratio of surface area of lagoon to reef-flat is smaller than in an atoll, and the lagoon is shallower.

Table reef: A small coral reef with neither central island nor lagoon.

The distinction between high islands as volcanic and low islands as coral reef forms is too simple, for there are many combinations of the two, as described above. Moreover, these combinations are further varied by being elevated above the sea as raised reefs. Thus there are partly raised and fully raised barrier reefs, almost atolls, atolls, and table reefs, as well as tilted forms with one side elevated and the other sunk beneath the sea.

The Atoll Environment

Atolls comprise the most numerous and distinctive form of calcareous reef. Bryan listed 309 in the Pacific, more than three times the number in all the rest of the world's oceans combined.[33]

Atolls are reefs of organic limestone that are partly, intermittently, or completely covered by water, and on which there are discontinuous, low sandy islets resulting from the accumulation of limestone debris, loose or consolidated, and occasional remnants of former high reef surfaces. These islets are usually not more than 5 to 10 feet above high-tide level, except for storm-built rubble ridges and wind-deposited dunes which rise but a few feet higher. The atoll is thus a limestone cap perched on the top of an underlying volcanic mountain or cluster of cones. This cap is commonly bowl-shaped at the surface with a ringlike ridge or reef enclosing a shallow body of water or lagoon, and in turn surrounded by the open sea.[34]

The primary distinctions to be noted on an atoll (Fig. 2) are the outer slope, reef front, seaward reef margin, reef flat, beach, islets, lagoon reef margin, lagoon slope, and lagoon floor.[35] Islets are most frequent on the eastern or windward sectors of the reef rim. Almost three-quarters of all atolls have islets on less than one-half of their circumference. The largest and widest islets coincide with wide portions of the reef where sharp outward bends occur. Reef widths tend to be greater in the general direction of prevailing winds, currents, and waves—the areas of greatest reef growth. Conversely, deep passes through reef rims, navigable to ocean-going vessels, occur most frequently on the leeward sides of atolls where reef growth is less vigorous or is inhibited.[36]

Waves commonly break on the seaward reef margin and water flows from the sea to the lagoon and back to the sea over the reef flat or through gaps in it. The flow may be in or out with the tides, or in over the windward and out over the leeward sides. The only natural source of fresh water on any atoll islet is the rain that falls there. If not caught on and evaporated from the plants or ground surface, it seeps quickly into the porous sediments. Larger islets are highly permeable and may contain at

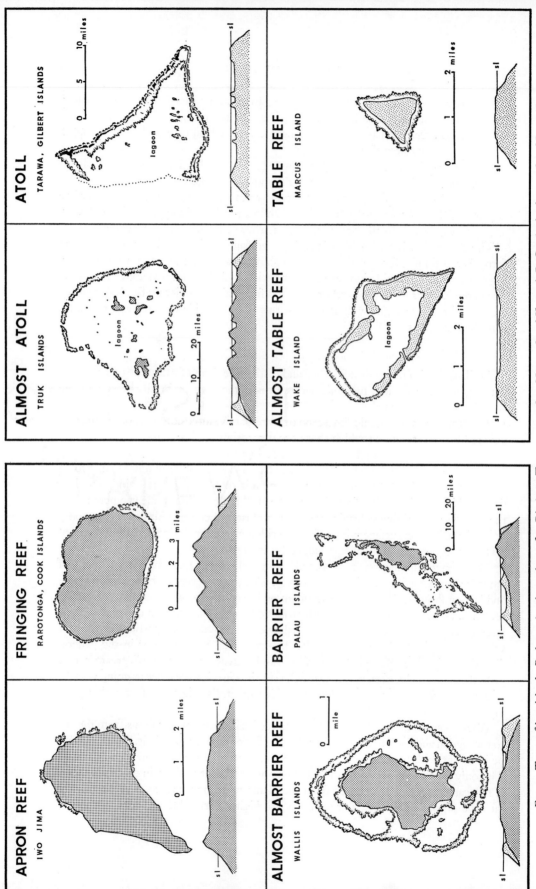

APRON REEF
IWO JIMA

FRINGING REEF
RAROTONGA, COOK ISLANDS

ALMOST ATOLL
TRUK ISLANDS

ATOLL
TARAWA, GILBERT ISLANDS

lagoon

ALMOST BARRIER REEF
WALLIS ISLANDS

BARRIER REEF
PALAU ISLANDS

ALMOST TABLE REEF
WAKE ISLAND

lagoon

TABLE REEF
MARCUS ISLAND

FIG. 1. Types of low islands. Redrawn by the author, after Risaburo Tayama, 1952 [see Note 32] and Kenneth B. Cumberland, 1956 [see Note 10].

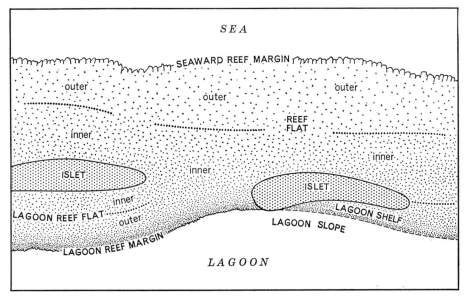

FIG. 2. Prominent landform features of an atoll. Redrawn by the author, after J. I. Tracey, Jr., P. E. Cloud, Jr., and K. O. Emery, 1955 [see Note 35].

shallow depth a lens of fresh ground water floating upon the underlying salt water and retarded by friction from free diffusion with it.[37]

CLIMATIC REGIONALIZATION IN THE PACIFIC

All kinds of climate, from tropical warmth to polar cold, are found in the Pacific. There are the foggy, wind-swept outer Aleutians, the contrasting seasonality of Japan between snowy winters and warm humid summers, the constant steaminess of the lowland interiors of Borneo or New Guinea, and the mild and salubrious climate of Hawaii and other mid-ocean islands. At or near the equator, temperatures remain nearly the same throughout the year, but everywhere else there are definite seasons. These differing climatic patterns are superimposed like a mantle over all islands of whatever origin, location, size, shape, and composition.

CIRCULATION REGIONS

There are five different kinds of atmospheric circulation regions (Fig. 3), within each of which are certain unique climatic features: (1) the "middle latitude" westerlies, (2) the trades, (3) the monsoons, (4) the doldrums (intertropical trough), and (5) the typhoons, which partly overlaps the others.[38]

1. In the middle-latitude realm occur the extra-tropical cyclones with their distinct frontal systems and the variety of weather patterns that they subsume: cold waves, general rains from occluded systems and from warm fronts, sharp cold-front storms, and the like.

2. The trade winds areas are those in which winds from the northeast quadrant in the Northern Hemisphere and from the southeast quadrant in the Southern Hemisphere occur at least 70 percent of the time in every month of the year, and more than

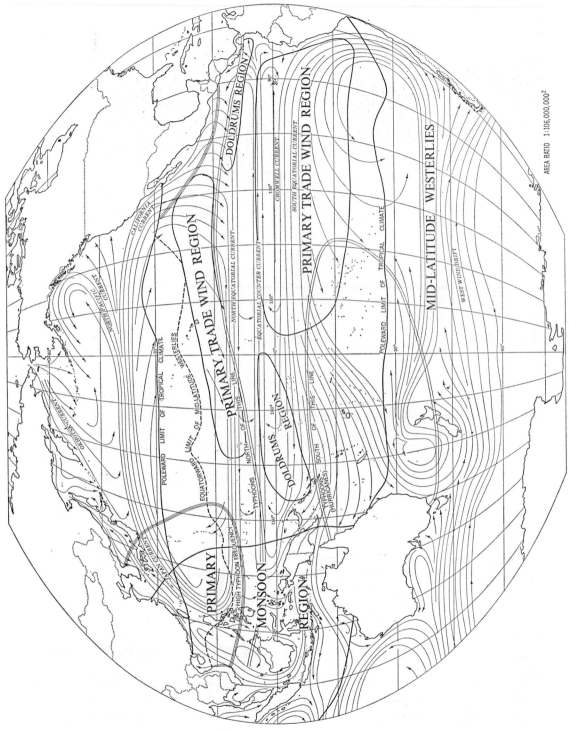

FIG. 3. Distribution of atmospheric circulation regions and ocean current circulations of the Pacific.
After David L. Phiseoverbook, 1958 [Note 38, p. 8] and John A. Knauss, 1961 [Note 42, pp. 106–107].

AREA RATIO 1:106,000,000²

85 percent during the summer months. On high islands within these regions, windward and leeward become directions of climatic importance, the windward coasts being cloudy and wet and the leeward coasts relatively cloudless and dry. The general climatic regime for the trade-wind regions is one of rather constant prevailing winds with scattered light or moderate showers and occasional rainless periods of a few to many days, interrupted periodically by rainy spells that are sometimes very pronounced and last for three to five days.

3. The monsoon region is in the far western Pacific between northern Australia and southern Japan.[39] The outstanding climatic characteristics are the seasonal reversal of winds and the marked seasonality of cloudiness and rainfall. Because the monsoon air masses contain waves and eddies, the rainy season is an alternation of spells of heavy and prolonged rains, moderate interrupted rains, and rainless weather sometimes with virtually clear skies. However, the heavy rains are far more prolonged and intense than in any other part of the tropics except for rain spells yielded by typhoons.

4. The doldrums regions are more poorly defined than the others. They are regions within which horizontal temperature gradients are insignificantly small and within which the rainfall is well distributed throughout the year. They are also regions of high humidity, considerable cloudiness, and low wind speeds.

5. The fifth circulation region is where typhoons occur. The tremendous winds and torrential rains generated by these storms are a serious land-use hazard.[40] Whereas the rainfall contribution may form a considerable part of the total annual precipitation, it may be of little value where run-off is high.

The five core regions outlined on Figure 3 are not mutually exclusive; neither do they cover all of the tropical Pacific. The intervening areas are transition zones, wherein characteristics fluctuate seasonally from those of one to another of the core regions.[41]

OCEAN CURRENTS

The currents in the surface layer of the ocean (Fig. 3) are characterized by vast closed anticyclonic eddies in the subtropical and tropical latitudes, and by smaller cyclonic eddies in the north temperate latitudes and the high southerly latitudes.[42] The wind-driven circulation of the surface waters involves a layer about 500 feet deep over almost the whole expanse of ocean. In the region of the westerlies, where strong west winds, stable in direction, prevail throughout almost the whole year, the circulation penetrates to 650 feet or more. But in the counter-current region of the doldrums, where light and unstable winds prevail, the wind-driven circulation is limited to depths of 150 to 250 feet.

At greater depths, the circulation is set up mainly by differences in ocean water density. The general circulatory pattern of the Pacific Ocean waters begins with the import of water from the Indian Ocean in the high southerly latitudes. By way of deep currents and bottom currents such water reaches the northern part of the Pacific and into the Sea of Okhotsk and Bering Sea. Gradually transformed, it rises in cyclonic eddies to the surface and turns back into the North Pacific. In the convergence zones these waters descend into the deep strata and are carried by the upper deep current to the south, where the general eastern transport in the high southerly latitudes takes them out into the Atlantic Ocean. The newest discoveries in oceanographic exploration are the equatorial undercurrent (Cromwell Current) and the south equatorial countercurrent.[43]

DISTRIBUTION OF RAINFALL

The climatic element of greatest variability in the Pacific is rainfall (Fig. 4). There are a number of desert and semiarid islands; many more are perennially very wet; on others, water availability is a feast-or-famine proposition, depending upon the season. Within the tropics, the seasonal and annual patterns of rainfall provide the best frame of reference for further differentiating the regional climates of the Pacific.[44]

Not quite half of the land area of the tropics is truly humid and a little more than half is seasonally wet-and-dry. In general, the truly humid region is centered at or near the equator and the wet-and-dry regions lie poleward on either side. Except at the very cores of the truly humid tropics, periodic drought is a common phenomenon; some islands are very dry indeed. The islands of the equatorial eastern Pacific have low rainfall: Canton, Enderbury, Howland, and Baker are virtually desert islands. On many atolls, especially those just south of the equator, as are the southern Gilbert and Phoenix islands, when conditions of the dry southeast trades prevail, more than a year will elapse with no rain at all; at other times, when conditions of the doldrums are dominant, more than the annual average may fall in one month.

CLIMATIC PATTERNS

Climatologically, the western part of the Pacific is basically different from its eastern sector (Fig. 4). The eastern portion, located at the root region of the subtropical anticyclone, is characterized by cold ocean currents, upper-air subsidence, marked trade inversion, stratiform clouds at night, and persistent drought, especially in the summer. Toward the far west, the water temperature rises, the trade inversion weakens, the air becomes conditionally or convectively unstable, cumulus clouds dominate, and rainfall, usually with a summer maximum, is abundant.[45]

The overwhelming dominance of ocean surface in the Southern Hemisphere makes possible a strong and relatively uninterrupted zonal circulation. The climatic pattern is far more latitudinally regular than in the Northern Hemisphere.[46] There are, however, certain anomalies.[47]

Because of the more vigorous westerly circulation in the Southern Hemisphere, stemming from the powerful Antarctic cold source and reduced continental friction, the longitudinal axis of the subtropical high in the eastern South Pacific lies closer to the equator than does its counterpart in the North Pacific. Accordingly, over the ocean the equatorial pressure trough is asymmetrically located to the north of the equator at all times of the year. One consequence is that all of the tropical climates of Pacific coastal South America are displaced northward of their expected latitudinal positions. Intense drought conditions are characteristic almost to the equator, then give way abruptly, on the north, to a zone of excessive wetness along the Pacific side of Colombia. The abnormal feature of the dry eastern equatorial Pacific is that the rainfall deficiency extends so far westward along the equator. The narrow dry zone in the equatorial Pacific which reaches westward from Ecuador for some 7000 miles is one of the earth's most striking climatic anomalies. Gentilli has called attention to the remarkably abrupt westward transition to wetter climates in the central Pacific and to the conspicuous wet tongue projecting east-southeast from the Solomon Islands toward the Samoa Islands and Tahiti.[48]

In New Zealand there are conspicuous contrasts in rainfall distribution between North Island and South Island, and within the latter between an extremely wet west and a subhumid east.[49] The climatic arrangement in Australia is almost perfect in its simplicity: dry climates occupy all but the northern, eastern, and parts of the southern margins of the continent. The greatest anomaly is the absence of a cool ocean current, fog, and extreme aridity along the west coast.

In Indonesia, one of the climatic peculiarities is the small amount of annual rainfall in the area from eastern Java to southernmost New Guinea. Annual rainfalls of less than 40 inches occur, coupled with dry seasons of seven to eight months. The long dry season coincides with the prevalence of southeast trades, while westerly flow prevails during the wet months. Along the eastern coasts of Asia, extreme winter continentality is the rule. Japan has spring and winter temperatures 4° to 8° F. cooler than for corresponding latitudes of coastal southeastern United States. Summer temperatures in Hokkaido and northern Honshu are abnormally low because of the cool Oyashio (current).

HABITATS FOR MAN

THE RESOURCE BASE

Earth materials, soil, altitude, landforms, location, and climate all combine to create the varied physical environments found among the Pacific islands. Many gradations occur between the luxuriant wet continental-type island and the barren desert sandy islet. In each of the four main types of islands there is a definite relationship among earth materials, landforms, water supply, soil, and mineral resources, with a resulting limitation to their biotic resources and utilization by man.

The *continental* islands have the greatest commercial value and the most varied and abundant natural resources; fertile soil covers much of their mature landforms. Geologically recent *volcanic islands* lack minerals of commercial value; land use is limited by conditions of landforms and rainfall. Most of these islands lie in the trade-wind belt, where moisture-laden winds strike their windward slopes making them wetter than the drier leeward slopes. Islands of *raised reef* also lack mineral resources except deposits of phosphate rock, and ground water is meager or lacking; unless rainfall is abundant, irrigation and water supply become problems. *Sea-level coral reefs* with their low sandy islets provide the most limited range of resources for human existence and are the most tenuous habitats for man in the Pacific. They lack mineral resources, except small deposits of guano from the droppings of sea birds. The soil of reef islets is relatively infertile, lacking humus, and fresh ground water is very limited, or may be brackish, or entirely lacking. Even where rainfall is abundant an atoll can support only meager land vegetation and animal life. On the other hand,

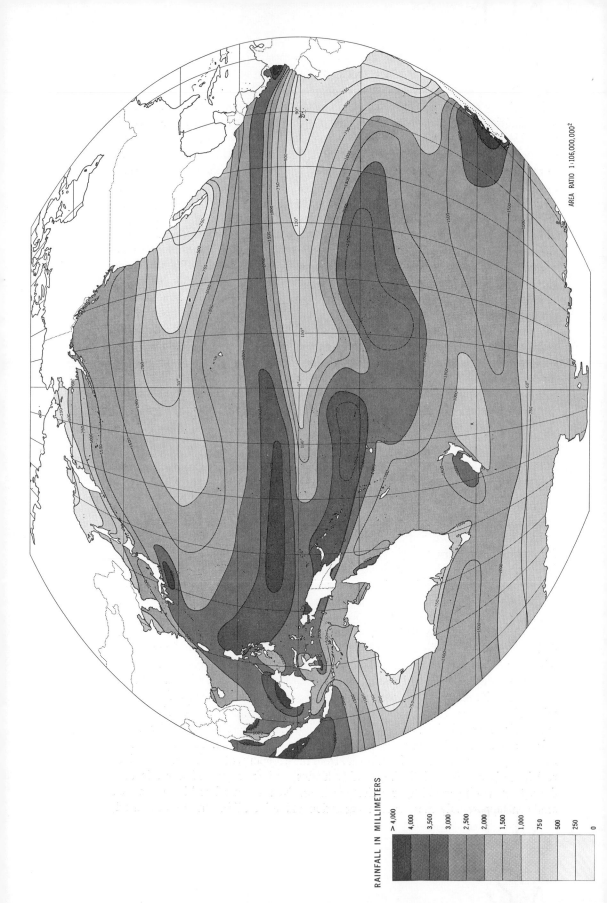

RAINFALL IN MILLIMETERS

> 4,000
4,000
3,500
3,000
2,500
2,000
1,500
1,000
750
500
250
0

AREA RATIO 1:106,000,000²

marine life is quite highly developed, both on the reefs and in the protected lagoon. Thus people and birds on an atoll obtain much of their sustenance from the sea.

MAN, SPACE, AND TIME

Man is an ancient occupant of the western Pacific margin, evolving from *Homo erectus* to *Homo sapiens* in the area from Java to north China. Man is new to oceanic islands.[50] In general, the farther away an island is from a continent, the less diverse are its land plants and animals. The populations of islands must pass through the sieves of difficulty of overseas transport, reach the islands, and surmount the mostly overwhelming hazards of survival and colonization. For example, there are about 550 kinds of land birds in New Guinea, but only four on Henderson Island isolated far to the east beyond Pitcairn Island. Age, area, and elevation are of fundamental importance to biotic development and distinctiveness.[51] A high island can develop a diversified biota, an atoll cannot.[52] Man has imported to the oceanic islands every important source of food.[53] Many of the plants and animals he has introduced purposely or accidentally have greatly altered, largely replaced, or exterminated delicately balanced naturally established organisms.[54] He has changed the island environments rapidly and drastically for his own benefit.[55] Man has had a profound and increasing impact as the dominant agent in discovering, investigating, and changing the face of the Pacific world.[56]

THE ART AND SCIENCE OF NAVIGATION IN RELATION TO GEOGRAPHICAL EXPLORATION BEFORE 1900

Norman J. W. Thrower*

Now at the threshold of navigation in extraterrestrial space, man has traveled a long way since his first uncertain wanderings over the face of the earth. In the history of geographical discovery the exploration of the Pacific has been a most important chapter, but many of the developments which have facilitated an understanding of this largest of oceans took place outside of the Pacific area. Hence, in this consideration of the relationship between geographical exploration and navigation, events not exclusively concerned with the Pacific will be discussed.

The purpose of this chapter is to sketch the progress of navigation and maritime discovery and to help prepare the reader for more detailed discussions of the contributions of various nations and organizations in the exploration of the Pacific Basin. This treatment is necessarily brief and introductory in character, with emphasis on Occidental or Western navigational practice. It is not the intention of the author to minimize the importance of the Pacific Islanders' knowledge of their own areas or the achievements of the peoples of the Far East in exploration and navigation. These topics are treated by the authors of the chapters dealing with contributions from those particular areas. But the view is here taken that the systematic navigation and survey of the Pacific Ocean and the documentation of this knowledge relates more directly to the mainstream of Western culture than to that of other areas.

The origins of the art and science of navigation can never be fully understood because journeys were made both on land and water long before the compilation of written records. Man was doubtless influenced to take to the water by observing floating objects and may have found, for example, that a log beside a stream might assist him in crossing to the other bank. At first he may have used his hands to propel himself and later employed a piece of wood as a crude oar. Various mythological explanations of the beginnings of the several elements of navigation are suggested in classical literature. In that great sea epic *The Odyssey* we not only recognize its hero as the prototype of the restless voyager, anxious to discover the world, but we can also learn something of the character and conduct of ships.[1]

CONTRIBUTIONS FROM ANTIQUITY

In considering contributions to the advancement of navigation and geographical exploration it is necessary to review, however briefly, the principal achievements of

---

*Dr. Thrower is professor of geography at the University of California, Los Angeles.

man in antiquity because of their bearing on subsequent events. Doubtless long before 1500 B.C., when we have a well-documented case, sea-going trading ships from Egypt were journeying far down the coast of Africa and returning with valuable cargoes.[2] Egyptian ascendancy in navigation passed to the Cretans and later to the Phoenicians who, from their centers of Tyre and Sidon, became the great long-distance sailors and traders of pre-Classical times. About 600 B.C., Phoenician sailors in the service of Necho, King of Egypt, may have circumnavigated Africa, an event reported later by Herodotus who cast doubt upon this remarkable accomplishment.[3] Cargoes from Ophir to King Solomon were also entrusted to the Phoenicians[4] who, in their own trading interests, reached as far as the Tin Isles (modern Cornwall) beyond the Pillars of Hercules.[5] In spite of these and other long journeys we have no evidence that the idea of a spherical earth occurred to the Phoenicians, whose knowledge of geography and navigation is largely lost to us because of their strong desire to keep these discoveries secret. In turn the Assyrians and the Persians extended their influence over Tyre and when, later, Alexander conquered the city, Phoenician sea power in the Levant came to an end.

It is from the Greeks particularly that we gain specific information of known lands and, of even greater importance, theories which were fundamental to further scientific progress. First among these was the recognition of the sphericity of the earth, a recognition which was born of philosophical reflections on the ideal form of bodies. This theory, which gained currency in the time of Plato (*ca.* 400 B.C.) but undoubtedly had its beginnings earlier among the Pythagorians,[6] replaced the idea of a cylindrical or a quadrangular earth which had been favored before this time.[7] Although the concept of a spherical earth was not immediately and universally accepted by Greek philosophers, it gave rise to further profitable speculations such as the division of the surface of the sphere into latitudinal zones (*klimata*).[8]

While these ideas were taking form, travelers, including in some instances men of letters, were extending the limits of the known world. Some of their journeys, such as that of Hanno of Carthage along the west coast of Africa to the Fortunate Isles (Canary Islands) and to the area now known as Sierra Leone, actually did little to advance geographical knowledge.[9] The vague reports supplied by this colony-planting expedition stand in contrast to the large amount of information both true and false arising from the conquests of Alexander the Great in Asia. Alexander was the pupil of Aristotle, whose encyclopedic works on many topics, including geographical subjects, were important in antiquity. Later, in translation, they were to be influential in both the East and West.

Military operations carried on under Alexander (died 323 B.C.) extended as far as northern India and doubled the area of the world known to the Greeks.[10] Of greater significance, as the result of these contacts, Hellenic philosophers came into possession of Babylonian astronomy and mathematics.[11] At approximately the same time that Alexander was conquering in the East, Pytheas made his famous voyage to the west and north. Although his reports were disbelieved by certain Greek writers such as Strabo, through whom we know of these travels, Pytheas visited Britain and may have circumnavigated the larger island. It is possible that he also journeyed far to the north of Scotland, and his reports about the climates of particular localities lend strong support to this idea.[12] In addition to this great achievement Pytheas, a native of Massilia (Marseille), calculated the latitude of his home city with remarkable accuracy, using a gnomon—a simple variation of the sundial[13]—and ascribed the tides to lunar influences.[14] He made observations of circumpolar stars in the Northern Hemisphere, recognized that there is no fixed Pole Star, and estimated that the Arctic Circle passed through Thule (latitude 66° N.).[15]

The growing body of information resulting from these and other observations and travels gave rise to theories which were to have a profound effect, centuries later, upon the exploration of the Pacific. The astronomical method of the determination of latitude provided the basis for the measurement of the earth. A well-known and remarkably accurate solution to this problem was achieved by Eratosthenes (276–194 B.C.) who measured, by means of a gnomon, the angular variation between Syene (Aswān), near the Tropic of Cancer, and Alexandria, Egypt. Knowing the estimated distance between these two places, which are roughly on the same meridian, he was able by the use of simple geometry to determine the degree of the arc subtended by this distance and thus to calculate the circumference of the earth.[16]

Eratosthenes, through whom, rather than Aristotle, the main current of scientific geography can be traced, was like other philosophers before him concerned with the extent of the inhabited world—the *oikoumene*. He considered that it extended over less than a quarter of the surface of the globe and also regarded the Ocean as a single continuous body of water covering the greater part of the sphere.[17] The existence of another continent or continents, unknown to the inhabitants of the Mediterranean world, was also postulated. Such speculations, which had been the concern of philosophers ever since the discovery of the sphericity of the earth, found their greatest exponent in Crates of Melos (second century B.C.). Crates conceived of four approximately symmetrical continents, two in the Northern Hemisphere and two in the Southern, possibly inhabited, separated from each other by two great streams of water, one flowing east-west and the other, north-south (Fig. 5). The idea of a great southern continent (later *Terra Australis*) persisted until finally disproved by the discoveries of Captain Cook in the Pacific during the second half of the eighteenth century.

FIG. 5. The Globe of Crates. (Reproduced by permission of John Bartholomew and Sons Ltd. from *Everyman's Classical Atlas*, J. M. Dent, Publishers.)

After Eratosthenes, geographical progress developed along two major lines. In the first place, a refinement of astronomical observation led ultimately to improvements in cartography, a subject treated in the following chapter of this volume. Secondly, there was the compilation by various writers of geographical treatises ranging from pilot books, of which the *Periplus of the Erythrean Sea* is an outstanding example, to the ambitious general descriptions of the known world such as Strabo's *Geographia*.[18] This latter work is also the principal source of information on the contributions of a number of philosophers whose ideas affected the progress of navigation and exploration, including Hipparchus of Nicaea. Hipparchus, who flourished in the middle of the second century B.C., introduced the idea of a systematic, imaginary grid of meridians and parallels crossing each other at right angles. He also proposed the method of the determination of difference in longitude by a comparison of observations made at two different points of the time of an eclipse.[19] Among his other enduring accomplishments are the compilation of a star list and the division of the great circle of the earth into 360 equal parts.[20]

The work of another Greek philosopher, Poseidonius (186–135 B.C.), had a particularly important effect on the course of the discovery of the earth. Poseidonius calculated the angular variation of the star Canopus at two locations, Rhodes and Alexandria, and, like Eratosthenes, estimated the circumference of the earth. It was the "corrected" figure of Poseidonius, roughly three-quarters of the actual earth circumference, that was accepted by later workers in preference to the larger estimate of Eratosthenes.[21] Thus Claudius Ptolemy (second century A.D.), the last figure of classical antiquity whose work demands mention because of the great influence it exerted on the subsequent course of scientific thought, adopted Poseidonius' calculation. Because of the perpetuation of this error by Ptolemy, whose authority both as an astronomer and cartographer was not seriously challenged for fourteen centuries, Columbus dared to sail westward in the hope of finding the coast of Asia.[22] Ptolemy also accepted and elaborated the prevailing geocentric theory of the universe in place of which, alone among the philosophers of antiquity, Aristarchus of Samos had proposed the rational alternative—the heliocentric theory.[23]

The astronomical and geographical systems of the Greeks, upon which navigational practice might be based, were generally accepted by the Romans, who themselves made only minor contributions to these sciences. It is true that the progress of Roman arms in western Europe provided more detailed information of that area which, centuries later, was to be a springboard from which exploration of the Pacific Ocean was to be undertaken. Moreover, Roman control which finally extended from Britain to beyond the Tigris and embraced all the land bordering the Mediterranean, made that sea free from piracy for the first time in several centuries. Roman vessels, such as the large Alexandrian grain ship in which St. Paul suffered shipwreck, were thus able to ply from port to port with only the elements to oppose them.[24]

We are unable to ascertain how much of the information provided by the philosophers filtered down to those concerned with the practical problems of navigation. Certain instruments devised by early astronomers such as the gnomon, the mural quadrant, the dioptra, and the scaphe would, of course, have no practical use on board ship. On the other hand the clepsydra (water glass) and also very simple forms of the astrolabe (star measurer) would have been of utility to the navigator though it is probable that such instruments were used only on land at this time. A number of the earliest references to navigation allude to soundings that were made either by a pole or by lead and line. Pillars and towers, including the most famous of these landmarks, the Pharos of Alexandria, were set up to assist pilots to find harbors or to warn them of dangerous offshore conditions.[25] Of the ships themselves we have evidence not only from the written record but also from paintings and carvings. There were two main types in the classical period, the warship of light construction which was propelled mainly by oars, and the trading ship which relied largely on the square sail. Roman vessels of the heaviest type were as big as large wooden ships of two thousand years later but were not nearly as maneuverable or manageable in heavy seas. Steering was accomplished by steering oars and later by the use of side or quarter rudders.[26] The earliest anchors appear to have been made of stone but at the end of the period under consideration iron anchors were in general use in the Mediterranean. Another aspect of navigation that must be mentioned because of its later significance, after the introduction of the compass, is the matter of direction. A number of methods of dividing the circle of the horizon were used in antiquity, but it was ultimately the four-fold (later eight-fold) system from which, with further subdivision, more elaborate wind roses were developed. Although fundamentally related to solar position the directions of the rose were designated by the names of winds. This idea found architectural expression in the well-known Wind Tower of Athens.[27]

EARLY PROGRESS IN THE EAST

Our survey of the progress of navigation and geographical exploration now takes us briefly to the Arab world, where a number of developments took place that were later to play an important part in the Great Age of Discoveries. Reference must be made to those remarkable Arab voyages from the Indian Ocean to the coast of China and therefore to the margins of the Pacific itself.[28] We have already alluded to contacts between the Mediterranean world and the Orient in antiquity. In fact, a ship canal connecting the Red Sea with the Nile permitted navigation intermittently, between east and west, from the time of Pharaoh Senusret (twentieth century B.C.).[29] Famous early voyages east of Suez include that of Scylax of Caryanda, under the auspices of Darius,[30] from India to the Red Sea, that of Nearchus (Alexander's admiral) from the Indus up the Persian Gulf,[31] and that of Hippalus who took advantage of the monsoonal winds to steer a direct course from Arabia to India.[32] This latter voyage is an excellent early example of the fact that, long before the Columbian period, navigators must have sailed out of sight of land for many days at a time.

The tradition of long-distance sailing thus established in the Indian Ocean was probably never entirely lost. Cosmas of Alexandria, known as Indicopleustes (sixth century A.D.), reports considerable maritime activity on the part of the Persians and even of the Abyssinians.[33] It is not possible to say with certainty when the first contacts were made by sea between the Arab world and the coast of China proper, but before 750 A.D. some Shi'ah Moslems settled on an island on the China coast and served as middlemen between the Chinese and foreigners in the sea-borne commerce which flourished at that time.[34] By the ninth century regular voyages were undertaken in frail, sewn-plank ships between ports on the Persian Gulf and those of south China, especially Kuang-chou (Canton), a fact substantiated by both Arab and Chinese sources.[35] The Sindbad stories arose from the experiences of the Moslem mariners of this period but sea commerce was by no means a one-way affair. Chinese junks occasionally sailed all the way to Bassora (Basra) on the Persian Gulf and visited Indian ports frequently, sometimes in great flotillas.[36]

Through these contacts, which were officially discouraged after the rise of the Ming dynasty (fourteenth century A.D.), scientific ideas were propagated. Although there is disagreement among scholars on this point, Arab seamen may have derived their knowledge of the magnetic needle from China, but some recent students favor the transmission of this instrument to Europe across the wastes of central Asia.[37] On land the magnetic needle was used to determine the meridian. In the practice of navigation among Islamic sailors the magnetic needle seems to have played only a minor role, which can be explained by the fact that the Arabs, like the Chinese, apparently found no satisfactory method of mounting the needle. In any case, a compass has much less utility in areas with prevailingly clear skies such as those in which the Arabs sailed, where greater confidence can be placed in celestial navigation.[38]

It is not surprising, therefore, to find that in the science of astronomy the Arabs made contributions of positive value to navigation. The major writings of Aristotle and Ptolemy, translated from Greek to Syriac and to Arabic (ca. 800 A.D.), formed a basis for Moslem astronomy and geography.[39] But the Peripatetic and Ptolemaic traditions were not merely preserved; in time they were criticized and in some particulars improved (for example, in the more accurate determination of geographical locations). These matters will be alluded to later on in our consideration of the impact of Islamic science on Christendom but now we turn to mention a development that was apparently transmitted westward by the Arabs—the lateen or triangular sail.[40] This device permits a vessel to sail closer to the wind (that is, to utilize the force of even oblique air movement) than the square sail used in classical antiquity and thus represents a most significant advance for long-distance voyaging. Both the Polynesians and the Arabs use the lateen, but whether this invention was borrowed or developed independently by the two peoples is impossible to state with certainty. The lateen sail, however, appeared in the eastern Mediterranean at least by the ninth century A.D., probably brought thence by the Arabs.[41] In the hands of the Byzantine sailors it was modified and then spread to the west and north to be available to European explorers of the Renaissance.

PROGRESS IN WESTERN EUROPE AND THE MEDITERRANEAN

While these technological advances were taking place in the East, Europe was emerging from the so-called Dark Ages, a period during which she had reached her lowest cultural level for centuries. This period, the early Middle Ages, although not now regarded as being so dark as formerly thought to be the case,[42] nevertheless is a period of minor importance in the study of navigation and oceanic exploration— particularly that of the Pacific. The Christian pilgrimages were largely land journeys and, although giving rise to their special literature, generally added little to geographical knowledge. Of greater interest are the voyages undertaken in northern Europe by Irish holy men who reached Iceland before the end of the eighth century, possibly following the route of migratory birds.[43] The skin-covered boats of the

Irish, like the wooden ships of shallow draft and high prow and stern of Germanic peoples of the same period, were better adapted to the generally rougher seas of the Atlantic fringe than were the contemporary Mediterranean vessels.

Explorations begun by the Irish were continued by the Vikings who reached Iceland (*ca.* 870 A.D.), settled in Greenland a little over a century later, and found Vineland (North America) around the year 1000.[44] Of the navigational methods of these hardy Norsemen we have only limited knowledge. Presumably lacking the magnetic needle, they made use of land-sighting birds, an extremely ancient navigational aid, and were keen observers of signs both of sky and sea. In addition to their voyages to the west, the Vikings expanded by means of river routes to the Caspian and Black Seas and, as Normans, established colonies along the coasts of Europe from Britain to Sicily.[45] In this way contact was made with the world of Islam, bringing results significant to navigation.

It is unnecessary for us to discuss the cosmological ideas of the early Middle Ages beyond mentioning the fact that while the theory of a spherical earth was never entirely lost, there were many who denied this concept. Thus Cosmas of Alexandria (Indicopleustes), a monk of the Eastern Church to whom reference has already been made, considered the earth to be oblong in shape.[46] Cosmas' writings were unknown in the West at this time but those of other workers such as Lactantius, who held similar views, influenced the Latin schoolmen;[47] Saint Augustine argues against inhabitants in the Antipodes in his writings.[48]

Although an intellectual revival in Europe can be said to have been under way by the eleventh century A.D., the beginnings of this movement may be traced even before this time. The reawakening is represented not only by Irish monks and by certain Carolingian scholars but also by figures such as Alfred the Great and the Venerable Bede. Bede was aware, apparently from personal observation, of the reasons for the retardation of tides, on which he composed a treatise, and was also one of those who supported the idea that the earth was a sphere. Alfred disseminated geographical knowledge through the translation of Latin works, critically edited, into the Anglo-Saxon.[49] The principal sources of information on the earth available to scholars in the West in the early Middle Ages were Latin translations of Aristotle, the work of Roman encyclopedists such as Pliny and Seneca, and the writings of later fabulists among whom Solinus and Macrobius were especially influential.[50] It is from the eleventh century that the intellectual pace quickens and a milieu conducive to great advances is created.

In the later Middle Ages almost every great ecclesiastical center could claim at least one savant whose scholarly interests were secular as well as sacred. Some of these studied or wrote upon phenomena including cosmology and magnetism, of concern in this study. Positive references to the use of the magnetic compass appear in European literature at the end of the twelfth century. Alexander Neckam, a monk of St. Albans who was resident at the University of Paris at this time, describes as being used on shipboard a needle mounted on a pivot that would revolve until it pointed north.[51] Since this is a considerable refinement over the more primitive method of floating the magnetized needle on cork or straw, we may assume that the device had been employed in northern Europe for some time and may have been in general use on larger vessels. A century later Albertus Magnus and Roger Bacon, both of whom advocated the experimental method in science, refer to magnetism in their writings.[52] Albertus and Roger, who apparently never met, both comment on the extent of the habitable world and to the latter we owe the interesting suggestion, born of his support of the terrestrial rather than the oceanic view of the earth, that the body of water separating Spain and India is not of great width. This statement, repeated by Pierre d'Ailly, influenced Columbus to attempt his discovery in the West.[53] Roger Bacon's friend, the French scholar Petrus Peregrinus (Pierre de Maricourt), wrote on magnetism, constructed compass-like instruments, and experimented with them. While he was in Italy Petrus wrote a tract on the properties of the lodestone, and was one of those who provided a link between scientific progress north and south of the Alps. Earlier in the thirteenth century John Holywood (Joannes de Sacrobosco) had compiled his *Tractatus De Sphera*, (Paris, 1493) an astronomical treatise that was destined to be the most influential European work in this field for the next four hundred years.[54]

Particularly in those areas of southern Europe conquered by the Moslems before the tenth century A.D., advances were now being made that were soon to alter navigational practice and, by doing so, geographical understanding. By direct contact with Islam the West not only fell heir to Arab learning but also rediscovered original Greek scientific writings. We have noted the voyages of the Arabs which, together with their equally remarkable land journeys, extended from Spain to China. Information on these travels and conquests was supplied by a large number of writers of whom Ibn Battūta and Al Idrīsī are outstanding examples. After undertaking extensive travels himself Idrīsī was invited to Sicily by its Norman ruler Roger II, for whom he compiled a great geographical treatise (*ca.* 1150 A.D.).[55] Even more significant to this study than these descriptive writings are the contributions of other Arab scholars such as Al Zarqālī whose astronomical observations had immediate utility. Zarqālī, who worked in Spain in the twelfth century, is one of a long line of Moslem astronomers who provided more precise data on geographical coordinates. He wrote a commentary on the astrological and astronomical *Toledo Tables*, in which he gives instructions for the use of the astrolabe and supplies a remarkably accurate figure for the length of the Mediterranean Sea.[56] Ptolemy, depending on itineraries and the writings of Marinus of Tyre, had estimated roughly 62° for the length of the Mediterranean. The figure was reduced to about 52° by Al Khwārizimī (ninth century A.D.) and to 42° by Zarqālī, who used observations of lunar eclipses made at observatories situated at both ends of the Mediterranean.[57] Writings by these Arab astronomers, as well as the works of Greek writers, including Ptolemy, were rendered into Latin through the efforts of a number of translators who were working in southern Europe at this time.[58] Among these the prolific Gerard of Cremona is perhaps the best known.

Maritime ascendancy meanwhile passed to the Italian cities—Amalfi, Pisa, and then to Genoa and Venice. From these last two centers, particularly, well-equipped vessels traded both within and beyond the confines of the Mediterranean Sea. The compass, consisting of a box containing a pivoted, magnetic needle mounted over a card on which sixteen and later thirty-two wind directions were painted, came into general use among Italian navigators.[59] The lateen sail was commonly employed in Europe by the eleventh century and, during the three hundred years following, the stern-post rudder gradually replaced the steering oar or quarter rudder on larger ships.[60] Charts as well as sailing directions (*portolani*), complete with bearings, distances, and notations on depths and anchorages, were available for frequently traversed seas. Another Mediterranean center of nautical science existed at this time in the Balearic Islands, where Catalan Jews, instrument makers and cartographers, enjoyed the patronage of the Kings of Aragon.[61] We should mention, if only in passing, Marco Polo, the Venetian whose travels took him at length to the China seas and whose journal, published after his return to Europe in 1295, gave that continent more than a glimpse of the splendid East.[62]

NAVIGATION AND THE EUROPEAN DISCOVERIES

It was in Portugal, at the southwestern extremity of Europe, that these threads were drawn together to produce a burst of maritime exploration unparalleled in history. At the outset the dominant personality in this movement was Prince Henry, born in 1394, the son of King John (João) I of Portugal and his English Queen, Philippa. Henry made the first of his four brief visits to north Africa in 1415, when the Portuguese took Ceuta from the Moors.[63] It was after 1419, particularly, when Prince Henry was appointed Governor of the Algarve, the most southwesterly province of Portugal, that he devoted his life to the initiation of geographical discovery and the patronage of navigation. Taking up his residence at Sagres near Cape Saint Vincent, Henry gathered all the geographical information he could assemble. He read the works of Arab geographers, interviewed travelers and merchants and acquired maps and instruments. This well-directed activity bore fruit when the island of Madeira was taken for Portugal by Henry's sailors in 1420. A few years later Henry's brother, Pedro, brought to Portugal from Venice a copy of Marco Polo's *Travels* and a *mappamundi*.[64] From this latter source Henry learned of the Azores, all of which were discovered, or rediscovered, by the Portuguese in the course of the following twenty-five years.

But it was Henry's burning desire to outflank the Moors and for this purpose he sent expedition after expedition down the west coast of Africa. At first the *barca* with square sail or the larger *barinel* which could also be rowed,[65] were used but later the *caravela*, developed from the Portuguese fishing vessel, gained favor. It was in small caravels, of from fifty to one hundred and fifty tons, fitted with a stern-rudder and one or two lateen sails, that the main Henrician discoveries were undertaken.[66] A landmark was achieved in 1444 with the rounding of Cap Vert—the westernmost point of continental Africa. Arrangements regarding African exploration were made between Henry and foreigners, including the Venetian, Alvise Cadamosto, who regarded Portuguese caravels as the best ships afloat.[67] The River Gambia was reached before 1460, the year of the death of Prince Henry who had established a tradition of continuous geographical discovery for which, centuries later, he was to earn the cognomen "The Navigator."

Prince Henry's method involved assembling geographical information and instructing in various aspects of navigational science. For this purpose Catalan Jews among others appear to have been employed but it is incorrect to conceive of a formal navigation school at Sagres. Of the instruments used aboard the ships at this time, we have only fragmentary information; indeed it became part of nautical practice not to disclose intelligence of any possible value to rivals. But we do know that the needle and the sailing chart were in use and the astrolabe and quadrant were employed for the observation of the *altura*—the meridional height of the sun or stars.[68] Henry also appears to have separated the functions of military commander and navigator in the expeditions he sponsored. But the great triumph of the life of Prince Henry, who stands as a transitional figure between the crusading Middle Ages and the Renaissance and who, in his work and in his person, fused the best of northern and southern Europe, was that the explorations he initiated were continued after his death. From the success of the sailors of Portugal other Europeans learned to discredit stories, fostered by the Arabs, of the impossibility of returning from the "Sea of Darkness." Soon other Atlantic states—Spain, France, England, and the Netherlands—joined in the discoveries that, in a few decades, were to bring the seamen of western Europe to the Pacific.

We need here only briefly recount the major events of the Great Age of European Discoveries. By 1475 the Portuguese had passed the equator and in 1488, Bartolomeu Dias returned to Portugal having doubled the Cape of Good Hope.[69] Less than ten years later Vasco da Gama embarked on his great voyage. Reaching Malindi on the east African coast, roughly 2500 miles north of the farthest point attained by Dias, Da Gama engaged an Arab pilot who could use instruments, including the kamal, and knew the sea route to India.[70] With this assistance Da Gama sailed to the Malabar Coast on a voyage which demonstrated that India could be reached from the Atlantic and also confirmed Dias' discovery of the peninsular character of southern Africa.[71] Two caravels of only fifty tons burden and a smaller store ship had been used by Dias, who later supervised the construction of Da Gama's fleet.[72] This consisted initially of four vessels, of which the largest was over a hundred and fifty tons, with square as well as lateen sails. Taking advantage of the northeast-southwest trade winds, Da Gama shaped a course to the Cape that avoided the calms of the Gulf of Guinea, setting a precedent to be followed for centuries. The best available navigational aids including a large wooden astrolabe for use on land were furnished to Da Gama who, like Dias, determined latitude by observation of the meridional altitude of the sun, especially in the Southern Hemisphere with its unfamiliar constellations. Bearings or courses came from the compass and distances were possibly estimated with the help of a *catena a poppa*, that is, a rope towed at the stern to determine the ship's leeway, or by a piece of wood thrown overboard (ship log) to provide a comparison with the moving vessel.[73]

Although Christopher Columbus, the next figure with whom we are concerned, sailed under the flag of Spain, it was in Portugal that he conceived the idea that by traveling westward he would find land in that direction.[74] Leaving his native Genoa in 1475, Columbus journeyed to the Levant and to England before taking up residence in Portugal in 1477. Here he became acquainted with leading explorers and studied navigational techniques. Failing to gain adequate support for his plans in Portugal, Columbus went to Spain where ultimately he secured royal patronage.[75] It is unnecessary to repeat here the well-known historical details of Columbus' epoch-making first voyage beyond mentioning that he left Spain on August 3, 1492, and, sailing by way of the Canary Islands, reached land (probably San Salvador in the Bahamas) on October 12. Less well known are the navigational practices employed by Columbus on this and his three subsequent voyages to the Indies (New World), all completed before the end of the year 1504. We know that he carried the mariner's astrolabe and the quadrant for finding the altitude of the North Star following the Portuguese practice. Particular interest attaches to Columbus' use of the magnetic compass and especially to his journal entry of the 13th of September, 1492, that "the needles turned a half point to North West and in the morning they turned somewhat more North West."[76]

Columbus may be credited with the first known Occidental reference to westerly magnetic variation though not to its discovery. This phenomenon was frequently observed as other great voyages in an east-west direction were undertaken during which, because of the uncertainty of longitudinal position, the navigational practice of running down the latitude was employed. This consisted of finding the latitude of the desired position and then sailing east or west as the case demanded. Latitude could be determined with considerable accuracy by astronomical observation taken in conjunction with ephemerides (tables of the positions of celestial bodies), which were compiled by astronomers before the practical navigator was ready to use them.

Information useful to the navigator soon began to be published in manuals, of which an early example is the anonymous Portuguese *Regimento do estrolabio e do quadrante* (Lisboa, 1509?). This work, based in part upon the observations of the Jewish astronomer Abraham Zacuto as well as upon the work of Sacrobosco, contains calculations for finding latitude by means of the Pole Star, a list of the latitude of known places, and a section on dead reckoning. Two Spanish works of a similar character are Pedro de Medina's *Arte de navegar en que se contienen todas las Reglas* ... (Valladolid, 1545), and Martin Cortés' *Breve compendio de la sphera y de la arte de navegar* ... (Sevilla, 1551),[77] (Plate 1, *following this page*).

The success of the voyages sponsored by Portugal and Spain encouraged others to engage in exploration. As early as 1496, John Cabot, a Genoese seaman, received letters patent from Henry VII of England for discovery in the West. In the following year, between the second and third voyages of Columbus, Cabot made a landfall on the northeastern coast of North America, probably the first by a European since the Vikings.[78] Meanwhile Portuguese and Spanish exploration flourished with undiminished vigor: witness the discovery of Brazil by Cabral on his voyage to India in 1500 for the former power and, for the latter, the explorations of Amerigo Vespucci in the Caribbean. Only a few years later, in 1513, the "Great South Sea" was sighted from a peak in Darien by Vasco Nuñez de Balboa.[79] These explorations, which revealed America to be a barrier on the way to the Indies rather than the Indies themselves as Columbus had believed, were eclipsed by the discoveries of Ferdinand Magellan (Fernão de Magalhães). Magellan's achievement in attaining a virtual circumnavigation of the globe can only be compared with those of Columbus and Da Gama, with whom he forms the great triumvirate of navigators. Details of the explorations of Magellan, who was Portuguese by birth and training but who

L'ARTE DEL
NAVEGAR,
IN LAQVAL SI CONTENGONO LE RE

gole, dechiarationi, secreti, & auisi, alla bona nauegation ne=
cessarij. Composta per l'Eccel. Dottor M. Pietro da Me
dina, & tradotta de lingua Spagnola in volgar Italia=
no, à beneficio, & vtilità de ciascadun Nauigante.

In Vinetia, ad instantia di Gioanbattista Pedrezano, libraro
al segno della Torre, à pie del ponte di Rialto.
Con Priuilegio del Illustriss. Senato Veneto. Per anni. xv.
M   D   LIIII.

The title page of *L'Arte del Navegar*—the first Italian edition of the influential Spanish nautical manual, *Arte de Navegar* by Pedro de Medina. This Italian version was published in 1554, nine years
after the appearance of the original Spanish edition. Medina's work, which was approved by the
Casa de Contratacion, was translated into several languages and served as a textbook on navigation
in the naval colleges of Europe. The attractive woodcut shows six ships being blown in various directions by the winds. The vessels are one- and two-masted caravels, a galley, and the larger *naos* used
by explorers in the period of the great discoveries. (Reproduced by permission from the copy of this
now rare work in Special Collections, University of California, Los Angeles.)

PLATE 1

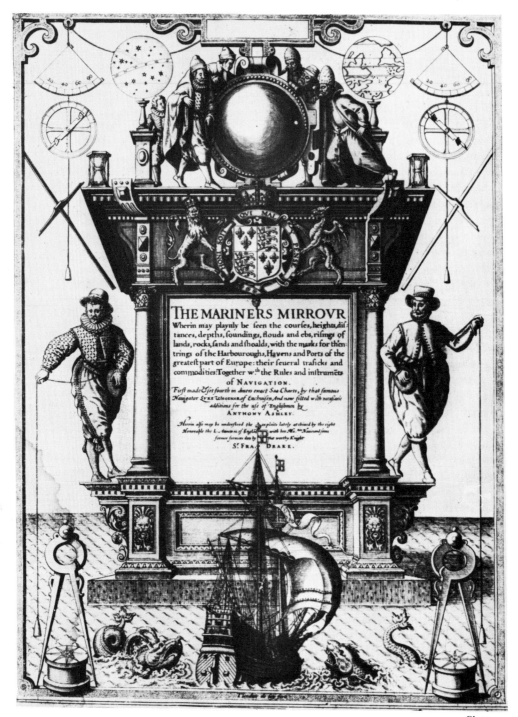

THE MARINERS MIRROVR
Wherin may playnly be seen the courses, heights, distances, depths, soundings, flouds and ebs, risings of lands, rocks, sands and shoalds, with the marks for then-trings of the Harbouroughs, Havens and Ports of the greatest part of Europe: their seueral traficks and commodities: Together w.th the Rules and instrumēts
OF NAVIGATION.
First made & set foorth in diuers exact Sea Charts, by that famous Nauigator Lvke Wagenar of Enchuisen And now fitted with necessarie additions for the vse of Englishmen by
ANTHONY ASHLEY.
Herein also may be vnderstood the Exploits lately atchived by the right Honorable the L. Admiral of England with her M.ties Nauie and some former seruices don by that worthy Knight
S.r FRA. DRAKE.

The title page of *The Mariners Mirrour* well illustrates the equipment of the navigator of the Renaissance. Reading from the top to the bottom, we can recognize the following navigational aids: terrestrial and celestial globes, quadrant, mariner's astrolabe, sand glass, balestilha or Jacob's staff (a simple form of the cross-staff), lead and line, dividers, and box compass. At the top center a group of mariners and an apprentice look toward the mirror which symbolizes the sea chart, while below is a well-fitted Flemish carrack of the period. The original *Spieghel der Zeevaert* was compiled by Lucas Janszoon Waghenaer of Enkhuizen and was published by Christophe Plantin at Leiden in two parts, in 1584 and 1585. Waghenaer brought together sailing charts and sailing directions in his work, which was popularly known as a "Waggoner" in English or "Charioteer" in French. A Latin edition appeared in 1586 and the first English edition, (illustrated above) in 1588. The English translation was the work of Anthony Ashley who made certain amendments to suit the needs of his patrons. The title page is by the well-known engraver Theodore de Bry, and closely resembles that of the *Spieghel* by Johannes a Doetecum. (Reproduced by permission of the Huntington Library, San Marino, California.)

PLATE 2

immortalized himself in the service of Spain, will be dealt with in other chapters of this volume. But we should note here that Magellan's perilous passage through the strait which bears his name, in 1520, opened the way for advances in navigation, three thousand years in the making, to be applied in that vast theater—the Pacific Ocean.[80]

Instructions issued to Magellan prior to his departure specifically directed him to prosecute his discoveries within the limits of the Spanish demarcation. This, of course, refers to the arrangements for the partition of the world between Spain and Portugal reached at the Treaty of Tordesillas (1494) which, in turn, was an outgrowth of four Papal Bulls promulgated during the previous year. This is not the place to consider the political and legal implications of this treaty, which was precipitated by the discoveries of Columbus; the rivalry between Spain and Portugal for overseas possessions can be traced back at least as far as 1415, when Prince Henry contested the claim of Castille to the Canary Islands.[81] Our special interest in the lines of demarcation relates to the problem of their placement, which could never be established with accuracy not only because of the rather ambiguous terms in the documents but more particularly because of the uncertainty of longitudinal position at this time.

We have mentioned the patronage extended to explorers by royal persons; in time this was supplemented by the establishment of institutes to foster the science of navigation. The Casa de la Contratación de las Indies performed this function in Spain.[82] As Pilot Major, Amerigo Vespucci presided over this influential body in which John Cabot's son, Sebastian, held important offices after 1518. Among other duties, the Casa was charged with responsibility for the training and examination of Spanish pilots but eventually, through conservatism, it tended to inhibit rather than promote progress. Although Spain and Portugal continued to produce explorers of skill and determination, before the end of the sixteenth century the initiative in both discovery and navigation had passed to the countries bordering the North Sea.

Enough has been said to indicate that northwestern Europeans were aware of the significance of the great voyages of discovery and desired to reap benefits themselves from this expansive movement. The example of patronage extended to Cabot by England was followed when Giovanni da Verrazano, a Florentine navigator, explored the mid-Atlantic coast of North America for France in 1527. Long before this date seamen from Dieppe, Rouen, Bristol, and Flemish ports had made more limited voyages to the Atlantic islands, but some years afterwards adventurers native to northwestern European countries were themselves conducting extended expeditions of discovery: Cartier in the Saint Lawrence, 1534; Willoughby and Chancellor in the northeast, 1553; Frobisher in the northwest, 1576; and Drake who circumnavigated the globe, 1577–1580.[83]

NAVIGATION AND THE SCIENTIFIC REVOLUTION

Concurrent with these events was the ushering-in of that period in which theorists on the land were relating experimentation to observation to a greater extent than ever before—the Scientific Revolution. Many of the advances made during this time had an effect, direct or indirect, upon the progress of navigation. Mention should be made of the publication *Nicolai Copernici Torinensis De revolutionibus orbium coelestium* . . . (Norimbergae, 1543) in which Copernicus advanced the heliocentric theory anticipated centuries earlier by the hypothesis of Aristarchus.[84] But before Copernicus, astronomers in the north such as Georg Peurbach and Regiomontanus (Johannes Mueller of Königsburg) through the technique of observation had attempted to revise the Ptolemaic literature.[85] In 1471 Regiomontanus and his student-patron Bernhard Walther established and equipped an observatory in Nurnberg.[86] From this center was issued a volume of *Ephemerides* (Venice, 1482 and later), calculated by Regiomontanus for the thirty-two years 1474–1506, which contained a recommendation for and explanation of the use of lunar distances for finding longitude at sea. This was one of several celestial methods for the solution of the longitude problem that received the support of astronomers. The practical suggestion of carrying timepieces aboard ship for this purpose appears to have originated with Reinerus Gemma (Frisius). Gemma, a contemporary of Copernicus, made this proposal in a chapter devoted to longitude in his *De Principiis Astronomiae & Cosmographiae*, . . . (Antwerpiae, 1530).[87]

Although the basic principle was sound, over two centuries were to elapse after Gemma's death before a portable timepiece was invented that permitted the accurate determination of longitude on the unstable deck of a ship. Of other methods for finding longitude, the variation (declination) of the compass appeared most promising to early investigators but eventually this was found to be unsatisfactory. Sebastian Cabot claimed to have discovered a means of finding longitudinal position by magnetic variation and held to this belief until his death in 1557.[88] Cabot did not disclose details of his secret but others were convinced that the intersection of a line of magnetic variation with latitude was the best indication of longitudinal position. Ever since the Middle Ages there had been a great interest in magnetism on the part of both scholars and practical men. Compass makers applied a "correction" to the needle to compensate for local variation, a practice that undoubtedly retarded a true understanding of the phenomenon. But it was the English instrument maker Robert Norman who, in 1581, described his discovery of the dip or inclination of the needle from the horizontal when magnetized.[89] This had been independently discovered in Germany but it was the work of the Englishman that laid the foundation for further understanding of magnetism, a science greatly elucidated by the researches of Norman's compatriot, William Gilbert. In . . . *De magnete, magneticisque corporibus* . . . (London, 1600), Gilbert enunciated the principle that the earth itself is a magnet—a fact that explains magnetic attraction north and south and also the dip or inclination of the needle. The medieval notion of the needle pointing to the Pole Star which had lost favor in the preceding fifty years was thus finally demolished. Gilbert, who was the climactic figure in Elizabethan science, also fostered Copernican views in England through his writings.[90]

William Gilbert and his English contemporaries benefited from the tradition of science and instrument making that had existed in Flanders and Germany for well over a century before the publication of *De magnete*. . . . We have already mentioned the contributions of Regiomontanus and of Gemma Frisius whose student, Mercator, was an instrument-maker as well as a cartographer. The transmission of theoretical and practical knowledge from the continent to England was accomplished both through foreigners and by Englishmen who traveled and studied abroad. Among the latter group John Dee, a Fellow of Trinity College, Cambridge, was particularly influential. We find him advising the explorers Chancellor and Frobisher on technical matters. It was one of Dee's students Stephen Borough, an observer of the operations of the Casa de la Contratación, who was instrumental in having the Spanish nautical manual *Arte de navegar* by Martin Cortés rendered in English.[91] A translation of this work, in which the suggestion is made that the magnetic pole and true earth pole are not the same, was undertaken by Richard Eden in 1561.[92] This translation provided the impetus for English writers to compile navigational manuals and as these proliferated new information was gradually incorporated. Paralleling this development was the production in the Low Countries of sea manuals containing tables, distances, soundings, and anchorages as well as charts. The superiority of the Dutch is this field was acknowledged when an English edition of the *Spiegel der Zeevaerdt* (*Mariner's Mirror*) was commissioned in 1588, after its approval by the Lord Admiral of England, Charles Howard of Effingham.[93] (Plate 2, *facing page 29.*)

Ships used for voyages of discovery underwent a considerable change in design from the time of Prince Henry to that of Sir Francis Drake. The *caravela latina* was replaced by the *caravela redonda*, with its three masts, characteristically, and square as well as lateen sails. In turn the long, narrow, and maneuverable caravel was superseded by the heavier and more seaworthy *nau* (Spanish *nao*), which was three masted and often of about four hundred tons burden. Frequently much larger than the *nau* but a variant of this vessel, the galleon gained increasing popularity during the sixteenth century.[94] At this period, in addition to navigational aids already mentioned, ship's inventories list the cross-staff.[95] This instrument, of considerable antiquity and known by a variety of names, consists of a rod with cross pieces fitted at right angles with which forward observation of the altitude of celestial bodies can be made. Unlike the mariner's astrolabe, the cross-staff could be successfully used by one man and was preferred on this account as well as for its greater accuracy under most conditions. Nevertheless, the astrolabe was still retained because of its superiority for the observation of large angles.

The Arctic explorer and writer on navigation, John Davis, was responsible for the invention of the backstaff, an important derivative of the cross-staff. In using the backstaff, as the name suggests, the observer's back is toward the object being observed and the serious problem of glare in the case of solar observation is eliminated.[96] Another instrument commonly carried aboard ship at this time was the nocturnal, which automatically provides the necessary correction to be applied on any bearing of the Guards of the Lesser Bear (Ursa Minor) from the Pole Star.[97] Equipped with the instruments discussed above the mariner was able to determine latitude to within a degree or so during the day or night, provided he was favored with clear weather. The plane chart on an equirectangular projection was still in general use at sea at the end of the sixteenth century although Gerhard Mercator had published the famous projection that bears his name in 1569. The properties of the Mercator chart on which any straight line is a loxodrome (line of constant compass direction) were analyzed by Edward Wright who outlined its mathematical basis in his *Certaine Errors In Navigation . . .* (London, 1599).[98] But it was about a century and a half later before the "true" or Mercator chart, on which the plotted course could be followed readily with the help of a compass, supplanted the plane chart in normal use.

Although the use of instruments and tables permitted latitude to be determined with reasonable accuracy, the problem of finding longitude at sea remained unsolved. It is true that before 1600 certain devices had been developed to assist the navigator in keeping a record of the distance sailed and thus to provide an approximation of longitude. One of these, mentioned as being used on Magellan's great voyage, was the log line and chip,[99] which consisted of a long cord attached to a weighted piece of wood, which was thrown overboard when the vessel was in motion. The chip remained stationary in the water while the line was payed out, an operation which was timed by a sand or water glass. After a short period the log line was hauled in and a measurement of the length of the line used provided an indication of the distance traveled in a specified time and therefore of the speed of the vessel. Eventually the log gave its name to the journal in which such records were kept. Another device to aid in dead reckoning was the traverseboard, on the surface of which the points of the compass were marked. A series of holes were bored along each rhumb and it was the responsibility of the helmsman to record, by means of pegs, the course made by the ship during each half hour of the watch.[100] Of course, not all shipmasters or even all explorers were willing to employ new navigational techniques or instruments; on the other hand some vessels were provided with equipment that was too complicated for use on shipboard.

While royal patronage, which had been so vital to the success of the earlier overseas discoveries, continued during and after the sixteenth century, support for exploration came increasingly from other sources—particularly from the various companies of merchant adventurers. Some indication of the relative strength of the merchant fleet at this period can be gained from the fact that the list of the English ships which defeated the Spanish Armada in 1588 records the names of four times as many vessels owned by merchant companies and master mariners as those belonging to the Queen.[101] The base of support was extended further when government-sponsored naval expeditions entered the field of discovery in the seventeenth century. Although information was often jealously guarded by both states and companies, greater knowledge of the oceans and coasts of the world resulted from the increased maritime activity. Occasionally an explorer was able to contribute to a better understanding of a scientific principle. For instance, Henry Hudson's Arctic travels added materially to the accumulated observations of the dip of the needle as well as to geographical discovery.[102] Most of the voyages were, of course, routine or operational in character but some were productive of those discoveries which unlocked the secrets of the Great South Sea. These explorations, undertaken by the sailors of various nations, form the subject of discussion in most of the chapters of this volume, and it is with concomitant progress in navigation that we may now particularly concern ourselves.

In the seventeenth century the marriage of experimentation and observation produced scientific advances even more remarkable than those of the preceding

years. Perhaps no individual better expresses the mood of this intellectual movement than Galileo Galilei. Learning of the recent invention of the telescope, Galileo
manufactured his own instruments with which he began an incredibly fruitful series
of observations.[103] In 1610, Galileo discovered Jupiter's satellites and later negotiated
with the Dutch government relative to observation of the occulations of these
bodies for the determination of longitude. It was another of Galileo's proposals, that
of adding a pendulum to a clock to regulate its movement, that appeared for a time
to provide a key to the problem.[104] The Dutch scientist Christiaan Huygens actually
produced such a timepiece in 1657 and some years later he prepared two marine
clocks fitted with short pendulums. However, the regularity of the pendulum was
destroyed by the motion of a ship as subsequent tests at sea revealed.[105] The tests
were closely watched by members of the newly founded Royal Society of London,
one of several scientific institutions created in the second half of the seventeenth
century that were to have a profound effect on the course of navigation and geographical discovery. Robert Hooke, the first curator of the Royal Society, designed
a timekeeper for use at sea that was made by the celebrated clockmaker, Thomas
Tompion.[106] The watch had a balance spring but no pendulum and was unsatisfactory because of the friction on the unjewelled bearings and the effect of temperature changes on the spring.

Hooke was appointed to serve on a Commission of Inquiry set up to examine the
claims of a Frenchman, the Sieur de St. Pierre, to have discovered an astronomical
solution to the longitude problem. The Commission found this method to be impracticable but the event had the effect of hastening the establishment of Greenwich
Observatory. The Royal Warrant for the building of the observatory specifically
included among its objectives ". . . the finding out of the longitude of places for
perfecting navigation . . . ."[107] Like Galileo, most astronomers preferred methods of
determining longitude that involved observation of heavenly bodies; accordingly, the
preparation of tables of lunar motion and of the positions of stars for the use of
mariners became an important part of the work at Greenwich. Scientists working at
the Paris Observatory, which was founded under the auspices of the Académie
des Sciences, generally agreed that astronomical observation was the rational
method of finding longitude. Indeed, great improvements did result in the determination of longitudinal position on land where careful observations were carried out by
astronomers. But at sea the problem remained unsolved and navigators understandably felt that scientists ashore had been of little assistance to them.

The variation of the compass[108] was a fata morgana that continued to be pursued in
the seventeenth century to provide the answer to the navigator's age-old longitude
problem. Encouragement in the search was provided by an error which was perpetuated in Gilbert's important work in the field of magnetism, namely, that the
variation at any one place on the earth would remain constant in the absence of any
great geographical change.[109] This idea was overthrown when Henry Gellibrand
established in 1634 that "the variation is accompanied with a variation" (secular
variation), a discovery resulting from the comparison of a number of observations of
the variation of the compass in Limehouse, London, stemming back over several
years to the work of John Gunter. In 1676, Henry Bond claimed in his book, *The*

longitude found: or, A treatise . . . (London, 1676), to have solved this problem by utilizing the dip of the needle. Bond made the assumption that the magnetic poles described small circles, very slowly, around the geographical poles and reiterated an earlier suggestion that the dip of the needle at any place was simply a function of the distance from the magnetic pole.

The inadequacy of Bond's proposition as a means of determining longitude became apparent as more data, including that provided by the astronomer Edmond Halley, revealed the complex nature of the earth's magnetic field. Halley, in 1698, was given the temporary rank of Captain in the Royal Navy and command of the pink, *Paramour*. The purpose of the appointment was to enable Halley to undertake a purely scientific expedition of a different character than the earlier explorations sponsored by Britain's navy.[110] Halley returned to England in 1700 after an extensive voyage through the Atlantic where he collected magnetic data which was embodied in his celebrated chart of that area. (Plate 3, *following page 38.*) Soon after this date a world chart incorporating information from other sources and with isogonic lines extending to the Pacific was compiled and published by Halley. This astronomer did much to put navigation on a more scientific basis and familiarized himself at first hand with the problems of the navigator.

While some scientists were concerned with navigational questions, contributions were made, from time to time, to theory as well as practice by seamen themselves. We have already alluded to the valuable work of the Arctic explorers Davis and Hudson. The intrepid Captain John Smith also contributed several practical ideas to navigational science[111] and we should also mention the accomplishments of William Dampier.[112] Dampier's observations on winds, storms, and currents, particularly for the low latitudes, made it possible to recognize systematic relations among these phenomena. The information was derived from the careful logs (journals) kept by Dampier, who in 1699 was recruited by the Royal Navy from the ranks of the buccaneers to lead an expedition to the Pacific.[113]

DEVELOPMENT AND CONSOLIDATION

In the early eighteenth century the necessity of finding a satisfactory method for the determination of longitude at sea was dramatically pointed up by the tragic loss of four British naval vessels with their complement of 2000 men including Admiral Sir Clowdisley Shovell.[114] The ships were wrecked in 1707 off the Scilly Isles as a result, in part, of lack of knowledge of longitudinal position. In the literature of the period the difficulty or even the impossibility of solving the problem was suggested[115] while imposters as well as inventors and scientists put forward their proposals. To pass judgment on these ideas a committee was appointed which included Edmond Halley and Sir Isaac Newton, the genius who generalized a gravitational theory from Kepler's laws of celestial motion. Newton supported the method of carrying timepieces for the determination of longitude at sea, putting it first among several methods that he discussed.[116] At the suggestion of the committee the British Government in 1714 offered a reward of £20,000 for any device that would give correct results up to thirty nautical miles (two minutes of time). Lesser awards were to be granted for less exact determination or for promising ideas, all of which were to be evaluated by a government-appointed Board of Longitude. The encouragement of ideas by means of such bounties, really a precursor of state-supported research, is an interesting facet of the history of science. Philip III of Spain had offered a prize for the solution to the longitude problem in 1598, while shortly after this date Holland promised a reward for the same purpose. Two years after the announcement of the British award, the French also offered prizes for an exact method of determining longitude at sea.

The effect of the action of Britain and France was to revive interest in the longitude dilemma and during the eighteenth century many ideas were advanced and reviewed. Jeremy Thacker was one of those who contributed to the production of more accurate timepieces through the invention of the auxiliary spring and understood that, ideally, watches should be kept at a constant temperature. He made the suggestion that the mechanism should be kept in a vacuum and in his *Longitude Examined* used the word chronometer for a marine timepiece.[117] It was a chronometer made by John Harrison that eventually won the reward offered by the British Government.[118]

Born in 1693, Harrison, who was largely self-educated, began making clocks in 1715. To overcome the problem of temperature change he fitted together strips of metal with different expansion rates and greatly improved the accuracy of watches by his creation of the practically frictionless "grasshopper" escapement. In 1728' Harrison communicated his plans for a marine timekeeper to Halley, who encouraged him to construct the mechanism. Harrison's clock, which was controlled by balances instead of a pendulum, was successfully tested at sea by the Board of Longitude. That body voted Harrison sums of money to enable him to work on other clocks and by 1759 he had produced a chronometer of vastly improved design. Two of Harrison's chronometers were tested again in 1761 during a voyage of five months duration and one of them performed within the limits of the specifications set up by Act of Parliament. Nevile Maskelyne, the Astronomer Royal, who compiled the British *Nautical Almanac*, was one of those who attempted to prevent Harrison from receiving the whole award but through the intervention of King George III, Harrison finally received the £20,000 in 1773. Copies of Harrison's small and accurate chronometer were made by horologists such as Kendall and Mudge, and were used by famous explorers including Cook, Bligh, Vancouver, and Flinders.

In spite of this, longitude continued to be determined by lunar distance. Captain Cook, for example, relied on this method by which "the moon's angular distance from the sun or a suitable star was observed; Greenwich time at the moment of observation was obtained from tables predicting the moon's motion and position in relation to other heavenly bodies; and a comparison with the local time gave the observer his longitude."[119] Because of the great cost of the instruments it was not until the middle of the next century that chronometers were in common use on merchant ships. Nevertheless the longitude problem, which had engaged the attention of men for centuries, was solved by the marine chronometer, which could accurately record the time of day at a point of origin for comparison with local time, wherever the navigator happened to be.

The eighteenth and the early nineteenth century was a period marked by consolidation and by progress affecting navigation in other directions also. Indeed, the

Board of Longitude disbursed over £100,000 during the century or so of its existence, but not all the money went to instrument makers or to British nationals. Thus £3000 was awarded in 1765 for lunar tables of great accuracy compiled by the German astronomer Tobias Mayer. Considerable improvements were also made in the design of altitude-measuring devices used in navigation. Newton had earlier described the application of double reflecting mirrors to an octant, but apparently the design was not carried out nor was it published until 1742, fifteen years after his death. Improved quadrants embodying this principle were proposed independently in the 1730s by Thomas Godfrey of Philadelphia and Thomas Hadley of London; both designs were evaluated and approved by the Royal Society.[120] More rapid and accurate observations of altitude than were possible with earlier instruments resulted from the use of the reflectors. The value of Hadley's quadrant was enhanced by the addition of a spirit level, enabling the instrument to be used without reference to the actual horizon,[121] and later a vernier was incorporated which further improved its accuracy. The sextant, invented in the mid-eighteenth century specifically for the determination of longitude by lunar observation, was an instrument of even greater refinement. Even toward the end of the nineteenth century, however, the quadrant, because of its simplicity, was preferred to the sextant for ordinary use.[122] Further impetus toward improvement in navigation was provided by the establishment, by various governments, of hydrographic offices; such a department was created in France in 1720, in Britain in 1795, and in the United States in the next century. In a sense the foundation of a hydrographic office in the United States was anticipated by the work of Nathaniel Bowditch, author of the *New American Practical Navigator* . . . (Newburyport, Mass., 1802). The copyright of this valuable nautical manual was bought by the U.S. Navy Hydrographic Office shortly after the Office was created in 1866.[123]

Meanwhile the design of the wooden ship progressed, reaching a high point in the United States at the end of the period now under consideration. Through the years masts were lengthened and the sail area greatly increased. The steering wheel was introduced in the early years of the eighteenth century. Toward the latter part of the same century, as a shortage of suitable timber developed in Europe, an increasing amount of metal came to be used on ships: copper sheathing to protect the bottom and iron for various structural members of frigates, schooners, men-of-war and merchantmen.[124] A definite gain in speed over all previous vessels was attained by American clipper ships built around the middle of the nineteenth century.[125] In contrast to the hardwood used on European vessels, the clippers were basically constructed of lighter softwood. The largest of these ships exceeded 2000 tons but many of the most significant discoveries were made in more modest vessels, for example, the modified British colliers used by Captain Cook in his explorations of the Pacific.[126]

The charting activities of the various hydrographic surveys are discussed elsewhere in this volume but we should mention here some other contributions of the personnel employed by hydrographic departments. The marine surveyor Matthew Flinders observed that iron on the ships produced errors in the compass and he invented a correcting bar to overcome this difficulty. Another Britisher, the hydrographer Sir Francis Beaufort, investigated problems of marine meteorology and originated the scale of wind intensity that bears his name. But it is Matthew Fontaine Maury, who became Superintendent of the U.S. Navy Depot of Charts and Instruments in 1842, who is generally regarded as being the founder of modern oceanic meteorology.[127] Maury's earlier work was based on old log books but by inducing shipmasters to keep records on specially prepared forms he was able to assemble a more complete body of information on weather elements at sea. After processing these data Maury made suggestions regarding the most advantageous routes for vessels and was an advocate of great-circle sailing in regions where wind patterns were favorable. A considerable saving in time on several much-traveled routes resulted from Maury's directions.[128] However, the gradual displacement of sailing vessels by steamships in the second half of the nineteenth century liberated shipping from dependence on the wind and also facilitated oceanographic investigations. An extended and detailed scientific survey, such as the *Challenger* expedition of 1872–1876, would probably not have been possible in sailing ships.[129]

Some of the varied scientific and technological achievements of the late eighteenth and the nineteenth century were applied to navigation only after further development and at a later date. These will be dealt with in subsequent chapters, and we now call attention to certain contributions that had more immediate application to navigation or which were designed specifically to solve navigational problems. Gradually the common log was superseded by mechanical devices that could more accurately measure the speed of a vessel and the distance run. Most of these mechanical logs took the form of a rotator placed in the water which at first had to be hauled aboard to be examined and later was refined so that it transmitted the number of revolutions to a dial fixed on the ship.[130] After the application of steam power to oceangoing vessels the revolutions of paddles and, later, propellers were increasingly used to indicate speed and distance measurements.

Concurrent with these changes was the substantial improvement in that age-old navigational aid—the lead and line for soundings. At first, soundings were confined to shallow coastal waters (during the Middle Ages there had even been opposition on theological grounds to the measurement of depths). With the resurgence of the spirit of scientific enquiry a desire to plumb the ocean deeps led to various ingenious solutions. In 1773 a depth of nearly seven hundred fathoms was measured with the aid of a number of sounding lines spliced together on the Arctic voyage of Captain Constantine Phipps.[131] Later Maury made use of a cannon shot attached to a ball of twine of known length for deep soundings; after the shot had been heaved overboard and reached the bottom the line was cut and the depth ascertained from the amount of twine remaining. Various devices for measuring depth utilizing a mechanism that recorded water pressure were invented in the nineteenth century. To an instrument of this type the physicist Lord Kelvin attached, in place of the usual hemp twine, a length of piano wire. The wire was found to be greatly superior to rope since it could be payed out and hauled in much more rapidly than the conventional line.[132] It was Lord Kelvin who, toward the end of the nineteenth century, made very significant improvements in the design of the magnetic compass. With the increased use of iron in ship construction it became evident that correctional devices additional to the Flinder's bar were needed to overcome the effects of local magnetism. For this purpose Sir George Airy had proposed, during the middle of the last century, that a system of permanent steel magnets and soft iron masses be introduced into the ship. But it was Kelvin's improved design of the magnetic compass including, particularly, his use of short, lightweight needles as compass magnets that increased the precision of this instrument under the altered circumstances.[133]

As steam-driven vessels became more commonplace great-circle sailing increased in popularity; the advantage of taking the shortest route between two points became especially evident in the vast expanses of the Pacific Ocean. Understandably, the plotting of such journeys brought into favor the gnomonic projection, which had been devised in classical antiquity but had been little used since that time. During the nineteenth century there was a notable increase in the number of lighthouses and buoys to mark the world's coastlands. Global standards applying to such navigational aids were recommended at the International Marine Conferences of 1889 and 1919, a work continued by the International Hydrographic Bureau in Monaco.[134] Before leaving the nineteenth century we should call attention to the effect of telegraphy upon navigation. Visual signals, including fire, had been used since early times and flag signaling was systematized during the eighteenth century. A mechanical semaphore device was employed on land in the 1790s and only a short time after this it was adapted from ship-to-shore and for ship-to-ship communication.[135] Practical developments in electrical telegraphy in the middle of the nineteenth century led to the transmission of time signals over long distances, which enabled navigators to check chronometers on ships while in port.[136] The laying of the transoceanic cables which made this possible is a fascinating and well-known chapter of the story of the sea that need not be repeated here.[137]

PROSPECT AND RETROSPECT

Some of the advances in navigation which have taken place in the twentieth century are discussed in Chapter 14 of this volume. These advances often had their theoretical or actual origin in earlier work and all of them were made possible through the more favorable attitude toward experimental science that had existed in the West since the seventeenth century. Thus, interest in the balloon, in the eighteenth and nineteenth centuries, particularly, led to the development of heavier-than-air machines which, in the twentieth century, were to revolutionize exploration, navigation and, through aerial photography, mapping. The much more rapid means of transport afforded by the airplane and, in the second half of the twentieth century, by the space vehicle, has been paralleled by the spectacular rise of electronic navigation systems including radio, radar, and longer range devices, including Loran. The use of this last-named system in the exploration of the Pacific is dealt with in some detail subsequently in this book. Other devices of direct or indirect use in navigation that have come into use in recent years include the gyro compass and the echo sounder. The former invention, which is built upon the theoretical basis provided by Foucalt's law of precession, allows an indication of true north irrespective of magnetic variation and local deviation. Earlier experiments in the speed with which sound travels through water were basic to the invention of automatic depth-finding mechanisms which permit a continuous trace of echo soundings to be made whilst a ship is in motion. Data

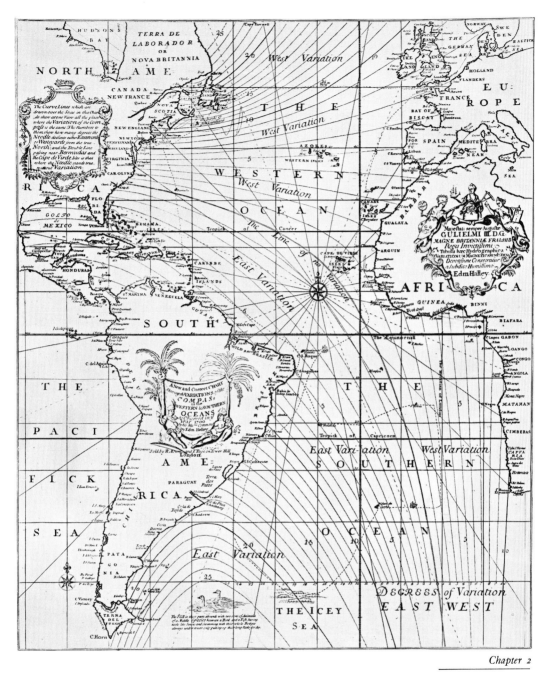

The Atlantic chart of lines of equal magnetic declination, by Edmond Halley (*ca.* 1700). Although the suggestion of employing this graphical means was made earlier, this is the first isomagnetic chart extant. It also appears to be the earliest example of any map employing isometric lines in series, the ancestor of numerous progeny and a device of infinite value in the representation of earth phenomena. One of the most important maps in the history of cartography, it was published soon after Halley's return to England from a scientific voyage (October 1698–September 1700). Already a scientist of considerable reputation and later to be the second Astronomer Royal, Halley undertook this voyage to test his geomagnetic theory by the accumulation of additional data on magnetic declination (variation). He observed the declination daily and it is assumed that he began the compilation of his map while on shipboard. The track of the vessel, the *Paramour*, is indicated on the map. Halley called the isogonic lines simply curve lines, though for a century after they were known as Halleyan lines. At one time the original was prominently exhibited at the Royal Society, London. Soon after the appearance of his Atlantic chart, Halley published a world map. The isogonic lines, however, did not extend across the Pacific on this map, which was published with revisions until 1758. (Reproduced by permission of the Royal Geographical Society, London.)

PLATE 3

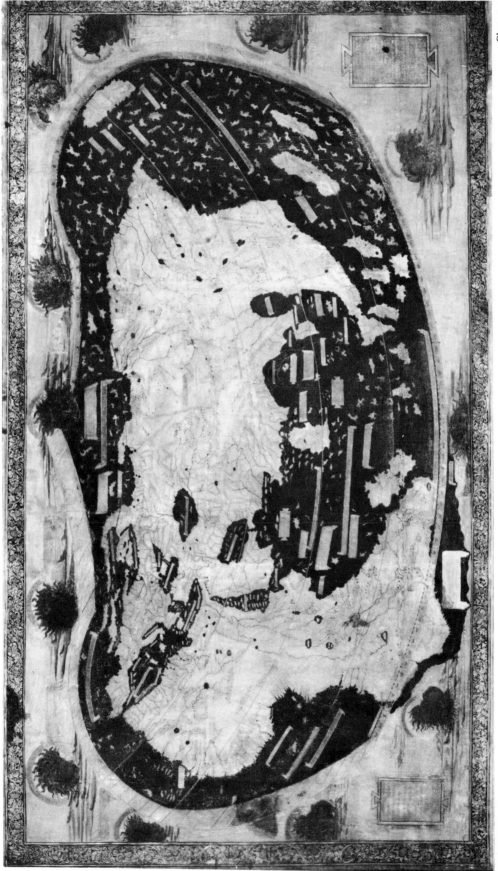

World map by Henricus Martellus Germanus, *ca.* 1490. (Courtesy of Yale University Library.)

Chapter 3

PLATE 4

supplied from these and other sources has enlarged our knowledge of the sea floor so that the true three-dimensional character of the oceans can at last be appreciated. In the future man's inventiveness will undoubtedly provide us with new tools which will play their part in the exploration of what has been called "inner space."

The desire of man to explore and the means by which this has been translated into reality are closely interrelated. While at some periods a leap forward into the unknown has been made with inadequate equipment, further progress in exploration has frequently awaited a scientific or technological advance. The story of the conquest of our predominantly water-covered planet is a fundamental part of man's general history. As we consider the exploration of the Pacific and the brave men who traversed its broad expanses, we do well to recall that philosophers, scientists, and inventors of many countries and of different times also played an essential part in unlocking the secrets of the greatest of oceans.

MAP COMPILATION, PRODUCTION, AND RESEARCH IN RELATION TO GEOGRAPHICAL EXPLORATION

RALEIGH A. SKELTON*

In the history of exploration, maps form a strong thread of continuity. At the level of action, a discovery must be located with precision on a map if it is to be picked up again by later travelers. The accuracy of a map is limited to that of the techniques of observation by which it is made. Imperfect mapping may render an initial discovery sterile, in the sense that its object is either not found again or wrongly identified by subsequent explorers. The first phase in discovery of an island (let us say) is closed, and the end of the beginning reached, only when the island is correctly located on the world map. How we describe the second phase depends on our definition of the term "discovery."[1]

At the level of thought, it is clear that the maps used or made by an explorer, if read with due precaution, throw light on his motives, his expectations, and his interpretation of what he found. They may tell us not only what he in fact discovered, but also what he supposed he had discovered, and what he thought about what he supposed he had discovered. The further we go back in time, the stronger is the element of hypothesis in the map. The early cartographer did not always lift his pen from the paper or vellum when he had traced a coastline to the limit of fact verified by experience. He often continued the line at the guidance of conjecture, analogy, or political interest, and we can expect no reliability diagram. In the interpretation of his end-product we must try to distinguish what part of it is a witness of truth, and what of supposition.

These truisms have particular relevance to the mapping of the Pacific, the largest of the oceans, with an area exceeding that of the entire land surface of the globe. To north and south it reaches the Arctic and Antarctic circles; the lands which bound it east and west at the equator are separated by 160 degrees of longitude; and the seaman may find himself 1500 miles from any land, even an islet. The wind systems channel navigation from east to west, under sail, into relatively narrow lanes. The fundamental factors in the exploration and mapping of this ocean have been its immense longitudinal extension, with few fixed points of reference, and the fact that, before the days of steam, voyages of discovery by Europeans had to be made from east to west or west to east within certain latitudes. Only when a reliable method of finding the longitude at sea became available could the disjunct landfalls of various expeditions be adjusted satisfactorily to one another and to the framework of the world map. Until then, discoveries made at different times wandered, apparently at random, over the maps, and geographical theorists enjoyed a rare liberty in adapting

---

*MR. SKELTON is superintendent of the Map Room in the British Museum in London.

them to hypotheses born in the study. It is not surprising that, with the exception of central Africa and the polar regions, the Pacific Ocean was the last great tract of the earth's surface of which the geography became known to Europeans with sufficient precision to be laid down on a trustworthy map.

CLASSICAL AND MEDIEVAL COSMOGRAPHY

European mapping of the Pacific from data of observation or experience begins only in the late Middle Ages and Renaissance. Even then, and indeed as late as the eighteenth century, cartographers incorporated into their rendering of the ocean theoretical elements which go back to the geographical thought of classical antiquity about the size and shape of the earth and about the distribution of land and water over its surface.[2] The Pacific exemplifies, in a peculiarly interesting way, the process by which early cartographers have habitually poured new wine into old bottles.

From the time when Aristotle demonstrated, and his authority established, the sphericity of the earth, Greek philosophers held divergent views on the extent of the ocean, on its relationship to the known habitable world (the *oikoumene*), and on the existence of other lands. No maps by them have survived, but the patterns which they had in mind can be reconstructed from their writings, or reports of them, and from derivative maps drawn in Roman or post-Roman times. The majority of philosophers supposed the ocean to cover the greater part of the earth's surface, surrounding the *oikoumene* and its "opposite continents" or antipodes. Thus the global geography of Crates of Mallos (second century B.C.) envisaged a continuous ocean with four land masses, divided by confluent seas which extended along the equatorial zone and between the poles (Fig. 5, in Chapter 2). In the northern hemisphere were the *oikoumene* and the lands of the *perioikoi*, south of the equator lay the "continents" of the *antoikoi* and the *antipodes*. This concept was challenged by Hipparchus (second century B.C.) and, by Marinus of Tyre and Claudius Ptolemaeus (Ptolemy) of Alexandria (both second century A.D.). Their theory that the oceans were surrounded by land is illustrated by the landlocked Indian Ocean in the world map by Agathodaemon (whose date is unknown) found in the earliest manuscripts of Ptolemy's treatise on map making, the *Geographike Hyphegesis* or (as the Renaissance called it) the *Geographia*. This delineation provides, in Lawrence C. Wroth's words, "a notable instance of the length to which a scholar will go in the application of an hypothesis," for it was inconsistent with information on the east coast of Africa available in Ptolemy's day.[3]

More germane to the present study are Ptolemy's estimates of the circumference of the earth and of the longitudinal extension to be ascribed to Eurasia. Following Marinus, he reduced Eratosthenes' figure for the size of the earth, which was of roughly the correct order, by one-sixth, making only 50 (instead of 60) geographical miles to a degree. In mapping the habitable world, Ptolemy depended on the reckonings of distance recorded by travelers, from which he computed the coordinates of places listed in Books II–VII of the *Geographia*. They led him to give an exaggerated east-west extension to the *oikoumene*, which in his map embraces over 180 degrees of longitude. Although Ptolemy had little influence on European cartography until the end of the Middle Ages, these errors lent substance to the opinion expressed by schoolmen of the fourteenth and fifteenth centuries that "the sea is little between the farthest bound of Spain from the east and the nearest of India from the west" and that "this sea is navigable in a few days if the wind is favorable."[4] The maps (whether Ptolemy's or later compilations) in the Byzantine manuscripts of the *Geographia* which reached Italy at the beginning of the fifteenth century, and in the early printed editions, presented this world picture in an absolute form which gave it authority in the geographical enterprise and cartography of the Renaissance.

Although, as early as the fifth century B.C., Herodotus had scoffed at cartographers of his day who made "the ocean stream to run all round the earth, and the earth itself to be an exact circle . . . with Europe and Asia just of the same size," this—and not Ptolemy's—was the model adopted by Roman geographers, and taken over from them by the Christian Fathers. The circular disc, or *orbis terrarum*, representing the *oikoumene* surrounded by the ocean sea, with east—and the Earthly Paradise—to the top, gave diagrammatic expression to the cosmography of the Church and provided a vehicle for iconographic illustration of scriptural, historical, or legendary lore. From the seventh to the tenth centuries the *mappaemundi* drawn by monastic scribes —the T-O or wheel maps—borrowed from the writings and maps of Latin geographers their pattern of land and sea and nine-tenths of their nomenclature, and even the great world maps of Ebstorf and Hereford (thirteenth century) clearly betray their Roman origins.

Yet, alongside the disc-shaped model of the *orbis terrarum*, the antipodean concept of Crates held its own among the Romans, and it can be traced in residual form throughout the Middle Ages, either in late derivatives from Roman cartography (such as the world map of the fifth-century Carthaginian Martianus Capella, preserved in twelfth- and thirteenth-century copies) or in maps and diagrams illustrating the theory of climatic zones (notably those in manuscripts of Ambrosius A. T. Macrobius: *Macrobii interpretatio in somnium Scipionis*). The Church Fathers did not repudiate the idea of an antipodean *adversus orbis*, but biblical authority led them to suppose that, if any lands lay beyond the ocean, they must be unpeopled.[5]

Thus the sources of the medieval world map, schematic in form and didactic in intention, were primarily literary, and its geographical content was drawn from verbal sources such as itineraries. Its formal structure, however much a creation of the mind, nevertheless admitted without difficulty the new elements brought to the notice of European cartographers, from the fourteenth century, by Marco Polo's account of his travels, and perhaps also by reports of the Franciscan missionaries who preceded him into east Asia. The seas which lapped the coasts of Cathay on the east were plainly a part of the circumambient ocean of the *mappaemundi*, which also represented an open sea passage into the Indian Ocean from the east, together with a peninsular Africa.

THE END OF THE MIDDLE AGES

At the very period, in the second half of the thirteenth century, when Marco Polo extended the European horizon to the shores of the Pacific Ocean, the prototype of the Mediterranean sailing chart seems to have come into existence. The earliest known portolan chart, drawn (it is supposed) a little before 1300, established a model of such maturity as to suggest the end, rather than the beginning, of an evolutionary process. This model was to be reproduced without structural alteration for nearly four centuries, arguing a successful adaptation of form to function. The appearance and character of the sea chart at this point in time can be explained by technical, economic, and social factors. It is associated with the introduction of the mariner's compass in southern Europe, and with the estimation of distance in sea miles (rather than in days' sailing) by Mediterranean seamen. The portolan chart was developed in the Italian maritime republics, where the mercantile middle class was becoming familiar with mensuration and mathematics, particularly angular measurement, which was unknown in land surveying until the sixteenth century. It served the sea-borne commerce of the Italian and Catalan ports, and embraced its trade routes, from the Black Sea to Flanders.

The world maps of the fourteenth and fifteenth centuries which incorporated into the *mappaemundi* new data from discovery and experience were to be drawn, for the most part, by men who had learned their trade by preparing pilot charts. Until the middle of the fifteenth century, in fact, the chartmakers were (so far as we know) the only professional cartographers. From the beginning of the previous century chartmakers' shops were actively at work in the seaports of north Italy and Catalonia. A Jewish "master of sea-charts" from Majorca entered the service of Prince Henry of Portugal in 1427, and may have taught his craft to the Portuguese. By the end of the fifteenth century Portugal had an official hydrographic office, and Spain followed suit in 1508.

When the chartmakers of southern Europe attempted to visualize the world beyond the trade routes familiar to them, they produced maps which graft on to the older cartographic patterns newer craftsmanship and more recent information from reports of travelers in Africa and Asia. Some maps, such as that of Giovanni da Carignano (*ca.* 1310) and the Catalan Atlas of Abraham Cresques (1375), are essentially nautical charts of the normal Mediterranean type, but extended to take in a great part of Africa and Asia and enriched by inland detail. The *mappaemundi* drawn in the last phase of the Middle Ages, from those of Fra Paolino Minorita and Petrus Vesconte (early fourteenth century) to that of Fra Mauro (1459), still show the traditional circular framework of the wheel maps, but with progressive modifications in construction and content under the influence of other cartographic models or of new geographical data. The eastward orientation is, though general, no longer uniform; maps are drawn with north to the top (perhaps under the influence of Ptolemy) or with south to the top (as in Arabic cartography). Jerusalem is displaced from the center, as the longitudinal extent of Europe, corrected from the portolan charts, is reduced in proportion to that of Asia. The delineation of Africa and the Atlantic islands is progressively extended by the Portuguese voyages of discovery and from reports of travelers in the Sudan and Near East. The world maps of this period, following the medieval tradition, invariably show open sea from the Indian Ocean westwards, to the south of Africa, and eastwards, into the ocean beyond Asia. But the cartographers did not necessarily owe this representation to the reading of Marco Polo, whose Asian geography was slow to find its way onto the world maps. A notable exception is the Catalan Atlas of 1375, in which the geography of central and east Asia is largely derived from Marco Polo and Odoric of Pordenone. Not until the middle of the fifteenth century was serious use to be made of Polo's book by cartographers; Fra Mauro's map, completed in 1459, was the first to name "Zimpagu," after Polo's "Chipangu."

The recovery, translation, and copying of Ptolemy's *Geographia* with its maps, during the fifteenth century, called into existence in Italy the professional mapmaker, a man competent in the mathematical cartography to which Ptolemy introduced the West. Cartographers of this new type, recruited generally (like the early printers) from decorative artists such as painters and illuminators, produced the "base map" on which, at the turn of the century, the great discoveries in the east and west were to be grafted. This world picture, which supplied the premises for the enterprise of Columbus, is exemplified in the large wall map of Henricus Martellus Germanus drawn at Florence *ca.* 1490, now in Yale University Library, and in the Nürnberg globe made by or for Martin Behaim in 1492 (Plate 4, *facing page 39*). These are the only two non-Ptolemaic world maps of the fifteenth century to be graduated in longitude, and so to give a precise quantitative statement of the width of the ocean which (it was supposed) divided westernmost Europe from easternmost Asia. Their estimate expressed the theoretical view of the Florentine cosmographer Paolo Toscanelli, whose reading of Marco Polo led him to extend Asia even further eastward than Ptolemy, leaving no more than 85 degrees of longitude for the ocean crossing from the Canaries to Cipangu. This was the hypothetical basis for the belief, apparent in embryonic form from the middle of the fifteenth century, and translated into action by Columbus and Cabot, that the East could be reached by sailing westward.

The map of Martellus, unlike earlier world maps, was developed from that of Ptolemy, with the necessary modification in the design of the Indian Ocean introduced by Bartolomeu Dias's passage of the Cape of Good Hope in his voyage of 1487–1488. The *terra incognita* by which Ptolemy closed the ocean on the south has been removed, but has left a residual trace in a great horn of land curving westward from southeast Asia (the "fourth peninsula," as it has been called by Roberto Almagià).[6] The idiosyncratic features of Martellus's map, representing a horizon of knowledge of 1488–1500, recur so frequently on early sixteenth century maps from widely separated workshops that a map of this character, if not by Martellus himself, must have come into circulation through the printing press, though no such map is known to survive.

THE DISCOVERY OF AMERICA

The principal centers to which first-hand intelligence of the great discoveries came were Spain and Portugal, the states which promoted them, and southern Germany, whose merchant houses had a commercial stake in them and sent factors with the fleets. Italy was a secondary but still more prolific center from which geographical information was disseminated in maps and printed texts. The extant maps from the official cartographic workshops of Spain and Portugal and the derivative maps produced by Italians are elaborately finished work, in which the rough sketches made by the seaman from observation (such as that of Hispaniola by Columbus) are completed by compilation from older models or by conjecture. On the channels by which "primary" geographical materials came into the hands of Italian or German cartographers, little information is available. We know however that the "Cantino" planisphere was obtained by an agent of the Duke of Ferrara from a Portuguese cartographer in Lisbon before the end of 1502, and that the "Caveri" planisphere, drawn at Genoa from a Portuguese prototype in or after 1502, came under the eyes of Martin Waldseemüller, at St. Dié in the Vosges, before 1507 (Plate 5, *following page 46*). The Alberto Cantino map was completed immediately after the return of the last Portuguese expedition whose results it showed; but the time lag between a discovery and its representation, even in official cartography, was usually much greater.

When they incorporated the first American landfalls by Columbus and Cabot into the world map, cartographers attempted to reconcile the sailing distances logged by these pioneers with their belief that they had reached the east coast of Asia. The world maps which first recorded these discoveries accordingly extended northeast Asia by an immense peninsula or promontory reaching as far east as the longitude of the Azores and closing any entry into the Pacific from the north. This representation is common both to those mapmakers who were unaware of the continuity of North and South America (*e.g.*, Contarini 1506, and Vesconte Maggiolo 1511) and to those who suspected or knew of this continuity (*e.g.*, Juan de la Cosa 1500, Franciscus Monachus 1529 (Plate 6, *following page 46*), Oronce Finé 1531 (Plate 7, *following page 46*.) Even when the longitudinal width of the North Atlantic was more correctly shown (as in Jacopo Gastaldi's world map of 1546) the isthmus between Asia and America continued to appear. The revision of this relationship and the insertion of a strait dividing the two continents came about by a process characteristic of Renaissance geography and combining classical authority, an inference from Marco Polo, and (we must suppose) some wishful thinking about possible navigable trade routes. The Strait of Anian was first named (so far as is known) in a pamphlet by Gastaldi in 1562 and laid down on Bolognino Zaltieri's map of North America in 1566. Thus the ancient concept of water-surrounded continents supplied a necessary link in the hypothetical route by which the nations of northern Europe sought a seaway to Cathay and the "Indies" by passages to the north of America and Asia. Born in the study, this feature remained on the world maps until Vitus Bering and James Cook navigated Bering Strait. Yet such is the tenacity of cartographic tradition that, even after Cook's third voyage became public, mapmakers could still —with the help of some newer "imaginary geography"—lay down a strait piercing the continent from the Pacific coast of North America in a lower latitude, until George Vancouver's survey of this coast, in the last decade of the eighteenth century, finally discredited the fantasy.

SPANISH AND PORTUGUESE MAPPING OF THE DISCOVERIES

With the exception of La Cosa's map (the date of which—1500—seems to stand up to skeptical criticism), the earliest Portuguese and Spanish maps illustrating the great discoveries were apparently prepared under official auspices. The Casa da Guiné (or Mina), later called Casa da Índia, in Lisbon was certainly in existence, as

an administrative department for overseas exploration and settlement, before the end
of the fifteenth century. There is no documentary evidence before the third quarter
of the next century that its functions included the supervision of hydrography, but
royal charters from the second and third decades of the sixteenth century refer to
individual cartographers as the King's "servants" and "masters of navigation charts,"
and Armando Cortesão has argued with good reason that an official hydrographic
office, as attested by later documents, formed part of the Casa da Índia at a very
early date.[7] This argument is perhaps reinforced by the fact that the Spanish Casa de
la Contratación de las Indias, established at Seville in 1508 with very similar functions
to those of the Casa da Índia, included among its staff, from the beginning, a Pilot
Major responsible for the instruction and licensing of pilots, for the examination of
sea charts, and for the compilation and maintenance of a master chart (*padrón general*)
"of all the lands and islands of the Indies."[8]

La Cosa's map—the only extant Spanish world map before 1525—appears to admit the claims of Columbus and Cabot to have reached east Asia, but the earliest
surviving Portuguese world maps, drawn in the first decade of the century, suggest
by inference that their makers did not concede these claims. It was a German cartographer, Martin Waldseemüller, whose "inspired guess," in Lawrence C. Wroth's
words, first gave expression on a map to the continental character of America and,
consequently, to the existence of the Pacific Ocean.[9] Waldseemüller's world map of
1507, in which this speculative delineation appears, was a woodcut printed in an
edition of 1000 copies, and it consequently came under the eyes of far more readers
than the manuscript maps so far considered. It illustrates the public diffusion of
geographical discoveries and ideas, throughout Europe and at both academic and
popular levels, by the application of printing to map reproduction. Up to the second
quarter of the sixteenth century, most printed maps appeared in books, not many
separate sheet maps were printed, and few of these have survived. From about 1540,
when the superior medium of copper-plate engraving (compared with woodcut) for
the rendering of maps established itself, the copious cartographic output of Roman
and Venetian engravers and printsellers supplied the European market, not only with
original maps of Italian authorship, but also with finely engraved copies of work by
mapmakers of other countries. For the remoter lands and oceans, the primary source
of the Italian maps, sometimes at several removes, was of course the official cartography of Spain and Portugal, the countries under whose flags the oceanic discoveries
had been made, although elements of interpretation are not absent, as in the work of
Gastaldi, the most distinguished of the Italian map compilers.

The "governmental" character of Spanish and Portuguese cartography, interpreting the diplomatic settlement reached by the two countries in the Treaty of Tordesillas (1494), was to affect the mapping of the Pacific. The Spice Islands (Moluccas)
tended to be located on Spanish maps to the east, on Portuguese maps to the west, of
the antipodal continuation of the *raya* or demarcation line; and when Magellan sailed
in 1519 to establish the Spanish claim he was using maps drawn by Portuguese
cartographers in the service of Spain. These maps, though not now extant, evidently showed a navigable passage into the Pacific through or around South America,
and laid down the Moluccas east of an *antiraya* perhaps drawn—as in later Spanish

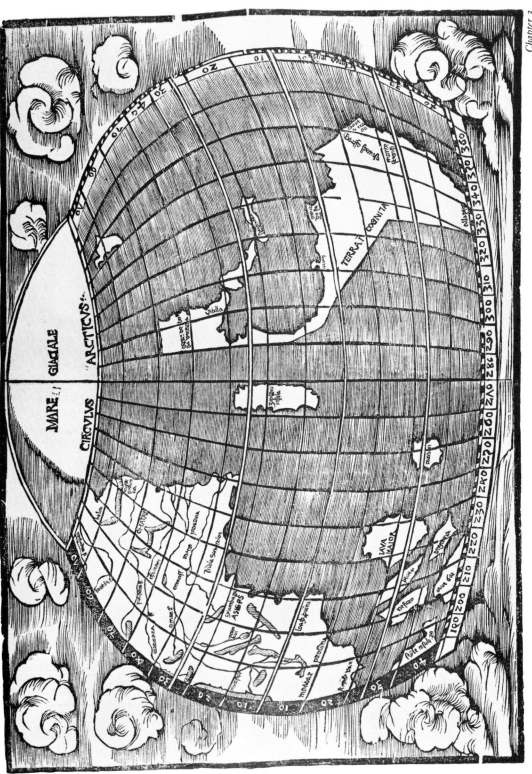

The Western Hemisphere, by Joannes Stobnicza, 1512; copied from an inset of Waldseemuller's world map of 1507. (Courtesy of British Museum.)

PLATE 5

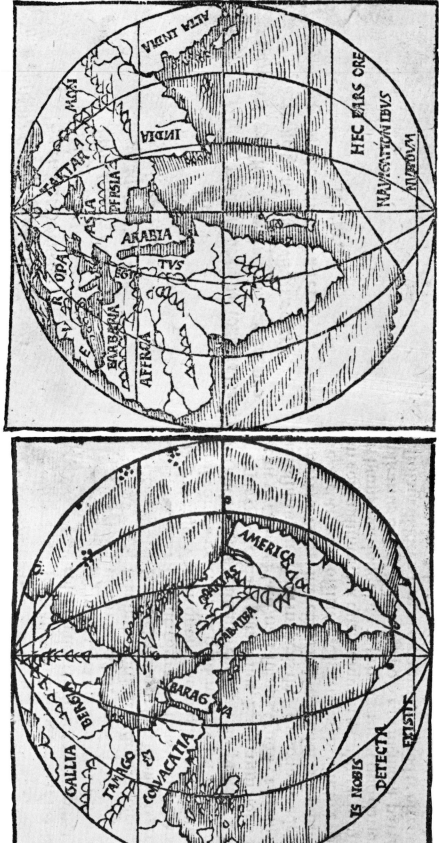

Hemispheric world map by Franciscus Monachus, 1529. (Courtesy of British Museum.)

PLATE 6

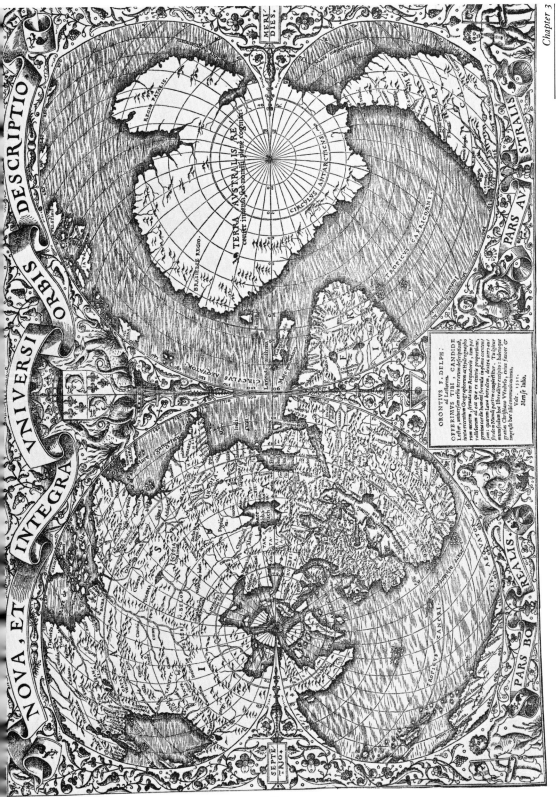

Cordiform world map by Oronce Fine, 1531. (Courtesy of British Museum.)

PLATE 7

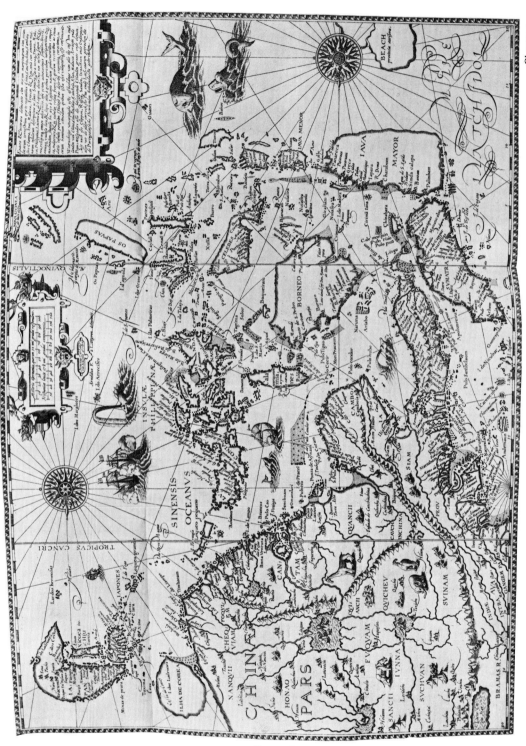

PLATE 8

Map of Southeast Asia and the Southwest Pacific, from Linschoten's *Itinerario*, Amsterdam, 1595. Note that east is to the top. (Courtesy of British Museum.)

maps—through or near the Malay Peninsula. These features characterize the earliest printed map which appears to show knowledge of Magellan's circumnavigation, the little woodcut hemispheres of Franciscus Monachus published at Malines (Mechelen) in 1529. They are presented, with more authority, in the manuscript world maps drawn in Spain by Nuño García de Toreno (1522–1525) and by Diogo Ribeiro (1525 —ca. 1532), the first cosmographer appointed to the Casa de la Contratación of Seville. Ribeiro was aware of the unreliability of the longitudinal data at his disposal, a problem which theoreticians of this century, from Sebastian Cabot and Pedro Nuñes to Petrus Plancius and Simon Stevin, attempted to solve by association with magnetic variation. Nonetheless, no doubt from his interpretation of the voyage of the *Vitoria*, he notably improved the delineation of the Pacific, increasing its longitudinal extension, between the coast of Peru and the Moluccas, to about 125 degrees (correct distance, about 150 degrees), an estimation which was better than that of many later mapmakers.

The appointment of Ribeiro, a Portuguese, to a senior scientific office in the Spanish administration illustrates the superior esteem in which Portuguese cartographers and their work, especially in the mapping of the Far East and the Pacific, were held throughout the century. The dependence of Spanish explorers on them is exemplified in the instructions given in 1564 to Miguel de Legazpi, *conquistador* of the Philippines, which required him to "try to see the sea-charts which they [the Portuguese] use in their navigation, and if you can obtain some of them, even by buying, you are to do so, or at least get a copy of one of them."[10]

TERRA AUSTRALIS

With characteristic realism Ribeiro's world maps show the southern shores of the Strait of Magellan only vestigially, with no indication of any continental land extending along the south of the Atlantic and Pacific Oceans. Although Magellan's men, as they traversed the Strait, "thought the land to the left to consist of islands," the earliest printed maps to record his passage—those of Franciscus Monachus (1529) and Oronce Finé (1531)—depicted an immense southern continent reaching to the South Pole and first named by Finé "Terra Australis" (Plates 6, 7). The feature was introduced into world geography by the mapmakers along converging lines of theory and inference. In part a legacy from medieval cosmography (*e.g.*, the Macrobian maps), in part developed from the rendering of South America by some Renaissance geographers (such as Johann Schöner), the concept was given a pseudo-scientific basis of theory by learned cartographers from the sixteenth to the eighteenth century, reviving the classical hypothesis that the lands of the northern and southern hemispheres must be in equipoise. Thus Gerard Mercator's argument, in his world chart of 1569, that there must be "under the Antarctic Pole a continent so great that, with the southern parts of Asia, and the new India or America, it should have a weight equal to the other lands," was echoed by Alexander Dalrymple's declaration, in 1767, that a Southern Continent "was wanting on the South of the Equator to counterpoise the land on the North, and to maintain the equilibrium necessary for the earth's motion."[11] For two and a half centuries after Fernão de Magalhães (Magellan), cartographers were to lay down "Terra Australis" on their maps and to gather evidence, from reports of islands sighted and from physical geography, for its existence and outline.[12]

EXPLORERS AND CARTOGRAPHERS

By the end of the sixteenth century the main questions concerning the general geography of the Pacific Ocean and its littoral lands had received theoretical answers which were not to be fully tested by experience for another two centuries. Serious cartographers were already conscious of the structural defects in the deductive processes by which these answers were formulated. Although navigators still used quadratic plane charts which gave misleading results in determining their easting or westing in higher latitudes, a number of projections had been devised to demonstrate the convergence of meridians. The character of the rhumb line was understood, and Mercator's projection, although slow to be adopted, enabled the seaman to plot as a straight line on his chart a course on a compass bearing. The declination of the compass and its local differences were recognized, although the secular variation was not to be detected until the seventeenth century. Observations for declination had indeed been systematically made and collected, in the belief that the local declination varied east and west of a magnetic zero meridian and so corresponded to difference in longitude. Isogonic lines were even traced over the Pacific by an anonymous Portuguese cartographer about 1585,[13] but in the earliest isogonic world map, published by Edmund Halley in 1702, the lines of equal declination were, for want of reliable data, not continued over the Pacific.

Latitudes, from observations with cross-staff or quadrant, were of tolerable accuracy, especially if taken on land, but the problem of longitude could not be solved until an accurate timekeeper had been developed. Before the eighteenth century the mapping of the continental coasts to east and west of the ocean, so far as they had been frequented by Europeans, was accordingly far in advance of that of Polynesia and the southwest Pacific. These coasts trend mainly north and south, so that the relative latitudes of their principal features supplied a satisfactory outline. By the end of the sixteenth century the Portuguese had created a cartographic model for the coasts of Malaya, Indonesia, and China as far north as Korea; the layout and orientation of the Japanese islands had been established; and the Pacific coasts of America, from the Strait of Magellan to northern California, had been traced by the Spaniards. But the dead reckoning by which the longitudinal position of island landfalls in the ocean was plotted was subject to factors of which little was known—principally the leeway due to ocean currents. Even Captain Cook, when he sighted New Zealand in October 1769, found his dead reckoning, taken from Cape Horn, to be four degrees short of his ship's position as determined by observation.

The perplexity into which mapmakers and explorers led one another in consequence of such great errors in longitude is most clearly displayed in the cartographic history of the great island group of the Solomons. Discovered by Alvaro Mendaña de Neiva in 1567, and laid down by his pilots 85 degrees (1700 leagues) west of Peru, i.e., some 25 degrees east of their true position, they were sought in vain by two later Spanish expeditions, those of Mendaña himself in 1595–1596 and of Quirós in 1605–

1606. World maps of the sixteenth century, such as that of Ortelius 1587, drew them—more or less correctly—off the eastern tip of New Guinea, though still displaced far to the east. Robert Dudley in 1646 even identified them with the Marquesas (Mendaña's discovery of 1595), 70 degrees east of their true longitude, and Alexander Dalrymple correlated them with Dampier's discovery of New Britain. Their very existence was doubted, and some mapmakers did not even show them on the Pacific chart. In the years 1767, 1768, and 1769 three expeditions passed through the islands and gave new names without recognizing them as Mendaña's discovery. Louis-Antoine de Bougainville, the leader of one of them, concluded in 1768 that "if there were any such islands, their situation was wrongly laid down."

THE DUTCH IN THE DISCOVERY AND MAPPING
OF THE PACIFIC

During the second half of the sixteenth century the map production of the southern Netherlands outstripped that of Italy in volume, quality, and commercial success. Antwerp had by the middle of the century become the emporium for commodities of the East, and was said to do more business in a week than Venice did in a year. Here the map industry had its roots, nourished by the activity of the city's engraving shops and printing houses and by the humanist interests of its mercantile middle-class, and here the synoptic forms of map publication pioneered by the atlases of Abraham Ortelius (1570) and Gerard de Jode (1578) began their long career. But it was no accident that the first printed sea-atlas of modern character, Lucas Jansz. Waghenaer's *Spieghel der zeevaert . . .* (1584–1585), came from the presses transferred from Antwerp to Leiden in 1583 by the master printer Christophe Plantin, and that Waghenaer's second pilot book, the *Thresoor der zeevaert* (1592), was published from 1593 onward at Amsterdam.

After the liberation of the United Provinces from Spain the political, economic, and scientific activity of the northern Netherlands offered freer scope to cartography in the service of maritime enterprise. Antwerp gave way to Amsterdam as the center of the great Dutch map industry which was to dominate the European market throughout the seventeenth century and to play a significant part in its country's overseas expansion. The commercial success of the Amsterdam map publishers was due to the highly developed organization of their workshops for compilation, engraving, and printing. They were also in close touch with the mercantile interests which promoted voyages for exploration and trade, and during the period of Dutch ascendancy in the Pacific the cartography of the Netherlands was to record, with commendable accuracy and little time lag, advances in geographical knowledge made by new discoveries, whether planned or fortuitous.

In the second half of the sixteenth century the nations of northwest Europe, to whom the southern routes into the Pacific were denied by Spain and Portugal, had sought Arctic passages to the Spice Islands (Moluccas). When these hopes were frustrated, first the Dutch and then the English (encouraged by the successful circumnavigations of Francis Drake and of Thomas Cavendish) challenged both the Portuguese monopoly of the route by the Cape of Good Hope and Portugal's commercial empire in the East, where (as Richard Hakluyt wrote in 1599) "their strength is nothing so great as heretofore hath bene supposed."

Before the first Dutch expedition (that of Cornelis de Houtman in 1595) sailed eastwards by the Cape of Good Hope, the English and Dutch were already well supplied with information, both by written report and in cartographic form, on the East Indian trade and navigation. This was either Portuguese in origin or furnished by travelers such as the English Jesuit Thomas Stevens, who in 1579 went "as a passenger in the Portugale Fleete" to Goa, or Jan Huyghen van Linschoten, who spent nine years in the Portuguese Indies before returning to his (and Waghenaer's) native town of Enkhuizen, on the Zuider Zee. During his sojourn in Goa, Linschoten had assiduously collected Portuguese *roteiros* (sailing directions) for navigation of the eastern seas, with other hydrographic materials, and these were printed in the second part of his *Itinerario*, published in 1595. Earlier than this, Portuguese charts were already circulating in the Netherlands. Even Waghenaer's general chart of northwest Europe (in the *Spieghel*, 1584) had been derived from a Portuguese model. In 1592, the year in which Waghenaer printed in his *Thresoor* sailing directions for the China Sea by Linschoten's friend Dirck Gerritsz Pomp, the States-General authorized the Amsterdam printer Cornelis Claesz "to print . . . all the 25 special sea-charts which he obtained at the instance of Petrus Plancius, but at his own expense, from Bartolomeu Lasso, cosmographer of the King of Spain, embracing the sea-coasts of the whole world."[14]

The material thus procured from the Portuguese cartographer was used by Plancius in his large world map of 1592 and in some sectional charts, evidently printed by Claesz about this date, six of which are known. It also supplied the five engraved charts in Linschoten's *Itinerario* (Plate 8, *facing page 47*), which were presumably also compiled by Plancius, that of the East Indies being described in its title as "drawn from the most correct charts and rutters used to-day by the Portuguese pilots." This was to remain for many years the prototype for Dutch cartography of the Malay Archipelago and southwest Pacific, with modifications introduced by explorers. Thus Houtman's traverse of the south coast of Java in 1597 showed it "neither to be so broad nor to extend so far south as the chart draws it" and demonstrated that the island could not form part of Terra Australis.

As the Dutch extended their maritime enterprise in the East, ousted the Portuguese from their trading bases, and entered the phase of exploitation, their cartographic activities were given an administrative structure analogous to that of Spain. On the formation of the United East India Company in 1602, Plancius, who has been well called "the father of Dutch colonial cartography," was appointed cartographer to the new company; from 1619 to 1632 the post was held by Hessel Gerritsz, and then (together with that of cartographer to the States-General) by Willem Janszoon Blaeu, from 1633 to 1638, and by his son Joan. How the system worked in its maturity under the Blaeus can be gathered by inference. The Dutch pilots and captains were supplied with charts of the eastern navigation drawn in Blaeu's workshop, and were required on their return to deliver the charts to Blaeu with their corrections. The practice thus formalized enabled the prototype or master chart to be continuously revised and improved. Charts were also drawn at Batavia, the center of government in the East, and these too were forwarded to Blaeu for information and copying. In this way the navigation routes and coasts frequented by Dutch shipping were systematically covered by a regular hydrographic service, and new discoveries were promptly incorporated in the standard charts and even published with little delay.

The "great map of the South Sea" often cited by Tasman in the journal of his voyage of 1642–1643, a manuscript chart of the Pacific (now in the Bibliothèque Nationale, Paris) drawn by Gerritsz in 1622, illustrates the cross-fertilization of Dutch cartography and exploration in this period.[15] In a legend on the construction of the map, Gerritsz refers to the defects of the plane chart, whose users "will not wonder to see the great breadth between the most eastern and western places which are situated far north and south," and he affirms the longitudinal width of the Pacific shown in Spanish maps to be exaggerated by about one-twelfth. Gerritsz' map, which distinguishes Spanish from Dutch discoveries by a color code, was designed to depict the voyage of Jacob Le Maire and Willem Schouten (1615–1616) whose track across the Pacific is marked, and to reconcile their landfalls with those of Mendaña and Quirós.

The dead reckoning of Dutch navigators, using the log and line developed in the second half of the sixteenth century, was more accurate than that of their Spanish predecessors. Gerritsz, plotting Le Maire's track from the daily runs logged in his journal, had to lay down the two islands ("Coques" and "Verraders") discovered by Le Maire in the northern Tonga Islands, and his Hoorn Islands just off the New Hebrides of Quirós (although they are separated by some 17 to 19 degrees of longitude), the whole group thus formed being labelled "Islas de Salomon" and lying under the lee of New Guinea. The courses adopted by Abel Janszoon Tasman and his pilots in February 1643 can only be understood if we suppose this representation to have been under their eyes.

Sailing north from Nomuka, in the Tonga Islands, to latitude 17° S., and then westward to run down the latitude of the Hoorn Islands (as represented by Gerritsz), Tasman found himself among the northern islets of the Fiji Islands. These were taken by his pilot to be "the islands which in the large chart are drawn southwest of the Hoorn Islands, for which reason he was of the opinion that we ought to shape our course close to the wind somewhat to the north in order to keep clear of the coast of New Guinea, since this is a lee shore." Here is a classic instance in which a skillful navigator trusted, and was deceived by, his chart in preference to his own much more reliable reckoning of westing made good.

The misleading character of the plane chart in higher latitudes, remarked by Gerritsz, was responsible for the chance discovery of the west coast of Australia. In passage from the Cape of Good Hope to Java, the earlier Dutch fleets had sailed with the monsoon by way of India, but from 1611 Dutch captains were laying an easterly course from the Cape of Good Hope to the longitude of Java before turning north. The difficulty of fixing a ship's position on the run from the Cape, when plotted on the plane charts in use by seamen, was remarked by the governor-general Jan Pieterszoon Coen. "In 28½ S. we came upon the land of Eenrdracht [on the west coast of Australia] . . . In the plane charts the reckonings of our pilots were still 300–350 miles from any land . . . although the reckoning of the [Mercator] chart with increasing degrees showed only 120 miles, and the reckoning by the terrestrial globe only 50 miles distance from the land."[16] The uncertainty with which easting could be determined by dead reckoning led inevitably to unforeseen landfalls on the Australian coasts. A chart by Gerritsz, engraved in 1618 and revised after 1627, provides almost the only contemporary testimony to a number of such landfalls on the west and northwest, between 1616 and 1622, as well as of the striking Dutch discoveries along the south coast in 1627. Such is the value of the cartographic record of exploration in this period.

NATIONAL CARTOGRAPHY

The Dutch government was not the only one to show increasing awareness of the significance of maps. With the growth and entrenchment of national states in Europe during the sixteenth century, the questions raised by contemplation of the world map—the continuity of the New World, its relationship to east Asia, the possibility of northern passages, the existence of a southern continent—became geopolitical issues. In the course of the seventeenth and eighteenth centuries, original mapping emerged as essentially an instrument of national policy, partly conscious and officially inspired, partly spontaneous and actuated by private enterprise. In the political field, maps served for the demarcation of frontiers and the assertion of sovereignty over newly found lands; in the economic sphere, for property assessment, for the inventory of national resources and the expansion of overseas trade; in administration, for communications; in military affairs, for strategic and tactical planning, offensive or defensive. This is the threshold of the period (extending into our own day) in which scientific enquiry and technological practice have been brought into the service of the State, whether for economic interest or political control or simply for prestige; it begins the age of the government scientist. In the same period, by a paradox which is only apparent, the concept of a free science was to grow, as the following story suggests.

In November 1768 H. M. bark *Endeavour*, Captain James Cook, called at Rio de Janeiro, on the first leg of her voyage round the world. The chilly reception which Cook received, in somewhat farcical circumstances, from the Portuguese Viceroy illustrates the fusion—or confusion—of political and scientific motives in men's minds. Cook's instructions from the Admiralty required him to convey the Royal Society's observers to Tahiti, where they were to record the transit of Venus across the sun as a means of determining the distance of the sun from the earth. This was a purely scientific objective. But the Admiralty's additional secret instructions to Cook called for exploration of the South Pacific Ocean, where they had "reason to imagine that a continent, or land of great extent, may be found." Here there were political and economic overtones, and the expedition was in this sense an act of national policy. Cook had also to make "surveys and draughts," and his voyage was in fact to produce an outstanding feat of hydrographic survey. The Viceroy at Rio de Janeiro refused the facilities normally available to an English warship. He was probably no geographer, and uninterested in the southern continent, but he suspected Cook of espionage on his port defenses or of unauthorized trade. The astronomical observations in the Pacific, which the English commander quoted as the purpose of his voyage, meant nothing to the Viceroy; the Portuguese, we are told, thought that this implied "to observe, as they well knew, how the North Star moves to the South Pole"! Here there was no common ground—but Cook came away with a plan of the harbor fortifications.

SCIENTIFIC CARTOGRAPHY

It is generally true that the mapmaker's resources, in tools and methods, have developed most rapidly in periods of accelerated economic and social change. This applies no less to the mapping of the world than to that of single countries. During the seventeenth and eighteenth centuries, indeed, the productive cartographic industries of the Netherlands, France, England, and Germany continued to exercise a conservative influence. The life of a copperplate was prolonged, by husbandry and reworking, long after the map engraved on it had outlived its usefulness; for the commercial map dealer the "sale of the work" (in Cook's words) was more important than its reliability. Parallel with this reactionary trend, however, the "reformation of cartography" which took place, mainly on French initiative, between about 1670 and 1750, laid the geodetic foundations both for national mapping and for the world map, and provided the basis for eighteenth-century cartography. It involved, in succession, redetermining the shape and size of the earth; ascertaining the extent and form of the land masses and oceans by accurately fixing the coordinate positions of a great number of points; and precise "infilling" survey, where possible by trigonometrical methods.

The measurement of arcs of the meridian in France (1669 and 1700–1718) and, for high and low latitudes, in Lapland and Peru (1736–1745) established the earth's figure as an oblate spheroid, flattened at the poles, and provided more correct estimates for the length of a degree in various latitudes. The number of positions accurately determined by astronomical observation increased from 40 in 1682 to 109 in 1706; by 1817 it had risen to over 6000. Instruments for angular observation—the altazimuth theodolite, the reflecting sextant—were perfected; combined with the telescope and the vernier scale, they supplied mapmakers with a growing stock of fixed control points. Thus the French cartographers of the first half of the eighteenth century were able to correct the outlines of Eurasia from the maps and observations of the Jesuit astronomers established at Peiping. The techniques of topographical and hydrographic survey, by triangulation from measured bases, were refined, and new standards of accuracy reached, in the national surveys organized by the governments of Europe, and by a few extra-European countries.

From the second half of the century, activity in exploration brought into the hands of cartographers an ever-increasing quantity of reliable data on positions, topography, and coastal outlines. The improved quality of this information was due to the lighter precision instruments with which the traveler was now equipped and which (unlike the cumbersome astronomical quadrant and theodolite) could be used in a route-traverse or on the deck of a ship. The reflecting sextant—"a portable observatory"—and the chronometer allowed him to plot his discoveries in latitude and longitude with sufficient accuracy to enable them to be picked up and reidentified from his map or chart. Discovery and mapping now went hand-in-hand. Although Captain Cook confessed to an ambition which "leads me not only farther than any man has been before me, but as far as I think it possible for man to go," he regarded the two tasks as essentially one and considered that "the world will hardly admit of an excuse for a man leaving a coast unexplored he has once discovered."

EXPLORATION AND HYDROGRAPHIC SURVEY:
18th–19th CENTURIES

These advances, both in method and in standards, are exemplified in the Pacific Ocean, the principal field of exploration during the second half of the eighteenth century. This was the period in which the voyages of Bougainville (1767–1769) (Plate 9, *facing this page*) and Cook (1768–1779) established the map of the South Pacific; when Antoine R. J. de Bruny d'Entrecasteaux (1791–1793) and Matthew Flinders (1798–1803) charted the coasts of Australia; and when basic surveys of the American and Asiatic shores of the North Pacific were made by Cook (1778–1779), La Pérouse (1785–1787), Alessandro Malaspina (1791–1792), and Vancouver (1792–1794). Within less than half a century the modern map of the Pacific, in its essentials, had been drawn, and the mythical elements which had so long haunted its geography, cartography, and exploration had been swept away. The southern continent in temperate latitudes, the fictitious lands north and east of Japan, the strait penetrating North America "from sea to sea," the land connection between New Guinea and Australia—these features were all discredited and removed from the map by the hydrographic surveys of the explorers. This was, however, no merely negative achievement. When Cook's voyages were over, only a handful of Polynesian islands remained undiscovered (the Îles Gambier, the northern Marquesas Islands, isolated islands of the Cook Islands and of the Tuamotu Archipelago). But it is more significant that any subsequent navigator using Cook's charts had no excuse for failing to find an island discovered by Cook. Although none of the expeditions named above was free from political or economic motives, it is evident that the element of survey, or (we may say) scientific research, became increasingly conspicuous in the instructions given to their commanders. We may compare the immense range of Cook's ten years of work in exploration and survey, in which the emphasis was on discovery, with Vancouver's meticulous charting of the intricate northwest coast of America, from latitudes 39° N. to 61° N., between 1792 and 1794, even if Vancouver's primary task was to investigate the existence of a northwest passage or lead from the Pacific into the Atlantic.

The rapidity of Cook's running surveys in the Pacific is indeed no less remarkable than their accuracy. On his first voyage the coasts of New Zealand (2400 miles) were charted in six months (Plate 10, *facing page 55*), and the east coast of Australia (2000 miles) in four months; on his second, the New Hebrides, extending over six degrees of latitude, were surveyed in six weeks; and on the third voyage he charted over 3000 miles of the Pacific seaboard of North America (with two major breaks) in little over four months. These extraordinary performances testify both to the commander's skill in inshore navigation and running survey and to the precision and use of his instruments, particularly the reflecting sextant, by now the marine surveyor's tool-of-all-work, which largely superseded the compass in taking horizontal angles. Thus in his circumnavigation of New Zealand (1769–1770), Cook made no use of dead reckoning; he plotted his track by fixing the ship's position from his courses and from intersecting rays on landmarks, adjusting it from time to time to

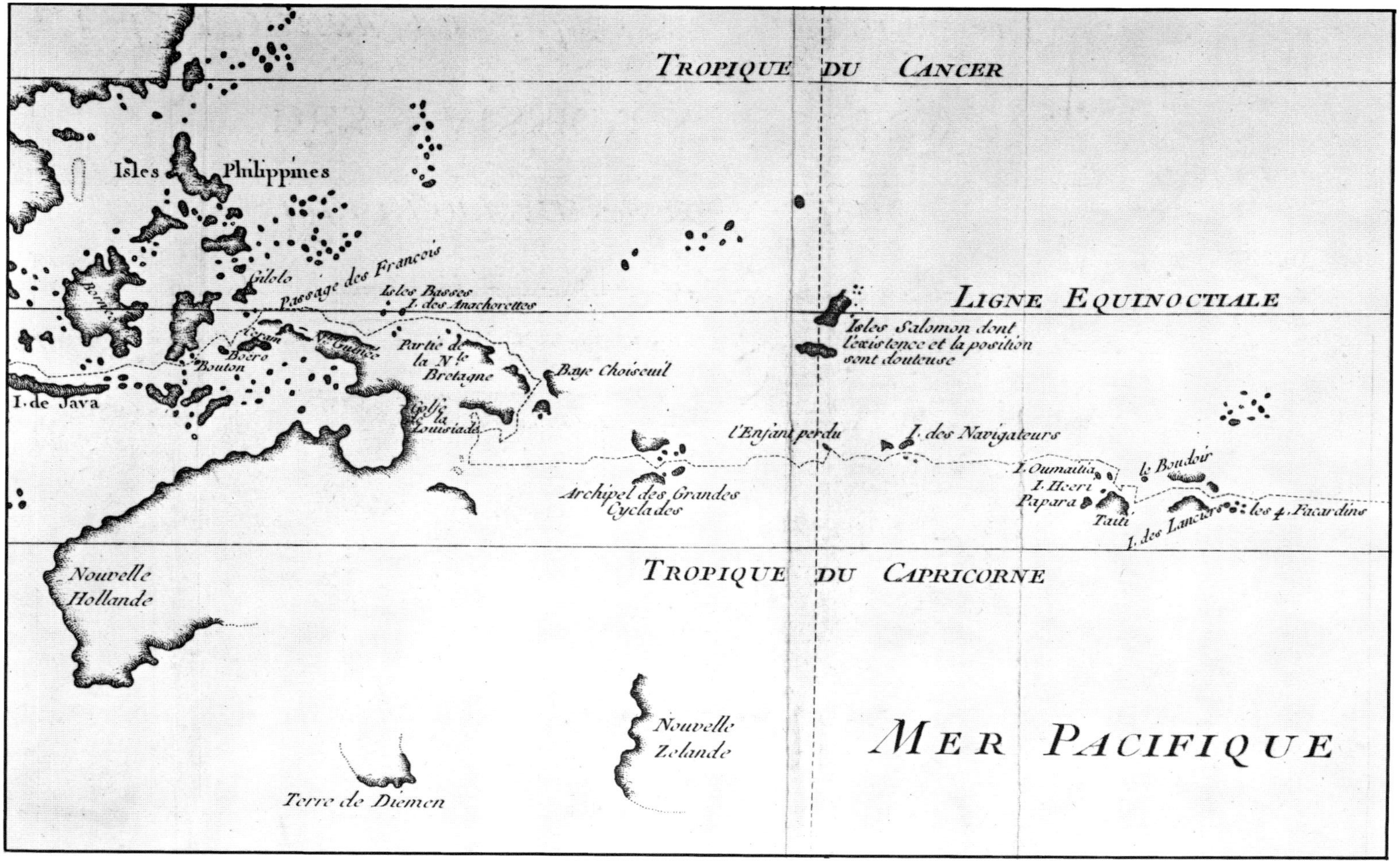

The search for the Solomon Islands. Bougainville's track across the Pacific in 1768. (Courtesy of British Museum.)

PLATE 9

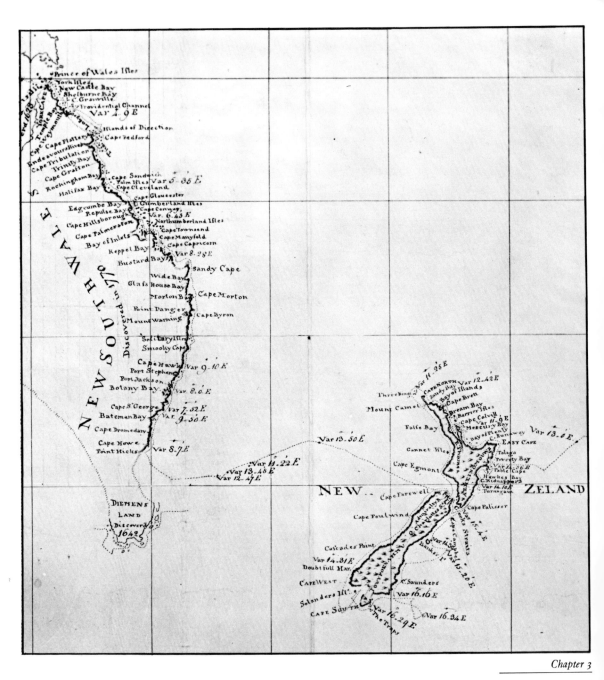

Cook's charting of New Zealand and the east coast of Australia, 1769–1770. (Courtesy of British Museum, Add. MS.7085.1.)

PLATE 10

the astronomical observations and making "no further use of the log than to connect those points of the track the ship was in when he took his angles and bearings."[17] The chart which this survey produced was notably exact in its latitudes and outline, and generally not more than half a degree out in longitude. Because Cook carried no chronometer on his first voyage the longitude was determined by the method of "lunar distances," and when that of Queen Charlotte Sound (his principal reference point for the survey laid down in 1770) was checked by the chronometer in 1773, on Cook's second voyage, it was found to have been 40' in error. Later in the century, the precision of the "waterwork," or charting of the sea bed offshore, was improved by the use of resection, that is, fixing the survey ship's position by observation of three rays on shore marks with sextant or reflecting circle. This method was employed by the hydrographer Charles F. Beautemps-Beaupré on D'Entrecasteaux's expedition of 1791–1793. About this time, a mechanical solution for such "running fixes" was provided by the station pointer (an English invention) which enabled the position of a boat, while sounding, to be rapidly determined by resection and plotted directly on the chart.

From this period any ship engaged on exploration or survey duties might be expected to bring back a much greater wealth of hydrographic data, and the constantly increasing volume of such information called for a regular service for the continuous revision of charts and for their supply to ships. In France, the Dépôt des Cartes et Plans de la Marine had, since its establishment in 1720, undertaken an ambitious program of chart publication, both in separate sheets and in the sea atlases for various *"navigations"* constituting the *Hydrographie française*. In England, the Hydrographic Department of the Admiralty, set up in 1795, developed its surveying service after 1811, and under the administration of Francis Beaufort (1829–55) assumed the responsibility for providing world coverage. During Beaufort's term of office as Hydrographer the number of Admiralty charts increased from 883 to over 2000; and in 1844, Matthew Fontaine Maury, then Superintendent of the Depot of Charts and Instruments at Washington, testified to the debt owed by "navigators of all nations" to Beaufort "for the . . . zeal with which he has conceived, and for the liberality he has shown in communicating, the surveys made from his office."[18] By 1885 nineteen countries had official hydrographic departments. Their significance in the extension of geographical knowledge was twofold. In the first place, as noted by Maury, their charts were generally available, and so provided a reliable "base map" for correction and completion by the explorer; in Lloyd A. Brown's words, "the very nature of the work performed by the various Hydrographic Surveys precluded isolation and secrecy, and from the beginning the benefits to be derived from international cooperation were apparent to all countries."[19] Secondly, national hydrographic offices have been active in promoting scientific exploration, notably in the polar regions and in the Pacific Ocean.

OCEANOGRAPHIC EXPLORATION AND RESEARCH

The eighteenth and nineteenth centuries saw the continuous enrichment of the content of maps, a process which has continued with progressive acceleration into our own day. The great increase in observed data has evoked cartographic techniques to represent the facts of many branches of knowledge in their structural or spatial relationship. This enlargement of the mapmaker's field has embraced on the one hand the physical phenomena of the lithosphere, the hydrosphere, and the atmosphere, and on the other various aspects of human geography. Even the eighteenth-century voyages of exploration are distinguished by the variety and fullness of their hydrologic and meteorological observations. From Cook's expeditions, for instance, we have, besides the usual records of tides, currents, and winds, regular observations for magnetic declination and dip, gravity observations by pendulum, and measurements of the temperature and salinity of sea water. Temperature observations to determine the limits of the Gulf Stream were made with Fahrenheit's thermometer by Benjamin Franklin in 1775 and Charles Blagden in 1776–1777. There were primitive attempts at deep-sea sounding, like that of Captain Constantine John Phipps who in 1773 reached a depth of 683 fathoms in latitude 65° N., longitude 3° E.

Systematic charting of the sea bottom and study of the physical and biological phenomena of the oceans were intensified during the nineteenth century with improved techniques for observation and recording. The instructions issued by Beaufort in 1837, besides requiring of his surveying officers the normal hydrographic data, called for meteorological, magnetic, biological, and geological records. Maury's standard reporting forms, or "abstract logs," which were adopted by an international conference at Brussels in 1853, provided the material for his wind and current charts and whale charts. The model for many oceanographic expeditions, under national auspices and with comprehensive scientific programmes, was that of the *Challenger* (1872–1876), which provided a broad synoptic view of physical and biological conditions in the Atlantic, Indian, and Pacific oceans. Since the early eighteenth century the cartographer's representational technique has therefore developed continuously to admit scientific data of various kinds onto his maps.

The most significant graphic device, and that of widest application, has been the isopleth or "curve line" of equal value. Long called the "Halleyan line" from its employment in Halley's isogonic charts of the Atlantic and the world (1701–1702), it is found, in the form of isobaths or underwater contours, in early bathymetric surveys in the Netherlands at the end of the sixteenth and beginning of the eighteenth centuries. The introduction of more accurate leveling instruments and of the aneroid barometer led to an increase in the number of reliable observed altitudes, to a greater interest in hypsometry and, under social and scientific pressures, to the general adoption of contouring in topographical maps during the nineteenth century. Submarine contours were introduced into the Russian official charts from 1834, and into the British from 1838; in the "Carte Bathymétrique des Océans" of the International Hydrographic Bureau they have come into universal use. The isopleth, largely on the initiative of Alexander von Humboldt and Hermann Berghaus, has found many other applications to cartography, notably in meteorological charts, synoptic weather charts, maps of terrestrial magnetism, and charts incorporating the data of quantitative oceanographical research.

With the evolution of apparatus for deep-sea sounding and sampling and of continuous recording instruments, the concept of exploratory survey has acquired a new dimension. Maury's broad vision of the scope of oceanography and his insistent advocacy of intensive scientific surveying of the Pacific Ocean, on an international basis, have alike been justified.

4

GEOGRAPHICAL KNOWLEDGE
OF THE PACIFIC PEOPLES

Gordon R. Lewthwaite*

When "stout Cortez" (or, to correct the poet,[1] Balboa)

> "Stared at the Pacific—and all his men
> Look'd at each other with a wild surmise—
> Silent, upon a peak in Darien"

they were not gazing upon a virgin sea. The occupation of the Pacific was an accomplished fact (Fig. 6). Across the span of the ocean, from north to south and from east to west, the Europeans found flourishing societies, and as they plotted their course from island to island it was, as often as not, the uncanny cunning of some native navigator which guided them to a sure landfall. And even when some discovered island was devoid of population, the crumbling ruins of sacred *marae* or the trace of some deserted garden gave mute evidence of former habitation. Everywhere the European Crusoe beached his boat, he found the footprints of Man Friday in the sand.

How this came about is by no means fully known. Speculation—not to say wild surmise—was lively enough in Balboa's day, and it has lost nothing of its vigor. Whence did the people come, and how did they reach such remote locations, mere pinpricks of land lost in an infinitude of water? Just what was the significance of their tales of gods and heroes fishing up the islands? And where, if anywhere, lay their ancestral Hawaikis and dim "spirit lands" such as Bulotu? Was their origin to be traced to Asia or to America, or perchance to some sunken continent? And were they, as Buck expressed it, fearless "Vikings of the Sunrise,"[2] boldly navigating their craft along well-chosen courses, or were they, as Sharp maintains, the victims of storm and current, helplessly drifting or steering blindly from obscured homelands and fortunate to plant their seed by happenstance on some unsuspected island?[3] And how much did they remember, or discover, of their vast environment of ocean and island and distant continental rim?

Such questions unfortunately remain partially unanswered, though refined techniques such as linguistic analysis and bloodtyping, archaeology, and carbon-dating, have increasingly reinforced or cancelled out the cherished traditions on which reliance was perforce placed during Oceania's age of scientific innocence. Not that the traditions can be expunged, but a more critical analysis has revealed a measure of contamination and post-contact rationalization (intentional or unconscious) and has shaken faith in their unsupported value, while the spade has uncovered a hitherto unsuspected time-depth in the ancient and often complex process of settlement. This chapter, in fact, is one which is written both too early and too late; too late to tap the resources of uncorrupted tradition and native navigational lore, and too early to

---

*Dr. Lewthwaite is professor of geography, San Fernando Valley State College at Northridge, California.

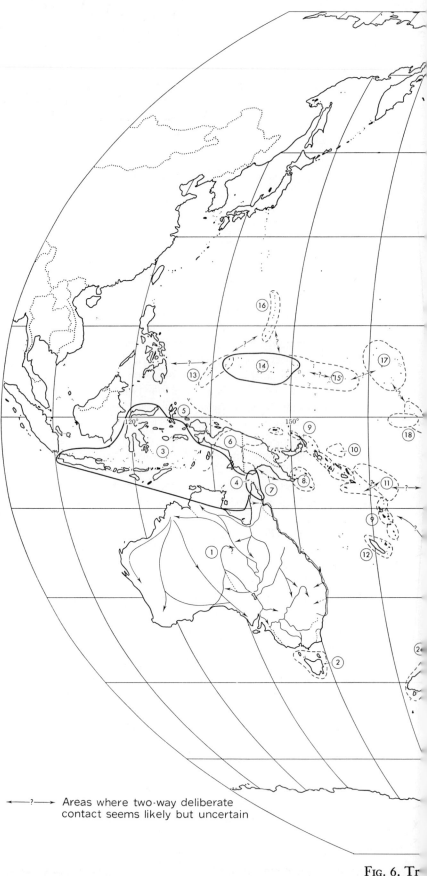

1. Australian trails (after McCarthy)

2. Tasmania

3. The World of the Arnhem Landers at the close of Indonesian contact (ca. 1900) (after Ronald M. and Catherine H. Berndt)

4. Torres Strait

5. Indonesia-New Guinea

6. Fly-Sepik trail

7. Papuan Gulf (Motu)

8. Papua-D'Entrecasteaux (Kula Ring)

9. Bismarck Archipelago-Solomons-New Hebrides: circles of discontinuous contact

10. Ontong Java

11. Santa Cruz-Banks Islands

12. New Caledonia-Loyalty Islands

13. Yap-Palau

14. "Gagil" sphere of Yapese hegemony

15. Eastern Micronesia

16. Mariana Islands

17. Marshall Islands

18. Gilbert Islands-Ocean Island (Banaba)

19. Ellice Islands-Rotuma Island

20. Tongan knowledge (suggested by data supplied to Cook)

21. Tokelaus (Union Islands)

22. Rakahanga Island-Manihiki Island

23. Tupaia's map (approximate bounds)

24. Society Islands-Tuamotu Archipelago

25. Southern Cook Islands

26. New Zealand

27. Chatham Islands

28. Marquesas Islands

29. Hawaiian Islands

30. Mangareva Island

31. Easter Island

32. South America—Galapagos Islands

→—?—→ Areas where two-way deliberate contact seems likely but uncertain

FIG. 6. Tr

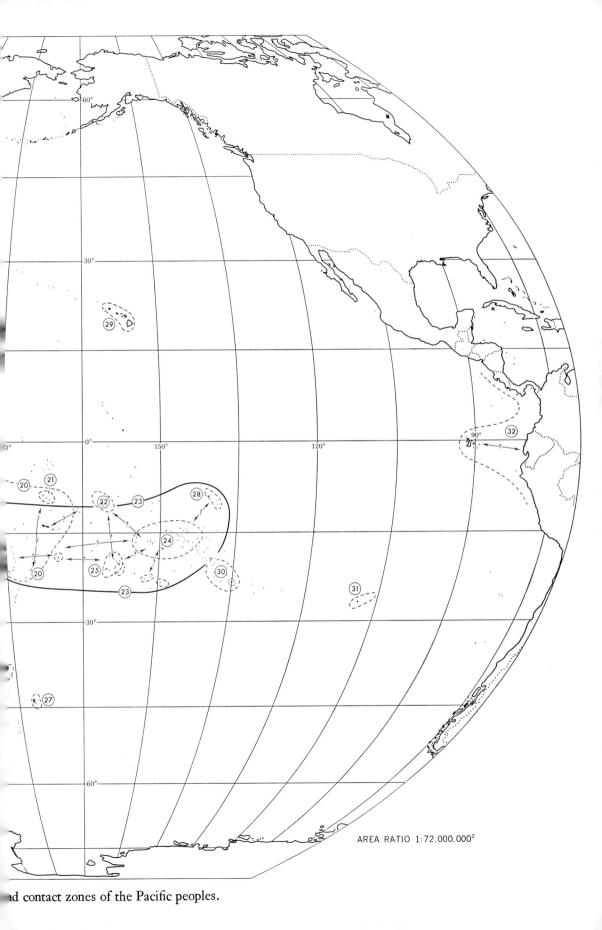

id contact zones of the Pacific peoples.

reap full benefit from the current thrust of scientific enquiry. Nothing seems more certain than the assumption that fresh modifications will be in order even as these paragraphs roll from the printer's press.

Nonetheless, something of value does in fact emerge from the records. Here ultimate problems of ethnic origins and trans-Pacific contact, while not wholly irrelevant, will recede into the background and the focus will shift to the patterns of contact and geographical knowledge which prevailed when Westerners first sought to chart the sea.

AUSTRALIAN ABORIGINES AND CONTINENTAL TRAILS

At the southwestern threshold of the Pacific lay *Terra Australis incognita*, virtually unknown and certainly neglected by Europeans until the time of James Cook. Although the Australian aborigines are usually assumed to have stood apart, isolated from the web of communications that linked the higher cultures of other lands, the assumption is only part-truth. Their very origins (if the theory of triple genesis holds good) lay in intergroup contact, the intermingling of ancient Negrito peoples with Ainoid and Veddoid immigrants; and the different regions of the continent remained linked by a web of trails. Nor did the widening of the barrier straits by glacial eustasy wholly sever Australia from the Asian archipelagoes, for its northern shores lay open to the maritime traffic of Indonesia and New Guinea.

The breadth of aboriginal knowledge must not, however, be exaggerated. It would seem that the ancient Tasmanians, though venturing in their frail craft to outlying islands, were cut off from the continent,[4] while continental peoples were largely confined to their tribal territories. Admittedly, these were mentally mapped with uncanny skill and there was a network of exchange which distributed goods far and wide across the land,[5] but more often than not such goods were simply passed from one sedentary group to another. Each controlled the local sector of a route vague in origin and unknown in termination. Thus the "merbok" partners consummated their ceremonial exchange without widespread travel, and the tropical shells so valued on southern shores had many a time been passed from hand to hand before they reached their destination.

Nevertheless, geographical knowledge was far from purely local. Memories of ancestral migration routes were woven into the traditions, and many a trail was beaten to distant regions rich in some material resource or endowed with the prestige of the supernatural. Virtually every horde gathering involved some interchange of information, and trails were carefully designated and neutralized to enable "innocent passage" across hundreds of miles of alien territory. Coast dwellers trekked to the inland bush to barter fish for opossum skins, while others resorted to the Queensland ranges for edible *Araucaria* cones, sought grinding stones in remote outcrops, or went in search of the narcotic *pitjuri* (*Duboisia hopwoodii*) in the far interior. Parties traveled 900 miles or more to collect the red ochre of Flinders Range, and incipient "markets" such as Ooldea evolved to facilitate the process of regional interchange.

Such local trails meshed into the great transcontinental trunk routes, some seven of which were delineated by McCarthy.[6] These naturally converged on resource-rich regions, traced the pattern of streams and water holes across the arid interior, or followed the coastal beaches. Several fanned south from Cape York Peninsula, an eastern route following the shoreline to Victoria and interior trails paralleling the beds of streams that drained toward Lake Eyre, and both systems joined in the Murray-Darling basin. From the northwestern shores of the continent, inland and coastal routes linked the Kimberley district and Arnhem Land with the southwest and with the Eyre Peninsula, and these in turn were interlinked with each other and the eastern network. Thus, from north to south and east to west the continent was interlaced with trails which at once repeated the patterns of prehistoric migrations and diffused at least hints of faraway places and their resources.

CONTACTS ACROSS THE NORTHERN SEAS

Nor were the aborigines of the north unaware of other lands. From the Kimberleys to Groote Eylandt the coast was washed by narrow seas whence came strange peoples from the northwest, Chinese and Arabs maybe, but more commonly seafarers from Indonesia.[7] Once, it seems, the Arnhem Landers knew only the offshore islands and hypothetical "Braglu," but the light-skinned "Baijini" (Sea Gypsies, perhaps) and their successors from the direction of Timor, Ceram, and especially Makasar, brought the Indies within their ken. Pearl-oyster and tortoise, sandalwood and trepang were precious in Asia, and the proas that came and went with the monsoons gave the hunters and gatherers of the north more than a glimpse of rice planting and pottery making, and introduced many an adventurous aboriginal crewman or concubine to the exciting life of Makasar, "the Mecca of the eastern Arnhem Landers."[8] Returning prodigals stirred their encampments with tales of strange animal life and polyglot populations, thronging market places and exotic foods, and transmitted a quite specific geographical knowledge of the island realm north to Halmahera and west to Java, though it was Timor, Timorlaut (Pulau Jamdena), and the Celebes which loomed largest in their consciousness.

The Arnhem Landers were apparently only vaguely aware of New Guinea, which was, however, better known to the inhabitants of Cape York Peninsula. These were made aware of their northern neighbor largely by the Papuans of certain islands in Torres Strait who cruised their outriggers for hundreds of miles across the narrows and through the sheltered waters behind the Great Barrier Reef, concentrating their traffic to some degree in Princess Charlotte Bay and the Batavia (Wenlock) River mouth, returning north to tap the trade of Mawata and Saibai in adjacent New Guinea.[9]

NEW GUINEA PEOPLES AND THEIR NEIGHBORS

New Guinea, thus linked to Australia on its southern flank, had more intimate contact with southeastern Asia. The unearthing of ancient Chinese pottery and the distribution of Asian glass beads gives evidence of at least indirect traffic in earlier times, though when Europeans arrived it was Indonesian influence which was paramount in western New Guinea. The blending of blood and custom was patent, sweeping claims of sovereignty were being made by the sultanates of Ternate and

Tidore, and slavers and traders from Makasar—Indonesians, Arabs, and Chinese—
were working from permanent local bases or arriving and departing with the monsoons. But the influence of southeast Asians was far from universal. Though occasional Indonesian or Filipino colonists may have penetrated eastward to Aitape and
New Ireland, their proas rarely prowled either the more rugged and unsubjugated
northern shores east from Teluk Sarera (Geelvink Bay) or the southern swamp-
forests of the "casuarina coast."[10]

While the Malaysian peoples knew something of New Guinea, it seems uncertain
how much the Papuans and Melanesians in general knew of the outer world and indeed of their own region. Not uncommonly they are contrasted with Micronesians
and Polynesians as ignorant landlubbers confined to their tribal boundaries. If a guess
may be hazarded on the basis of limited data, their horizons were in fact notably restricted. Rain forest, precipitous slopes, and sodden marshland interposed obstacles
enough, but more significant checks to the diffusion of geographical knowledge were
imposed by opaque screens of cultural contrasts, linguistic barriers, intergroup hostilities, and fear of alien spirits. Both in New Guinea and along the island chain, many
Melanesians were pronounced by European observers as untraveled beyond their immediate confines and ignorant of even the direction of villages a few miles away.

Nevertheless, this unawareness must not be exaggerated. Quite apart from widespread if tantalizingly vague traditions of migration, locational information was acquired by various means, warfare itself serving a geographical turn when knowledge
of enemy territory was gained, while ties of kinship and trade linked even distant
communities. Alien groups conducted "silent barter" or exchanged children to learn
each other's language, while regular markets attracted visitors from quite extensive
hinterlands. Regions endowed with skilled potters or resistant adze-stone were widely known; "beach" and "bush" peoples deigned to trade their respective surpluses;
and it could be said of most of New Guinea as of the Trusteeship that "the entire
territory is covered by countless small networks of intergroup trading complexes."[11]
Furthermore, these were frequently unified by great trunk routes such as that which
traversed the ranges from Torres Strait to the valley of the Sepik and elsewhere
crossed "the whole of New Guinea" from coast to coast.[12]

Though many of the shore dwellers were singularly lacking in maritime skills,
others were seafarers with broad horizons. Canoes from Teluk Sarera (Geelvink
Bay) sailed a hundred miles or more to offshore islands and ranged into the Indies,
while "the most adventurous of all this [Melanesian] race,"[13] the Motu of the eastern
Gulf of Papua, though favoring coastal navigation, took advantage of the monsoon
winds which propelled their double canoes and raft-like *lakatoi* across two hundred
miles of open sea, carrying thousands of pots to be exchanged for sago in the Fly
delta. Analogous traffic threaded the shores of Huon Gulf, and two great contact
zones linked the mainland with the island chains respectively extending southeastward and northeastward from New Guinea. To the southeast it was the "Argonauts
of the Western Pacific," the famed traders of the "kula ring," who moved from island
to island along seaways defined by landmark and guiding star,[14] while to the northeast the Triam and Siassi islanders of Dampier Strait played a considerable role in
the network of communications which joined New Guinea to the Bismarck Archi-

pelago and its outliers. And westward among the Admiralty Islands, the Manus traders stood pre-eminent.

ALONG THE MELANESIAN CHAIN

Southeastward from New Ireland extends the chain of Melanesian islands where traditions speak of a "far past, when peace, and free travel and intercourse and trade flourished,"[15] but where also early Europeans recorded limited and discontinuous circles of contact rather than a continuum of geographical knowledge, and a notable absence of sophisticated navigational techniques. Only the outer fringe, where Micronesians and Polynesians blended with Melanesians, was boldly maritime. The Bismarck Archipelago was linked to the Solomons by intermediate islanders such as the Tanga, but even the active Tanga were largely confined to a sixty-mile radius.[16] Among the Solomon Islanders and their immediate neighbors "beach" and "bush" peoples were frequently mutually ignorant, and though the records are studded with traditions of migrations and daring interisland raiding and trading which extended for hundreds of miles, the canoemen clung within eyeshot of the shore. The Santa Cruz seaman, by contrast, shared something of the maritime tradition and were reputedly the finest seamen in all of Melanesia, sailing star-courses, though not without confusion and loss, westward to the southern Solomons and Rennell and east to Tikopia.[17] The traditions of the Banks islanders also indicate extensive voyaging, though Codrington found their "world to consist of their own group, with the adjacent Torres Islands, the three or four northern New Hebrides and perhaps Tikopia, round which the ocean spread till it was shut in by the foundations of the sky."[18] The New Hebrideans were still more confined: though Santo people were aware of the Solomon and Santa Cruz islands there was little if any contact, while Harrisson found cause to accuse the Malekulans of "complete geographical ignorance."[19] And New Caledonia to the south lay in "extreme isolation,"[20] having contact only with its immediate neighborhood, from the Îles Belep to the Loyalty Islands.

While voyaging was too limited to link the Melanesian chain into an entity and promote mutual knowledge, the Melanesians were not wholly unaware of the outer world, nor was the outer world wholly unaware of them. Recent archaeology indicates a prehistoric continuum of culture which extended from New Caledonia to Melanesian Fiji and eastward into Polynesia,[21] nor was contact with other island realms wholly a thing of the past. The northeasterly screen of islands extending from Nuguria through Ontong Java and Sikaiana to Tikopia was populated by Micronesian and Polynesian communities not without contacts to the north and east. Not even the secluded villages of the New Hebrides and New Caledonia could discount the prospect of unwelcome visitation from the dimly realized Pacific—a canoe manned by Tongan warriors, as likely as not.

PEOPLING THE OPEN PACIFIC

Far beyond the festoons of Malaysian and Melanesian islands that extended an intermittent but substantial front to the open sea, there rolled the vast oceanic spaces of Micronesia and Polynesia. As the Chinese reported with telling aptness, beyond their shores stretched "the boundless place,"[22] endless waters from which men did

not return. And there the problems of navigational outreach and geographical knowledge reach their most acute—not to say contentious—forms. When Westerners
queried the islanders they uncovered a network of traditions, some of which were
clearly historical and precisely geographical and others which spoke uncertainly of
ancient homelands or "spirit lands," such as the Bulotu of the Fijians and western
Polynesians, and the Hawaiki to which most eastern Polynesians traced their origin.
Tales of warfare, migration, and heroic voyages were inextricably interwoven with
the supernatural; and lists of place names which defy identification, or suggest post-
European interpolation, are meshed into the chants. The vagueness of such locational
data may be partially gauged from the fact that Hawaiki alone has been identified
with places as far apart as Saba (Shabhah) in Arabia, Java, and Hawaii, Savai'i in
Samoa and Raiatea in the Societies, and Hakai Passage in British Columbia.[23] Smith
concluded that the traditions alluded to at least seven separate Hawaikis,[24] and along
with others Best credited the Maori with memories of the snow-crested Himalayas
and muddy ricefields of the Ganges,[25] memories which Heyerdahl[26] refers to the
flanks of the Andes.

But even if dubious legends of continental homelands are excluded from consideration, there remain numerous traditions of voyages which were interpreted as spanning the Pacific island world during a postulated "Golden Age" of Polynesian navigation. This was thought—to conflate somewhat variant viewpoints based on traditions
presumed to be genuine—to have followed the abandonment of cherished links with
Java and to have issued in a burst of exploration and settlement which reached its
climax after 1250 A.D. and terminated with the closing of the Polynesian "frontier"
about 1450 A.D. Tangiia was alleged to have inaugurated the era with a final visit to
Indonesia and a return voyage which continued beyond his Tahitian base to Easter
Island, followed by purposeful probes of the cold southern seas—a mere 20,000 miles
as Buck skeptically noted[27]—while Ui-te-Rangiora supposedly traversed the seas
from New Guinea to Easter Island and ventured south of Rapa into a region where
"foggy, misty and dark" waters were frequented by strange sea mammals and studded with icebergs.[28] Other voyagers allegedly returned with shrewd assessments of
New Zealand resources and circumstantial detail about New Guinea's negroid
peoples and resplendent bird life, while navigation was occasionally envisaged as
sufficiently exact for flotillas from far-flung Polynesia to arrive at the great *marae* of
Raiatea in synchronized precision. Small wonder that most agreed with Smith's
encomium: "Long before our ancestors had learnt to venture out of sight of land,
these bold sailors had explored the Antarctic seas and traversed the Pacific Ocean
from end to end. . . . Before such feats as theirs the navigations of the Phoenicians,
Arabs, Chinese and others sink into insignificance."[29]

A CHAPTER OF ACCIDENTS?

But such assertions are apt to breed their antitheses, and the concept of deliberate
long-range voyaging and exact geographical knowledge has been brusquely challenged, most particularly by Andrew Sharp. According to this interpretation, precise
navigation was impossible before Europeans developed precision instruments: dead
reckoning and orientation by sun and stars, winds and currents were but "crude
methods" whose inadequacy became evident once the broad target of a continental

shoreline was replaced by the miniscule isles of the Pacific. For courses set by sun and stars could be maintained only if these remained continuously in view—"a somewhat miraculous event," Sharp argued[30]—while subtle shifts of wind and current introduced imperceptible, or at least incalculable, degrees of set and drift. Once interrupted or deflected, the navigator could not recover his initial course, and even a minor directional error was compounded by distance.

These inescapable facts, it was insisted, both broadened the range of settlement and diminished the circle of geographical knowledge. The peopling of the Pacific was an involuntary process, the by-product not of a Golden Age but of navigational confusion. Untimely weather swept the unwary fisherman or the voyaging canoe from familiar waters to drift or run before the wind to oblivion—or to some lucky landfall. Return was impossible, for none could pinpoint the relative positions of the lost homeland and its fortuitous colony, nor were the "explorations" of voluntary or involuntary exiles and refugees admitted as more than a variation to the theme of chance: they forwandered unknown waters on one-way voyages. Only where wind and current were favorable and islands were grouped within the accepted navigational radius of two or three hundred miles did zones of deliberate contact develop, and Oceania was thus composed of "a number of little worlds, inaccessible except by accidental migration,"[31] and existing in a mutual ignorance which was relieved only by fading traditions of lost homelands and, perchance, the arrival of another canoe-load of castaways. The supposed Vikings of the Pacific, though not denied such skills as were conformable with their modest technology and imperious environment, were little more than the flotsam and jetsam of wind and wave.

Thus basic questions concerning the islanders' knowledge of land and sea have been answered in starkly contrasting fashion, nor is the end of the debate yet in sight. Sharp's contentions have found support from such authorities as Oliver,[32] Vayda,[33] and Ferdon,[34] Goodenough[35] and Hilder,[36] Sinclair[37] and Cumberland,[38] while others, including Emory[39] and Spoehr,[40] Suggs[41] and Duff,[42] Heyen[43] and Frankel,[44] Parsonson[45] and Dening,[46] have expressed a measure of dissent. Not that a dialectical polarization of viewpoints should obscure the areas of agreement. Sharp himself, in restatements of his hypothesis, has reemphasized the role of deliberate exiles and well-equipped canoes rather than "Captain Cook's forgotten theory" of storm-driven castaways, while arguments for the transfer of untended plants and livestock in unmanned canoes became somewhat muted. On the other hand, native tradition and European observers alike have always attributed a considerable role to accidental discovery, and it is generally agreed that such outliers as Hawaii, Easter Island, and New Zealand had long sunk into isolation, no matter what the nature or degree of ancient contact. Nor did later traditionalists sustain Percy Smith's contention that voyages spanned the seas from Indonesia to Easter Island. Buck[47] and Kelly[48] concluded that even Tangiia was confined to the central Pacific and that tales of Antarctic adventure were reducible to modest southerly probes duly embellished in the whaling era. Nor do contemporary authorities such as Suggs press any claim that long-range settlers were sailing to a destination foreknown or that the discovery of the Marquesas was followed by return voyages to ancestral Tonga.[49]

But beyond such points of agreement a cross fire of criticism confronts the assertion that long-range voyagers could not return and that contacts between distant areas were solely accidental. It has been affirmed, in refutation, that its advocates exaggerate the perils of the Pacific, fail to do justice to the skill and courage of native navigators, and overlook a concatenation of positive evidence to the contrary.

THE PACIFIC PACIFIC

The charge that the perils of the Pacific have been exaggerated rests on the observed fact that many a long voyage, accidental or deliberate, has in fact terminated in a successful landfall, and that the Ocean is not a notably treacherous one. The tropical Pacific can be roiled and clouded, but even in the stormy season fine spells are prolonged and sun and stars are seldom obscured for more than three days. In the fine season, which was normally chosen for voyaging by notably shrewd native navigators, the trades blow and good sailing conditions prevail with conspicuous regularity. Nor do wind patterns necessarily favor sailing in one direction only. Quite apart from zones where winds shift with the seasons, there are disturbances which sporadically replace easterlies with westerlies, carrying vessels in directions sheerly contrary to the prevailing winds.

As for the ocean itself, though Polynesian currents occasionally move with some velocity and may prove tricky in interrupted waters, they tend to marked regularity. Waves, it is true, may be characterized by irregularity, but swells are notably constant, and it was swells which the navigator most particularly noted. Nor was lateral drift necessarily more than a mere "landsman's bogy," sometimes cancelling out, but not insurmountable and accepted as an inevitable risk by any seaman worth his salt.[50] All in all, Heyen insists, "the general weather-wind-wave-current pattern is fairly consistent for the greater part of the year."[51]

The Haven-Finding Art

Furthermore, the navigators of Oceania had mastered their environment to a degree which evoked the awe of most European observers. Their ships—scarcely "canoes"—were manned by crews inured to the sea and alert to note any subtle nuance that might affect their course. Shifting winds and currents were betrayed by temperature and humidity, trailing feathers, and star bearings; and corrective action could be taken with sail, paddle, or giant steering oar. Even adverse winds did not necessarily baffle the Polynesian, for canoes could sail within six points of the wind, take steady slants through the trades, and tack their zigzag way to difficult targets. And if the worst came to the worst and they were driven off course, all was not necessarily lost. The seamen of Oceania are emphatically not prone to panic, and (as Heyen suggests) the exploration of the Pacific may have originated from just such conditions. Off course but refusing to be driven far downwind and away from home, they made long boards to north or south with a shrewd eye for the return tack.[52] It is perhaps significant that Pritchard, while ostensibly accepting the contemporaneous belief that settlement was accidental, hastened to add that involuntary voyagers "invariably preserved correctly the direction of their homes."[53]

Certainly, too, their vessels gave them some command of the sea. There may have been some degeneration in construction, as was true in Easter Island, Mangareva, and the Chatham Islands, and the rafts so persistently mentioned in early tradition were

Double canoes of Tahiti, by Sidney Parkinson, in John C. Beaglehole (ed.): . . . *Captain James Cook* . . . Vol. 1, Fig. 32, British Museum, Add. Ms. no. 23921.12 [see Note 102]. (Courtesy of The Hakluyt Society.)

PLATE 11

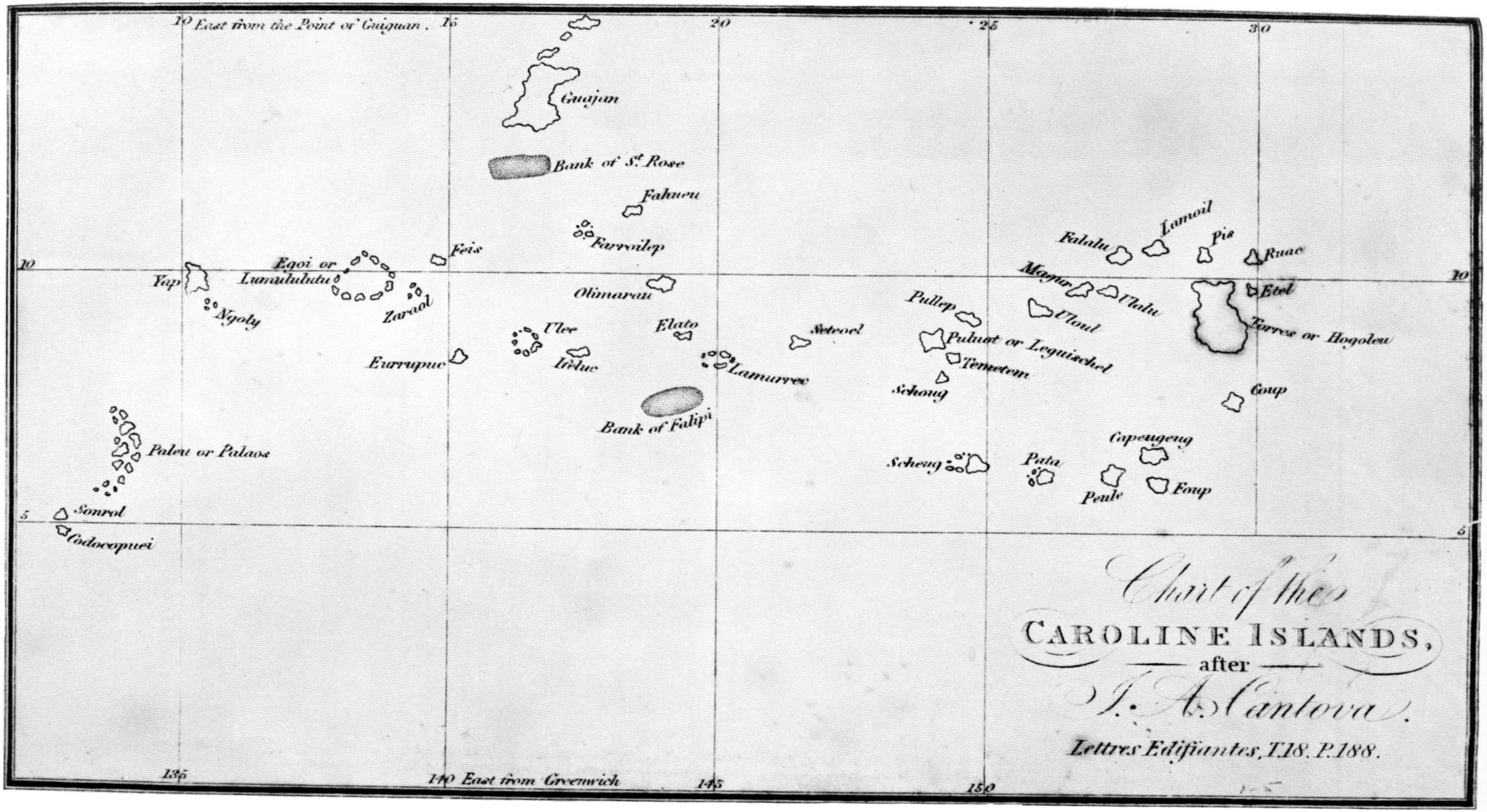

Juan A. Cantova's map, drawn by a missionary in Guam from data given by occidental voyagers from Faraulep in 1721. It indicates the contact zone of the western Carolines extending from Yap to Truk (Hogoleu). In Otto Kotzebue: *A Voyage of Discovery* . . . , Vol. 3, op. p. 412 [see Note 126]. (Courtesy of the Library of Congress.)

PLATE 12

not evident in the time of Cook, but the Englishman was quick to pronounce great double and outrigger canoes (Plate 11, *facing page 66*) such as those of Tonga to be "not only vessels of burden, but fit for distant navigation,"[54] swift and maneuverable. Cruising speeds, variously estimated at five to ten knots, enabled the craft to average 140 miles or more a day and brought the farthest outliers of Polynesia within two or three weeks of voyaging time. And the double voyaging canoes were well-found and provisioned, laden with water containers and foodstuffs, crop plants and livestock, to say nothing of scores and occasionally hundreds of people. Sometimes, too, flotillas moved in formation to increase the chance of landfall. Disasters there inevitably were, but it has reasonably been claimed that these most frequently involved tiny outriggers or European boats without benefit of skilled navigators.[55]

For skilled navigators there assuredly were, studious in the lore of sea and sky and guiding star. Much of this esoteric knowledge may have perished with the passing of the ancient priesthood, but even so the data are compelling. Cook found Polynesian weather predictions to be uncannily accurate, and roundly affirmed that "there was not a star in the hemisphere, fixed or erratic, that Tupia could not give a name to,"[56] while Andia found Society Islanders employing the concept of a sixteen-point compass and using wind, water, and especially "the rhumb of . . . particular stars" to pinpoint not only the islands but particular harbors "with as much precision as the most expert navigator of civilized nations could achieve."[57] Later investigators have reinforced the evidence. The Carolinians clinched their geographical knowledge by meshing it into a positively scientific astronomical system, and the mariners of the Gilberts named more than fifty stars that studded their "roof of voyaging."[58] And, though Makemson[59] may have incorporated much that seems apocryphal, the accumulation of data is impressive. The directions once cited as guiding the mariner from Hawaii to Tahiti or from the Societies to New Zealand are either fragmentary or fictitious, as, it seems, was the postulated use of the sacred Hawaiian calabash as a sextant.[60] Nevertheless, the astral directions from Pukapuka to Samoa are significantly accurate,[61] and the potential utility of stars in locating even distant islands has been indicated by Gatty[62] and Frankel[63]—though only if knowledge of the zenith stars were combined with latitude sailing, a knowledge which implies at least one earlier voyage of discovery without benefit of star guidance.

Moreover, even if accurate stellar observations were difficult if not precluded (as Hilder insists)[64] on the heaving sea, other indicators could be invoked. Initial directions were often guaranteed by aligning the departing vessel with landmarks—such as the "navigation stones" of Beru[65]—which were held in view till the guiding stars shone clear. And, though clinching evidence may be lacking, it seems that the departure of migrating land birds helped point the initial direction of search and, especially where migrations continued for weeks at a time as in the case of the cuckoo, far-ranging voyagers could follow their "long, low, ragged flight . . . to a certain landfall."[66] The bristle-thighed curlew (*Numenius tahitiensis*) and golden plover (*Pluvialis dominica*) winged their way between Hawaii and central Polynesia, and the longtailed and shining cuckoos (*Eudynamis taitensis* and *Calcites lucidus*) and godwits (*Limosa japponica*) flocked southwards to herald the New Zealand spring. Birds such as the terns were indicative of the proximity of the shore, and some species are said to have been released from canoes to be followed in their shoreward passage: certainly the landward flight of wildfowl was watched for in the twilight. But many a natural "homing device" was brought into play, such as the alignment of ocean swirls and their nocturnal luminescence, the hint of convection in shimmering "loom" or towering clouds, the green-tinted skyglow of a lagoon, the thunder of surf, the smell of land, drifting wood, or seaweed. Even today the island pilot is apt to ignore compass and chronometer and follow the intangible but certain guidance of delicate indicators scarcely suspected by the uninitiated.

The range of effectiveness of such techniques remains open to doubt, Sharp maintaining that homing aids were useful only close to home, and that star navigation lost its utility one or two hundred miles from land where deviations were no longer discernible,[67] while Hilder underscores the practical difficulties of locating the "slippery stone" of Polynesian parlance, the low island that scarcely crested the surface and was so readily overshot.[68] Others by contrast, and with equal appeal to instances, assert that though the risk of error might increase with the length of the voyage, the methods remained essentially valid no matter what the distance. Besides, it was not so much single islands but archipelagoes which offered targets for long-range voyages, and such insular clusters, with their overlapping circles of navigational sensitivity, multiplied the chances of a landfall.[69]

THE EVIDENCE OF TRADITION

It would seem, moreover, that if the traditions are brought into the balance a fairly generous evaluation of oceanic navigation and geographical knowledge must be accepted. Admittedly these traditions constitute evidence of mixed value. The mythical looms large, genealogies were distorted in the interests of upstart chiefs or conquering tribes, legends were imported or localized, identical place names were duplicated across the Pacific, and local names were changed from generation to generation. Vital segments of prehistory did slip through the very selective mesh of native memory, and elements of rationalization as well as fresh geographical data were also incorporated in facile and unwitting fashion in the post-contact era. Nor did the earliest Europeans always discover evidence of long voyages in Polynesian tales; indeed, it was explicitly affirmed that no "established fact or . . . probable conjecture" contradicted their initial assumption that migration was accidental.[70] Yet it was not long before others (though fully cognizant of the danger of confusing history and myth) became convinced by the interlocking of data that both historical fact and geographical knowledge were validly incorporated. Williams' efforts to locate Rarotonga have been cited as proof of the limitations of primitive navigation,[71] but Williams himself drew an opposite conclusion. In emphatic protest against the obuseness with which Europeans "perplexed [their] would-be informants with questions and doubts," he recorded his experience as "of universal importance to all persons in every scientific or other expedition who seek information from natives, as it shows the correctness of their knowledge." He insisted that not only was he given explicit sailing directions to Rarotonga but also circumstantial detail of that yet unknown island, of the Societies (especially Raiatea, the ancient center of worship) and of deliberate voyages to Tonga and even Rotuma. Such data convinced Williams "that at some former period more frequent communication must have existed between the islanders,"[72] and Ellis said as much of the Hawaiian traditions: embodied therein was evidence of voyages to lands afar.[73] Nor have recent decades of critical scrutiny and comparison with the data of archaeology and ethnology failed to confirm a solid residue. The tales of discovery seem too widespread and deeply rooted for excision, and to admit only such observations as Europeans put on paper during a brief and traumatic phase of Polynesian experience seems to narrow the evidence to the point of falsification. Most would conclude with Suggs[74] and Heyen[75] that the voyaging traditions stem not from fancy but from hard fact.

DISTRIBUTIONAL PATTERNS: RANDOM OR REGULAR?

Such traditions, it would seem, are also reinforced by the more tangible fact of regularities in the distributions of artifacts, crops, and livestock. Admittedly, irregularities (claimed as evidence of the random nature of settlement) do in fact appear, particularly in the distributions of the Polynesian livestock trilogy of pig, dog, and chicken, and most notably in the peripheral zone extending from New Zealand to Easter Island. New Zealand possessed only the dog, Niue along with Mangaia and Aitutaki lacked the pig, all three species were absent from Rapa and Mangareva and the dog from the Marquesas, while Easter islanders were left with the solitary chicken. The major crop plants were more regularly distributed, but this was explained as resulting from natural dispersal and especially from the fortuitous arrival of lost and often unmanned canoes, a process whereby plants "were dribbled along piecemeal over 3000 years from group to group and from island to island."[76]

But this would seem to involve too long a chapter of happy accidents. All three livestock species were present in most high islands, and the exceptions may be open to alternative explanations. Cook[77] and Andia[78] testified to the difficulties of shipping Polynesian pigs, while even well-established stock could be eliminated by feast or famine. Furthermore, archaeology (to reinforce the impression of distributional regularity) has now revealed that the dog once existed in the Marquesas and the pig and dog in Easter Island. And the same regularity appears in the repeating pattern of coconut and banana, breadfruit and paper mulberry, taro and yam, sweet potato and gourd. It seems difficult to conceive that some thirty species, characteristically associated in a horticultural complex throughout Polynesia, were fortuitously transported and established, while the omission of some tropical species from Easter Island, Rapa, and New Zealand suggests a veto by environmental factors. Merrill asserted that "all the basic food plants . . . other than a few fruit trees, had to be grown from underground parts . . . mostly carried from island to island in soil."[79] The untended establishment of such species as banana, breadfruit, and delicate tubers, let alone the progressive "dribbling" of a total crop and livestock complex, seems a mathematically remote contingency. Nor does it accord with archaeological evidence that early settlers, whether deliberately or by chance, arrived in the

Marquesas, Easter Island, and Hawaii in well-equipped expeditions with the full roster of crops and livestock ready to hand.[80]

Other distributions have also been cited as relevant to the point. Some erratic features of the culture of atolls in particular have been attributed by Vayda to the presumed impact of random arrivals,[81] while Duff, by contrast, inferred considerable regularity in interisland contacts from the pattern of adze-type distributions[82]—mere "straws to keep the argonauts of the Pacific afloat," retorted Sharp, re-affirming his conviction that such consistencies owed more to the pattern of wind and current.[83] Such riposte notwithstanding, there seems enough evidence to lend point to the opinion that, though the debate on the relative "roles of voluntary and involuntary voyages . . . seems one of the more intractable questions of oceanic prehistory," there are in fact both uniformities and variations "so ancient and so regular" that no multiplication of accidents can be deemed satisfactory.[84]

SOME TENTATIVE CONCLUSIONS: THE NATURE OF EXPLORATION

And so the debate goes on, though some suspect that evidence from native traditions and explorers' journals must be supplemented by fresh data from linguist, ethnobotanist, and archaeologist before any breakthrough can be registered. But the author feels that there are certain regularities in the evidence, and that some generalizations are fully warranted. It is patent that the accidental factor, including both castaway and exile groups, has been conspicuous. Sharp has thoroughly under-scored this point. But there were directional patterns which were rather consistently repeated. Admittedly, as Ferdon has tellingly insisted,[85] Pacific winds and currents are multidirectional and human migrations may have been the same, but it remains true that the observed direction of accidental movement has been overwhelmingly from east to west. Movements in the opposite direction have been comparatively rare. This was insisted upon by early observers such as Ellis,[86] Williams,[87] and Pritchard,[88] recently re-emphasized by a number of independent investigators,[89] and is consistent with the results produced by experimental "models" constructed by Ward and Webb and based on the play of wind and current.[90] This accords with the undoubted direction of much Oceanian settlement and with the contemporary hypothesis that eastern Polynesia was largely populated from the Marquesas, but it also suggests that accident may have played a lesser role in the primary eastward movement.

It seems equally evident that drifting voyagers did not easily panic, let alone abandon hope of return. To compress a variety of instances, they remained notably free from psychological stress, being disturbed neither by the passage of time, the prospect of death, or the severance of family ties.[91] Though some never attempted to return home, this was often a matter of inclination rather than of inability. Pritchard noted that they preserved the direction of their lost homes by means of sun, moon, and wind,[92] while Forster was intrigued to find that Tupaia, by such means as observation of the fixed stars, was able to point the direction of Tahiti throughout the year-long and circuitous voyage to Java.[93] Sharp has challenged the navigational relevance of this fact,[94] but it surely hints at an ability to record directions and guide subsequent search. Kotzebue claimed evidence that the Caroline Islanders preserved star directions to the Marianas through centuries of disuse.[95]

But though the means may be obscure, it seems clear that at least occasional return across great ocean spaces was a reality. It is surely significant that the oft-cited drift of two canoes from the Carolines to the Philippines in 1696 was followed by an offer to return home and initiate traffic with the Spaniards, that one member of the crew had previously been to Mindanao and found his way home quite explicitly without a hint of European help, and was happier "in this his second voyage."[96] It is also in accord with Chamisso's report that Carolinians were finding their way back from the Philippines to the west and the Marshalls to the east, and that one return voyage traversed 2300 miles from Aur via Nugor (Nukuoro) and Ulea (Wolei Atoll) to Yap.[97] In later years Sittig reported another Micronesian return voyage of 1100 kilometers (685 miles),[98] and Weckler noted the nonchalance with which the Mokilese accepted a 900-mile return from the Gilberts.[99] In central Polynesia voyagers blown from Fakaofu boldly pressed on across hundreds of miles of sea from Nassau Island to Palmerston and on to Mangaia,[100] and Beechey gave evidence that the castaways blown 600 miles eastward to the Tuamotus were methodically pursuing their return to Tahiti.[101] Tupaia said that Society islanders sailed westward for ten days (at least 400 leagues or 1200 miles, in Cook's estimation) and returned in thirty-day voyages[102]—surely indicative of an ability to tack their way home over considerable distances. It is here maintained that the pattern included both accidental discovery and perhaps occasional and groping but nevertheless deliberate return, the pattern which Ratzel described as "dispersion . . . first through storms and currents, then by voluntary migration," followed by development of contacts of "the most varied kind."[103]

Not that all dispersion was necessarily involuntary. There is no reason to doubt that the pressures and opportunities which fostered deliberate migration in Asia continued into Oceania, and the variations on the theme were legion. Strife and famine, crime and punishment, an almost oriental passion to save face, the search for fish or feather, frustration and overcrowding in the home village, "pride, prestige and predatory economics," to say nothing of the sheer desire to see the wide world that lay beyond the insular horizon—all the motives that goaded men of other lands to lift anchor operated with intensity within the narrowed circle of the reef. Sometimes leaders sought to alleviate local pressures by encouraging exploration and overseas settlement. As Porter found in the troubled Marquesas, great canoes laden with men and women and crops and livestock periodically set forth in search of peace and plenty in rumored islands to the west. Some expeditions doubtless perished at sea whilst others beached their craft in safety. In this instance return voyages seem not to have taken place;[104] indeed, the very circumstances which promoted departure often sufficed to preclude return. But sometimes it was the homecoming that gave relish to the expedition. Williams was told that one young blood who swaggered ashore with tales of distant adventures provoked such envy that "it became the object of ambition with every adventurous chief to discover other lands and on his return to bring some article of value to his home island,"[105] and Firth, probing Tikopian history, found that among the many who sailed forth on *forau* at least some returned to enlarge "the range of knowledge of the outside world for all Tikopia."[106]

Thus it is here concluded that at least some "elbow room" must be left for long-range purposeful exploration, and that the difficulties of two-way navigation should not be exaggerated into impossibility. It would seem, rather, that voyaging covered the entire spectrum between hapless drifting and carefully planned expeditions that ranged afar before returning home. Accident and purpose need not, of course, be pressed into complete dichotomy. Some voyages that began by accident ended in deliberate return, while others that raised anchor with clear intent were fortunate to sail into some unsuspected haven rather than the jaws of the giant *Tridacna* that gaped open before the audacious Polynesian. For Sharp has administered a merited rebuke to speculation. Whether or not a Golden Age of Exploration ever existed remains uncertain, but it is his critic Dening who affirms that "insofar as Sharp has impugned the picture of casual and far-reaching excursions through the Pacific, he would seem to be correct."[107] And, though Sharp may have drawn the perimeters of insular knowledge too tightly, it cannot be doubted that many areas of Oceania were in fact existing in mutual ignorance when European sails first broke the horizon. Yet each archipelago had its particular range of knowledge and ignorance, and local variations require separate consideration.

MICRONESIANS: MASTERS OF THE SEA

It is Micronesia which current opinion favors as the major gateway to the Pacific, and western Micronesia remained within the threshold of Asia. Neither the routes nor the methods of occupation are yet clear, but the currents that pour northeasterly through the Djailolo Passage and the winds of the southwestern monsoon may well have enforced or guided penetration. Negritoid elements seem evident in Yap and Palau in the southwest as well as in northeastern Micronesia, and Melanesian influences were not excluded, but it was the stamp of Southeast Asia which prevailed. The Palaus were occupied by 2000 B.C. and the Marianas and portions of the Carolines before 1500 B.C., but the eastern Carolines may have remained fallow until Malayo-Polynesians moved north from either the Bismarck-New Guinea area or the New Hebrides, or perchance from both. It seems, too, that the basaltic islands were colonized some time before population spilled into the low islands and began the evolution of an atoll culture which was superbly adjusted to its maritime environment.

Opinions differ as to the manner of penetration. Doubtless the occupation of the Palaus was incidental to the thronging maritime traffic of southeast Asia and particularly of the Philippines and Moluccas, and the later movement into eastern Micronesia may well have been (as Goodenough surmises)[108] the fortuitous result of wind and current. Spoehr, however, believes the thrust into Micronesia was preceded by the development of maritime skills which enabled man to "traverse truly awe-inspiring distances across the open sea" in fully laden vessels,[109] and points out the significant fact that the Palaus are linked by the flyways of migrating birds to both the Philippines and Japan.[110] And, as Osborne intimates, the Djailolo current may have favored accidental dispersal from the Moluccas but it is skill which seems implied when contrary currents were traversed by migrants from the Philippines.[111]

Whatever the nature of the original migrations, Micronesia witnessed a most extraordinary evolution of maritime skill based on the reading of sea and sky. The astronomical systems were apparently locally developed with precise reference to navigation rather than to agriculture, and took full advantage of their latitude. Pole Star and Southern Cross were both in view, and only trifling error was introduced by the assumption that the axis of the Carolines formed the terrestrial equator, and correlated also with the celestial equator. Though particularly appropriate to east-west sailing, their system was sufficiently comprehensive to guide voyaging in all directions. "A vast and minute knowledge of the rising and setting positions of stars through the seasons" was incorporated in both sidereal compass and calendar. The thirty-two points of the sidereal compass were fixed by the azimuths of the stars, while the calendar was coordinated with the sequence of the stars in their rising and their relative altitudes. A far-flung network of interisland exchange and refinement of knowledge bore fruit in the development of a "rudimentary science," a definite international system[112] which incorporated a wealth of inherited information and provided a framework into which fresh data were progressively meshed. Only the European impact interrupted a spreading process whereby sidereal and lunar months were being coordinated, and westerners were astonished at the facile accuracy with which Caroline navigators sketched maps to oblige. Star bearings, voyaging times, and alternative landfalls were precisely indicated.

But only in the Marshall Islands, it seems, was there an incipient development of a "true cartography"[113] in the pre-European era—if indeed it was pre-European, an assertion not unchallenged.[114] These maps (Fig. 7) were based not on stellar directions (which seem to have been locally less significant than in the Carolines and Gilberts) but upon a scrutiny of the sea so painstaking and methodical that it was unrivalled even in Polynesia. Ocean currents, long and regular deep-sea swells and their deflection around island obstacles, the nodes or swirls that patterned the disturbed seas that flanked the islands—such were the elements most commonly indicated on Marshallese sea charts. These were simple lattices of wood or coconut-leaf midrib curved to show the swells and joined to show the swirls, with cowrie shells to mark the islands and leaf strips to suggest the currents and navigational directions (Fig. 7). Cartographically unsophisticated and highly irregular, they were individualistic mnemonic devices as much as maps, yet hints of positional accuracy were significantly present. The three types differed. The simple *mattang*, designed to aid instruction, showed the oceanic fronts and swells deployed around a single island, the more complex *meddo* incorporated a cluster of four or more islands, and the elaborate *rebbalib* covered the Rataks or Raliks or even the entire Marshall archipelago.

But interisland voyaging required seaworthy vessels as well as an intimate knowledge of sky and sea, and such vessels the Micronesians possessed in unusual measure. With possible exceptions (such as Truk where at least the memory was preserved) they lacked the double canoe but placed a well-founded faith in their superb "flying proas." Constructed with gently convex hulls and outriggers counterpoised by platforms, these craft were fitted with removable lateen sails and masts

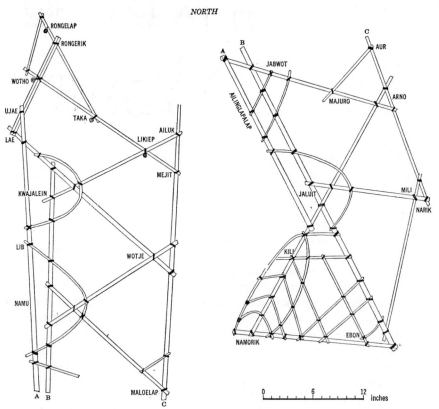

FIG. 7. Two stick charts, of the *meddo* type, from the Marshall Islands. The drawings (considerably reduced) represent most of the islands. Collection of Bernice P. Bishop Museum, Honolulu. (Courtesy of Edwin H. Bryan, Jr.)

pivoted amidships. Trim and incredibly handy, they combined a minimum and predictable tendency to slip sideways with the stability essential to ride out a storm, could move with undeviating straightness or progress with the characteristic "gentle zigzag" so advantageous in star navigation,[115] and reverse direction by simply shifting mast and sail. Their ability to sail close to the wind and their speed (perhaps dubiously reported as over 20 knots for sustained distances) were humbling to Europeans; Dampier reported one as covering over 480 leagues (1440 miles) from Guam to Manila in four days.[116]

Such craft were utilized with a sensitive skill born of determination and discipline. From the Carolines comes the report that none could marry until his dexterity with the proa had been demonstrated before critical elders,[117] while in the Carolines and Gilberts future pilots were trained in distinctive schools. Gilbertese youths were drilled to perfection in long lists of navigation stars and only after they could pinpoint these on the ceiling of their training house were they taken to the shore to survey the constellations of the open sky.[118] Though there was much that was esoteric and jealously guarded, the arts of navigation appear to have been diffused more widely than in aristocratic Polynesia, and fresh data were woven into a more tautly correlated system.

MICRONESIA AND ASIA

Thus the Micronesians were enabled to range the seas with notable freedom, but how far did they range? And was there consciousness of Asia? To Force, it appears that Palauans were at least vaguely aware of Indonesia and the Philippines, for "countless waves of migration must have ebbed and flowed through this aperture to the farther reaches of Oceania . . . . A long history of racial admixture is attested to by Palauan folk tales, which provide evidence of contact with Yap, the Philippines, the central Carolines, and Melanesia,"[119] and the legends incorporate references to the arrival of "whites"—Portuguese some think, or perchance Arab traders. Indeed, if culture traits give valid hints, western Micronesia was bombarded with Asian influences—whether by accident or design—and even the distant Carolines may have felt the Asian touch. It may well have been the sultanates of the Indies which were emulated in the pattern of island empires, and Indonesian cities which inspired the cyclopean structures of Ponape and Kusaie so strangely exemplified at Nanmatol, "The Venice of the Pacific."[120]

But it was in the western islands rather than the Carolines that the strongest influences were manifest: the intricate terracing of the Palaus, the sweet potatoes brought from the Philippines to Yap, the rice of Guam, treasured glass beads, and a wealth of pottery—especially the abundant red ware of the Marianas which has been invoked as defining the eastern fringe of the Malaysian tradition.[121] Osborne has concluded that the glass beads and gorgets of Palau were introduced from Indonesia and perhaps also from the Philippines and China by seafarers who came "occasionally in early times and who certainly visited the islands in the seventeenth and eighteenth centuries."[122] Traditions relating the ancient origin of glass beads imply at least accidental contact with Formosa and vague northern islands currently identified with Japan but more probably Okinawa,[123] a suggestion in accord with Mason's view that some knew of Formosa as well as the Philippines and the Celebes.[124] Yap and Palau may, in fact, have represented the remotest fringe of a farflung trading network which linked western Micronesia with southeast Asia and indirectly with the distant Mediterranean.

Thus there is solid evidence for substantial contact between western Micronesia and the rim of Asia, but the involvement of central Micronesia seems less clear. For Micronesia was scarcely an entity, and current opinion tends to favor the view that while the western chain from Palau to the Marianas was peopled directly from Asia, the eastern islands were primarily populated from the south and remained unconscious of the Asian continent.

But the latter conclusion seems open to challenge. As Burney noted, it could be inferred from the earliest Spanish contacts that Filipinos and Carolinians "were not wholly strangers to each other"[125] and in the early nineteenth century Chamisso learned that "those islanders frequently visited these [Philippine] coasts, sometimes by accident and sometimes by design," and found "their way back from Radack again to their home," thus covering a span of ocean almost as broad as the Atlantic (Plate 12, *facing page 67*).[126] And later ethnologists such as Sarfert[127] and Hambruch,[128] impressed with the demonstrated competence of the navigators of their time, felt impelled to the conclusion that pre-contact Carolinians must also have been aware of the vast circuit of shore extending from Asia through the Philippines to New Guinea and the Bismarck Archipelago, and eastward to Nauru and the Marshalls (Plate 13, *following page 80*).

CONTACTS WITHIN THE MICRONESIAN REGION

But whatever the ultimate judgment on Asian contacts, there are intimations that many a voyage brought Micronesians into mutual contact. The Palauans sent fleets of *kaep* racing north and south through the length of their archipelago, while the Yapese cruised to Palau and on to Peleliu and beyond to quarry their great discs of calcite and return, perilously laden, across nearly three hundred miles of sea. There is reason, too, to suspect that they visited Guam;[129] certainly they voyaged westwards, sometimes swept along in the great current which broke on the wall of the Philippines, and moved eastwards from island to island through the Carolines to Ponape some 1300 miles away and perhaps even to Kusaie.[130] Indeed, it was this web of navigation that confirmed the far-flung spiritual hegemony—or supernatural blackmail—exercised by the Gagil district of Yap. Fleets of canoes from islands extending almost as far east as Truk came laden for trade and tribute, gathering at Ulithi for the final run. It was this "Gagil sphere" which in practice formed the universe for the inhabitants of Ulithi, though they had also contact with Truk, Ngulu, and less directly with the Marianas; their vaguer penumbra of awareness included Palau, Ponape and Kusaie, the Marshalls, the Gilberts and even New Guinea, though the Ellice Islands lay beyond their ken.[131]

The people of Puluwat also sent their fleets to Yap and contacted the Marshalls and Gilberts through Kusaie. With their distinctive navigation school they won the reputation of being the finest pilots (not to say pirates) of Micronesia,[132] and the effectiveness with which their stellar system registered a fund of impersonal data was demonstrated when, at the German behest, a navigator swiftly sailed 390 miles to Ponape, an island he had never seen.[133] And beyond the circle of Truk, which lay outside the Gagil sphere, the situation was analogous: intimate contact with neighboring islands favored by the pattern of winds, fading into "an outer world which shades off imperceptibly through islands whose inhabitants are known, to other islands which at least these other islanders know."[134] And it seems that long and daring Trukese expeditions had occasionally probed the seas eastward to Ponape and Kusaie and far west to Yap and Guam and distant Saipan. Thus it was that the islanders accumulated a range of information invoking repeated European admiration. One Carolinian pilot, stated Arago, not only precisely located every island in his archipelago on a map composed of corn grains, but also defined their accessibility and products, neglecting "nothing which could prove to us that he was acquainted with the geography of one part of the Pacific."[135]

Outside the Carolinian archipelago, however, contacts are less precisely known. Sharp favors the view that voyages north to the Marianas began only with Spanish encouragement,[136] but there is cause to believe that these were rather a renewal of ancient ties.[137] Chamorros fleeing Guam before the Spanish invaders had found refuge in Uleai (Woleai Atoll) and Lamotrek, and it was a fleet from Lamotrek which, probing across 400 miles of open sea for islands allegedly known in tradition, rediscovered Guam in 1788 and initiated contacts which evolved into annual trading voyages. And though it was largely Carolinians who came to link the outer islands of the Marianas chain to Guam and to each other, this had not always been so, for in ancient times the proas of the native Marianans moved freely north and south across their trade winds. In early Spanish times, indeed, locally based craft ran clear to Manila.[138] But whether ancient contacts existed with the Bonins to the north only archaeology can reveal: though plausibly suggested as one route into Oceania, the Bonins were uninhabited when discovered.

Not so the northeastern quadrant of Micronesia, the Marshall Islands, where navigators were noted for the perceptive intensity with which they conned the sea rather than the sky, and for the simple but telling skill displayed in their sea charts (Fig. 7). The latter were effective only where islands were known and appropriately clustered, but the range of Marshallese knowledge was not defined by such frameworks. It seems possible that peaceful voyaging was largely concentrated in the separate circles of the northern Rataks and the politically unified Raliks,[139] but warfare sent the restive islanders roving throughout both archipelagoes, with the possible exception of several outlying atolls. Sailing under skilled pilots and in formations designed to comb a broad span of ocean, they have been considered the farthest-ranging of all Oceanic peoples, variously reported as covering from 600 to well over 1000 nautical miles on their expeditions,[140] of raiding Kusaie, of being aware of Truk and its neighborhood, and of appearing in the Gilbert and even the Ellice groups. Their knowledge of these southerly atolls would seem, however, to have been derived from castaways, though Carolinian contacts appear more deliberate. It will suffice to note that Europeans reported the occasional return of wandering Marshallese from the Carolines and the Marianas.

THE GILBERT AND ELLICE ISLANDS: MICRONESIAN-POLYNESIAN BORDERLAND

Thus the Marshallese made at least tentative acquaintance with other Micronesians, including the inhabitants of the northern Gilberts and perhaps the Ellice Islands. Here, in a zone where Micronesia merges into Polynesia and song and story tell of origins as far east as Samoa, stellar knowledge was developed to a nicety. Europeans were quick to note the rigor of the training whereby would-be pilots were introduced to the mysteries of the starry sky, and the beaches of some islands are checkered by crumbling "voyaging stones," range marks duly aligned to guide the departing canoe to its chosen destination—a system which Hilder described as the zenith of Oceanic navigational acumen.[141] Yet Hilder, skeptical of long voyaging, affirms that these guiding stones were seldom oriented to targets beyond a radius of 100 miles, and Sharp, citing the records of the Wilkes expedition of 1841, insists that even sporadic Gilbertese contact was confined to the central islands of their chain, and that the Ellice Islanders (though possibly aware of Tonga through Rotuman contacts) shared mutual ignorance with their Gilbertese neighbors.[142]

But this interpretation would seem unduly constrictive. Wilkes and his compatriots stressed that it was a recent development of hostility which had curbed travel in the Gilberts, and that about a hundred years earlier one navigator had reportedly "voyaged to every island in the group . . . to see the world."[143] Gilbertese navigators seemingly moved back and forth to Banaba or Ocean Island 250 miles away,[144] and the Banabans themselves may have invaded Kusaie. The inhabitants of some of the islands that fringed the Melanesian chain[145] to the south witnessed repeated arrivals from and perhaps departures to the Caroline, Gilbert, and Ellice islands, absorbed the cultural characteristics of these northern neighbors, and apparently possessed quite specific information about such islands as Vaitupu, Nukulailai, and Funafuti in the Ellice group.[146] The Ellice Islanders themselves exhibited an "intimate acquaintance" with the Tokelau Islands and Rotuma, appear to have suffered from Tongan raiders, and knew something of Samoa.[147] And there are hints that memories of ancient origins and contacts were preserved. Grimble believed that parallels between island names in the Ellice Islands and Djailolo Passage were too close to be accidental, and accepted as valid (though possibly imported from an ancient homeland) a Gilbertese tradition that ancestral voyagers to the farthest east had found the ocean bounded by a continuous wall of land.[148]

FIJI, SAMOA, AND TONGA: A NETWORK OF CONTACT

While recent scholarship might stress parallels with Melanesian rather than Indonesian nomenclature and dismiss vaguer intimations as mythical rather than historical,[149] even a strictly historical approach cannot fail to include the essentially Polynesian Ellice Islands within the periphery of the great contact zone which had Fiji, Samoa, and Tonga as its clustering nuclei. These three groups, though far from identical in ethnic character or in range of contact, were nevertheless linked by frequented seaways and mutual influence, and that of ancient origin. In recent years archaeologists have uncovered evidence that Polynesians anciently occupied at least parts of Fiji, and that elements of the culture of ancient New Caledonia, which was occupied perhaps a thousand years B.C., were shared by Fiji, Tonga, and Samoa. Suggs has emphatically affirmed that a far-flung network of deliberate voyaging extended far beyond "the circumscribed Fiji-Tonga-Samoa area."[150]

This affirmation may perhaps overleap current evidence; what is certain is the fact that Europeans found Tongan seamen to be masters of the surrounding seas, though they were then adopting ships of Fijian design. Apparently prompted by Micronesian and Melanesian practice, Fijians had evolved two magnificent canoe types, great outriggers or *camakau* which rivalled their prototype, the flying proa, in maneuverability, and huge *ndrua*, deemed the "largest, swiftest and most seaworthy double canoes ever constructed in Oceania."[151] These canoes, up to 120 feet long and 50 feet wide, were occasionally commodious enough to carry hundreds of warriors and their provisions. Controlled by their huge steering oars, they could face contrary weather with notable ease, sailing even within three points of the wind, though faring ill when it blew directly aft. Such were the craft that inspired emulation, and though Lauan and Tongan shipwrights were favored by Fijian chiefs for their craftsmanship and navigational finesse, it was Fijian designs which set the fashion. By the late eighteenth century marauding Tongans were eagerly abandoning their traditional *tongiaki* for the *ndrua* (which they bought or seized) or the *kalia*, which followed its pattern.

But, ship design apart, the Fijian contribution to geographical knowledge may be questioned. In fact, the very maneuverability of their craft may have reduced their range, for few were storm-driven into unfamiliar waters although occasional reports speak of them as sailing far afield. Lawry characterized the Fijians as boldly venturing on "somewhat distant voyages,"[152] and Wilkes found them "daring navigators" making long voyages to Tonga, Rotuma, and Samoa.[153] Speiser credited them with sailing to the New Hebrides, while occasionally Fijian vessels were reported at New Caledonia, at Tikopia, and in the waters of the Gilberts and Ellices.[154] It may be suspected, however, that such voyages were primarily accidental. Although the Fijians accounted the neighboring Yasawas a distant land, Williams asserted that they never sailed beyond the waters of their own archipelago,[155] Mariner[156] and Dillon[157] affirmed that none ever ventured to Tonga or back without Tongan assistance, and their legends are notably silent regarding Samoa.[158]

Similar doubts have been expressed concerning the outreach of the Samoans, and that despite the title of "Navigators' Islands" early bestowed upon their homeland. To various observers they seemed "quite a domestic people" who rarely ventured beyond eyeshot of the shore,[159] traveling freely only along the axis of their archipelago, never reaching Tonga save in Tongan craft, and lacking contact with even Wallis Island. Buck, claiming that voyaging traditions were conspicuous by their absence, later alloted Samoans but a minor role in the unveiling of Polynesia.[160]

Such assumptions may well be challenged. Quite apart from the thrust of the spade which reveals a hitherto unsuspected depth of occupation[161] (silence of traditions notwithstanding), others claim a substantial body of evidence for voyaging. Bitter warfare and sometimes intermarriage kept Samoans fully cognizant of Tonga. Some are reputed to have regularly visited Wallis and Rotuma, and willingly or willy-nilly, colonists pushed westward to the Gilberts and apparently on to Ocean Island and the Melanesian fringe.[162] To the north they occupied the Tokelau Islands or Union Group, and there are strong traditions of purposeful voyages to and from the Gilberts, Atafu, and Pukapuka.[163] Apparently, too, there was easterly contact with Niue[164] and Rarotonga,[165] and some families in Samoa cherish traditions which claim voyaging between Tau and Tahiti[166]—a contact also suggested by Tupaia's claim to have visited elusive "Manua." And if, as Hale[167] and de Quatrefages[168] maintained, Savai'i was indeed the ancestral Hawaiki of eastern Polynesia, then memories of Samoa were carried afar.

Yet in early European times it was the Tongans who were unchallenged as "the Phoenicians of southern Polynesia,"[169] the active factor in the vigorous traffic which knit together the triangle of Fiji, Samoa, and Tonga. Cook was given a list of over 150 islands of which "the most considerable in this neighbourhood, that we now heard of (and we heard a great deal about them) are Hamoa, Vavaoo and Feejee . . . No European, that we know of, had, as yet, seen any one of them."[170] An early missionary report which adopted the thesis that Polynesian voyaging was severely restricted exempted the sailors of Tongatapu, for they maintained "an extensive and intimate connection . . . with other islands," moving freely across the favoring trades of the Tonga Archipelago and beyond to Fiji and Samoa—though these were postulated as the only other groups within range.[171] But this latter restriction seems dubious. Diapea reported young Tongan bloods as voyaging "600 or 800 or even 1000 miles, being not infrequently absent a year or two . . . wandering and gadding from island to island" as far afield as Wallis and Île Futuna,[172] while Thompson believed that ancient sagas gave evidence of voyaging to the Line Islands,[173] and Tokelau was perhaps the "Toggelao" made known to Cook. And the Tongan adventurer Kau Moala, though deflected off course when sailing from Fiji to Vavau, and from Vavau to Samoa, was yet able to choose landfalls at Île Futuna and finally at lonely Rotuma 500 miles to the northwest, eventually returning home by way of Fiji.[174]

ACROSS THE MELANESIAN TRENCH?

Nor did the Tongan contacts terminate with Rotuma, for Vaitupu, one thousand miles away in the Ellice Islands, was also included in the list of islands which the Tongans supplied to Cook, and southwestward lay the Melanesian chain with its peripheral screen of islands and atolls where Tongan and Samoan influences were unmistakably present. It has been argued that the undoubted Polynesian presence reflected nothing more than the arrival of fortuitous voyagers stranded in unfamiliar Melanesian waters, but though this may be difficult to disprove it is yet difficult to credit. True enough, the frequency with which the Tongan craft arrived may have reflected the tendency of *tongiaki* to drift before the storm. But traditions report the arrival of at least one well-equipped flotilla of five canoes, indicate that marauders moved with malice aforethought from island to island, and cite warnings that the departing raiders would return with reinforcements.[175]

Such contacts, accidental and purposeful, armed and peaceful, seem to have extended along the length of the Melanesian chain, at least to Sikaiana and Ontong Java, and the tribes of parts of the Loyalties and New Caledonia jealously preserve the traditions of the arriving canoes.[176] It may well be, as Parsonson maintains, that it was Tongan vessels which Quirós saw preparing to return from Santa Cruz (Ndeni), that the "Manicolo" of which the Taumakoans spoke was Wainkoro (Vanikoro) in Vanua Levu, that voyagers from the Polynesian fringe sailed more than 1200 miles to Fiji to secure the valuable *vesi* wood (*Intsia bijuga*) from Natewa Bay, and that it was malarial mosquitoes rather than geographical ignorance which curbed the Polynesian penetration of Melanesia.[177] And it may also be that the traditions of "Bulotu" so cherished in Fiji and western Polynesia refer not to a "spirit land" but to some Melanesian island such as the San Cristóbal favored by Guppy[178] and Woodford,[179] or (as Parsonson thinks) New Guinea itself.[180] Certainly, Bulotu sometimes appeared in tradition as solid earth whence fine yams and taro were procured, inhabited by bright-plumaged birds as well as crocodiles, but pestiferous with disease which "infected mortal bodies with speedy death."[181]

Most authorities probably would admit to continuing uncertainties both in regard to particular identifications and the general pattern of Polynesian and Melanesian contact. As Sharp emphasizes in his reiterated denial of two-way voyaging across

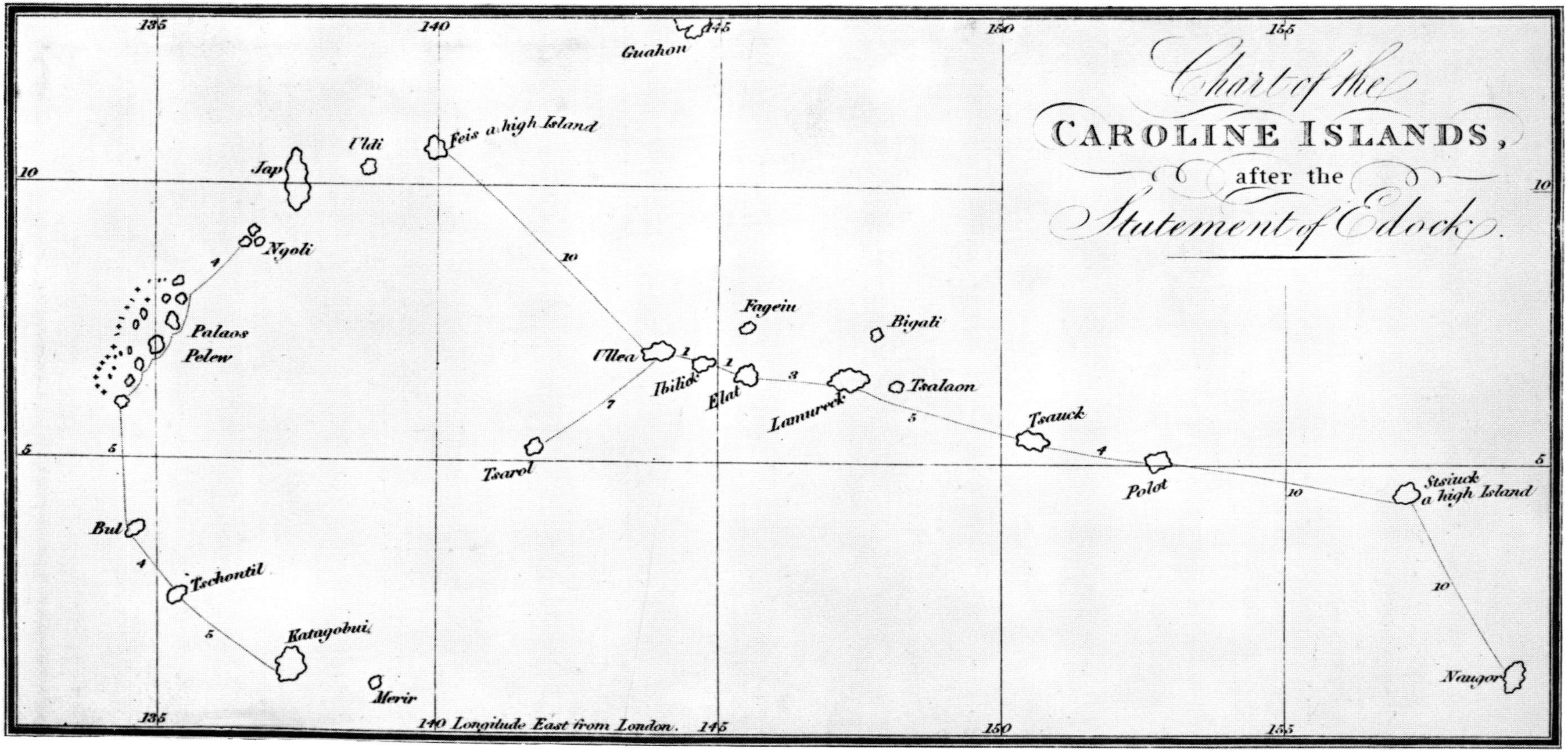

This chart was drawn for Otto von Kotzebue's expedition and was based on information supplied by Edock, a western Carolinian voyager who was found in the Marshall Islands. In Otto Kotzebue: *A Voyage of Discovery . . .*, Vol. 2, at end of vol. [see Note 95]. (Courtesy of the Library of Congress.)

PLATE 13

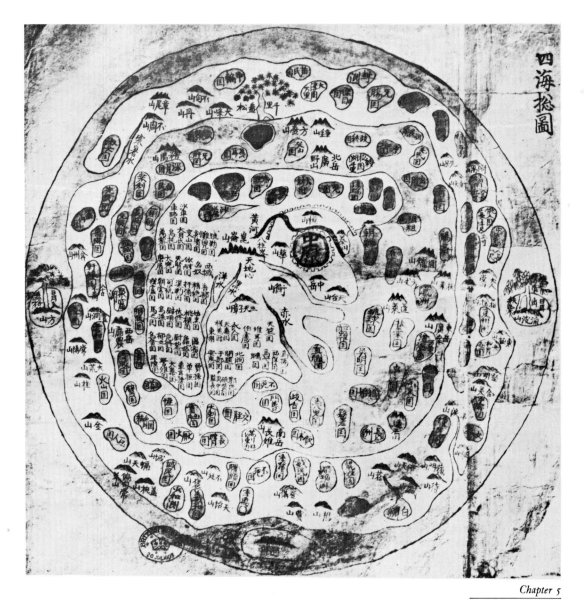

An early Chinese concept of the world. Hirosi Nakamura [see Note 1]. (British Museum, courtesy of *Imago Mundi.*)

PLATE 14

the Melanesian trench, the Manicolo to which Quirós was pointed seems to have lain southwards in Vanikoro or Malekula rather than eastwards in Fiji,[182] and Dillon found the Tongan chief Thubow quite ignorant of these Melanesian islands.[183] Admittedly, later investigators in Melanesia were told of vaguely defined connections with Fiji, Tonga, and Samoa and, as Woodford pointed out, Rotumans were aware of both Tonga and the Melanesian fringe.[184] But this establishes only a thin chain of contact, and it may be significant that Tikopian tradition indicates the cessation of Tongan visits and that the Tikopian seafarers seem to have become aware of Fiji only in the post-European era.[185] On current evidence "probable, not proven" would seem the fairest verdict on the issue of voyaging across the Melanesian trench.

THE HORIZONS OF THE SOCIETIES

A similar indecisive verdict appears appropriate on the question as to whether or not return voyages spanned the seas between western and eastern Polynesia. Tongan and Samoan outreach (and probably return) seems to have extended northeastward to the Tokelaus, eastward to Niue, and perhaps southeast as far as Rarotonga. But it remains a moot question whether two-way voyagers were spanning the further gap eastward to the Societies.

The Societies were undoubtedly the source of far-reaching voyages, though an earlier orthodoxy which postulated them as the initial source of all eastern Polynesian exploration and settlement now seems untenable.[186] It may well be, as Buck believed, that the ancestors of the eastern Polynesians migrated eastward through Micronesia, but current evidence scarcely sustains his thesis that the first landfall was made at Bora Bora and that Raiatea and Tahiti became the hub whence voyagers launched forth to populate the vast triangle which extended from Hawaii to Easter Island and New Zealand. It seems virtually certain that the Marquesas were populated by an expedition from either Tonga[187] or Samoa,[188] and evidence is strong that it was the Marquesans who beached the first canoes in Hawaii, Mangareva, Easter Island, and perhaps even Tahiti itself.

Yet when Cook arrived the Society Islanders seem to have had a much wider knowledge of the Pacific than the Marquesans or other eastern Polynesians.[189] If the chants placed on record in 1817[190] were uncontaminated, the "new lands" they had discovered and their "circuit of navigation" included "burning Vaihi" (Hawaii), the Marquesas, Mangareva, Rarotonga, and (in one version collected at a later date) New Zealand.[191] But incorporation of data acquired during early European contacts seems likely and presumed identifications are all too tenuous. For instance does "burning Vaihi" in fact refer to Hawaii or to Savai'i?[192] And Tupaia's evidence suggests a more restricted radius: at Cook's behest, this Raiatean geographer directed the sketching of a map which delineated much of undiscovered central Polynesia, yet conspicuously omitted Hawaii and New Zealand. Not that the map offers conclusive evidence as to what was or was not included in the world of the Society islanders. Some items seem to have been omitted from the map or rendered unidentifiable by a nomenclature now obsolete, unattuned ears distorted the Polynesian place names, and, as Hale concluded, there was a partial transposition of north and south. Furthermore, there are lingering suspicions that the original map was modified by concurrent European tampering.[193] When all due allowances have been made, however, the scope of the map remains impressive. Fiji and Tonga, Samoa and the Cooks, the Australs and the Tuamotus—virtually all major islands from Rotuma to the Marquesas—are represented. Even excluding the plea of the overly enthusiastic Percy Smith that New Guinea should also be recognized,[194] it seems likely that still more information could be yielded by further linguistic analysis of Tupaia's data—surely one of the most pressing of needs!

This broad sense of location does not, of course, imply an equally vast span of precise or effective knowledge based on actual contact, but it also seems difficult to concede that it represented no more than an accretion of fragmentary data derived from fortuitous arrivals who preserved the general direction of their homelands. This latter view seems scarcely consistent with the impression of orderly knowledge, with the ring of truth in Tupaia's claim that he had sailed ten days to the east and spent thirty returning, and with the anomalous fact that though the Tongans stood to profit more from the prevailing westward drift of accidental voyagers, they seem to have remained ignorant of eastern Polynesia. Perhaps, as Sharp has recently postulated, the preservation of greater breadth of Tahitian knowledge reflects the preservation of "vestigial memories" of Tonga and Samoa in the Societies,[195] but it could also reflect the tales of returning voyagers. It is surely significant that though Cook placed Anderson's opposing views on record, his early and independent judgement was that only "long and distant voyages" could account for "the knowledge of the islands in these seas they seem to have."[196] And how did Tupaia know that Oheavai (Savai'i) was the "father of all the islands"[197] unless there was some way to spread the news? If such knowledge came from Savai'i, then Savai'i had been in contact with its colonies and passed the news on to Tahiti; otherwise, the Tahitians had found out by direct communication with "all the islands," whatever that phrase might mean.

Such communication need not always have been deliberate or permanent. Tupaia's statement that his father knew of southern islands beyond his own ken[198] is hint enough of that, and a clear indication that the range of Polynesian voyaging should not be cut to fit the strait jacket postulated for any single generation. In the particular case of Tupaia, personal observations were largely limited to the Societies along with Rurutu and "Manua," uncertainly identified with Manua in Samoa or Manuae in the Cooks or even Tubuai.[199] As a pilot, Tupaia was sometimes confident and sometimes confused, obviously, as Cook wrote, a "very intelligent person," knowing "more of the geography of the islands situated in these seas, their produce, and the religion, laws and customs of their inhabitants than anyone we had met with," yet hitherto having "hardly . . . an idea of any land being larger than Otaheite."[200] Bougainville said as much of his own pilot, Aotourou, who knew one place as much as fifteen days' sail away, yet stumbled on unsuspected Samoa and thought it France.[201]

It is improbable, indeed, that the navigators of the Societies—or any other islands for that matter—had precisely identical mental constructs of their region. Even the scanty information recorded by Europeans makes it clear that different pilots knew different areas. But there are also intimations of "a common store of knowledge variously known,"[202] data derived from former generations and contact with other voyagers. And even in Cook's time the nuclear region of active contact included the Societies themselves, the northern atolls of the Tuamotus perhaps as far south as Hao, and some at least of the Australs and the Cooks. Tupaia had Rurutu located, Raevavae adzes were used at Raiatea, Atiu and Rarotonga were well known and, as Dening stresses, it is significant that Tahitians sailed confidently westward to tiny and isolated Mopelia despite contrary returning winds and a perilous backdrop of fifteen hundred miles of open sea. And they may have sailed even further. Apart from the fact that western Polynesia appeared on Tupaia's map, Cook was told of ten-day voyages in that direction, and Parsonson insists that biological evidence (not yet in print) will clinch the question in the affirmative.[203]

Contact with Samoa and Tonga apart, it does seem certain that the Cook Islands fell within the purview of Tahiti and linked the genealogies of eastern and western Polynesia.[204] The Society Islands, Samoa, and Tonga all appear to be cited in Rarotongan traditions of tribal origins and voyages, and recent archaeological work confirms previous indications that there were strong affinities with both East and West.[205] Current opinion may well reject former interpretations which acclaimed Ru and Tangiia as explorers of the breadth of the Pacific and withdraw credence from the detailed narratives of expeditions returning from New Zealand laden with greenstone and moa flesh, but there can be little doubt that the Cook Islanders knew something of each other and of the outer world as well. The absence of the pig from Mangaia and Aitutaki may suggest a degree of isolation from the active contact zone which included Atiu, Mauke, Mitiaro, and Rarotonga,[206] but marauders from Aitutaki are claimed as raiding throughout the archipelago.[207] Furthermore, there is evidence of outside contacts. It seems probable that Niue was known, Williams was convinced that there had been two-way voyaging between the Cooks and the Societies (especially the pagan center of Raiatea),[208] Cook Islanders sang of sailing to Tahiti,[209] Tahitians are said to have repeatedly raided these distant neighbors,[210] and Spanish visitors to Tahiti were told the sailing times to Atiu and Rarotonga.[211] Moreover, if tales be true, even the far northern atolls of Manihiki and Pukapuka were linked to Rarotonga in two-way voyaging.[212]

If Tahitians had been in contact with Rarotonga they were also aware of the Australs, as was indicated by the renown of Raevavae adzes and Tupaia's claim to have visited Rurutu.[213] But it is not so clear that the Australs themselves were in mutual contact. Aitken reported that modern Tubuains never embarked on long voyages, though if tradition be true their forebears were in close communication with Raevavae and sailed to Tahiti, Bora Bora, and the Tuamotus.[214] But in Cook's day Rapa may have faded from Tahitian consciousness: Tupaia confessed that his father had spoken of islands further south which were unknown to him.[215]

FARTHEST SOUTH: THE ISOLATION OF AOTEAROA

Still further southwestward lay New Zealand, clearly beyond the pale. It seems certain that Aotearoa, if such it may be called, had long been forgotten, and doubts remain whether it had ever been reported back to Rarotonga and the Societies.

Cook's report was meager; the Maoris told only of ancestral "Hawaiki" (frequently but over-precisely identified with Raiatea) and their discovery of unidentified "Ulimaroa" or "Olhemaroa"—a large land with hogs, lying to the northwest.[216] But the tally grew as later investigation disclosed a pattern of traditions relating to discovery—traditions long regarded as orthodox, chanting long lists of place names suggestive of the mid-Pacific,[217] telling of a partially accidental discovery by Kupe about 925 A.D. and later Toi and Whatonga, and finally the coming of "the Fleet" following precise navigational directions about 1350 A.D., and then the cessation of return voyages to central Polynesia.[218]

But it is now evident that such traditions, at least in their written form, have been both embellished and rationalized or fused as in the tales of Kupe and Toi.[219] The progress of critical evaluation is far from complete, nor has archaeological investigation yet produced full clarification. Current evidence favors the view that Polynesians from the Societies and Cooks had reached New Zealand by 750 A.D. if not earlier, and had begun the development of the "Moa-hunter" culture. It may be that this evolved into "classic Maori" either independently or through the influence of later arrivals, but the concepts of a single "Fleet" and deliberate voyaging are both questioned.[220] But even if the canoes of the "Fleet" should prove to have arrived centuries apart, deliberate navigation seems more than possible. As Dening has insisted, New Zealand presented a broad front to observant Polynesians: a direct line of migrating birds, an eastward-trailing line of seaweed, and changing currents and temperatures rendered it "a target difficult to miss."[221] At least one well-equipped expedition seems implied by the introduction of delicate food plants, and the reality of return voyaging is at least suggested by Maori traditions of an expedition to secure sweet potatoes, by the alleged discovery of "Ulimaroa," by the claims of some Cook islanders to New Zealand contacts and origin,[222] and by the discovery of greenstone (unfortunately undated and inconclusive) in a Cook Island site.[223] It now seems confirmed that the pre-European Maori, rightly or wrongly, believed that some had returned to Hawaiki, and that this lay in a northeasterly direction.

But it also seems clear that when the *pakeha* arrived Maori contacts were in practice confined to New Zealand. There, place names may have perpetuated some ancient memories, and usually-luckless exiles or migrants occasionally came ashore.[224] There was considerable travel within the country: though it was "percussion exchange" from group to adjacent group as well as more direct long-range contact[225] which distributed resources such as greenstone and obsidian, it is clear that the geographical peculiarities of different regions were widely known. But though the Kermadec Islands to the north may have been referred to in tradition,[226] the Chatham Islands (five hundred miles to the east) seem to have been beyond Maori horizons although their Moriori inhabitants preserved memories of New Zealand.[227] Nor have intimations of Maori landfalls on the Australian coast been confirmed,[228] while the adzes and banana gardens of uninhabited Norfolk Island point to visitors from the tropics rather than from cooler Aotearoa.[229]

Tahiti and Its Eastern Neighbors

If the southern outpost of Polynesia had faded from Tahitian memory, not so the neighboring archipelagoes to the east. The northern Tuamotus were not only visited for their pearl shell and feathers but were populated by "the most daring and successful navigators" of the eastern seas.[230] Lacking heavy timber, Tuamotuan craftsmen (who were eagerly sought in Tahiti) lashed a patchwork of planks into shapely and resilient *pahi* hulls and ranged boldly for trade and spoil through their atoll-studded seas and westward to the Societies. And they may well have been alerted to other lands to the east by the arrival of flotsam and jetsam from South America.[231]

On the eastward flank, both Society Islanders and Tuamotuans seem to have had at least sporadic contact with the Marquesans, who may indeed have been directly or indirectly ancestral to them. Apparently deriving its initial settlers from a well-manned Tongan or Samoan exploring expedition or lost canoe,[232] the Marquesas became a source-region whence sailed explorers or exiles to populate eastern Polynesia. Rightly or wrongly, their recorded traditions are claimed as evidence of voyages to Fiji and Samoa, Tonga and Rarotonga, the Societies and Hawaii,[233] the Australs and the Tuamotus, though again questions of identification will not down. And investigation now points decisively to Marquesans as beaching the first canoes in some Tuamotu atolls and Mangareva, on Easter Island and Hawaii, and perhaps (to reverse earlier concepts) in the Societies themselves. Not that the eighteenth-century Marquesans knew as much. Though the Spaniards found them planning expeditions against dark-skinned people (perhaps the sun-tanned atoll-dwellers of the Tuamotus)[234] in 1595, and though crowding, war, and local encouragement were still impelling expeditions into the unknown in Porter's day,[235] there seems to have been little if any "feedback"—a supposition which is conformable with the likely thesis that (apart from cherished Tongan names) knowledge was then restricted to the home archipelago and probably some of the Tuamotus, while Tahitian awareness of four or more Marquesan islands could be accounted for by the arrival of one-way voyagers from the east.[236]

HAWAII: NORTHERN OUTPOST

If it was the culture of the Marquesas which spread northwards through earliest Hawaii, it was obscured by later and powerful Tahitian influences,[237] a fact strongly suggesting truth in the conviction expressed by Ellis that though Hawaiians affirmed their ignorance of Tahiti before European contacts, their "traditions furnish very strong evidence that [they] were acquainted with the existence of the Marquesan and Society Islands long before visited by Captain Cook," and that other islands were also within their purview.[238] Certainly the traditions subsequently gathered are laced with references to far-flung voyages,[239] and many believe that the voyages of Hema and Pamakau to Tahiti have substance, and that the indefinite lands of "Kahiki" and "Polapola" may have indeed meant Tahiti and Bora Bora. Stokes thought traditions of visits to the great and exotic land of Haupokane to be strongly sug-gestive of Mexico,[240] nor have advocates of American contacts failed to attach Polynesian significance to the incurved shell fishhooks and plank canoes of the Santa Barbara region of California. Undoubtedly, the repeated drifting of the "Oregon pine" treasured by canoe builders, and the sporadic arrival of Chinese and Japanese castaways, made for awareness of lands beyond the horizon.[241] Even if authoritative opinion be a consensus, little credence can be given to local claims that even in Cook's time there were southern contacts with Samoa or Tahiti: two-way contact was maintained only along the Hawaiian chain, and even there the western outliers of Nihoa and Necker were abandoned and the latter had vanished even from tradition.[242]

FARTHEST EAST

As with the northern apex of Polynesia, so with the eastern islands. In early contact times, Mangareva seems to have been unknown in the Marquesas and the Societies which variously influenced it, but Mangarevans still maintained contact with nearby Temoe and the southern Tuamotus,[243] while Pitcairn, though strewn with the relics of former occupance, was deserted and probably forgotten. And the lonely Easter islanders, wrote Forster, knew of no other lands,[244] though it is evident that they fished and fowled at Isla Sala y Gómez two hundred miles to the east,[245] and preserved memories of lands elsewhere. It now seems probable that lush "Marae Renga" whence Hotu Metua fled was a Marquesan island and that, if Barthel is right, the *rongorongo* tablets speak of the Society Islands and particularly of Raiatea.[246]

But beyond Easter Island rolled a vast expanse of ocean which separated (or perchance united) Polynesia and the Americas. And here the tale of prehistoric contact is clouded with unresolved disputes. Parallels between the high cultures of Asia and the Americas, Peruvian pottery in the Galapagos Islands, Japanese-style pottery in Ecuador,[247] Polynesian-type artifacts on American shores, Inca traditions of Tupac Yupanqui and his long voyages into western waters,[248] Polynesian traditions such as that of the Marquesan canoe *Kahua* sailing eastward to the great land of "Te Fiti,"[249] or of canoes arriving at Easter Island from an arid "land of ridges"[250]—the tally is confusing and still inconclusive. Yet conflicting opinions should not obscure the virtually unanimous agreement that Polynesians and American Indians had in fact been in contact. The distribution of the sweet potato, whether by balsa raft or Polynesian canoe, seems proof enough.

Thus by one means or another the broad Pacific had been spanned, and an established pattern of both uncertain tradition and firm geographical knowledge was soon to guide European thrusts into the "unknown," to be verified by strange instruments, and charted by alien hands. The story of Tupac Yupanqui was but one of the traditions which inspired Spaniards and others to sail forth into the Great Ocean, and Tupaia was but the most famous among many who pointed the directions of distant islands and identified the guiding stars of the great South Sea. Even so did Quirós have Tumai list some sixty islands on the borders of Melanesia[251] and Kotzebue have Edock chart the Carolines or Lagediack to guide him in the Marshalls,[252] while Bougainville had his Aotourou[253] and Andia his Pukuro.[254] But such selection seems invidious. These are but names plucked at random from the long and often nameless tally of island navigators who were to join their knowledge and acumen with European technology in the making of the Pacific map.

5

GEOGRAPHICAL EXPLORATION BY THE CHINESE

Chiao-min Hsieh*

Throughout most of their long history of cultural and scientific development, the Chinese people have been but passively interested in the Pacific Ocean. Believing that no land existed beyond the Pacific, most early Chinese explorers directed their expeditions westward. Progressively, however, the Chinese acquired geographical knowledge of the Pacific that was based on the observations of travelers. Some traveled in the cause of religion, some were involved in political missions, some were engaged in trade, and some were on military expeditions. In spite of the diversity of their purposes, these pilgrims, diplomats, traders, and admirals all added their store of experience and observation to the growth of Chinese knowledge about the Pacific. Historical records indicate that from time to time the Chinese authorities sent out maritime exploring expeditions, notably those to Japan as early as the second and third centuries B.C. and to southeast Asia, India, and Africa during the fifteenth century A.D. Interestingly, as early as the second and third centuries B.C., Chinese philosophers and cosmographers appeared to conceive of China as the center of the world. The "world" was surrounded by four seas, one of which, the Pacific, spread eastward from China's east coast. The Chinese appeared to be aware of a large land mass (Asia) that continued west from China to meet the western sea. Apparently there have been few, if any, planned deep penetrations of the Pacific Ocean by the Chinese during their long history.

But Chinese traders, religious figures, and, in several instances, military exploring expeditions, did follow the land and water trade routes to India and beyond to Africa and the Middle East, and possibly even to Australia, prior to the Renaissance and the era of initial European exploration of the Pacific in the sixteenth century. Indeed, centuries before European explorers began their penetration of the Pacific Ocean the ports of southern China were carrying on a brisk trade with the Moslem world. It is obvious from records of these and related sources of economic intercourse that knowledge of a vast eastern ocean, however fragmentary, had become part of the general geographical knowledge of the fraternity of philosophers, cosmographers, and commercial interests of the Middle East before the tenth century A.D. These contacts and the diffusion of knowledge that inevitably resulted must have reached the Mediterranean and European countries long before Columbus and Magellan set sail into the "unknown." The role of the Chinese and that of the intrepid Arab sailors in diffusing this knowledge cannot be minimized. The following remarks cover only the highlights of this history as it pertains to Chinese exploration.

---

*Dr. Hsieh is professor of geography at The Catholic University of America, Washington, D.C.

EARLY CHINESE CONCEPTS OF THE WORLD AND ITS OCEANS

The earliest knowledge the Chinese had of the Pacific was based on religious belief, philosophical thinking, and astronomical observations. This is evident from the ancient geographical books and world maps.[1] *Shan Hai Ching* (Classic of Mountains and Seas), probably the oldest traveler's guide in the world, shows the Chinese concept of the world prior to the Ch'in Dynasty (earlier than 200 B.C.).[2] From this book we may surmise that the ancient Chinese believed China was in the middle of the world and that it was surrounded by oceans, which in turn were the limits of the universe (Plate 14, *facing page 81*). Accordingly, they recognized "four seas," which meant four limits.[3] *Mu Tien Tze Chuan* (An Account of the Travels of the Emperor Mu), is a semilegendary geographical work, produced between 475 and 221 B.C.[4] Neither book is a scientific geography; each is a religious or symbolic cosmography.[5]

Early Chinese knowledge of the Pacific is reflected not only in their religious beliefs but also in their philosophical thinking.[6] Chuang Tzu, a philosopher, in 300 B.C. stated that if a man goes north from Yen (Hopeh Province) and another man goes south from Yueh (Chekiang Province), they will meet at the end of their journey, although they started in opposite directions. He also mentioned that the same thing would be true if they traveled east-west. From these statements we may deduce that the ancient Chinese had the idea that the earth is round.

With the development of astronomical observation, the Chinese enlarged their knowledge of the Pacific. Wang Ch'ung, an astronomer who lived during the Han Dynasty, recorded his observation of the sun in his book entitled *Lun Heng* (Discourses Weighed in the Balance), which expanded the world concept of the Chinese people and modified their cosmology.[7]

Religious motives have led the Chinese to explore the Pacific.[8] In ancient China the inhabitants of Hopeh and Shantung provinces along the east coast were influenced by the idea of looking for the immortals.[9] The authentic court record of the Ch'in Empire, *Ch'in Chi*, states that in the year 219 B.C. a mission was sent by the Ch'in emperor to seek a "longevity herb" that was reputed to grow on the "Great Immortal Island of the Eastern Sea" (Fig. 8). The leader of the mission was a Taoist named Hsu Fu. He was authorized to conscript several thousand young men and women and to obtain the necessary resources, including grain, seeds, and livestock for the expedition. He also was authorized to conscript the services of artisans in all trades, including navigators. The mission's journey began at the city of Lang-yu in Shantung Province. In 210 B.C. Hsu returned to Lang-yu to ask the Emperor for a grant of "expert archers and special bows" to clear away sharks from the path of his ships. He was granted the equipment and was sent out again to complete his mission. Shortly after the envoy's departure the Ch'in emperor died.

The Ch'in Dynasty was succeeded by the Han. An officer who was stationed on the east coast of China in the Han Dynasty recorded that Hsu Fu went to a place "of flat plains and great lakes," remained there, made himself king, and did not return to China. Tingsen S. Wei notes that east of China only three islands have flat plains and great lakes: Hokkaido and Honshu of Japan, and Luzon of the Philippine Islands. But Hokkaido is too far north and Luzon is too far south to be reached by such an

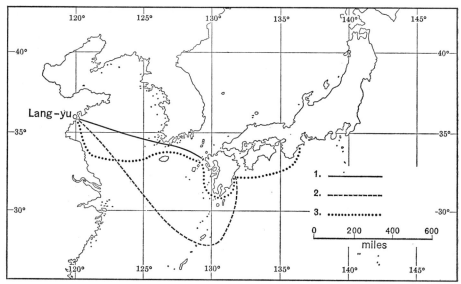

FIG. 8. Approximate routes of Hsu Fu's three expeditions. After Tingsen S. Wei [Note 10].

early eastbound voyage from Lang-yu in Shantung Province. In addition, neither Hokkaido nor Luzon has artifacts of the Ch'in and Han dynasties. Honshu is the only accessible island of that description which abounds in such artifacts. And so, says Wei, "the so-called 'Great Immortal Island of the Eastern Sea,' which Hsu Fu visited, was nowhere but Japan."[10] Wei further theorizes that Emperor Jimmu Tenno, the founder of the Japanese Empire, could be none other than Hsu Fu, the envoy from Ch'in.[11] Wei compares the timetable, the place, and the artifacts, and makes every effort to support this conclusion.[12] However, Wei's conclusion has not received wholehearted support from Japanese scholars, and has even encountered some opposition.[13]

Despite the fact that Wei's study is not generally accepted in Japan, the following facts, recorded in Japan, may convince us that the Chinese of the Ch'in Dynasty did explore and settle in Japan:

1. Japanese are well-known as seal hunters. For over a thousand years, the center of seal hunting has been Kumano in Yamato Prefecture (Honshu), a place where it is believed Hsu Fu first landed. It is recorded in Chinese history that in the Ch'in era the Chinese knew how to hunt seals, and Hsu apparently brought with him from China a number of seal hunters, perhaps the "expert archers and special bows." In Kumano there is a base for hunting seals, called Taigi-machi and sometimes Tachi-no-Oura, which means the "coastal area where the people from Ch'in settled." The captains of seal-hunting ships are called the "people from Ch'in."

2. According to Japanese historians, the Japanese first used rice, agricultural implements, iron ore, and textiles about the year 200 B.C. It will be recalled that in 219 B.C. Hsu Fu brought grain seeds and all kinds of artisans to the ". . . Island of the Eastern Sea."

3. In a Japanese book listing family names, published in 815 A.D., fifteen clans are

listed with the family name of Ch'in. These persons probably were the descendants of Hsu's subordinates, for the Chinese who migrated to Japan after the Ch'in Dynasty would have called themselves "Han People" or "Tang People," and not "Ch'in People."

While the Taoists were exploring northward from China, the Buddhists traveled southwest to India, the birthplace of Buddhism. The earliest Buddhist pilgrim, who brought to China much knowledge about the countries of southeastern Asia, was Fa Hsien. Fa Hsien set out for India in 399 A.D. by way of central Asia and returned to Chang-an fifteen years later by way of the Indian Ocean and the South China Sea, after visiting almost every part of India.[14] In 414 Fa Hsien took the commercial boat from Calcutta to Ceylon, where he stayed for two years, and then sailed to Java.[15] From Java he went to Canton, China's main port at that time. When Fa Hsien returned to China he wrote a book entitled *Fo Kuo Chi* (Records of Buddhist Countries), which may be identified as the chief geographical textbook of the countries of southeastern Asia during this period.[16]

Religious pilgrims were not the only men who wrote of foreign countries bordered by the Pacific Ocean. As time went on, ambassadors and envoys also made considerable contributions to Chinese geographical literature. In 1124 A.D. Hsu Ching, an official on the staff of a Chinese ambassador to Korea, wrote an account of his voyage and of Korea.[17] The title of the book is *Hsuan-Ho Feng shih Kao-li thu Ching* (Illustrated Record of an Embassy to Korea in the Hsuan Ho Reign Period). Though the book was not printed until 1167, it brought to China geographical knowledge of Korea and of the northwestern part of the Pacific Ocean.

EXPLORATIONS BY CHENG HO

The peak of China's geographical knowledge of the Pacific and Indian oceans was reached in the sixteenth century through military expeditions led by Admiral Cheng Ho, the most illustrious Chinese marine explorer.[18] During a period of twenty-eight years, from 1405 to 1433, Cheng Ho led seven exploring expeditions into the Pacific and Indian oceans and visited more than thirty-seven countries.[19] The areas he visited included such distant places as Persia and the Red Sea in the northwest, the east coast of Africa in the farthest west, and Taiwan in the east.[20]

Not only was Cheng Ho China's greatest marine explorer, but he was also one of the earliest systematic, trained navigators in world history.[21] Development of overseas commerce at the end of the fifteenth century brought about the need for an improvement in shipbuilding techniques and the introduction of the compass. Many explorers from Spain, Portugal, and Holland were active on the oceans of the world. Vasco da Gama is generally considered to be the first person to travel the sea route between Europe, Asia, and Africa. Cheng Ho's exploration of the sea route between these three continents, however, took place earlier than Da Gama's by eighty or ninety years.

Cheng Ho was commonly known as the "three eunuch" and was a Moslem. He was born in 1371 in the city of K'un-yang (now Chin-nung) in Yunnan Province.[22] When Cheng was twelve his father died, and he went to Peiping (Peking) and became a eunuch. His original last name was Ma; "Cheng" was the name given him by the Ming court.[23] His wit and talent soon made him the favorite of Emperor Chu

Ti, and Cheng helped him with military affairs. In 1405, the third year of the Yung-lo reign, Cheng Ho, then 35 years old, was chosen as the leader of a large exploring expedition that was to cross the South China Sea and explore the Indian Ocean. During the succeeding seventeen years Cheng Ho was leader of six significant exploring expeditions that ranged through the South Pacific and the Indian Ocean. On his return from his sixth expedition in 1422 he found that Emperor Chu Ti had died and that Chu Ti's son had taken his place on the throne. Cheng was no longer the favored officer at the court, though in 1432, at the age of 62, he commanded his seventh expedition. His explorations were criticized by the court as "poor to [an impoverishment of] the country." He served as a military officer in Nanking for two years and died in 1435 at the age of 65. The basic or guiding reasons for Cheng Ho's expeditions are not generally known and have become a topic for academic research.[24] The expeditions stopped as suddenly as they had begun, for reasons which are obscure.[25]

Cheng Ho's expeditions are well known in a popular way, but the details and accomplishments are not. Even the dates of his sailings are in doubt, and the information in the basic records differs. The following brief summary of his seven explorations is based on three kinds of sources: (1) the official record and the annals of the reigns of the Ming Dynasty, (2) tablet inscriptions discovered on the coast of Fukien Province, and (3) three books written by members of Cheng's expeditions.[26]

The First Expedition: The first expedition left China in July 1405, and returned in October, 1407. It set sail from Liu-chia-chang (near present Shanghai) and proceeded south to Fukien. In the winter of the same year it set out for voyages in the Pacific, including in its itinerary the Philippines, Java, Sumatra, Malaya, Ceylon, and Calicut on the west coast of India. On this expedition, Cheng led a force of more than 27,800 men in sixty-two large ships. He set up a consulate in Palembang, the first overseas office to be established by the Chinese.

The Second Expedition: The second expedition lasted from October 1407 to August 1409. The voyage was similar to the first one and never extended beyond the west coast of India.

The Third Expedition: Leaving China in October 1409, Cheng led forty-eight ships on his third expedition, visited the west coast of India, and returned in July 1411. When he reached Malacca, he built a wooden-walled city with four towers. Within the city he built a large compound which became a storage place for food and other supplies and the supply center for his later expeditions.

The Fourth Expedition: The fourth expedition left China in October 1413 and returned in August 1415. During this exploration Cheng's expedition reached the Persian Gulf, the Red Sea, and the east coast of Africa.

The Fifth Expedition: The fifth expedition lasted from May 1417 to August 1419. Cheng reached his farthest western point, the east coast of Africa south of the equator. He returned to China with princes and family members from seventeen countries, establishing diplomatic relations between these countries of southeastern Africa and the Ming Dynasty. Cheng also brought back ostriches, zebras, and giraffes, which were seen in China for the first time, and a good deal of geographical and cartographical information.[27]

The Sixth Expedition: The sixth voyage was the shortest of the seven, lasting from February 1421 to September 1422. During this expedition, Cheng traveled only as far as Sumatra; the expedition from there on was led by his subordinate officers, Yang Ching and Hung Pao.

The Seventh Expedition: The seventh voyage of Cheng Ho was his last. This time Cheng left many tablet inscriptions and written records and so we know more of this expedition than of the others. The complement of 26,755 persons included soldiers, sailors, cooks, medical

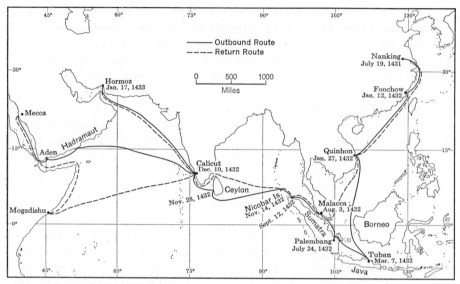

Fig. 9. Cheng Ho's seventh voyage. After Hsien Ta (Note 35), Chu Chieh (Note 22), and Hsu Yü-hu (Note 23).

doctors, and carpenters. He left Nanking in July 1431 for Foochow. He waited there until the next year, when he voyaged as far west as the Red Sea and the coast of Africa, returning to China in July 1433 (Fig. 9). This time Cheng brought back ambassadors from more than ten countries.

Some people have advanced the theory that a part of one of Cheng Ho's expeditions may even have traveled to Australia.[28] One piece of evidence in support of this theory is a stone statue of the God of Longevity (now in an Australian museum) that was unearthed in Darwin, Australia, in 1870. It is believed that while he was in Java, Cheng Ho may have sent some of his men to Australia to offer sacrifices to Canopus, which the Chinese considered to be the star that governs the lives of human beings. The Chinese referred to Canopus as the God of Longevity of the South Pole. Cheng Ho's party must have mistaken Australia for the South Pole.

Cheng Ho's seven expeditions not only enriched Chinese knowledge about the Pacific and Indian Oceans but they also improved the country's internal economy. The results may be summarized as follows:

1. *Contributions to oceanic geography.* Cheng Ho brought back scientific knowledge, especially of navigation, of the waters he explored, particularly in the Pacific and Indian oceans and in the Red Sea. Cheng Ho's expeditions were responsible for the publication of several books of great importance to geographic knowledge about the Pacific and the Indian oceans. The earliest, in 1434, was the *Hsi-Yang Fan Kuo Chih,* (Record of the Barbarian Countries in the Western Ocean) by Kung Chen. The second, which quickly followed the first was *Hsing Chha Sheng Lan* (Triumphant Vision of the Starring Raft). Then in 1451, Ma Huan, one of the Chinese Moslem interpreters, produced the *Ying Yai Sheng Lan* (Triumphant Vision of the Boundless Ocean). All of these authors had been officers under Cheng Ho. Their books provide much information about the people and countries visited by the expeditions and in-

clude invaluable geographical material concerning the southwestern Pacific Ocean. Even today, these books are useful references for the historical geography of southeast Asia. Because of Cheng Ho's expeditions in the fifteenth century, the Chinese had geographical knowledge of the lands as far west as Egypt, and apparently were aware of the east coast of Africa. They had a vague idea of the Arabian peninsula, the Red Sea, and southwestern Asia. Cheng Ho's expeditions served as the basis of Chinese geographical knowledge of the Southwest Pacific for about 200 years. With the coming of westerners such as Matteo Ricci, who introduced to China much knowledge of the world, these views were modified to fit the results of more recent geographical explorations.

2. *Increased Chinese migration to, and transportation and trade with the South Seas.* Cheng Ho's expeditions no doubt greatly influenced subsequent Chinese migration to Southeast Asia. Cheng Ho was the pioneer who opened the navigation route from China to the Indian Ocean, the Red Sea, and the eastern coast of Africa. Before Cheng Ho's voyages, the Indian Ocean was dominated by ships sent out by Arabian and Persian merchants. No Chinese ships had ever reached the Red Sea. Cheng combined his knowledge of astronomy and of geography and produced his well-known navigation map. On the map he showed in detail the location of different countries, sea routes, harbors, sand bars, and islands. Cheng Ho's navigation handbook was an important help to sailors in the area. In the daytime, Cheng used the compass to determine directions and at night he used the stars. His expeditions greatly increased trade between China and countries in southeastern Asia. From China merchants exported silk, porcelain, copper, and some medicines; and imported rare stones, spices, and jade. Canton, Ch'uan-chou, Yang-chou, and Ning-po became important ports.

3. *Influence on China's internal economy.* The opening of foreign markets along the shores of the Indian Ocean stimulated China's handicraft industry, the most important products of which were silk textiles and porcelain. The city of Soō-chow had been manufacturing silk since the Sung and Yuan dynasties. After Cheng's voyages, Soō-chow became the center of handicrafts, Ching-te of porcelain production, Sung-kiang of cotton textile manufacturing, Wu-wu of dyeing, and Tsung-kua of iron-ore smelting.

It would be interesting to know in how many and in what kinds of ships Cheng Ho sailed. Cheng's ship was usually called the "jewel ship," because it carried the treasures he brought back from foreign lands. A drawing found in the *Wu Pei Chih* (Notes on Military Preparation) is supposed to show the type of ship that Cheng used (Fig. 10). Unfortunately, the historical records on Cheng Ho's "jewel ship" are fragmentary and conflicting.[29]

It is also important to note what kinds of maps were made and used by Cheng Ho and his associates. In the *Wu Pei Chih* there are maps that occupy twenty-four pages. The book includes one page for an introduction, two pages for showing the stars, and one blank page. Neither the source nor the authorship of the maps are mentioned in the introduction, which consists of only 142 words. Mao Yuan-yi, the author of *Wu Pei Chih,* dated his preface 1621. The general consensus among scholars is that the sheets of map in *Wu Pei Chih* were not made prior to 1433 and that they must have been made by Cheng Ho's staff.[30] The map begins at Nanking and ends on the east coast of Africa (Fig. 11), showing Kenya and Mogadishu, about 4 degrees south

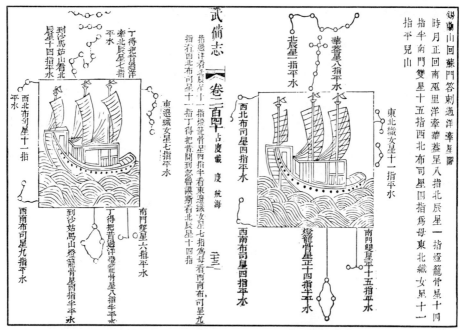

FIG. 10. Example of the kind of boat Cheng Ho may have used. Reproduced from Yüan-Yi Mao: *Wu pei chih*, vol. 240, n.d., n.p. (Courtesy of the Library of Congress.)

of the equator. On this map are 500 place names, about 200 of which apply to China, and the rest to other parts of southeast Asia and to Africa.[31] Cheng's map offered the most complete knowledge in Chinese, before the fifteenth century, about Africa and southeast Asia. The map provides more detailed geographical information about the coast of China and the westernmost Pacific than about other parts of the southeast Asian coast. The Chinese coast is shown on a scale that averages about one to one million, but this varies with different sections. The sea routes are shown on the map by a series of dotted lines, along which at appropriate intervals are columns of characters specifying the compass directions, the distances in watches of 2.4 hours each, soundings, and other sailing directions.[32] Of the total of 500 place names, to date about 350 have been identified.

Since the compiler of the map is unknown, it seems probable that on each voyage the navigating officers drew new maps incorporating data that appeared on previous maps and bringing them up to date. The numerous and serious errors and omissions suggest that the cited copy may be an incomplete draft. It should be noted that compass directions are shown for the route of navigation from Nanking to the north of Sumatra, whereas from west of Ceylon and along the west coast of India, the Arabian Peninsula, and the eastern coast of Africa, compass directions as well as the location of stars are shown, apparently to assist the navigator in determining direction.[33] Paul Pelliot insists that this map reflects Arabian influence,[34] but Hsien believes that this is not so.[35] Cheng's map remains one of the most interesting historical cartographic records of the coasts of China, southeast Asia, and India and constitutes a fascinating subject for intensive and exacting research.

FIG. 11. Four sections of Chengo Ho's map. *Above*, two sections covering the area in the vicinity of the mouth of the Yangtze River. *Below*, two sections covering part of the east coast of Africa. Reproduced from Yüan-yi Mao: *Wu pei chih*, vol. 240, n.d., n.p. (Courtesy of the Library of Congress.)

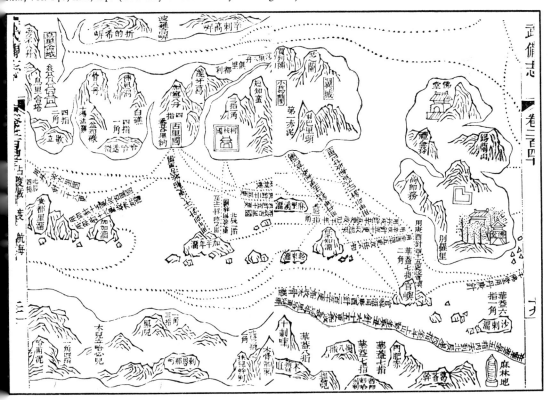

GEOGRAPHICAL EXPLORATION BY THE JAPANESE

Nobuo Muroga*

The Japanese were active in the waters of east Asia in the sixteenth century, when Iberian navigators made their first appearance. Most of them were armed smugglers called "Wako" (Japanese pirate) who plagued the entire coast from Korea to south China. Later Toyotomi* Hideyoshi, who governed the whole of Japan, undertook to secure control of foreign trade, and his policy was followed by Tokugawa Ieyasu, the founder of the Edo shogunate. They issued trading licenses stamped with a red seal, hence the name "Shuin-sen" or Red Seal ship. At the beginning of the seventeenth century numbers of Red Seal ships ranged the coast of southeast Asia and Japanese settlements were established in the Philippine Islands, Indochina, and Thailand.[1]

Under these circumstances the Japanese made their first contact with Europeans, which resulted in the propagation of Christianity among them and the introduction of Western sciences. Progress in Japanese navigation owes much to the influence of the West. In 1618 a Nagasaki seaman named Ikeda Koun compiled a book known as *Genna Kokai-ki* (Sailing Guide in the Genna Era) in which he gave an account of what he had learned from the Spanish trader Manuel Gonzalves. The charts used by Red Seal ships were drawn up after the model of European portolan charts. Some copies of these early charts actually used in South Seas navigation are still extant, and show that the Japanese cartographers of those days were well acquainted with Western map making. Western-style ships also began to be constructed about the beginning of the seventeenth century. An example is the Spanish "naveta"-type ship built by the shogunate shipwrights for Date Masamune, the feudal lord of Sendai, who sent his envoy to the Vatican by this ship in 1613.[2] Some Japanese made their way into the Pacific Ocean, and some even visited European countries. It is perhaps safe to say that the Japanese were at that time sufficiently well equipped to join with the Europeans in exploration of the uncharted seas of the world.

The shogunate authorities, however, came to suspect that the dangerous influence of foreign thought might well shake the feudal system to its foundations. The proscription against Christiantity commenced with the expulsion of the Jesuits in 1587. In 1636 Japan's door was closed to all Western countries except Holland which was given permission to continue its trade at Nagasaki although it was severely restricted. The national isolation policy thus established was consistently followed until the fall of the shogunate in the middle of the nineteenth century. This restrained the Japanese in their overseas expansion. Under such severe circumstances their ex-

---

*Personal names of Japanese noted in the text of this chapter retain the Japanese form of surname or family name first and the given or individual name second.

*Dr. Muroga is professor of geography at Tokai University, Tokyo, Japan.

peditions were restricted to the regions immediately circumjacent to and including the islands on which they lived (Fig. 12).

THE NORTHERN FRONTIER I.

From ancient times the Japanese had entertained a lively interest in the north-eastern part of their country where an uncivilized people called Ezo lived.[3] Japanese old tales frequently glorify war heroes who fought these ferocious barbarians and explored the little-known land of Ezo.

According to the *Nihon Shoki* (Chronicle of Japan), written in 720 A.D., Admiral Abe-no-Hirafu, commanding a fleet of 200 vessels, in 658–660 A.D. made an expedition against the people of Mishihase in the far north of Ezo and reached the hitherto unknown islands of Watari and Herohe. Though these islands still remain to be identified, there is a possibility that Admiral Abe actually was aware of the geo-graphical relationship between Japan's northern border and the northeastern part of the continent, for as a result of his expedition the so-called Mishihase came to be considered as identical to Shukushin or Su-shên, the people of Manchuria mentioned in Chinese classics.[4]

Regardless of the geographical implications of Abe-no-Hirafu's expedition to the far north, it was not until the end of the twelfth century that the Japanese gained complete control of northeastern Honshu (the main island of Japan), even to its northern extremity. Since then the name Ezo came to be applied only to the lands and aborigines north of the Tsugaru-kaikyō (strait), and present-day Hokkaido was called Ezo-ga-shima (the Isle of Ezo) where small Japanese colonies began to be planted. At the close of the sixteenth century Matsumae Yoshihiro, who had domi-nated the Japanese settlers, obtained official approval as the feudal lord of Ezo. Throughout the Edo period Japanese settlements were chiefly confined to the Matsumae district, that is, the southwestern corner of Hokkaido, and the revenues of the Matsumae clan were largely derived from the trade with the aborigines (the Ainu), in fur and products of the sea.

From early times these items were shipped to Osaka and Kyōto. Through such commercial relations the people of the cities were given information, often inac-curate, of the far-off land of Ezo, which in turn was transmitted to Europe by Jesuit priests and foreign traders. The first European traveler in Ezo was Girolamo de Angelis, S.J., who visited the Matsumae district in 1618 and 1621 and prepared a map and reports of the island. It is also well known that in 1643 Maarten Gerritszoon Vries made his voyage of exploration along the western coast of Hokkaido and Sakhalin, a voyage which had such strong influence on later maps of the North Pacific Basin. It would appear that these Europeans took an active interest in the geographical relations between Ezo, Tatary, and America in hopes of discovering the North Passage through the imaginary Strait of Anian or unveiling the fabulous islands of gold and silver.[5]

Japanese interest in this northern area, however, generally was quite the opposite. It is true that a few persons in power, such as Tokugawa Ieyasu, gave ear to geo-graphical information supplied by the Westerners. But Ezo was for the Japanese nothing more than a territory bordering on their own homeland, and they did not

Fig. 12. Routes of principal explorations by the Japanese, 1675–1809.

KAMCHATKA

SEA OF OKHOTSK

Strait of Mamiya

Nanio

Santan

Delen

Karafuto or Kita-Ezo
(Sakhalin)

Kita Soya Misaki

C. Kita-Shiretoko

Shumushu
(Shumshu)

Chishima (Kuril) Islands

Kushunnai

Naibutsu

Aniwa Bay

Soya Strait

Shiranushi

Soya

C. Shiretoko

Uruppu (Urup)

Etorofu (Iturup)

Kunashiri (Kunashir)

Nemuro

Amur R.

EZO
(Hokkaido)

Atsukeshi

Uchiura Bay

Hakodate

Matsumae

Tsugaru Strait

SEA OF JAPAN

HONSHU

Edo
(Tokyo)

Shimoda

Izu Islands

Korea

Kyoto

Osaka

SHIKOKU

KYUSHU

Nagasaki

Kagoshima

Tane

Yaku

Huang R.

Chichi

Ogasawara (Bonin)
Islands

EAST CHINA SEA

Yangtze R.

Amami

Nansei (Ryukyu) Islands

Okinawa

Formosa

0 200 400 600
Miles

- - - - - Shimaya, 1675
-·-·-·- Sea Route to Ryukyu Is.
- - - Yamaguchi and Mogami, 1786
——— Mamiya Rinzo, 1808
·········· Mamiya Rinzo, 1809

appear to be interested in its exploration as a problem of world geography. This may well be the reason why early Japanese maps of Ezo included so little geographical information about circumjacent areas.[6]

According to the *Shiragi no Kiroku*, a genealogy of the Matsumaes, Matsumae Yoshihiro presented a map of Ezo to Tokugawa Ieyasu in 1599. It is also reported that in 1634 Takahashi Giemon made a survey of the Matsumae district by order of the lord and in 1636 Murakami Hironori prepared a map of the entire island of Ezo. In the same year Matsumae authorities sent an expedition as far north as south Sakhalin. No records of these expeditions exist, but they must have prepared some maps and presented them to the shogunate. The islands of Ezo represented in the official map of Japan compiled later by the shogunate are presumably of Matsumae origin. Their configuration is far from accurate, but many place names in Hokkaido suggest that the surveyors made a complete circuit of the island. For the Kuril Islands (Chishima-rettō or Kuril'skiye Ostrova) the names of every island from Kunashiri (Ostrov Kunashir) up to Shumushu (Ostrov Shumshu) are given, though not in the proper sequence. Sakhalin is represented as an island with place names only in its southern part. It is of much interest to note that a place name on the lower Amur River was included by mistake. This name must have been learned from natives of Sakhalin who bartered with the people of Manchuria. From very early days they had practiced the so-called "Santan trade" by which Chinese goods were brought to the Ainu of Hokkaido through Sakhalin and then were passed on to the Japanese in Matsumae. The early expeditions to Sakhalin probably were an attempt to investigate the actual condition of this channel of trade in which the Matsumae government was so vitally interested.

In those days the shogunate authorities in Edo were little informed of affairs of the Ezo area, for the Matsumaes had chosen to keep secret the information in their sphere of influence. But the revolt of the Ainu in 1669 directed considerable public attention to the north. Tokugawa Mitsukuni, the Lord of Mito, who had been ambitious to develop the northern territory, built a ship named *Kaifu-maru* which he equipped with various Western navigational instruments and in 1687 sent it on an expedition to Ezo. In the next year the *Kaifu-maru* reached the mouth of the Ishikarigawa, traded with the Ainu, and made a survey of the inland region.[7]

In 1720 Arai Hakuseki, the excellent scholar-statesman of the shogunate government, published *Ezo-shi* (Description of Ezo), the first geography of the northern region. At about the same time certain Confucian scholars, such as Namikawa Tenmin, advocated the exploitation of Ezo, and his brother Namikawa Seisho went so far as to experiment with the possibility of growing rice in a cold climate. In 1737, Sakakura Genjiro was commissioned by the shogunate to prospect Ezo for gold and silver. These attempts were motivated by a desire on the part of the ruling class to solidify the financial foundation of the feudal system which had been threatened by the rapid rise of the merchants and the remarkable growth of money economy. Thus, the time was getting ripe for the exploration of the Ezo area by the shogunate. An added impetus to exploration was given by the emergence of the Russians in the North Pacific area.

The Russians, having occupied Kamchatka early in the eighteenth century, began to knock at the northern door of isolated Japan.[8] In 1739 a squadron commanded by Lieutenant Martin Spanberg, detached from the exploratory fleet under Captain Vitus Bering, appeared off the coast of Rikuzen and Awa, provinces of the main island of Japan. The squadron went away in silence, leaving only one playing card and two silver coins. Contact between the Japanese and Russians became more frequent in the Kuril Islands until 1778 and 1779, when the Russians came to Nemuro and Atsukeshi (Akkeshi), in eastern Hokkaido, asking to open trade with Japan through the Matsumae government.

The Japanese authorities, owing to an utter lack of overseas information, could not realize the full significance of such a Russian request. But before this, the Dutch Factory at Nagasaki received letters from a Hungarian fugitive named Benyovsky who had escaped from Kamchatka in 1771. Benyovsky warned of Russia's aggressive designs upon Japan. Those who learned of this portentious information from Dutch interpreters showed great concern, and not a few writers argued for the development of the northern area as a national defense against foreign aggression. Among them was Hayashi Shihei, who published the noted *Sangoku Tsuran Zusetsu* (General Account of Three Countries, Illustrated) in 1785, giving a geopolitical description of the regions adjacent to Japan proper.[9]

It is worthy of special mention that a map of Ezo appended to this book shows a strange peninsula named Karafuto facing southeastward to the Island of Ezo (Hokkaido) (Plate 15, *following this page*). It also shows another island, named Sagaren (Sakhalin), to the east of the estuary of the Amur River. This imaginary peninsula of Karafuto separated from the island of Sakhalin appears to have been inspired by Jean B. B. d'Anville's map or some of its descendants.[10] Despite the representation of Karafuto as an island on the aforementioned shogunate maps, the vague knowledge of Santan trade which brought the Chinese goods from the continent encouraged the Japanese to suppose that Karafuto was in fact a peninsula. Two distinguished authors of northern geography, Arai Hakuseki and Matsumae Hironaga, also leaned to that opinion.[11] Therefore, the Japanese were likely to accept D'Anville's inaccurate geographical interpretation.

Is Karafuto a peninsula or an island? Is it true that Karafuto and Sakhalin are two entirely different places? These questions were left unsolved until subsequent planned explorations were undertaken by the shogunate government.

THE NORTHERN FRONTIER II.

Exploration of Ezo by the shogunate was directly induced by Kudo Heisuke, a friend of Hayashi Shihei. In his *Akaezo Fusetsu-ko* (Considerations of Reports on the Red Ezo or Russia) submitted to the shogunate authorities in 1783, Kudo emphasized that the development of the Ezo area was a matter of urgent necessity to forestall Russia's descent from the north. Tanuma Okizugu, the leader of the shogunate administration, was greatly impressed by Kudo's suggestion, for he too had fostered the idea of exploiting these uncultivated lands and of promoting foreign trade to tap this source of revenue for the treasury.[12]

Consequently, in 1785, an expedition, headed by Sato Genrokuro and four other officers, was sent to Ezo by the shogunate. There the expedition divided into two

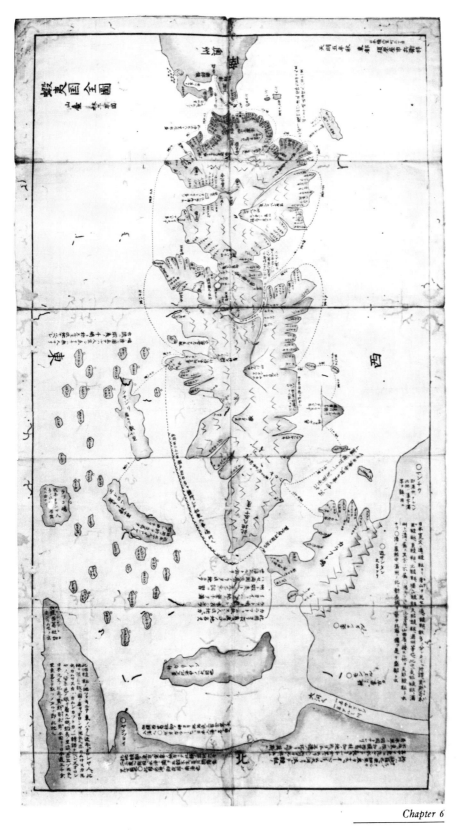

Chapter 6

Map of Ezo by Hayashi Shihei, 1785 [see Note 9].

PLATE 15

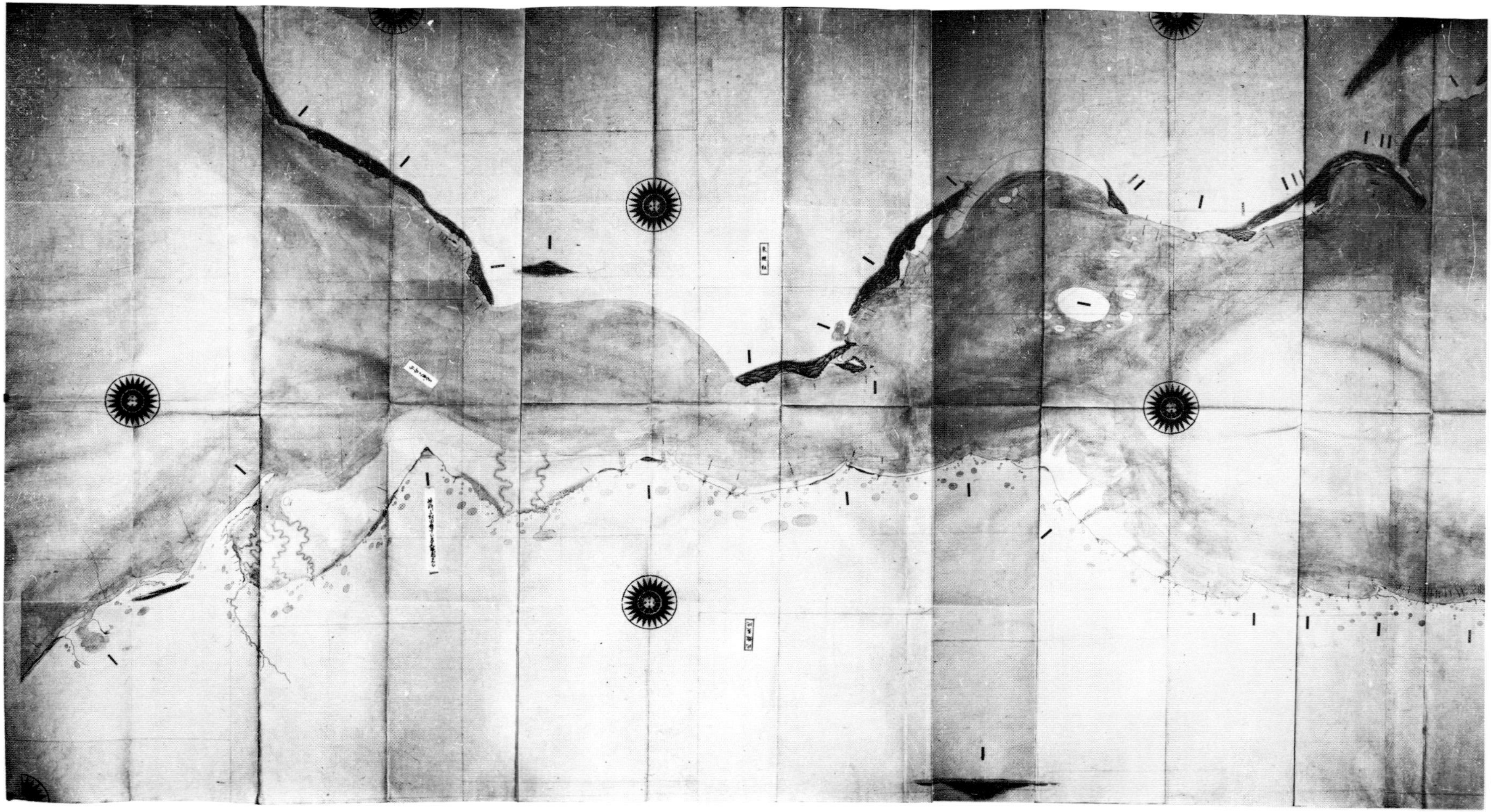

A portion of the map of Karafuto and eastern Tatary surveyed by Mamiya Rinzo in 1809, showing the channel between Karafuto and the mainland. Scale of original 1:36,000. (Courtesy of the Cabinet Library, Tokyo, Japan.)

Chapter 6

PLATE 16

parties and made a successful survey of the entire coast of Hokkaido. One of the parties went to Sakhalin and on the way back spent the winter at Sōya, in the northernmost district of Hokkaido, in order to make an observation of cold weather conditions. But five members of the party, including the leader Iobara Yaroku, died there of disease because of inadequate supplies and insufficient protection from the rigors of winter.

In the following year the expedition concentrated its efforts primarily on an exploration of the Kuril Islands and Sakhalin. Yamaguchi Tetsugoro, accompanied by Mogami Tokunai, was the first Japanese to set foot on Uruppu Island (Ostrov Urup) via Etorofu (Ostrov Iturup). Another party under Oishi Ippei reached Kushunnai (Il'inskiy, in latitude 47° 59' N.) on the west coast of Sakhalin. These explorations, which covered a period of two years, marked a great step forward in the geographical knowledge of the northern area. Their results were embodied in *Ezo-zoshi* (Accounts of Ezo) by Mogami Tokunai, *Hokkai-ki* (Essay on the North Sea) by Oishi Ippei, and *Ezo Shui* (Gleanings of Ezo) by Sato Genrokuro, as well as in the reports submitted to the shogunate.

The maps prepared by them were a considerable improvement over those of their predecessors, especially for the southern Kuril Islands and the east coast of Hokkaido. As Professor Takakura has pointed out, such cartographical success was mainly due to the surveying skill of Mogami Tokunai. Petty official that he was, Mogami joined the expedition upon the recommendation of his teacher, Honda Toshiaki, the illustrious scholar of Western learning who had a far-sighted view of the development of the northern territory. Later Mogami found favor with Minister Matsudaira Sadanobu, Tanuma's successor, and was actively engaged on subsequent expeditions as an expert explorer of the northern region.[13]

Meanwhile the Russians were continuing their advance toward the south. In 1792 a Russian brigantine *Ekaterina* carrying Adam Laxman, special envoy of Empress Catherine II, came to Nemuro near the eastern tip of Hokkaido. He returned some Japanese castaways rescued by the Russians,[14] and presented to Matsumae officials a request for trade with the shogunate. He could not get a definite reply from the shogunate and went home in the following year without any satisfactory results. In 1796 and 1797, fast on the heels of the Russians, the British corvette *Providence* under Captain William R. Broughton touched twice at ports in Uchiura-wan, in western Hokkaido, during her extensive survey of the Pacific Ocean.

These events were a great shock to the shogunate authorities, and they came to realize the necessity of bringing Ezo under their direct control. In 1798 the shogunate dispatched to Ezo a large inspection party of 180 members under the leadership of Okochi Masahisa and others. It is worthy of notice that a member of its detachment to the Sōya district, headed by Mitsuhashi Shigetaka, traveled up the Teshio-gawa (river) to its headwaters and then descended the Ishikari-gawa to its mouth, thus exploring the unknown inland region of northern Hokkaido.

In the following year the so-called East Ezo district, extending along the southern coast of Hokkaido to Cape Shiretoko, was transferred from the Matsumae's control to the hands of the shogunate, and development of the area was begun. At the same time the precise land surveying of Ezo was attempted. In 1800, the celebrated cartographer Ino Tadataka prepared a new map from original survey of the area from Hakodate to Nemuro. The rest of the island was surveyed later by Mamiya Rinzo, who had learned the art of surveying under Ino. The map of Hokkaido thus completed has a very accurate coastline, though the inland section is left almost blank.[15]

In the Kuril Islands, Kondo Morishige, who was in charge of the islands on the occasion of the expedition of 1798, made efforts to open up Etorofu-jima (Ostrov Iturup). In these efforts he had the assistance of the famous trader Takadaya Kahe. Using various sources, including information from the natives and works by Europeans as well as by Chinese, Kondo later completed a geographical study of the northern border. His researches are embodied in his *Henyo Bunkai Zuko* (Consideration of Border Regions with Maps) written in 1804, which is one of the most excellent works in the historical geography of the Ezo area. In Sakhalin, too, further explorations were carried out successively by Takahashi Hiromitsu in 1790, Mogami Tokunai in 1792, and Takahashi Jidayu and Nakamura Kojuro in 1801. Takahashi and Nakamura explored as far north as Naibutsu on the east coast and Kita Soya Misaki on the west coast. Fairly accurate maps of southern Sakhalin Island were portrayed from the data thus obtained, but the authors' knowledge of the northern part of the island was restricted to what could be learned by talking to natives on the island. The question as to whether or not Sakhalin was a peninsula remained unsettled.[16]

Western explorers of the late eighteenth and early nineteenth centuries, such as Jean F. de G. de La Pérouse, William R. Broughton, and Ivan F. von Kruzenshtern, were quite doubtful of the insularity of Sakhalin. Kruzenshtern, captain of the Russian ship *Nadezhda*, with the Russian envoy Nikolai P. Rezanov on board, visited Nagasaki in 1804. On his return to Kamchatka he made an exploratory voyage to Sakhalin, but as he could not discover the through passage between the island and the mainland, he mistook the strait as a large landlocked bay.

The mission of this second Russian embassy to Japan was again to urge that the Japanese government establish commercial relations with Russia.[17] However, having met with the flat refusal of the shogunate, the Russians took retaliatory measures upon Japanese residents on Etorofu-jima and on Sakhalin. During this crisis the shogunate took direct control of the whole area of Ezo, including Sakhalin in 1807, and reinforced the coast defenses of the territory.

At this time, the shogunate authorities adopted the proposal of Takahashi Kageyasu, the shogunate's eminent astronomer, to dispatch an expedition to Sakhalin to obtain more reliable information. In 1808, by order of the shogunate, Mamiya Rinzo and Matsuda Denjuro undertook an expedition along two routes. Matsuda explored the west coast of Sakhalin as far north as Cape Nakko (Mys Lakh), while Mamiya reached Cape Kita-Shiretoko (Mys Terpeniya) on the east coast, successfully traversed the mountains, and finally joined Matsuda's party on the west coast. This exploratory journey convinced them that Sakhalin was in fact an island, and they so reported to the shogunate.

The next year, Mamiya, after having passed the winter at Sōya in Hokkaido, proceeded to Sakhalin Island and reached Nanio, on the northern outlet of the narrow channel between the island and the mainland. Then, proceeding across the channel to the mainland he at last reached Delen' on the lower Amur River, where the Chinese government had an outpost for trade with the natives. In November of the lunar calendar 1809, he returned to Matsumae from a long and arduous journey which had yielded a rich harvest of geographical knowledge of the northern area. His on-the-spot observations at Delen' especially threw great light on the actual conditions of the 'Santan trade. But the most tangible result of his expedition was his success in confirming the existence of the strait between Sakhalin and the continent, and the certainty that Sakhalin was an island. Thus finally was solved the long-standing question concerning the geography of this northern area.[18]

The results of the expedition of 1808–1809 were embodied in Matsuda's *Hokui-dan* (An Account of Northern Ezo), Mamiya's *Kita-Ezo Zusetsu* (Illustrated Description of Northern Ezo), and *Totatsu Kiko* (A Journey to Eastern Tatary), and a very accurate map of Sakhalin Island and of the lower Amur region on the scale of 1 : 36,000 prepared by Mamiya (Plate 16, *facing page 101*). On the basis of these reports and maps, Takahashi Kageyasu published his comprehensive view of the geography of the northern area in his *Hokui Kosho* (A Study of Northern Ezo), and included the results of these explorations in his *Nippon Henkai Ryakuzu* (Outline Map of Japan and its Neighboring Regions) published in 1809, and the *Shintei Bankoku Zenzu* (Newly Revised Map of the World) in 1810, which were the most accurate maps of these regions available in those days. Philipp Franz von Siebold, who learned of Mamiya's achievements through Takahashi, named the channel between Sakhalin Island and the mainland the Strait of Mamiya (Tatar Strait) after its discoverer.[19] It is well known that Captain Kruzenshtern, seeing Siebold's collection of Japanese maps, remarked "Les Japonais m'ont vaincu!" However, since Mamiya Rinzo had not explored the east coast of northern Sakhalin Island, credit for its accurate mapping should be given to that eminent Russian captain, who had gone around the northern tip of the island.

About this time Russian pressure in the Far East weakened because of her preoccupation with the Napoleonic Wars. In 1811 Russian Captain Vasilii M. Golovnin was captured by Japanese guards on Kunashiri (Ostrov Kunashir), but the matter was peacefully settled and relations between Japan and Russia in this area temporarily improved. Under such circumstances the shogunate government, which had been in financial difficulty, in 1811 gave back the whole territory of Ezo to the Matsumaes. As a consequence, systematic exploration ceased.

In time, and because of persistent international pressures, the shogunate had to abandon the long-continued policy of national isolation. During 1853 American Commodore Matthew C. Perry and Russian Vice-Admiral Evfimii V. Putiatin came to Japan and demanded the opening of formal intercourse with the shogunate government. Recognizing the inevitable need to open the doors to international relations, the shogunate in 1854 concluded a Treaty of Amity and Friendship with the United States, Russia, and England. At the same time, Japan made a joint agreement with Russia regarding the delimitation of Japan's northern frontier. The treaty stipulated that in the Kuril Islands the line of demarcation was between Ostrov Iturup and Ostrov Urup, but that Sakhalin Island was to be maintained under joint occupation of the two countries, in rather vague terms, permitting both Japanese and Russians to settle there as they wished.[20] With due consideration to this agreement the shogunate in the same year dispatched Hori Toshihiro, Muragaki Norimasa, and others to Sakhalin Island on a tour of inspection. In 1855 the shogunate reinstated its official control of Ezo and resumed the survey and development of the area.

Japanese explorations during the period 1854–1868, that is, from Japan's opening of foreign intercourse to the downfall of the shogunate, were characterized by detailed surveys and voluminous reports. Under a commission from the shogunate, Maeda Natsukage compiled 210 volumes of *Ezo Shiryo* (Archives of Ezo), spending six years (1854–1860) in the task. His disciple, Megata Tatewaki, and others made a survey of the coast of Hokkaido and of Sakhalin Island in 1856–57. The *Ezo Rekishin-kenzu* and *Kita-Ezo Rekishinkenzu* (Map of Ezo and Northern Ezo from Field Survey) and 53 volumes of *Ezo Jitchi Kenkoroku* (Accounts of Actual Observation of Ezo Area) were the outstanding products of these surveys. The former two are a kind of perspective map drawn minutely on a scale of 3.6 *sun* (= 10.9 cm) to 1 *ri* (= 4km).

The inland regions left open on Ino-Mamiya maps are shown in detail on the *Tozai-Ezo Sansen Chiri Torishirabe Zu* (Topographical Map of East and West Ezo), *i.e.*, Hokkaido, and on the *Kita-Ezo Sansen Chiri Torishirabe Zu* (Topographical Map of Northern Ezo), *i.e.*, Sakhalin. These were completed by Matsuura Takeshiro in 1859 after years of laborious field survey. The former consists of twenty-eight sheets and the latter of twenty-two, each sheet showing an area of one degree of latitude by one degree of longitude. It should be added that these maps are the crowning work of the long, patient geographical exploration conducted by the shogunate throughout the Edo period.[21]

Up to this time, however, no Japanese had penetrated to the northern end of Sakhalin. In 1865 Okamoto Bunpei and Nishimura Denkuro made a complete circuit of Sakhalin Island, including the northern tip of the island. Their reports were published in Nishimura's *Karafuto Junkai-ki* (An Account of Travel Round Karafuto) and Okamoto's *Kyokuhoku Nikki* (Journal from the Farthest North) and *Kita-Ezo Shinshi* (New Geography of Northern Ezo). Thus, geographical exploration of the Ezo area by the Japanese had been pretty well completed by the end of the Edo period.

The North Pacific area, especially that including the northern border of Japan, was one of the regions which long remained unclear on maps of the world. Despite the severe restrictions imposed by Japan's closed-door policy, the results of exploration by the Japanese found their way into Europe and made a significant contribution to the advancement of geographical knowledge of this large region.

It is of special significance to note that these explorations encouraged a scientific way of thinking among Japanese intellectuals. Under the strong influence of Chinese learning, Japanese scholars of those days leaned heavily on the authority of the classic tradition and tended to appraise scientific results by testing their consistency with the doctrines of the classical literature. But the untamed wildernesses and the uncivilized natives of the desolate north were not responsive to this classical approach. Therefore, Japanese scholars had to abandon the ancient tradition and make studies of natural features and life of inhabitants of the Ezo area with the more objective approach they had learned from the Western sciences transmitted to Japan, especially through the Dutch.[22] Consequently, there appeared some excellent works about Ezo in the fields of botany, ethnology, and philology.[23] While most of the works on the Japanese homeland remained under the influence of Chinese classicism, the aforementioned reports and books and those in the field of geography concerning the Ezo area show every indication of scientific objectivity in their detailed descriptions and precise observations. The seeds of Western geographical sciences introduced through Nagasaki thus found favorable soil in the Ezo area and grew until they flourished in the Meiji era.

Ezo is of course but a small part of the vast Pacific Basin. But national survival and international pressures forced the isolated Japanese to join in geographical exploration by the Westerners, cultivated their scientific perception, and eventually led them to full participation in international society. The historical significance of the Ezo area far outshadows that of the relative smallness of the geographical area involved.

THE SOUTHERN ISLANDS: RYUKYU AND BONIN ISLANDS

Early in the seventh century, as recorded in some historical documents, the Japanese had been in contact with the Ryukyu Islands (Nansei-shotō), which stretch southward as an arc from the Japanese mainland.[24] In the latter half of that century, these islands were acquiring importance as a midway point on the new route to China, for Japanese influence over Korea was on the wane, and the route to the Asiatic continent through the Korean peninsula became insecure. In 679 A.D. the Japanese government in Yamato dispatched an exploratory party to Tanega-shima near Kyushu. The party returned in 681 A.D. and submitted to the Imperial Court a map and an interesting report on the customs of the inhabitants and the products of the island. Again, in 698 A.D., an expeditionary force on a larger scale was sent out. This resulted in the annexation by Japan of the southern islands, including Okinawa, as a new province of Tane.

Subsequently the government opened up a new route from Kyushu to the mouth of the Yangtze River in the East China Sea, using the southern islands as a relay base. But in the ninth century, when commerce with China decreased, Japanese authorities lost interest in these islands, and in 824 A.D. the province of Tane was merged with the province of Ōsumi (south Kyushu). Consequently, Japanese dominance within the islands was confined to a certain few locations near Kyushu, and exploration was not resumed until the beginning of the seventeenth century.

It is commonly believed that the Kingdom of Ryukyu was founded toward the close of the twelfth century and that it later grew in power, uniting all the islands south of Amami-ō-shima under its control. In the fifteenth century the kingdom enjoyed prosperity which depended upon the extensive intermediate trade with east and southeast Asian countries. The Japanese, for their part, regarded Ryukyu as their dependency, for the kingdom regularly sent an envoy on a tribute-paying mission to the Ashikaga Shogunate in Kyoto.

Frequent negligence in payment of tribute in the later sixteenth century furnished the Japanese with a pretext for sending a punitive expedition to the kingdom. With the approval of the Tokugawa Shogunate, Shimazu Iehisa, Lord of Satsuma, whose

domain comprised south Kyushu and a part of the northern Ryukyu Islands, in 1609
sent a force of 3000 men to the Kingdom of Ryukyu and occupied all of its dependent
islands without meeting any vigorous resistance. The primary aim of this expedition
was to secure the profits from the trade with China through Ryukyu, for in those days
the Chinese government had strictly prohibited commercial intercourse with Japan.
Therefore, Shimazu gave nominal independence to the Kingdom of Ryukyu, and, even
keeping secret its subjection to Japan, made the kingdom continue to trade with
China as before.[25]   The Shimazu government undertook a large-scale survey of the
southern islands primarily for the purpose of gathering data for administration. In
1610, 168 members of the exploratory party led by fourteen chief surveyors covered
all the islands of the Ryukyus. The data thus accumulated were compiled into the
huge *Kenchi-cho* (Cadastral Book) in 270 volumes, which contained a detailed description of villages, rice paddies, fields, cattle, useful plants, fishing boats, and sal-
terns on every island.

Presumably, by using such data obtained from the Shimazu government, Arai
Hakuseki wrote the *Nanto-shi* (Description of the Southern Islands) in 1719. The
fairly accurate maps of the Ryukyu Islands appended to it were also based on maps
originally prepared by the Shimazu officials. As Shimazu's materials were not opened
to the public, Arai's *Nanto-shi* was the primary source of knowledge about the Ryukyu Islands during the Edo period. Hayashi Shihei in his *Sangoku Tsuran* also borrowed
much from that work, especially for his chapter describing the Ryukyu Islands.

It is interesting to note that the exploration of the Ryukyu Islands, unlike that of
Ezo, was not conducted by the shogunate but by the local government. The reason for
this is probably found in the fact that, from the diplomatic and financial point of view,
the shogunate found it expedient to leave the affairs of Ryukyu to the discretion of the
Shimazu clan, which was powerful enough to assume complete control of such an
island kingdom. Even in the nineteenth century, when vessels from Western countries
came to Okinawa to establish friendly relations with the Kingdom of Ryukyu, negotiations were left entirely in the hands of the Shimazus. The Kingdom of Ryukyu
was officially incorporated into Japan, as Okinawa prefecture, at the beginning of the
Meiji era.

Exploration by the Japanese was also made to a small island group about 600 miles
south of Edo (Tokyo). These islands are said to have been discovered in 1593 by
Ogasawara Sadayori, hence the name Ogasawara-gunto (Bonin Islands).[26] There is
no reliable evidence, however, to corroborate his voyage of exploration to the southern sea. During the Edo period these islands were generally known as "Mujinto" or
"Buninto" (no-man's island) which has been corrupted to "Bonin" by Westerners.
This designation appears to have originated with some castaways who, on their return in 1670, reported that the islands were fertile but uninhabited.

The shogunate authorities were much interested in this information and commissioned Shimaya Ichizaemon, an expert seaman of Nagasaki who was familiar with
the Western art of navigation, to make an exploration of the islands.[27] By order of the
shogunate, a so-called "foreign style" ship was especially constructed at Nagasaki for
this expedition. In April of the lunar calendar 1675, Shimaya sailed from Shimoda
with his party of thirty-two men, and after a voyage of about a week, arrived in the
Bonin Islands. There they surveyed every island nearby for about one month, pre-

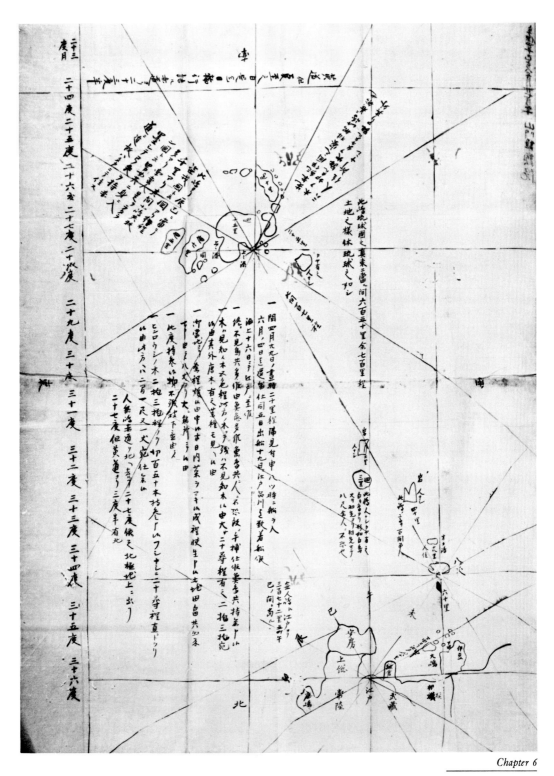

A rough copy (1719) of a map of the Ogasawara Islands appended to the report of the expedition led by Shimaya Ichizaemon in 1675 [see Note 27]. (Courtesy of Itaru Imai.)

PLATE 17

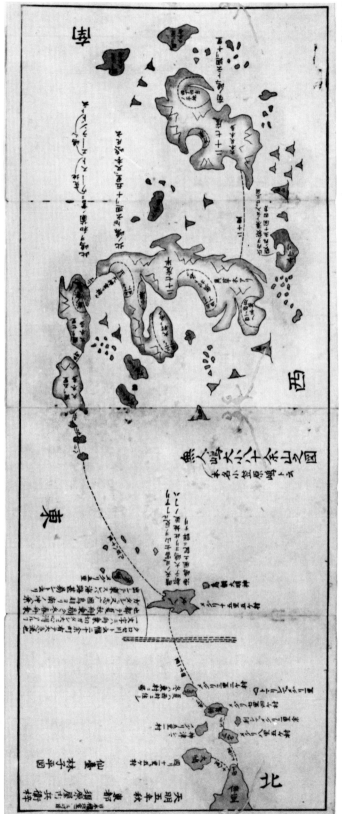

Map of the Ogasawara Islands by Hayashi Shihei, 1785 [see Note 9]. North is at left.

PLATE 18

pared maps and collected various plants and other products. In July they returned to Edo, leaving behind five fowl and a wooden shrine bearing the inscription "Within the Boundaries of Great Japan."²⁸

The report of the expedition and two maps (Plate 17, *following page 106*) were submitted to the shogunate. The *Mujinto Norimae Zu* (Chart of Navigation to the Bonin Islands) made by Shimaya is a rare example, for this age, of a portolan chart in the European style.²⁹ These Western arts of map making, shipbuilding, and navigation are the heritage of the trade with the West by Red Seal ships, and Shimaya's voyage to the Bonins can be said to have been the last case of putting them into practical use. Subsequent attempts by the shogunate to explore the islands ended in failure, giving evidence that Japan, under its strict isolation policy, had already fallen backward in the art of navigation.³⁰

In 1785 Hayashi Shihei published the aforementioned *Sangoku Tsuran*, in which he referred to Shimaya's report and emphasized the necessity of the exploitation of the Bonin Islands (Plate 18, *facing this page*). This aroused public interest in the islands, and in 1839 some merchants of Ezo attempted to establish a settlement there. But it came to a tragic end when the noted progressive scholars of Western learning, Watanabe Kazan, Takano Choei, and others were implicated in the scheme and were punished with death by the obdurately conservative shogunate officials.³¹ Meanwhile, Westerners preceded the Japanese in planting a colony there.

The Bonin Islands appear to have been known by Westerners as early as the sixteenth century. At the beginning of the nineteenth century, when British and American whalers extended their wide-ranging activities to the vicinity of these islands, Westerners began to take a real interest in them. In 1827, Captain Frederick W. Beechey came to the Bonins on board the *H.M.S. Blossom* and left there a copper plate with an inscription asserting the British possession of the islands. Acting on Beechey's report, two Americans and three Europeans accompanied by some twenty-five Kanakas came from Hawaii in 1830 to be the first immigrants to the Bonin Islands.³²

Years later a repatriated castaway informed the shogunate of what had occurred in the islands. The news also came through Commodore Matthew C. Perry, whose fleet had visited there in 1853 with the intention of laying claim to the islands. Realizing the seriousness of the situation, the shogunate commanded Foreign Affairs Commissioner Mizuno Tadanori to determine how matters stood in the islands. In 1861 Mizuno and his party of thirty men went to the Bonins on the *Kanrin-maru*, a shogunate warship purchased from Holland. They hoisted the Japanese flag on the main island (Chichi-shima) and told the Western immigrants that the island belonged to Japan. During its stay of two and a half months, the Mizuno party made a detailed investigation of all the islands and prepared a set of very accurate maps which used improved surveying techniques.³³

These two expeditions to the Bonin Islands are excellent examples of planned maritime exploration during the Edo period. They are characterized by the use of the most advanced type of seagoing ship then in Japan and an improved science of navigation learned from the West which enabled the Japanese to explore far-off islands in the vast ocean. However, because of the prohibition of overseas voyages by the Japanese government, such expeditions could be permitted solely on the premise that the islands had originally been within Japanese territory. This excessive restriction of exploration during the period of isolation proved to be a severe handicap to the colonial growth of Japan in subsequent times.

THE DAWN OF MODERN JAPAN

In 1868 the Tokugawa Shogunate was replaced by the Meiji government and Japan, liberated from its bondage to feudalism, was admitted into the family of nations. A vast horizon opened before the Japanese and they bent every effort to absorb Western scientific knowledge to overcome the general backwardness caused by long-standing national isolation. New industries were opened up under governmental protection and various land and marine surveys were inaugurated to cover the whole extent of Japanese territory.

In 1879 the Tokyo Geographical Society was founded and patterned after the English model (The Royal Geographical Society), under the presidency of Prince Kitashirakawa Yoshihisa.[34] Subsequently the Society carried out extensive surveys, mainly in Korea, Manchuria, and China, backed by Japan's political and economic expansion in these regions. Japan's scientific activity in the Pacific Ocean area during the nineteenth century was not so remarkable as it was on the continent. In 1874 Japan and Russia exchanged Sakhalin Island for the northern Kurils. But the development of these islands made little progress until 1893, when an exploring party headed by Lieutenant Gunji Shigetada conducted an exploration of the northern Kurils. In 1896 Gunji and his followers settled a small colony on the northernmost island of Shumushu (Ostrov Shumshu) to develop the cod fisheries in the Sea of Okhotsk and in the North Pacific Ocean. This was the forerunner of Japan's deep-sea fisheries.[35] In the south, the island of Formosa was annexed to Japan in 1895 as the result of the Sino-Japanese War, and exploration of this newly acquired territory was made principally by the national government. Scientific exploration of the sea was also taken up by the Meiji government. In 1871 a Hydrographic Division was established in Japan and Yanagi Narayoshi was appointed to be its head.[36] Yanagi was an expert hydrographer who had made a joint survey in Seto Naikai (the Japanese Inland Sea) with the British H.M.S. *Sylvia* in 1870. Under his distinguished direction the systematic hydrographic survey of the entire coast of Japan was begun in 1882.[37] Systematic observation of the ocean currents was for the first time carried out in 1893 by Dr. Wada Yuji of the Central Meteorological Observatory. His intensive researches threw new light on scientific aspects of the Kuroshio (Japan Current) and other currents in the seas circumjacent to Japan.[38]

It was not until the twentieth century, however, that comprehensive and detailed scientific explorations of the sea achieved results sufficiently adequate and large-scale to make comprehensive contributions to knowledge in this field. Japanese occupation of the former German-held Micronesian Islands, near the end of World War I, encouraged her to increase her scientific activity in the Pacific area. Japan's scientific exploration of the Pacific Basin during the latter half of the nineteenth century was of a pioneer nature, but it set the stage for the numerous and varied contributions that she has made to our geographical knowledge in the twentieth century (see Chapter 14).

GEOGRAPHICAL EXPLORATION BY THE SPANIARDS

Donald D. Brand*

This and the following chapter do not incorporate a startling discovery, report a new document, or make a daringly different identification; they merely constitute a survey. But they do comprise a reminder of the great and courageous accomplishments of Iberians beginning long before the days of Tasman and of Cook. Furthermore, the eastern Pacific waters and coastlands are given more consideration than normally is the case with discussions of explorations in the Pacific Ocean. My chief concern has been the selection of events worthy of mention, the judicious choice among routes and identifications of discoveries made by other students in this field, and the indication (where advisable and possible) of the location of primary documents and reliable reproductions.

The way has been made easier by the compilations and collections of such authorities as Peter Martyr and Giovanni B. Ramusio, through James Burney and Martín Fernández de Navarrete (hereinafter referred to simply as Navarrete), to the great historical collections published in Spain and Portugal in the nineteenth and twentieth centuries, and the publications of the Hakluyt Society and the Linschoten-Vereeniging.[1]

To the critical judgement of such as Jean N. Buache, Burney, and Navarrete, I have added the modern scholarship of the various editors for the Hakluyt Society, as well as that expressed in other writings by such as José T. Medina, John C. Beaglehole, Armando Cortesão, and the Visconde de Lagôa, and the expert identifications by many others including especially Henry B. Guppy, Carl E. Meinicke, Erik W. Dahlgren, Henry R. Wagner, H. E. Maude, and Andrew Sharp.[2]

For our purposes the Pacific extends from the Americas to the east coasts of Japan, the Philippines, Moluccas, and Australia, and from the Bering Sea to Antarctica. Such writers as Burney, Brigham, and Wroth[3] have helped to establish these bounds. We are not concerned with the Asiatic waters along the western shores of the Pacific since there was little for the European to discover there. The Chinese, Japanese, Indonesians, Indians, Persians, and Arabs who navigated in these waters represented for the most part civilized peoples who made charts and kept records. The time span that we will attempt to cover is from 1511/13 to the nineteenth-century elimination of imperial Spain from the Pacific.

My procedure has been to read the published primary documents, with especial attention to editions and versions having editorial comment and notations, as well as the histories and other writings by individuals who had access to information no longer available—such as Oviedo, Barros, and Herrera. Also, I have examined most of the charts and maps available in reproductions, as well as a few unpublished charts,

*Dr. Brand is professor of geography at the University of Texas, Austin, Texas.

maps, and documents. Because I have personal acquaintance with only a very minor fraction of the coasts and islands of the Pacific, I have relied heavily on the identifications by Meinicke and by Sharp.[4]

There are many kinds of information which the reader has a right to expect, even in a brief survey such as this. Unfortunately, the data on the nature of the ships and their equipment, the crews, provisions and diet, and the daily regime of working the ships are uneven, usually scanty, and often almost totally lacking. This holds true also for the instruments and methods of navigation, and the resultant logs, accounts, and charts, as well as data concerning latitude and longitude, magnetic declination, winds, currents, soundings, morphology of coasts and islands, biota, ethnology, etc. There are three principal reasons for this situation. Many things that were commonplace were not considered worthy of mention or description. Excessive nationalistic jealousy dictated policies of studied occultation of information. Apparently much material has been lost or destroyed through fire, earthquake, and flood, as well as by shipwreck, theft, improper storage, and by poor cataloging in archives, libraries, and museums.

However, there still exists a very large number of pertinent documents as yet unpublished in the Archivo General de Indias, Sevilla, as well as in the Archivo Nacional da Torre de Tombo, Lisboa, the Museo Naval, Madrid, the British Museum, London, the Vatican Library, etc.[5] Here it should be pointed out, as Spaniards and Portuguese are doing increasingly, that the navigators and other officials of Spain and Portugal observed widely and made many detailed reports and charts—in fact, were specifically required to do so.[6]

NAVIGATION

The known extant documents provide very little information concerning the ships specifically involved in the exploration of the Pacific. Commonly we are informed only of the number of ships in an expeditionary fleet (usually ranging from two to five), the proper names (most commonly *Santa María, Santiago, Victoria, Trinidad, San Pedro, San Pablo, San Francisco, San Juan*, and other names of saints), type of sailing vessel, tonnage, and the names of the captains and pilots. The type is given only by such designations as *nave, nao, navío*, and *galeón* (usually for the larger ships), *caravela, bergantín, patax* or *patache*, and *bajel*. Differences in local usages and changes of meanings through time make it extremely difficult to determine size, shape, rigging, and armament. For example, there seems to be no information available concerning the number of decks and masts and the rigging of the famous *Victoria*, which was the first ship to circumnavigate the globe.[7] Even when tonnages are given, there is little agreement as to the conversion of the sixteenth and seventeenth century *toneles de porte* into modern tons of capacity. Most commonly 10 Spanish *toneles de porte* are considered to be the equivalent of 12 modern *toneladas de capacidad*.[8]

The methods and instruments of navigation and the details of working a ship are seldom noted in the available literature. Furthermore, most of the formal reports and "logs" of the expeditionary leaders and chief pilots—from Magellan to Malaspina— either are lost or unpublished. We can only assume that the methods outlined and the instruments recommended in the more popular manuals of the time were those actually employed.[9] At the time of Magellan the chief navigational instruments con-

sisted of the astrolabe for precision, the quadrant for less precise observations, the
magnetic needle or mariner's compass (*aguja de marear*), dividers, and sailing charts
(*cartas de marear*). The *ballestilla* or cross-staff does not appear in the Pacific until
later in the century. The nature and development of the various techniques and instruments have been discussed by many historians and by some practical navigators,
but unfortunately most of these writers have had one or another regional or national
bias.[10]

Apparently all ships carried a supply of magnetized needles mounted on a card.
By the time of Magellan, navigators were well aware of magnetic declination, and
the various Spanish expeditions were instructed to make special observations on this
matter. Both Portuguese and Spanish experts, such as João de Castro and Alonso de
Santa Cruz, made maps showing magnetic declination. Santa Cruz corresponded
with Antonio de Mendoza, the viceroy of New Spain, and the Mendocine expeditions in the Pacific checked also on the problem of magnetic variation. Unfortunately, the extant "logs" give little information on these topics, and the results of
observations on the various voyages must be sought in the writings of the stay-at-
home experts in Europe.[11]

Speed and distance traversed were estimated on the basis of experience and current observations. Apparently there was no use of a *corredera* or "log" until some uncertain time late in the seventeenth century. Elapsed time was obtained from hour-
glasses or sandclocks and solar observations. Distances were stated in Iberian sea
leagues (evaluated as about 3.43 nautical miles or roughly four English statute land
miles), and *grados* or degrees (for Magellan equal to 16 2/3 marine leagues).

Latitude at sea was obtained almost exclusively by observing the altitude of the
sun at local noon by astrolabe or quadrant and applying corrections from tables such
as those of Zacuto. The range in error normally seems to have been between 10 and
60 minutes, usually toward the south, and rarely did the error amount to more than
30 minutes. This accuracy is remarkable when one considers the crudity of the instruments and the difficulties in making accurate readings on the deck of a relatively
small ship. Despite many statements by chroniclers and historians concerning the obtaining of latitude from observations on the North Pole Star or two of the stars in
the Southern Cross and other stars of the southern firmament, I have found no evidence for this in the available "logs" by Iberian mariners in the Pacific region. On
occasion such observations were made on land, but at sea—if the sun were not sufficiently visible at noon—the pilot (who was the officer in charge of the details of
navigation) would wait until the sun could be observed at noon, even though this
might mean a wait of many days.[12]

Longitude never was determined accurately by the Iberian navigators in the Pacific
region during the period of their great voyages, except on rare occasions and then
apparently by accident. Spain did not use exact chronometers until 1774, and apparently no Spanish ship having such chronometers reached the Pacific region until about
1785. Among the many methods suggested for obtaining precise longitude, apparently those involving lunar distances and the observation of lunar eclipses were best.
In both cases, however, the astronomical tables and the instruments were too poor
during several centuries, and the conditions on shipboard were too unfavorable. Nevertheless, lunar eclipses—which at best were not frequent enough or visible in the

appropriate regions—did provide the best approximations available for places in the New World such as Mexico City and Lima whence longitudes could be calculated for Pacific ports such as Acapulco and Callao.[13]

Precise determination of longitude had not been of much concern to the people of the Mediterranean and Atlantic coasts of Europe. It was not until the papal bulls and sanctions of 1452 to 1514, and the treaties between Spain and Portugal of 1479 to 1524, which ultimately established and recognized a Line of Demarcation between Portuguese and Spanish hemispheres, that an urgent need developed for precise determination of longitude. The primary Line of Demarcation came to be accepted as running near the present meridian of longitude 47° W. (Greenwich). In the controversy over which nation possessed or had access to the Moluccas it became of imperative importance to determine the location of the opposing meridian 180° around the globe. Ultimately Charles I of Spain (Emperor Charles V) effectively quitclaimed or sold his rights to the Moluccas 1524–29, although Spain retained the Philippine Islands which also were in the Portuguese hemisphere, and this particular problem became academic. Nevertheless, for years we are confronted with confused references to longitude based on the Line of Demarcation or on a too-frequently not specified primary meridian or *línea meridiana*. Frequently the Spanish astrologers (astronomers) used the meridian of Salamanca or of Toledo, while the navigators used Sevilla, Cádiz, and most frequently that of the Canary Islands.[14]

MAPS AND CHARTS

The sailing charts (*cartas de marear*) used by the Spanish navigators were prepared by cartographers in the Casa de Contratación in Sevilla, or by mapmakers under contract to the Casa de Contratación. The source of the data entered on these charts, which were specially prepared for each of the earlier expeditions, was theoretically and by law a master chart of the world known as the Padrón General de las Indias. This Padrón General was initiated about 1512, and presumably was kept up-to-date with the new data in the *diarios* and *derroteros* which had to be turned in after each voyage. For more effective presentation of data the master chart of the world was also kept on six regional charts having a larger scale. Eventually, three of these regional *padrones generales* covered the Pacific Ocean: one for the eastern Pacific and the coast from the Strait of Magellan to California, one for the northern Pacific from New Spain to the Philippines, and one for the region from Japan, China, the Philippines, and the Moluccas to the east coast of Africa.

Since practically all navigation to the Indies was monopolized or directed by the Spanish crown, there never was a need for a large number of sailing charts. Consequently, there was no necessity for a large edition of a sailing chart and all such charts were made by hand during the sixteenth century and most of the seventeenth century. The upshot has been that nearly all the *padrones generales* and derived *cartas de marear* of the sixteenth and seventeenth centuries have disappeared. This means that it is virtually impossible to trace the development of the map of the Pacific through official Spanish charts and maps.

Nevertheless, a considerable corpus of charts exists which embodies the results of Spanish voyages (Plates 19 and 20, *facing this page*). A relatively small number of

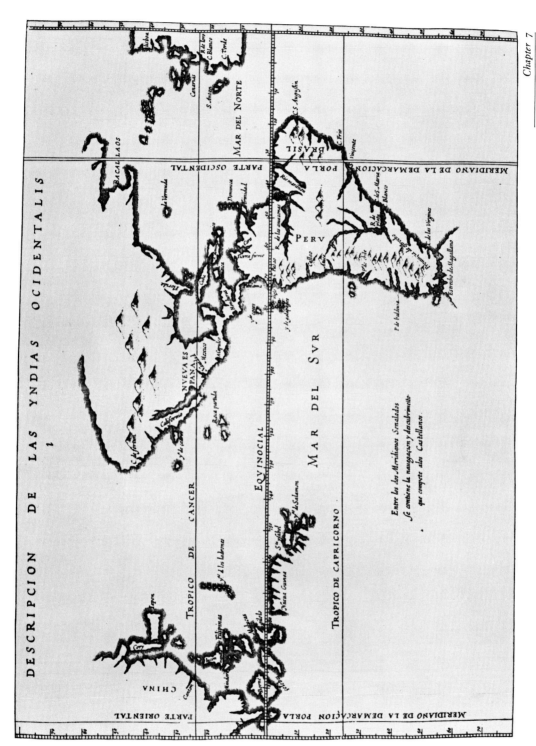

"Descripcion [map] de las Yndias Occidentalis," in Antonio de Herrera y Tordesillas: see Note 24, Vol. 1, Plate 1, between pages 6 and 7.

PLATE 19

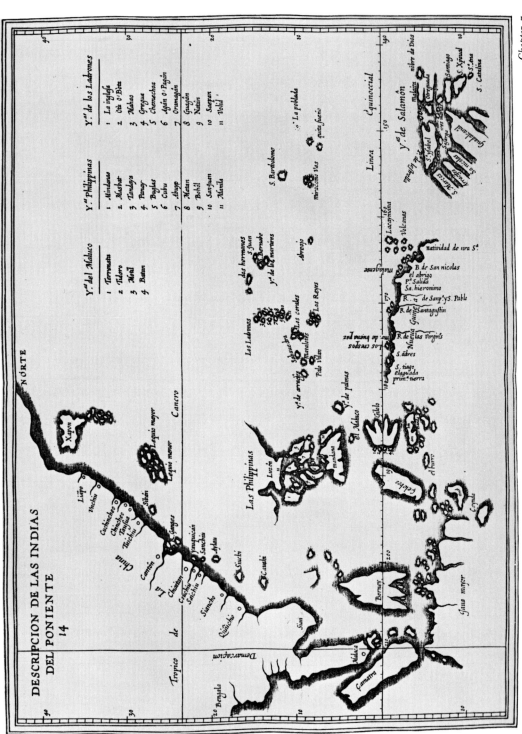

DESCRIPCION DE LAS INDIAS
DEL PONIENTE
14

Y.ᵃˢ del Maluco

1 Terrenate
2 Tidoro
3 Motil
4 Batan

Y.ˢ Philippinas

1 Mindanao
2 Mushat
3 Tandaya
4 Panay
5 Buglas
6 Cubu
7 Abuyo
8 Matan
9 Boholl
10 Sariffuan
11 Manila

Y.ᵃˢ de los Ladrones

1 La inglesa
2 Oʈa O'Bota
3 Maluao
4 Gregua
5 chemechoa
6 Agán o'Pagán
7 Orsomagan
8 Guajan
9 Natan
10 Saepan
11 Volil'

NÓRTE

Cancro

Trópico   de

Demarcacion

Linea   Equinoccial

PLATE 20

"Descripcion [map] de las Yndias del Poniente," in Antonio de Herrera y Tordesillas: see Note 24, Vol. 1, Plate 14, between pages 190 and 191.

Chapter 7

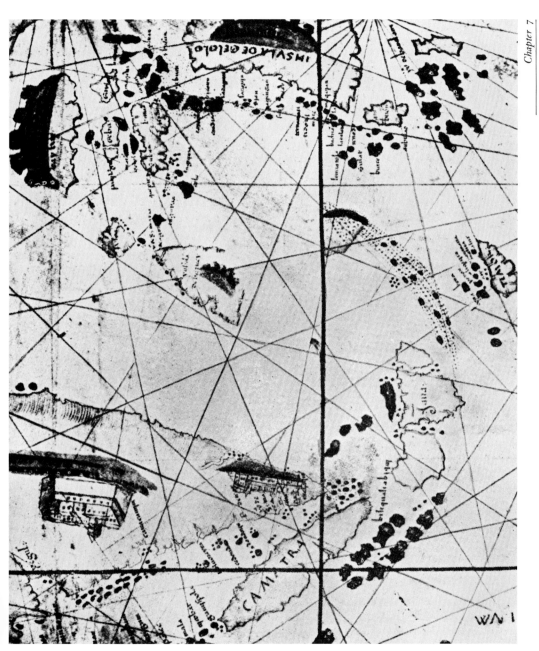

The East Indies, in a manuscript map by Nuño García de Toreno, 1522, reproduced in R. A. Skelton: see Note 11, Fig. 87 on page 141. (Courtesy of R. A. Skelton.)

PLATE 21

The East Indies, in a manuscript sea-atlas by Diogo Homem, 1558, reproduced in R. A. Skelton: see Note 11, Fig. 89 on page 142. (Courtesy of R. A. Skelton.)

PLATE 22

these charts were made by officials (cartographers, cosmographers, pilots, et al.) who had been employed by the Spanish crown, such as Nuño García de Toreno (Plate 21), Diego Ribero, Alonso de Chaves, Sebastian Cabot, Pedro de Medina, Alonso de Santa Cruz, and Juan López de Velasco. Nearly all of the charts by these cartographers that have been preserved are of the "library type," and they probably were made for royalty, nobles, ecclesiastics, wealthy merchants, and other important patrons and personages. The great bulk of the charts, both manuscript and printed, were by individuals not connected with the Casa de Contratación, and were produced in the great cartographic and publishing centers of Italy, France, the Low Countries, and England. There is good reason to believe that during the sixteenth century and well into the seventeenth century many pilots and other informed persons who were acquainted with the Spanish voyages, charts, and sailing directions, went to one or another of the centers of commerce and publication—especially to Antwerp and Amsterdam—and either with malice or because of need divulged their information. Consequently, we must depend in great part on "second-hand" maps and charts, or on cartographic items concerning which experts differ widely as to author, date, and authenticity. As I do not have sufficient competence, time, space, or local resources to discuss the evolution of the map of the Pacific by Spaniards or as a result of Spanish voyages, I will cite a number of the collections and studies that are most helpful.[15]

THE MOLUCCAN VOYAGES: 1519–1529

In September of 1513, Vasco Núñez de Balboa crossed the isthmus of Darién and became the first European to see the Pacific Ocean from its eastern shores. This discovery of the South Sea accelerated Spanish search for a passage through or around the great land mass which was already accepted by many as not being a part of the (East) Indies. With the voyage of Magellan was initiated the second phase of the Spanish search for a route west to the Indies which had commenced with Columbus in 1492. The decade 1519 to 1529 embraces what the Spaniards called Expediciones al Maluco, for which most of the documents are to be found in the collection termed Papeles del Maluco in the Archivo General de Indias, Sevilla.

MAGELLAN'S EXPEDITION

Captain Fernão de Magalhães (Ferdinand Magellan), a member of the Portuguese petty nobility, arrived in Sevilla on October 20, 1517. He had left the services of the Portuguese crown because of studied slights from King Manoel I. With the aid of some Portuguese in Spain, the powerful Bishop of Burgos (Juan de Fonseca, vice-president of the Council of the Indies), and Cristóbal de Haro (Spanish representative of the "Spice Trust" and German bankers such as the Fuggers), Magellan obtained consent from the crown to lead an expedition by sea westward which would locate a passage around the south end of the New World continent and on to the Moluccas. This expedition was subsidized by the Crown and by Haro.[16]

After nearly eighteen months of preparation, during which jealous Spaniards and the agents of the Portuguese king did all they could to stop or delay the outfitting of the fleet, five small vessels sailed from the port of Sanlúcar de Barrameda at the mouth of the Río Guadalquivir on or about September 20, 1519. The five *naos* (vessels)[17] were the flagship *Trinidad* of 110 *toneles de porte*, the *San Antonio* (120 *toneles*), the *Concepción* (90 *toneles*), the *Victoria* (85 *toneles*), and the *Santiago* (75 *toneles*).[18] Each ship had a captain, a pilot (except the *San Antonio* which had two and the *Santiago* on which the captain also served as pilot), a *maestre* (master in charge of the crew working the ship), and a *contramaestre* (boatswain); and these individuals ranked in the order listed in commanding, navigating, and working the ship. Of the captains who sailed from Spain, not one returned; of the pilots, only the deserter Esteban Gómez on the *San Antonio*; and of the masters, only Elcano.[19]

Food for the personnel, estimated to have been between 265 and 280, and calculated to be sufficient for two years (some documents say three years), consisted of biscuit, flour, rice, fish, pork, cheese, chick-peas, lentils, broad beans, wine, vinegar, olive oil, mustard, onion, garlic, capers, honey, sugar, salt, almonds, raisins, prunes, figs, quince preserves, six cows, and three pigs. The equipment for navigation supplied by the crown consisted of 23 sailing charts (all presumably made by Nuño García), six pairs of dividing compasses, 21 wooden quadrants, six metal astrolabes and one of wood, 35 magnetic needles (*agujas de marear*), and 18 sand clocks. Armament consisted of 71 guns (*lombardos* or mortars), 50 muskets, 60 crossbows, 1000 lances, and assorted swords, daggers, bucklers, helmets, and other items of personal armor. Other equipment included anchors, mooring lines, small boats, sounding equipment, medical supplies, goods for trade and gifts, and quantities of lead, iron, copper, pitch, and similar essential raw materials. Although listed in official documents, much of the above was not available to Magellan in the Pacific as he discovered, too late, that through chicanery in Sevilla many things never actually were placed in the ships. Also, the wreck of the *Santiago* on the Patagonian coast and the desertion of the *San Antonio* during the traverse of the Strait of Magellan rendered his situation even more desperate while crossing the Pacific.

After an eventful voyage from Spain, the details of which do not concern us, Magellan wintered at San Julián on the Patagonian coast, March 31 to August 24, 1520. On October 21, 1520, the headland approach to the Strait was seen and named Cabo de las Once Mil Vírgenes (Cabo Vírgenes today) from the saints day.[20] Here Pigafetta makes a remark that has puzzled historians to this day. He writes "But the captain-general who knew where to sail to find a well-hidden strait, which he saw depicted on a map in the treasury of the king of Portugal, which was made by that excellent man, Martin de Boemia, . . ."[21] It is the consensus of modern scholarship that Pigafetta confused Martin of Behaim with Johann Schöner. Furthermore, it is today commonly accepted that any pre-Magellanic representation of a strait was pure accident or based on conjecture. Magellan himself was not positive of the location of the strait (which he probably reasoned existed by analogy between South America and south Africa, as first suggested by Alexander Humboldt), and he is credited with saying, while at the Río Santa Cruz, that they would follow along the coast until they found either a strait or the end of the land even though they had to sail as far as latitude 75° S.[22]

The Magellanic fleet, now consisting only of the *Trinidad*, *Victoria*, and *Concepción*, sailed out of the troubled waters of the strait on or about November 28, 1520, past Cabo Deseado (now Cabo Pilar) into the sea which Magellan named Pacific[23]

(Fig. 13). For two days and three nights they sailed NW, N, and NNE, and then on December 1 two *mogotes* (hilly islands) were seen some 20 leagues to the east in about latitude 48° S. Apparently, based on Albo's log, the route was essentially parallel to the Chilean coast until about the 16th of December at which time, and approximately in the latitude of Concepción, it became apparent that the coast of the mainland was swinging in eastward increasingly.[24] However, there is little agreement among the five sources (Albo in Navarrete pp. 216–217; Barros dec. 3, lib. 5, cap. 10; Brito in Navarrete p. 309; Herrera in dec. 2, lib. 9, cap. 15, pp. 345–346; and Mafra in Lagôa 2:69) with details concerning the voyage in the southeast Pacific. Mafra has the fleet sailing north to latitude 30° S. before turning to the northwest. Brito says north to latitude 32° S. and then WNW. Herrera takes them to latitude 32°20′ S. and on December 18 heads them NW and WNW. Albo, who gives nearly daily latitudes and headings, on December 16 changes the heading from an easterly component to N by NW in about latitude 36°30′ S. Barros, Brito, Herrera, and Mafra are agreed that upon entering the Pacific Magellan had ordered a northerly course so as to reach a warmer climate as soon as possible. Herrera states explicitly that when Magellan had left behind the cold and stormy seas with contrary winds (the prevailing westerlies of the "Roaring Forties") the wind began to shift aft and the ships were able to head toward the northwest with a stern breeze.

If we follow the majority of the reconstructions, of the past one hundred years, of Magellan's route, we must trace it through the Tuamotu (Paumotu or Low) Archipelago and the southern Line Islands to a crossing of the equator between longitudes 160° and 170° W. In terms of the few data at our disposal, such a general routing seems reasonable. However, we should here note the route suggested by George Nunn (cited in note 16) which goes far north via Clipperton Island and Isla Clarión before turning west. Although Nunn presents his case well, despite a number of patent errors, we cannot agree with it. Nunn's main point is that Albo's log was falsified (as were other accounts) because he had to reduce the distances sailed in order to maintain Spanish claims to the Moluccas. Nunn's assumption is gratuitous, since Albo nowhere gives longitudes and distances sailed while between South America and the Philippines, and Nunn makes his own interpretations from the latitudes and headings given by Albo. Especially unacceptable is Nunn's assumption that Magellan did not have his pilots correct for declination of the magnetic needle (specifically stated to have been done in Pigafetta, p. 93, and noted in the *Genoese Pilot*, p. 403 as amounting to almost two *cuartos* or points—about 22°30′—to the northwest). The correction could be made on the same basis that led to Magellan's discovery of the declination, *i.e.*, by observation of the noon sun and of the Southern Cross and other stars of the austral firmament as the Portuguese had been doing for some time. However, the most important reason for believing that Magellan sailed north along the Chilean coast into the latitude of the 30°s and then headed in a west-northwesterly direction is that Magellan, in view of the extreme shortage of food at the time of leaving the Strait, would have sailed the theoretically shortest route available, taking advantage of the first favorable winds. The route as plotted by Nunn is some 15 to 20 equatorial degrees longer than the route as normally plotted.

Considering the discrepancies and vagueness in the ten "primary" sources[25] con-

Mariana Is.

Guam

Philippine Is.

Samar

Cebú

Mindanao

Sulu
Sea

Caroline   Islands

Ternate

Halmahera

Borneo

120°

150°

Admiralty Is.

New Guinea

Espinosa 1522

Saavedra

1529

Salazar   1526

Marshall Is.

Gilbert Is.

180°

1528

Elcano

1521-1522

—————Magellan, 1520-1522
– – – –Loaisa, 1526
- - - - -Guevara, 1526
–·–·–·–Saavedra, 1527-1529
–+–+–+–Grijalva, 1536-1537

||||||||||||| Coasts discovered and charted by Spanish expeditions
        prior to the intrusion of non-Iberians in 1578 (Drake)

FIG. 13. Viages

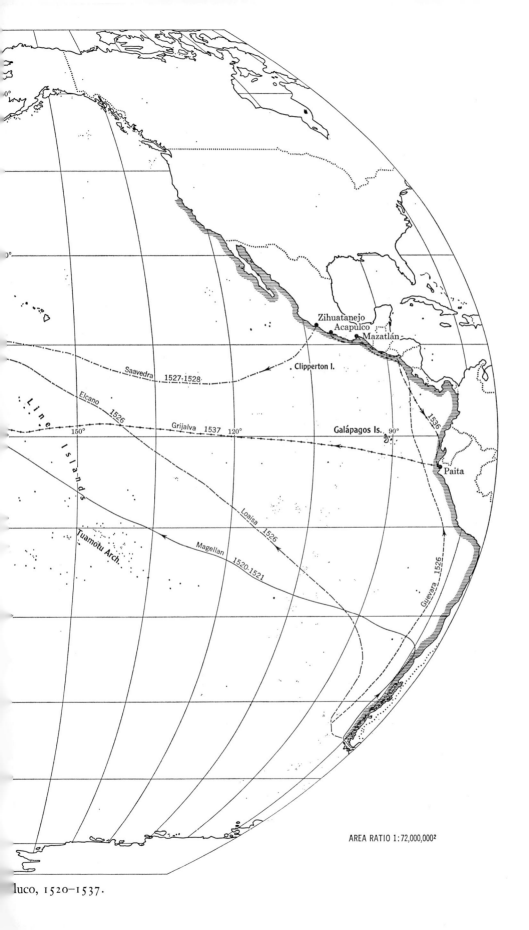

Zihuatanejo
Acapulco
Mazatlán

Saavedra   1527-1528

• Clipperton I.

Line

Elcano   1526

Islands

Grijalva   1537   120°

150°

Galápagos Is.   90°

1526

Paita

Loaisa   1526

Tuamotu Arch.

Magellan   1520-1521

Guevara   1526

AREA RATIO 1:72,000,000²

luco, 1520–1537.

cerning the location of two uninhabited islands seen about January 24 and February 4, 1521 (dates given only in Albo), it would be ridiculous to insist on any identifications. San Pablo most commonly has been identified with Pukapuka, Fangahina (Fakahina), and Angatau (Fangatau) in the Tuamotu Archipelago, and also Malden Island. Tiburones has been identified with Caroline, Flint Island, and Vostok Island in the southern Line Islands, and also with Jarvis Island.[26] Only six of the sources (Albo, Barros, Brito, Genoese Pilot, Herrera, and Pigafetta) give any clues as to where and when the equator was crossed, and only three are specific. Albo dates the crossing between February 12 and 13, 1521. Pigafetta states that the equator was crossed 122° from the Line of Demarcation. Barros claims, from inspecting one of Magellan's charts, that Magellan sailed past longitude 180° and then turned north to cross the equator. Little can be done with these data.

We are on more certain ground with the discovery on March 6, 1521, of two or three islands in an archipelago which the expedition named Islas de los Ladrones and Islas de las Velas Latinas.[27] These were almost certainly Guam, Rota, and possibly Saipan, in the southern Mariana Islands. The fleet remained at Guam until March 9, recapturing a stolen boat and obtaining water and food. Here Pigafetta (pp. 95–103) obtained the first notes recorded on the ethnography of a people (Chamorros) in Oceania.

After a week of sailing W by SW the expedition saw land and sailed NW towards it, but, discovering that the land extended northward and was bordered by reefs, they turned to the south and sailed around the southeast cape of Samar (actually Sungi Point on Candolu Island) and anchored off uninhabited Homonhón Island.[28] A week was spent here in resting the invalids on land, enjoying fresh water from local springs, and in obtaining food and information (by signs) from friendly natives who lived on nearby Suluan Island. From Homonhón the three ships traversed the Surigao Strait to Limasawa Island (Mazaua, Masana, etc.) in the Mindanao Sea. The details of what happened after this are not pertinent to our chapter. However, a brief summary is necessary to serve as background for the adventures of the *Trinidad*.

On Limasawa, Henrique de Malaca (the servant-slave of Magellan, acquired in Malacca and reputed to be a native of Sumatra, the Moluccas, and even the Philippines) was able to converse with the natives, who spoke a Visayan language. Henrique, if from the Moluccas or the Philippines, was the first person to circumnavigate the globe. From Limasawa the fleet, piloted by natives, went to Cebú. On April 27, 1521, Magellan was killed on nearby Mactan Island. The consensus of modern scholarship is that Magellan had not sailed into Philippine or Moluccan waters while based at Malacca about 1511–1512. Consequently Magellan missed by a little both circumnavigating the globe and reaching the Moluccas. After the death of Magellan and the subsequent slaughter of other leaders of the expedition, the *Concepción* was burned on Bohol, and the *Trinidad* and the *Victoria* wandered rather aimlessly to Mindanao, Cagayan Sulu Island, Palawan, Brunei in Borneo, and finally eastward again to southwestern Mindanao, the Sarangani Islands (where pilots were acquired), Kepulauan Sangihe, between Pulau Maju and Pulau Tifore in the Molucca Sea, and arrived at Tidore in the Moluccas on November 8, 1521. By this time Gonzalo Gómez de Espinosa (who had started out as *alguacil mayor* or peace officer or constable of the fleet) was captain of the *Trinidad* and of the expedition, and Juan Sebastián del Cano (Elcano, and other forms) had advanced from master of the *Concepción* to captain of the *Victoria*.

Magellan's friend Francisco Serrão, whose letters apparently had inspired Magellan to make the great voyage, had died earlier in the year. However, both ships were loaded with cloves and prepared to sail for Spain around the Cape of Good Hope. The *Trinidad* sprang a huge leak while still in port (the basic documents are explicit on this point), and the *Victoria* departed alone December 21, 1521. The *Victoria* reached Sanlúcar de Barrameda September 6, 1522, and discovered that in circumnavigating the globe a day had been lost. The *Trinidad*, after some three months of repair work, sailed from Tidore April 6, 1522, with Gonzalo Gómez de Espinosa as captain, Juan Bautista de Punzorol as master, and León Pancaldo as pilot.

Now the *Trinidad* began the first of what was to be five unsuccessful attempts between 1522 and 1545, to sail eastward across the Pacific. After sailing around the north end of Halmahera (known then as Batachina and Gilolo), and obtaining their last supplies at some port on the east coast (probably on Kaoe Bay, now Teluk Kai), the *Trinidad* headed eastward for Panamá (Fig. 13). However, contrary winds soon forced Gómez de Espinosa to turn northward.[29] About May 3 and/or May 6 two small islands (which were named San Antonio and San Juan) were discovered in approximately latitude 5° N. These have been identified as Tobi and Merir or Pulo Anna and, more logically, as the Sonsorol Islands.[30] After passing through the extreme southwesterly Caroline Islands, the *Trinidad* discovered fourteen islands between latitudes 12° and 20° N., from one of which (Chyquom, Quamgragram, Magrague, Magregua, or Grega) in about latitude 19° N. a native was taken on board. This island is most likely modern Agrihan (or Agrigan) in the Marianas. Thence the *Trinidad* sailed on June 11 to latitude 42° or 43° N., where bitter cold, twelve days of storm, insufficient food, and mortal sickness caused Gómez de Espinosa to turn back toward the Moluccas. It is impossible to determine how far the *Trinidad* advanced eastward, but it probably was to a point between longitudes 150° and 160° E. On August 22 the *Trinidad* anchored among three small islands to obtain water and food. Here the native deserted along with three members of the crew. The largest of these islands (Pamõ or Mão) in approximately latitude 20° N. probably gave its name to the present Maug Islands. By some time prior to October 20, 1522, the *Trinidad* was back in the Moluccas, where the ship and crew surrendered to the Portuguese under Brito. While being unloaded at Ternate the *Trinidad* broke up on the beach. Thus ended the Magellanic expedition in the Pacific.

Post Magellanic Expeditions

No sooner had Cristóbal de Haro shipped off to Antwerp the cloves brought back on the *Victoria* than he was aiding the Spanish crown in planning and outfitting another expedition to the Moluccas. This second expedition to the Moluccas sailed from La Coruña (where a short-lived Casa de Contratación for the spice trade was established) on July 24, 1525. The fleet, consisting of seven ships which ranged in tonnage from 300 for the flagship *Santa María de la Victoria* to 50 for the *patache* or tender *Santiago*, was under the command of Frey García Jofre de Loaisa, with Juan

Sebastián de Elcano as pilot major. After many delays and misfortunes four of the ships sailed out of the Strait of Magellan into the Pacific on May 26, 1526 (Fig. 13). A great storm on June 1, in about latitude 47°30′ S., separated the ships and they never were together again.

One of these ships, the *San Lesmes* commanded by Francisco de Hoces, disappeared completely. In the *relación* by Urdaneta, however, we learn that when a storm separated the ships January 26, 1526, while they were still at the Atlantic end of the Strait of Magellan, the *San Lesmes* was driven along the east side of Tierra del Fuego (and probably Staten Island, now Isla de los Estados) to about latitude 55° S. Upon rejoining the fleet Hoces reported that they had seen what seemed to be the end of the land.[31] This report, together with the belief of Magellan that the Tierra de los Fuegos was an island (Transylvanus in Navarrete 1837, vol. 4, p. 266) indicate that we should give the early Spaniards some credit for this determination.

The tiny tender *Santiago*, captained by Santiago de Guevara (a brother-in-law of Elcano), finding itself alone and with very little food, headed north for New Spain (Fig. 13). Land was first seen on July 11, 1526 (apparently in Nicaragua or El Salvador), and on July 25 a landing was made at the little village of Mazatlán near Tehuantepec, México. This was the first voyage from South America to México, but details are few.[32]

The *Santa María del Parral*, under Jorge Manrique de Nájera, somehow crossed the Pacific and made a landing on Mindanao shortly after the flagship had reached the Moluccas. There was an attack by natives, a mutiny, and wreck on the Kepulauan Sangihe. The few facts known are gleaned from the accounts of Urdaneta and De la Torre.

The route followed by the flagship *Santa María de la Victoria* apparently (from Uriarte's log) crossed the equator July 25/26, much farther to the east than the crossing by Magellan. Despite having on board three individuals who had been with Magellan, and improved charts constructed by Nuño García and Diego Ribero, the route differed at first apparently because of a number of storms, and later (after the deaths of Loaisa, July 30 and Elcano, August 4) because an attempt was made for a time to reach Japan. However, on August 9 in about latitude 12° N. it was agreed to head west for the Marianas and Moluccas. For three days, August 21–23, the ship was by an atoll with a long lagoon of green water, in latitude 14°2′ N., but a strong current and lack of anchorage prevented a landing. This island, named San Bartolomé, can most plausibly be identified with Taongi (Pokaakku or Gaspar Rico) atoll—the northernmost atoll in the Marshall Islands.[33] The discovery nominally can be credited to Toribio Alonso de Salazar, who was captain from August 4 until his death September 10/13.

On September 4, landfall was made in the southern Marianas and some six days were spent in obtaining water and food on what undoubtedly was Guam. Here also was picked up Gonzalo de Vigo (lone survivor of those who had deserted from the *Trinidad* in 1522), and eleven natives to work the pumps. Sailing west and southwest toward the Moluccas the ship reached latitude 5°7′ N. before winds and currents drove it northward to the northeast coast of Mindanao. A change in the wind allowed the *Santa María* to anchor at the Puerto de Vizaya, October 6, 1526, in a bay which can be identified with Liañgá Bay or possibly Bislig Bay on the northeast coast of Mindanao. On October 15, the *Santa María* headed out northwards to reach Cebú, but contrary winds forced the ship south, and the *Santa María* reached the Moluccas at the end of October via the Sarangani Islands and Pulau-pulau Talaud. Thus the *Santa María*, now under Martín Iñiguez de Carquisano, added to European knowledge that segment of the western periphery of the open Pacific between northeast Mindanao and northern Halmahera. The remainder of the activities of the *Santa María* and its crew do not concern us, except as they relate to the voyage of Saavedra Cerón. It is interesting, however, to note that the pilot Uriarte, apparently accompanied by Urdaneta, made a complete circuit of Halmahera about 1528, in a galley or brigantine constructed on the island.

The third and last Spanish expedition to the Moluccas which actually plied Pacific waters was one sent out by Hernán Cortés from México at the command of the Spanish crown to succor or obtain information about the Loaisa expedition and survivors from the *Trinidad*.

Three small ships built for Cortés near the mouth of the Zacatula River (Río Balsas) were placed under the command of Cortés' relative Alvaro de Saavedra Cerón. They sailed from the port of Zihuatanejo in Guerrero, México, October 31, 1527. After a storm on December 15, while sailing west near the parallel of latitude 11° N., two of the ships sailed out of sight and presumably were lost and only the flagship *Florida* continued the voyage to the Moluccas, which were reached March 30, 1528 (Fig. 13). During the voyage, on December 29, 1527, an inhabited island was seen which the pilot erroneously identified as one of the Marianas. After a day or two of unsuccessful attempts to land, the *Florida* headed westward and on January 1, 1528, encountered a group of populated islands where the ship remained until January 8, obtaining water and taking the latitude, which was 11° N.[34] The island first discovered probably was the Utirik-Taka atoll complex, and the group visited January 1–8 and named Islas de los Reyes most likely was the Rongelap-Ailinginae atoll complex—both in the northern Marshall Islands. The unfortunate misidentification of these islands as the Marianas by the pilot has confused cartographers, navigators, and historians ever since.

From these islands the *Florida* sailed westward and sighted land on February 1, which land apparently was one of the islands off the northeast coast of Mindanao. The ship was careened on an islet near the bay where the Loaisa ships had been in 1526, several survivors of the *Santa María del Parral* were picked up, and Tidore in the Moluccas was reached March 30, 1528, after sailing via the Sarangani Islands and Pulau Maju. This was the first crossing of the Pacific, from México to the Philippines, north of the equator.

Saavedra, in 1528 and 1529, made two unsuccessful attempts to return eastward across the Pacific to México (Fig. 13). On the first voyage, June 12 to November 19, 1528, the Kepulauan Schouten (Islas de Oro, or Paine) were discovered, Papua was coasted for many leagues (Meneses had discovered West New Guinea earlier), the Admiralty Islands were discovered, and an island group in the Carolines was discovered in latitude 7° N. Then the *Florida* encountered strong contrary winds in latitude 14° N. and returned past one of the islands of the Marianas and the coast of

Mindanao to the Moluccas. The second attempt, May 3 to December 8, 1529, followed the earlier route as far as Manus in the Admiralty Islands (Urais la Grande).
This time the *Florida* was able to sail northeastwardly to latitude 31° N. before contrary winds forced a return via one of the Marianas (where food and water were
obtained), the coast of Mindanao, and the Pulau-pulau Talaud. Some islands inhabited
by tattooed people were seen in latitude 6° or 7° N., (Islas de los Pintados which are
probably Ponape and Ant in the eastern Carolines); a week later several low islands
were sighted (possibly Ujelang Atoll); and a week was spent on some low islands in
latitude 11°30' N. with many coconut palm trees (Islas de los Jardines, probably
Eniwetok Atoll in the Marshall Islands). Since Saavedra died some time in October,
in about latitude 21° N., all of the above discoveries can be credited to him.[35]

Although the Spanish monarch had pawned (actually quitclaimed and sold) the
Moluccas to Portugal in 1529, there were two more Spanish expeditions that com-
monly are included in the Viages al Maluco. In 1536, Cortés sent two ships from
Acapulco, México, with supplies for Pizarro in Perú. The tender *Trinidad* under
Fernando de Alvarado returned to México, possibly sighting the Galápagos Islands
in passage. The larger *Santiago*, captained by Hernando de Grijalva sailed from Paita,
Perú, early in April 1537, on an exploratory voyage westward (Fig. 13). According
to Galvão,[36] the *Santiago* sailed in the vicinity of the equator, discovered the island
of Acea more than a thousand leagues from Perú in latitude 2° N., then later on
passed an island where fishermen were seen (Los Pescadores). The crew mutinied,
killed Grijalva, and sailed west to Papua where many islands were seen including
Haime (probably Paine, visited by Saavedra). Their rotten ship went to pieces under
them and they were captured by western Papuans; ultimately, seven were ransomed
in 1538 and 1539 by Galvão (the governor of the Moluccas). This voyage is notable
as the first crossing of the Pacific along and south of the equator. Acea has been
identified as Christmas Island in the northern Line Islands, or as one of the northern
Gilbert Islands; and the Isla de los Pescadores is almost undoubtedly one of the
northern Gilberts.[37]

The expedition headed by Ruy López de Villalobos was for the purposes of discovery, exploration, colonization, and missionary work. A fleet of six vessels sailed
from the port of Juan Gallego (on Bahía Navidad, Jalisco, México), November 1,
1542 (Fig. 14). The fleet passed through the Islas de Revillagigedo, the Marshalls,
and the northeastern Caroline Islands, and reached the Vizaya coast of northeastern
Mindanao on February 2, 1543. In the Revillagigedos, Isla San Benedicto (incor-
rectly identified with the Santo Tomás of Grijalva, 1533), and Isla Socorro (the
Santo Tomás of Grijalva which was named La Añublada) were rediscovered, and
Isla Roca Partida was discovered. In the Marshall Islands, between December 25,
1542 and January 6, 1543, three island groups or atoll complexes were discovered or
rediscovered. The first was thought to be part of Saavedra's Los Reyes, and the
names Los Corales and Los Jardines were applied to the other two. These islands,
recorded as being between latitudes 9° and 10° N., cannot be identified definitely and
many guesses have been made on the subject. Sharp[38] favors Wotje, Kwajalein, and
Ujelang. On January 23, 1543, the fleet passed an island where natives in boats ad-
dressed them in Spanish saying "Buenos días, Matalotes," whence the island was
named Isla de los Matalotes. This island has been identified with various of the

Carolines and most probably is Fais. Three days later large islands surrounded by reefs were passed which were named Los Arrecifes, and which probably were Yap or possibly Ulithi.

The expedition spent a month on Mindanao and, after an unsuccessful attempt to reach Limasawa Island, sailed down to the Sarangani Islands for a year. Several parties were sent out for food and incidentally explored the southern and eastern coasts of Mindanao and the Leyte-Samar region. At this time, in 1543, the name Islas Felipinas was applied to the Leyte-Samar group of islands.[39]

In August of 1543, Villalobos sent Bernardo de la Torre in the *San Juan de Letran* on what was to become the fourth unsuccessful Spanish attempt to sail eastward across the Pacific (Fig. 14). The *San Juan* sailed from the Sarangani Islands, via Leyte and Samar, north and eastward through the central Marianas and the Volcano Islands and reached latitude 30° N. on October 18 before adverse winds forced a return to the Philippines. The three islands in latitudes 16° and 17° N. named Abreojos (Abriojos) and Las Dos Hermanas probably were the Farallón de Medinilla, Anatahan, and Sariguan. The three islands in latitudes 24° and 25° N., one of which had a volcano with three active vents, undoubtedly were the Volcano Islands which include Iwo-jima. Another island seen on an eastwardly track in about latitude 26° N. probably was Marcus Island.[40]

A little-noted fact concerning the voyage of the *San Juan* is that on its return voyage under De la Torre it was the first European ship to use the San Bernardino Strait. Furthermore, it was the first to pass through the San Juanico Strait between Samar and Leyte;[41] and was also the first to circumnavigate Mindanao. Early in 1544, before the return to the Sarangani Islands, the *San Juan*, somewhere to the east of Mindanao, discovered an island covered with coconut palm trees which led to the appearance on many maps of an Isla de Palmas or Isla de las Palmeras. Possibly this island was Siargao.

By the time of the return of the *San Juan*, Villalobos had moved to Tidore. In May of 1545, the *San Juan* was sent out again, now under Iñigo Ortiz de Retes, to attempt a more southern route to New Spain. Going by way of the Pulau Pulau Talaud and Kepulauan Schouten, the *San Juan* coasted New Guinea for several months and apparently reached a point between latitudes 4° and 5° S. before contrary winds and currents forced a return to Tidore (Fig. 14). Many islands were encountered, to some of which names were given, and several can be identified with islands visited by the expeditions of Saavedra 1529, and Grijalva 1537-38. On June 20, 1545, at the San Antonio River (probably Mamberamo) in latitude 2° S., possession was taken for Spain of the great island which was given the name of Nueva Guinea.[42]

THE SOUTH AMERICAN PACIFIC: 1513-1580

After discovering the South Sea in 1513, Balboa made plans for further exploration. Several small sailing ships were built 1517-1518, and these began to explore the coasts of the Gulf of Panamá in October of 1518. These were the first European ships to sail on the waters of the Pacific Ocean.[43]

In 1522, Pascual de Andagoya took the ships built by Balboa a short distance down the coast southeast from the Pearl Islands (Archipiélago de las Perlas). Thus began

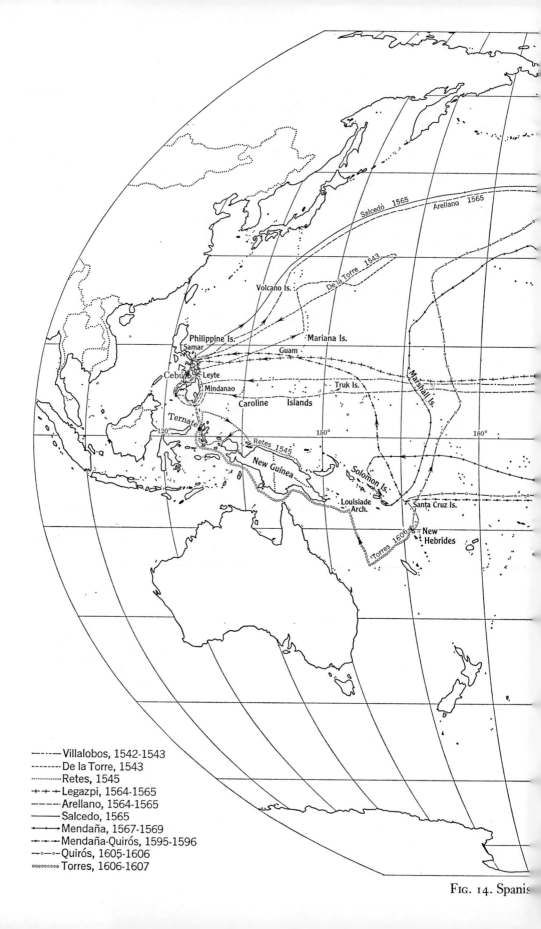

Salcedo 1565 Arellano 1565

De la Torre 1543

Volcano Is.

Philippine Is.
Samar
Cebú Leyte
Mindanao

Mariana Is.
Guam

Truk Is.

Caroline Islands

Marshall Is.

Ternate

Retes 1545

New Guinea

Solomon Is.

Louisiade Arch.

Santa Cruz Is.

Torres 1606-8 New Hebrides

120°   150°   180°

—---— Villalobos, 1542-1543
------- De la Torre, 1543
··········· Retes, 1545
+ + + Legazpi, 1564-1565
— — — Arellano, 1564-1565
——— Salcedo, 1565
—•—→ Mendaña, 1567-1569
—·—·— Mendaña-Quirós, 1595-1596
—•—○—•— Quirós, 1605-1606
ᵒᵒᵒᵒᵒᵒᵒᵒᵒ Torres, 1606-1607

FIG. 14. Spanis

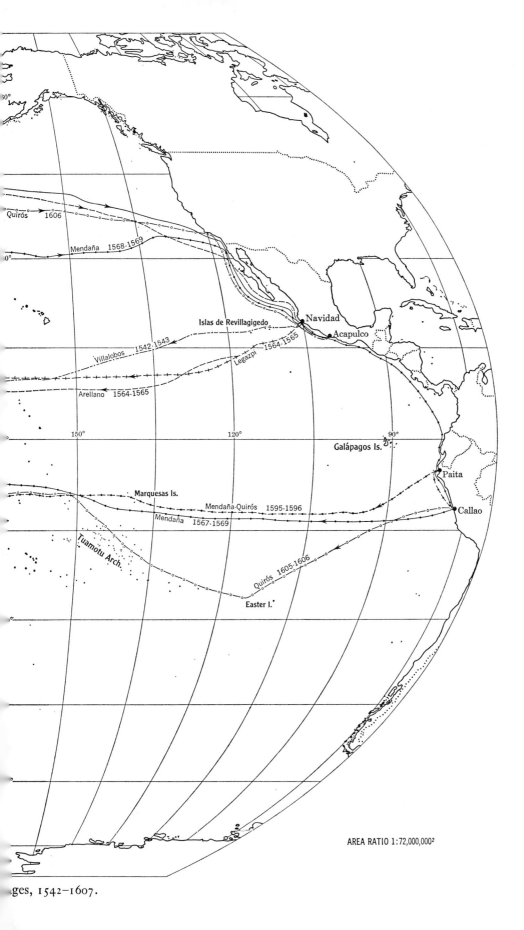

Quirós   1606

Mendaña   1568-1569

Islas de Revillagigedo   Navidad
Acapulco

Villalobos   1542-1543
Legazpi   1564-1565

Arellano   1564-1565

150°   120°   90°

Galápagos Is.

Paita

Marquesas Is.
Mendaña-Quirós   1595-1596
Callao
Mendaña   1567-1569

Tuamotu Arch.

Quirós   1605-1606

Easter I.

AREA RATIO 1:72,000,000²

ges, 1542–1607.

the advance along the South American coast. Although the details of the Peruvian epic do not concern us, a few dates will provide perspective. Pizarro, Almagro, and the expert pilot Bartolomé Ruiz de Estrada reached the Río San Juan in 1524. In 1526–1527 Tumbes was reached, and Ruiz sailed on as far as latitude 9° S; and in 1532–1533 much of Incaic Perú was conquered. Alonso Quintero sailed from Callao to latitude 32° 46' S. (near Valparaiso) in 1536; Juan Bautista de Pastene sailed from Valparaíso to latitude 41° S. in 1544; and in 1551 Valdivia was founded. Meanwhile, Isla de Malpelo and the Galápagos Islands were discovered.

Isla de Malpelo is in latitude 3° 59' N. about 230 miles SSW from Punta Mala, Panamá, and 250 miles west of the Río San Juan delta in Colombia. Although we do not know the name of the discoverer, the island appears on maps of the 1530s, and Cieza de León wrote that a ship in 1542, carrying the Governor of Perú, Vaca de Castro, from Panamá to Buenaventura came to this island which the sailors already knew and called Mal Pelo.[44]

Fray Tomás de Berlanga, Bishop of Castilla del Oro (Panamá) left Panamá February 23, 1535, to visit Perú. His ship coasted southward, was becalmed on the eighth day, and strong currents carried it westward where land was sighted March 10, 1535. Two islands were searched for water and two other islands were sighted. In his account Berlanga mentioned the giant *galápagos*, iguanas, sea lions and other elements of the biota and also the volcanic scoria.[45] In 1546, Captain Diego de Rivadeneira, sailing from Quilca, Perú, to San José de Istapa (Iztapa), Guatemala, passed through the Galápagos and noted a smoking volcano.[46]

In 1540, a little-known third passage of the Strait of Magellan was made by one ship under Captain Alonso de Camargo. An expedition sponsored by the Bishop of Plasencia, consisting of four ships, sailed from Sevilla in August of 1539, to occupy and colonize the Strait of Magellan area. The one ship (name unknown) which passed through the Strait about January/February of 1540, had an intimate and pain-ful acquaintance with the islands of southern Chile before arriving in Quilca, Perú, in 1541. Although a *relación* of the voyage existed in the middle of the sixteenth century, there are today essentially no basic records of the voyage. There are, however, numerous but brief contemporary mentions of the event, and there is at least one interesting cartographic result. On the Santa Cruz world map of 1542 (in the Royal Library in Stockholm), three "Yslas vistas de lexos" are shown in the southeastern Pacific. Also, Santa Cruz, in his *Islario*, mentions that a ship of the Bishop of Plansencia's expedition saw three islands at a distance to the west which were about 200 leagues NW from the Straits and 100 leagues from the Chilean coast, in about latitude 42° S. Although the latitude is quite a bit off, there scarcely can be any identification for these islands other than the Islas Juan Fernández which are three in number and which are about one hundred Spanish sea leagues (400 miles) from the Chilean coast.[47] Thus ended in practical oblivion the expedition which resulted in the third passage of the Strait, and the first to provide detailed information concerning the coast between the Strait and Valparaiso.

In the 1550s two expeditions went out from Valdivia, Chile, to survey the south Chilean coast and the Strait of Magellan. The first, under Captain Francisco de Ulloa with Francisco Cortés Ojeda as a pilot, left Valdivia in October of 1553. It followed the coastline and channels to the Strait and surveyed 30 leagues of the Strait in January of 1554, but returned to Valdivia before reaching the Atlantic end of the Strait. In November of 1557, an expedition under Captain Juan Ladrillero in the *San Luis* and Francisco Cortés Ojeda (Hojea) in the *San Salvador* was sent out from Valdivia by the Chilean governor García Hurtado de Mendoza. The two ships became separated in December and effectively conducted two campaigns of exploration. Cortés did not quite reach the Strait, and returned to Valdivia October 1, 1558 with an account that provided more ethnographic data than hydrographic information. Ladrillero sailed all the way through the Strait to the Atlantic end, where he took possession August 9, 1558, and was back in Concepción by the middle of 1559. The outstanding achievement of the Ladrillero voyage was a detailed account of the hydrography of the Chilean archipelagos and the Strait of Magellan which was not improved upon until the nineteenth century.[48]

There is no primary source concerning the discovery of Isla San Ambrosio and Isla San Félix and the discovery or rediscovery of the Islas Juan Fernández. However, the closely reasoned argument of Medina, supported by sixteenth century documentary material, indicates that "San Félix and San Amber" were discovered November 6 and the islands that were to become known as the Islas Juan Fernández were sighted November 22, 1574 while Juan Fernández was voyaging from Perú to Chile. Juan Fernández was universally given credit for discovering a new route from Perú to Chile. By going farther out to sea and avoiding the strong coastal current, he reduced the previous time of from three to six months for a voyage hugging the coast to one month. Juan Fernández also may have made a voyage westward in 1576, which resulted in the discovery of Easter Island or even New Zealand as suggested by some writers. Although possible, this voyage is not probable.[49]

THE NORTH AMERICAN PACIFIC: 1513–1603

Exploration by seagoing sailing ships along the Pacific coast of North America began in 1519, when two of the ships constructed by Balboa (the *San Cristóbal* and the *Santa Mar'a de la Buena Esperanza*) were used by Gaspar de Espinosa and the pilot Juan de Castañeda to coast westward nearly to the entrance of the Golfo de Nicoya (Salinas = Sanlúcar = Chira = Güetares = Orotiña = Nicaragua = San Vicente in the sixteenth century).[50] In January of 1522, after building four ships on the Pearl Islands (Archipiélago de las Perlas), Gil González de Avila and the pilot Andrés Niño sailed westward past the coasts explored by Espinosa and Castañeda. Actually, González de Avila (Dávila) soon debarked to explore and conquer in Costa Rica and Nicaragua by land, and the pilot Andrés Niño sailed as far as the Gulf of Fonseca (which was named at this time) and possibly as far as Guatemala or even Chiapas. Upon their return to Panamá in June 1523, González de Avila claimed that Niño sailed 350 leagues past the Golfo de Nicoya to latitude 17° 30′ N.[51]

The Isla del Coco (known for a time as Santa Cruz) some 300 miles SSW from Costa Rica, was discovered on some unrecorded voyage between 1523 and 1534, possibly during Pedro de Alvarado's voyage early in 1534, from Nicaragua to Ecuador, or the earlier voyage of Holguín sent by Alvarado to obtain news from Perú. The evidence lies in the fact that Oviedo, in his *Sumario de la Natural Historia de las Indias,* Toledo, 1526 (written after leaving Panamá in 1523), mentions coconut palms only for two areas in Pacific coastal Panamá, but in his *Historia General y Natural de las Indias,* lib. 9, cap. 4 (in a portion written between 1525 and 1534, and published in Sevilla in 1535) Oviedo mentions that more luxurious groves of coconut palms than in the two areas mentioned previously were on an island (reported to him by the pilot Pedro Corzo) 100 leagues or more from Perú (*i.e.,* South America) 230 leagues from Panamá, and 130 leagues from the Puerto de la Possessión (Corinto, Nicaragua). The Isla de los Cocos began to appear on maps in 1541.

Between 1519 and 1539 most of the Pacific coastlands from Panamá to modern Sonora in México had been explored and conquered, primarily by land expeditions. During the period 1517 to 1530 at least six shipyards between Panamá and Zacatula in western México turned out ships for local trade and exploration, and to search for a passage or strait between the Atlantic and Pacific, as well as to cross the Pacific to the Spice Islands. In the 1530s there were more than forty locally built ships making coasting trips between such ports as Chametla, Matanchel (Matanchen), Santiago (Manzanillo), Acapulco, Huatulco, Santiago (Puerto de Tehuantepec), Iztapa (Puerto de Guatemala), Acajutla (Puerto de Sonsonate), El Realejo, and Panamá, and as far as Ecuador and Perú.[52] Apparently the pilots of these ships coasted without charts and depended on sight, soundings, and memory, just as most of the skippers of the coasting *lanchas* still do. As a consequence, most of the very large number of coastal features and anchorages along the Mexican-Central American coast were not incorporated in charts and *derroteros* to be sent to the Casa de Contratación. The ultimate result was that the charts and maps by European cartographers of the sixteenth century show only a scanty and haphazard representation of place names along this coast.

However, exploration northwestward from the Reino de México or New Spain proper resulted in a number of reports and charts which reached Spain. The first ships built on the Pacific coast of México, at Zacatula, made their first voyage (a "shake-down cruise") from Zacatula to Bahía Manzanillo under Saavedra in 1527. The second lot of Mexican-built ships sailed from Acapulco in 1532, under Diego Hurtado de Mendoza and discovered the Islas Tres Marías on their way into the Gulf of California. In 1533, two ships sailed from Tehuantepec, one of which (under the mutineer Fortún Jiménez) discovered Lower California, and the other (the *San Lazaro*) under Hernando de Grijalva discovered the islands now known as the Islas de Revillagigedo.[53] These explorations in the waters off southwestern México, 1527 to 1534, have been given little consideration by historians as compared with the explorations that commenced in 1539.[54]

In September of 1539, Cortés sent Francisco de Ulloa from Acapulco with three ships to explore the region to the north and west of Santa Cruz (La Paz area of Lower California). Ulloa reached the head of the Gulf of California in September. Then, doubling around the peninsula, the Pacific coast of Lower California was explored, Isla Cedros was discovered about January 4, 1540, and (continuing with only the *Trinidad*) Ulloa explored as far north as some point between latitudes 30° and 32° N. In 1541, the Viceroy Mendoza sent Francisco de Bolaños out from Navidad to explore the coasts recently discovered for his opponent Cortés. Bolaños apparently did not get as far north as Isla Cedros, but his voyage is of interest because he probably named not only Cabo San Lucas but also laid the foundation for the use of the name California by applying it to a small bay near the southeastern end of the peninsula.[55]

In June of 1542, the Viceroy Mendoza sent out Juan Rodríguez Cabrillo (a Portuguese whose name normally is rendered in Spanish form) from Navidad with two ships. Cabrillo and, after his death, his pilot Bartolomé Ferrer discovered and explored what is today California (including the Santa Barbara Channel Islands area) to at least Point Arena in latitude 38° 57′ N. (Cabo de Fortunas, of Ferrer). None of the names applied by Cabrillo persisted as they were replaced by names given by Vizcaíno.[56]

Beginning in 1565, many of the Spanish ships returning to México from the Philippines coasted the Californias. However, no detailed exploration of this coast was attempted until the survey expedition of Sebastián Rodríguez Cermeño, who was instructed to sail from the Philippines and reach the North American coast farther north than latitude 41° credited to Cabrillo-Ferrer, and then search along the California coast for good ports of refuge to be utilized by the "Manila galleons" in case of need. Cermeño apparently reached the California coast in the vicinity of Point Saint George (latitude 41° 45′ N.) on November 4, 1595, but the detailed survey was carried out only partially because his ship *San Agustín* was wrecked within the month and the survivors were more interested in reaching México safely than in examining all the coastal indentations in their ship's boat, which reached the coast of Jalisco January 7, 1596. It remained for the 1602–1603 expedition of Sebastián Vizcaíno to chart the coast in detail from Acapulco to a point on the Oregon coast, possibly to Cape Blanco in latitude 42° 53′ N. This was a very important voyage in its results, as the resultant *derroteros*, charts, and place names were incorporated into the official *derrotero* for the Acapulco-Manila route (which was used with little change for the next 200 years), and a great number of the place names are still in use.[57]

PHILIPPINE ISLANDS AND THE "MANILA GALLEONS": 1564–1815

On November 21, 1564, an expedition consisting of four ships constructed at Navidad sailed from the anchorage at Melaque in Bahía Navidad. The purpose of this expedition, commanded by Miguel López de Legazpi (Fig. 14), was to explore and conquer the Philippine Islands, establish trade relations, and find a feasible route back across the Pacific to New Spain. On January 9, 1565, the main fleet (the *San Lucas* under Captain Alonso de Arellano having become separated on December 1) discovered a small island which was named Los Barbudos because the men were bearded. Other islands and island groups encountered were Los Placeres, Isla de Los Pájaros, Las Hermanas or Los Corales, some low islands and reefs, and Guam in the Marianas. Samar was sighted on February 14, and ultimately headquarters were established on Cebú.[58]

The *San Lucas*, under Arellano with Lope Martín as pilot, encountered some eight islands, groups of islands, and reefs, before reaching Mindanao on January 29, 1565 (Fig. 14). These, in the order seen, have been identified by Sharp as Likiep (36 isletas), Kwajalein (Dos Vecinos), and Lib (Nadadores) in the Marshalls; reefs of the Oroluk Atoll or Minto Reef (Mira como Vas); and Truk Islands (islas altas), Pulap Atoll (tres isletas), Sorol (isla), and Ngulu (isla) in the Carolines. After several months in Mindanao waters, including sailing clockwise around it into the Mindanao Sea, the *San Lucas* left the Philippines via the San Bernardino Strait on April 22, 1565. Heading east, northeast, and north, as currents and winds dictated, the *San Lucas* passed an isolated high rock in about latitude 31° N. (either Lot's Wife, now Sōfu-gan, or Smith Island, now Sumisu-jima, in the Izu shotō division of the Nanpō Shotō, now Nampō-shotō), then advanced in a northeasterly direction to a high of about latitude 43° N.; after which wind and current delivered the ship off the coast of Lower California in latitude 27° 45' N. on July 16, 1565. On August 9, 1565, the *San Lucas* arrived in the Puerto de Navidad, having completed the first recorded crossing of the Pacific from west to east.[59]

The official return trip from Cebú was begun June 1, 1565, by the *San Pedro*, under Felipe de Salcedo with Rodrigo de la Isla Espinosa as pilot, and accompanied by Urdaneta (who had been with Loaisa) and the co-pilot Esteban Rodríguez. The route of the *San Pedro* (Fig. 14) apparently was much like that of the *San Lucas* except that it was farther to the west in the early part of the voyage and in about latitude 20° N. a rock-and-reef like a ship (Parace Vela) was sighted June 21. Landfall was made on the American coast in about latitude 33° 45' N. on September 18. The *San Pedro* was off Navidad October 1 and anchored in Acapulco October 8, 1565. The *San Lucas* took 110 days from the San Bernardino Strait to Navidad and the *San Pedro* required 114 days for that portion of the voyage.

The voyage of the *San Pedro* in 1565 began the long history of trade between the Far East and New Spain, as the *San Pedro* carried a small quantity of spices to Acapulco. The ship going east became known as the Nao de China and "Manila galleon" (after Philippine headquarters were moved from Cebú to Manila in 1571), and the ship going west was termed the Nao de Acapulco. In a very few years the routes used became standardized and even mandatory, so that few discoveries were made unless a ship were blown off course by a storm. The Acapulco ship left New Spain between November and April (usually in February or March), sailed south and southwest to between latitudes 11° and 10° N., then made westing in general between 12° and 14° N., utilizing the *brisas* or northeast trade winds. The Manila ship left between May and September (usually between the middle of June and the middle of August), and—once out of the *embocadero* of San Bernardino Strait—sailed east then northeast making use of the *vendaval* or southwest monsoon until in the sweep of the Japanese Current and the prevailing westerlies, which resulted in a landfall on the American mainland somewhere between latitude 43° and 27° N., after which the ship coasted for the most part to Acapulco. The American landfall most commonly was between latitudes 33° and 27° N., and apparently an attempt was made to approach the Californias on a route which passed in sight of Isla de Guadalupe and/or Isla Cedros.[60]

We have space to comment briefly on only a few of the more interesting voyages of the 250-year *carrera de Acapulco*. In May of 1566, the *San Gerónimo* was sent from Acapulco to join Legazpi, with Lope Martín as pilot. Led by Martín, the crew mutinied, killed the captain, and sailed through four groups of islands in the Marshalls (on the last of which a counter-mutiny resulted in the marooning of Martín and some companions). The *San Gerónimo* continued to the Philippines via Rota and Guam. Only the islands where Martín was left can be identified confidently as Ujelang.

The much-publicized voyage of Francisco Gali in 1584, from Macao to Acapulco, deserves no mention except for the story that soon gained currency about several rich islands somewhere to the east or southeast of Japan. Gali saw none of these, but within a few years a number of Spanish ships attempted to locate the Isla del Armenio, and the Islas Ricas de Oro y de Plata, which islands also began to appear on maps. The equally publicized voyage of Pedro de Unamuno (Unamunu) in 1587, from Macao to Acapulco, is scarcely more deserving of mention. However, Unamuno did encounter two Islas sin Provecho in about latitude 25° 30' N. (probably in the Volcano Islands). He made a decided effort to locate the Islas Rica de Oro and Rica de Plata, and Isla del Armenio, and had an interesting sojourn on the San Luis Obispo (County) coast in California. Not a Manila galleon, but nevertheless a ship which sailed from Macao to Acapulco was that of the Portuguese João da Gama in 1590. Land reported to have been seen in relatively high latitudes north of Japan gave rise to a "Gama land" on maps of the seventeenth and eighteenth centuries. This may have been a part of the Japanese coast or possibly the Kuril Islands.[61]

In 1596, the *San Felipe* sailed from Manila for Acapulco, but a storm which partially disabled the ship forced it to seek refuge on the coast of Shikoku, where it was confiscated. This may have been the first Spanish ship to seek refuge in a Japanese harbor. In 1605, the *Espíritu Santo*, under Hernando de los Ríos Coronel, made the voyage from Cavite to Acapulco. The *diario* of Ríos Coronel includes acute observations on currents, winds, and declination of the magnetic needle, and probably the first formal notice of Los Alijos Rocks (rocks like ships under sail) which are 150 miles off Lower California in latitude 24° 57' N. Sebastián Vizcaíno in 1611 transported a Japanese delegation from New Spain back to Japan; made a hydrographic survey (including soundings of ports that might be used in case of need by Manila galleons) of the east coast of Honshu from about latitude 41° or 40° N. in the northeast down to the vicinity of Osaka; explored for the Islas Rica de Plata and Rica de Oro; and was back in Acapulco January 25, 1614. Four copies of a chart showing the results of the Honshu survey were made, of which two were left in Japan and two were retained. Apparently all copies have disappeared.[62]

In 1686, either the Acapulco galleon *Santa Rosa* or its escort the *Santo Niño*, while sailing south of the Marianas to avoid the English privateer *Cygnet*, encountered a large inhabited island which was named Carolina in honor of the Spanish king and also San Bernabé because of the day (June 11). This island could have been Ulithi, Yap, or Fais. In any case, this probably was the origin of the ultimate name Carolines for the extensive group.[63] In 1694, a small tender under Andrés de Arriola, en route from Manila to Acapulco, when nearly out of food and water after passing the Marianas, found an uncharted island with edible birds and water. This was possibly Marcus Island (perhaps seen by De La Torre in 1543) or Wake Island (discovered by Mendaña in 1568).

In 1702 and 1706, surveys were made by the Manila galleons of the Volcano Islands (Kazan-rettō) and the Arzobispo Islands (Bonin Islands or Ogasawara-guntō). The three Volcano Islands were discovered by De la Torre in 1543, and were frequently mentioned in the logs of the Manila galleons. Although discovery of the Bonins is commonly credited to the Dutch in 1639, it does not seem probable that the Spaniards could have missed these islands in nearly a century of voyaging in that general region prior to the Dutch "discovery." Unfortunately, the logs and charts extant are quite confusing as to names and locations of islands encountered in this area. At least one island (probably Lot's Wife, now Sōfu-gan) in the Izu-shotō was discovered by Spaniards in the sixteenth century.[64]

In the latter part of the eighteenth century the Spaniards explored routes north of Luzón and south of Mindanao as alternatives to the San Bernardino Strait route. Neither route was used much, but the explorations of the *Buen Fin* (alias *Nuestra Señora de la Consolación*) in 1773, piloted by Felipe Thompson (Fig. 15), discovered the Bajo de San Felix (Helen Reef in the western Carolines), and encountered the Islas de la Pasión (Ngatik Atoll) and a reef complex (Oroluk), to break the monotony of the long voyage to San Blas in New Spain.[65] A different version of this southern route was traced by Francisco Antonio Maurelle (Mourelle) in *La Princesa* (alias *Nuestra Señora del Rosario*) who sailed from the east coast of Luzón November 21, 1780, with urgent dispatches for the Viceroy of New Spain. Fear of enemy (English) ships, and the unfavorable season caused Maurelle to sail toward the southeast where his pilot José Vázquez had some acquaintance from his voyage on the *Buen Fin*. The islands encountered on this leg of the voyage (Fig. 15) included the Ninigo Islands, Hermit Islands, Admiralty Islands, northern islands of the Bismarck Archipelago, and various of the Tonga Islands. In about latitude 26° S. Maurelle gave up his attempt to cross the Pacific in southern latitudes and turned back through the Tongas and the Ellice Islands to Guam, and thence (after a stay of three weeks) to New Spain where he reached San Blas on September 27, 1781. Names were given to many of the islands seen or visited, but probably Maurelle's achievements were the first firm description of the Hermit Islands, of the Vavau Group in the Tongas, and of Nanumanga and Nanomea in the Ellices, and the discovery of Tench in the Bismarcks and Fonualei and Toku in the Tongas.[66]

The Manila-Acapulco route began to decline in importance with the liberalization of Spanish trade laws (1767–1778). In 1768, the town, port, and shipyards of San Blas (in modern Nayarit, México) were founded, and San Blas soon became the headquarters of the Spanish navy in the northeast Pacific. The last Nao de China (the *Magallanes*) arrived in New Spain in 1815, and was unloaded in San Blas in 1816.

THE SPANIARDS IN THE SOUTH PACIFIC: 1567–1793

Due in large part to the arguments of Pedro Sarmiento de Gamboa (gifted anthropologist, historian, cosmographer, and navigator), Castro (the governor-general of Perú) in 1567, sent out an expedition to discover and convert a gold-rich Terra Australis assumed to be out in the South Sea. Castro placed his nephew Alvaro de Mendaña de Neira in charge of the expedition, which consisted of the flagship *Los Reyes* on which was the pilot-major Hernán Gallego, and the *Todos Santos* under Sarmiento. The two ships left Callao November 19, 1567, sailing in a westerly direction (Fig. 14). On January 15 or 16, 1568, an inhabited island was sighted which was named Isla de Jesús, but contrary winds prevented a landing. This was the first discovery of an island in the Ellice group, almost certainly to be identified with Nui.[67] Continuing westward, an extensive reef area with a number of islets was encountered February 1, 1568, to which was given the name Bajos de la Candelaria. This probably was the atoll of Ontong Java, so named by Tasman in 1643. On February 7, having turned to the southwest, a mountainous island was seen which was named Santa Ysabel de la Estrella. This was the island of Santa Isabel in the group which came to be known as the Solomon Islands (probably because of all the rumors of gold) in 1569, shortly after the expedition had reported its findings to the Spanish officials in New Spain on the return voyage. Headquarters were established on Santa Isabel, a small brig (the *Santiago*) for local exploration was constructed, and a number of islands were discovered during a stay of six months which involved a shifting of headquarters to Guadalcanal Island and three exploration voyages in the brig.[68] Among the islands discovered were, besides Santa Isabel, Malaita (Isla de Ramos), the Nggela Group (Isla de la Pascua Florida, etc.), Savo (Sesarga), Guadalcanal, the New Georgia Group, Choiseul (San Marcos), Ulawa (La Treguada or Uraba), Olu Malau Islands (Tres Marías), Ugi (San Juan), and San Cristóbal (Santiago and San Christóval).

The islands were left August 17, 1568, on the return voyage via New Spain. A cluster of reefs and inhabited islets were encountered September 17 which were named the Bajos de San Mateo (possibly Namu Atoll or some other atoll in the Ralik Chain in the Marshalls). About October 3 the isolated Isla de San Francisco (Wake Island, as first identified by Guppy) was discovered. About October 16, in latitude 33° N. the two ships became separated, but both made landfall on the northern coast of Baja California in December, and within three days of each other (January 22 and January 25, 1569) the *capitana* and the *almirante* anchored in the bay of Santiago de Colima (Bahía Manzanillo). Leaving Manzanillo in March, and coasting via El Realejo in Nicaragua, the expedition was back in Perú before the end of summer of 1569. So ended the first of three Peruvian expeditions which contributed greatly to the exploration of the South Pacific.

After long years of disappointing delay, Mendaña received support from the Peruvian viceroy García Hurtado de Mendoza for an expedition to convert and colonize the Solomon Islands. The recent intrusion of English ships (under Drake in 1578, Cavendish in 1586, and Hawkins in 1593) into the hitherto "Spanish lake," undoubtedly was influential in bringing about consent and support for this expedition. A fleet of four ships commanded by Mendaña, with the Portuguese Pedro Fernández de Quirós as pilot-major, sailed westward from Paita June 16, 1595 (Fig. 14). On July 21, 1595, an inhabited island was encountered which was named Magdalena, and the next two weeks were spent in discovering San Pedro, Dominica, and Santa Cristina on which a landing was made. To this group of islands (specifically modern Fatu Hiva, Motane, Hiva Oa, and Tahuata) was given the name Las Marquesas de Mendoza, and here was obtained the first ethnographic information recorded for a Polynesian people. The Marquesas were left on August 5, and on August 20 were seen four small low islands which were named Las Islas de San Bernardo (Danger Islands or Pukapuka in the northern Cook Islands, not to be confused with the Pukapuka of the Tuamotus). Continuing in general between latitudes

Maurelle 1781
Buen F
Thompson 1773
Mariana Is.
Guam
Manila
Philippine Is.
Caroline   Islands
Maurelle
120°   150°   180°
1780

Tong

NEW ZEAL

.... González, 1770
– – – – Boenechea, 1772-1775
–·–·–·– *Buen Fin*, 1773
– – – – · Pérez, 1774
–o–o–o– Hezeta and Bodega, 1775*
············ Arteaga and Bodega, 1779*
–·–·–·–·– Maurelle, 1780-1781
———— Malaspina, 1790-1793

||||||||||||||| Coasts discovered and explored by the Spaniards
          after 1578 and prior to Cook's voyage of 1778
    * Return voyage not shown

Fɪɢ. 15. Spani

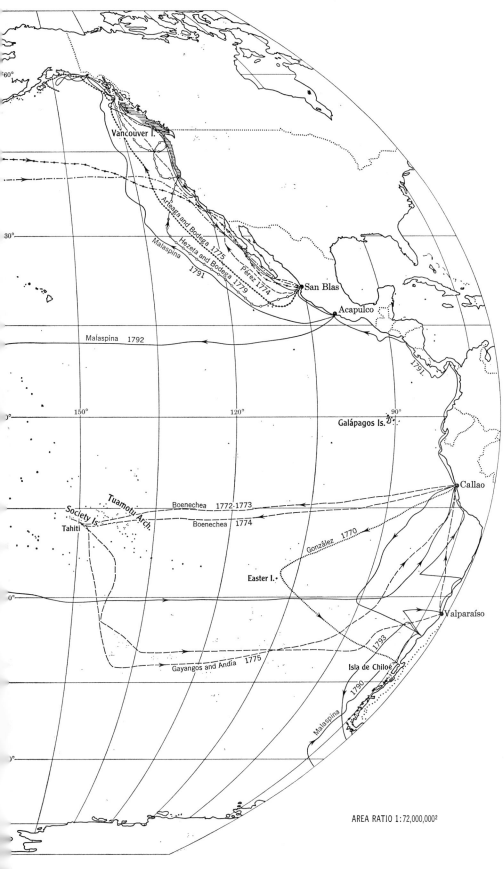

60

Vancouver I.

30°

Arteaga and Bodega 1775

Malaspina

Hezeta and Bodega 1779

Pérez 1774

San Blas

Acapulco

Malaspina   1792

1791

150°   120°   90°

Galápagos Is.

Callao

Boenechea   1772-1773

Tuamotu Arch.

Society Is.   Boenechea   1774

Tahiti

González   1770

Easter I.

Valparaíso

1793

Gayangos and Andía   1775

Isla de Chiloé

1790

Malaspina

AREA RATIO 1:72,000,000²

10° and 11° S., an isolated reef-fringed islet was discovered August 29, which was named La Solitaria (Nurakita, also Niulakita or Sophia)—southernmost of the Ellice Islands.[69]

The Santa Cruz Islands were discovered September 7, 1595, but before a landing was made the next day on Santa Cruz (Ndeni) the *almirante Santa Ysabel* disappeared and never was heard from again. A settlement was made on Santa Cruz, and exploration resulted in discovery of the nearby Swallow Islands, the volcano island of Tinakula, and Utupua, and the probable sighting of Vanikoro to the southeast. However, dissention and anarchy soon prevailed among the settlers. Mendaña died October 18, 1595, Mendaña's widow Doña Ysabel Barreto assumed command of the expedition, and the islands were abandoned November 18, 1595. The ability of the pilot-major Quirós enabled the flagship *San Gerónimo* to reach the Philippines January 14 and anchor off Cavite February 10, 1596, but the galliot *San Felipe* was forced to make port in Mindanao, and the frigate *Santa Catalina* was wrecked on an unidentified coast, with a loss of all hands and the body of Mendaña. En route to Manila, the *San Gerónimo* on December 21, 1595, encountered Ponape in the Carolines and discovered the nearby islets of Pakin. From these islands the *San Gerónimo* proceeded, via the southern Marianas (January 3), to the entrance of San Bernardino Strait. In Manila a report on the expedition was presented to the Lieutenant Governor Antonio de Morga. The *San Gerónimo* was repaired and refitted. Doña Ysabel married the cousin of the governor of the Philippines, and the *San Gerónimo*, under Quirós and carrying Doña Ysabel and her new husband, sailed from Cavite August 10, 1596 and arrived in Acapulco December 11, 1596. Quirós then continued on another ship back to Perú, where he arrived at Paita May 3, 1597 (not 1598 as often stated).[70]

After several years in Europe obtaining the backing of the Pope and other notables, Quirós was given permission to lead an expedition to discover and convert the great Terra Australis which he was convinced lay close to the Santa Cruz and Solomon Islands. On December 21, 1605, the fleet, consisting of the *capitana San Pedro y San Pablo*, the *almirante San Pedro*, and the sailing launch *Los Tres Reyes Magos*, sailed from Callao in a southwesterly direction to about latitude 26° S. (Fig. 14). Changing to a northwesterly direction on January 22, 1606, the Isla de la Encarnación (Ducie) was sighted January 26, and January 29–30 San Juan Bautista (Henderson Island) was sighted and visited. Between February 3 and 15 the expedition discovered Santelmo (Marutea—South Marutea), Las Cuatro Coronadas or Las Vírgenes (the Actaeon Group), San Miguel Arcángel (Vairaatea), La Conversión de San Pablo (Hao) where a landing was made and natives were encountered, La Decena (Tauere or perhaps Amanu), La Sagitaria (Rekareka, now Tehuata or possibly Raroia), and La Fugitiva (Raroia or Takume)—all in the Tuamotu Archipelago. On February 21 a landing was made on an island at first believed to be the San Bernardo of Mendaña but which was later named Isla de Pescado and recognized as a new discovery (Caroline Atoll in the Line Islands, which possibly had been sighted by Magellan). March 2–4 were spent at the Isla de Gente Hermosa or Isla del Peregrino (Rakahanga in the northern Cook Islands), whose inhabitants impressed the Spaniards greatly by their physical beauty.[71]

Quirós did not locate either the Solomon Islands or the Santa Cruz Islands proper, but landfall was made April 7 in the Duff Islands where some ten days were spent with the Polynesians on Taumako (Disappointment). On April 18 the fleet sailed to the southeast, coasted Tucopia (Tikopia) on a southerly route, then sailed west to the southern islands of the Banks Islands, April 25 and 26. Names were given to San Marcos (Merelav/Mera Lava/Star Peak), Virgen María or Santa María (Gaua), and other islands including modern Vanua Lava and Ureparapara. At the end of April an undifferentiated land mass was sighted to the southeast which was composed of Aurora (Maewe), Pentecost, and Oba islands, in the northern New Hebrides. On May 1 the fleet anchored in Saint Philip and Saint James Bay on the northeast side of Espíritu Santo Island.

The month of May was devoted to exploration of Espíritu Santo Island, establishment of a settlement, and initiation of the great work of conversion to Christianity to which Quirós was completely committed. The island and the region were formally taken possession of for the crown of Spain and were named Austrialia del Espíritu Santo. By this time Quirós seems to have become a sick and vacillating person, grasped by religious bigotry and incapable of command and decision. The upshot was that Quirós decided to abandon the island and, about June 11, 1606, the three vessels prepared to sail. The flagship *San Pedro y San Pablo*, with Quirós and the chief pilot Gaspar González de Leza, became separated from the other two ships on which were the *almirante* Luis Vaez de Torres and Diego Prado y Tovar. This has been explained as an accident due to wind and current, or to mutiny, and as an outright desertion. In any case, the flagship headed at first for the Philippines but then shifted to the track for New Spain. On July 8 the Isla del Buen Viaje was sighted which most probably was in the Makin Atoll in the northern Gilberts. After gaining latitude 38° N. the ship sailed on a track that gave a landfall about September 23 on the California coast in about latitude 34° N. Navidad was reached October 20 and, after a stay in Navidad until November 15, the ship anchored in Bahía de Acapulco November 23, 1606. Quirós was bankrupt and ill, but nevertheless managed to cross México overland and reach Spain the next year. After turning out some 50 *memoriales* and more than 200 maps Quirós was given a hypocritical promise of backing for another expedition, but he died in Panamá in 1615, before he discovered the intended treachery. So ended the last of the great Iberian explorers of Spain's century of glory in the Pacific. Apparently Quirós' admiral Torres had died previously, probably in the Philippines.

After Torres and Prado had searched in vain for the *capitana*, they sailed southwestward to about latitude 21° S., in obedience to their written instructions. Then they sailed northward to reach the Philippine Islands, but were not able to clear the islands and reefs at the southeastern tip of New Guinea, after being shunted westward by Tagula and other islands and reefs in the Louisiade Archipelago (Fig. 14). This forced Torres to sail along the south side and around New Guinea to the Moluccas. In the process Torres discovered the strait which was named after him by Dalrymple in 1767, and proved that New Guinea was a huge island and not part of the great southern continent. Although Torres may have seen the Cape York Peninsula of Australia, this is not likely and—in any case—the Dutch had reached that continent a few months earlier. Torres left the launch in Ternate, and reached Manila May 22, 1607, where his ship soon was requisitioned. Shortly after writing a narrative letter to the King, Torres passed out of the view of history until the British captured Manila in 1762, and Dalrymple discovered a copy of Torres' letter among documents that had been seized.[72]

The entrance of non-Iberians into the Pacific via the Strait of Magellan (Drake, et al.) renewed Spanish interest in that region. Sarmiento led a two-ship expedition (1579–81) from Perú which carefully surveyed the Strait and then continued on to Spain. This was the first voyage from the Pacific to Europe by way of the Strait. In 1581 a large expedition left Spain to colonize and fortify the Strait area, but the attempt ended in a tragic fiasco.[73] In 1618–1619, as a result of the 1615–1616 voyage of Le Maire and Schouten and the discovery of the Strait between Tierra del Fuego and Isla de los Estados, the brothers Bartolomé García de Nodal and Gonzalo Nodal carried out an extremely efficient voyage of exploration which resulted in the discovery of numerous islands south and west of Tierra del Fuego and the first circumnavigation of that island.[74]

RENEWAL OF SPANISH INTEREST: 1720–1793

For a century there is little of value for our theme. In 1720, while a captive in Lima, the English privateer William Betagh became acquainted with a French Captain Thaylet, who had recently been sent by the Peruvian viceroy to locate some inhabited islands in about latitude 10° S. which had been visited by two different Spanish ships, carried there accidentally by winds and currents. Although Captain Thaylet was not able to locate these islands in two months of searching, there is good reason to believe that the islands involved were the Marquesas.[75]

During the years 1735–1745, the Spanish naval officers Jorge Juan and Antonio de Ulloa were in the Pacific region of South America. Intermittently from 1736 to 1744, they participated in the survey of an arc of a meridian in Ecuador. From 1740 to 1743, the two officers organized the coastal defenses of the Viceroyalty of Perú against possible attacks by the English squadron commanded by Anson. In these years they commanded two ships which cruised the southeastern Pacific, during which time five trips were made to the Islas Juan Fernández and the islands were surveyed. In the 1750s Antonio de Ulloa returned to the Pacific and commanded the *San Rafael;* in 1758, he was one of the first navigators in the Pacific to consistently use lemon juice as an antiscorbutic. Ulloa attained a high southern latitude of 60° S., and was the first to comment on the aurora australis, which he observed south of Cape Horn. Altogether, Ulloa and Juan were among the most scientific observers and navigators in the Pacific during the eighteenth century.[76]

As a result of increased British and Dutch activity, and to forestall the establishment of a "foreign" naval base or colony in the eastern Pacific, the Peruvian viceroy Amat sent out an expedition in 1770 to locate and take possession of land reportedly discovered by Edward Davis in 1687. Captain Felipe González y Haedo in the *San Lorenzo* and Captain Antonio Domonte in the *Santa Rosalia* left Callao October 10, 1770, and on November 15 discovered an island which was named San Carlos, of which possession was taken for Spain (Fig. 15). About a week was spent here. After some further but fruitless cruising, the ships returned to the mainland where they anchored off Isla de Chiloé December 15, 1770. This "discovery" was recognized by the Spaniards to be a rediscovery of Easter Island, which Roggeween had found in 1722.[77]

News of the discovery of the Society Islands by Wallis in 1767, and the visits there of Bougainville in 1768 and Cook in 1769, stirred the Peruvian viceroy to further activity. On September 26, 1772, Domingo de Boenechea left Callao in the *Santa María Magdalena* (alias *El Aguila*) and reached Tahiti November 8, having discovered San Simón y Judas (Tauere) and rediscovered San Quintín (Haraiki) and Todos Santos (Anaa) which had been found by Bougainville in 1768 (Fig. 15). After a month-long survey, *El Aguila* returned to South America, where it anchored in Valparaíso on February 21, 1773.

On the basis of the information obtained, a second expedition was sent out to establish a mission and obtain further geographic and anthropologic data. The second expedition consisted of *El Aguila* under Boenechea and a cargo ship the *San Miguel* (alias *Júpiter*) under its owner José de Andía y Varela. Sailing from Callao September 20, 1774, and following approximately the same route as before through the Tuamotus, the expedition reached Tahiti November 15 (Fig. 15). En route the two ships became separated, so that Boenechea discovered San Narciso (Tatakoto) and San Julián (Tahanea), and Andía rediscovered the Isla de las Animas (Amanu) which had been sighted by Quirós in 1606. Two priests, a cook, and an interpreter (a Spaniard from Perú who had learned the language from some Tahitians taken back to Perú in 1772–1773) were established in a mission. The return trip to Perú (Fig. 15) was headed by Tomás Gayangos, as Boenechea had died on Tahiti January 6, 1775. On the return Santa Rosa (Raevavae) in the Austral Islands (Îles Australes) was discovered on February 5, 1775. The Spanish period (1772–1776) in the Society Islands was completed by Cayetano de Lángara y Huarte in *El Aguila*. He left Callao September 27, 1775, picked up the disillusioned mission group on Tahiti, and was back in Callao February 18, 1776.[78]

One more Spanish voyage in the south Pacific should be mentioned, since it resulted in adding a long name for a tiny island on the map of the Pacific. In 1793, the captain of a Spanish ship discovered the heap of rocks in latitude 26° 27′ S. and longitude 105° 21′ W. which he named for himself, Isla Sala y Gómez. The basic documentation is unknown to me.

THE SPANIARDS IN THE NORTHEAST PACIFIC: 1769–1795

In the northeast Pacific, stimulated by activities of the Russians and the British, maritime exploration was primarily along the coast north of California. In 1768, a naval base had been established in San Blas, and the settling of missions, towns, and presidios in (Alta) California began in 1769. During the period 1774 to 1792, a dozen Spanish expeditions originating in San Blas or Acapulco explored the coasts of what are today Washington, British Columbia, and Alaska as far as Unalaska in the Aleutians. The sequence of European exploration in this region was: Bering sailed through the Bering Strait in 1728; Bering and Chirikof in 1741, from about Dixon Entrance north and westward; Pérez in 1774 sailed to Dixon Entrance; Hezeta and Bodega, 1775, sailed to Kruzof Island in the Alexander Archipelago and latitude 58° N. in the Gulf of Alaska; Cook in 1778 surveyed the coast from Oregon to Bering

Strait; Arteaga and Bodega, 1779, explored north to Kenai Peninsula and Kodiak Island; and from 1785 on, there were many exploratory and commercial expeditions. Thanks to the Spanish policy of secrecy, versus the impressive publications that resulted from the voyages of Cook, La Pérouse, and Vancouver, and as a result of the application of diplomatic persuasion backed by greater military strength which forced Spain (1790–1795) to give up her claims and her settlements to Great Britain, the world at large has not realized that the Spaniards, up to 1795, had made more discoveries and had carried out more exploration and had made more charts of the Washington-British Columbia-Panhandle of Alaska coast than had the British, French, and American navigators combined.

I do not have the space here to detail the work of the Spaniards which, furthermore, has been covered in recent literature. The least I can do is to list the principal voyages with the dates, officers, and ships involved. The first voyage was that from San Blas, January 25 to November 3, 1774, in the frigate *Santiago* (alias *Nueva Galicia*), under Juan José Pérez Hernández with Esteban José Martínez as navigator (Fig. 15). Among discoveries were the features later to be known as Vancouver Island, the entrance to Nootka Sound, and the Olympic Mountains. The second voyage from San Blas, March 16 to November 3, 1775, in the *Santiago* under Bruno de Hezeta with Pérez second in command, and the schooner *Sonora* (alias *Felicidad*) under Juan Francisco de la Bodega y Quadra with Francisco Antonio Maurelle as navigator, sailed by way of Isla Socorro as far north as the Alexander Archipelago. At this time Bodega and Maurelle decided that Isla Socorro was the same as the Santo Tomás discovered by Grijalva. On the return voyage of Hezeta, who was separated from Bodega, the entrance to the Columbia River was seen. In some fashion information from this voyage reached the hands of Cook before he commenced his third and last voyage. Possibly Cook obtained a copy of the Maurelle diary, which was published in 1781 by Barrington from a manuscript the origins of which are unknown. Apparently, however, the Spanish ambassador in London made available some unspecified materials to the British Admiralty in 1776.

Ignacio Arteaga in the frigate *La Princesa* (alias *Nuestra Señora del Rosario*), accompanied by Bodega in *La Favorita* (alias *Neustra Señora de los Remedios*) with Maurelle second in command, made the third voyage from San Blas, February 11 to November 21, 1779. This expedition had been so long delayed that Cook, in 1778, anticipated it in discoveries in southern Alaska. The fourth voyage from San Blas, March to October of 1788, was made by Martínez in another *La Princesa* (alias *Concepción*), accompanied by González López de Haro in the *San Carlos* (alias *Filipino*). The fifth voyage from San Blas, February 17 to September and December of 1789, was by Martínez and López de Haro in the same ships, and resulted in the building of a fort on what came to be known for a time as the Island of Quadra and Vancouver.

What turned into three expeditions left San Blas on February 3, 1790. This squadron consisted of *La Princesa* under Francisco Eliza, the *San Carlos* under Salvador Fidalgo, and the *Princesa Real* under Manuel Quimper. In 1791, further exploration was carried out by Eliza in the *San Carlos* (which had been brought up to Nootka by Ramón Saavedra), and the *Santa Saturnina* (alias *Horcasitas*) under José María Narváez and later Juan Carrasco. From June to August 1791, Alessandro Malaspina in the *Descubierta* and José Bustamante y Guerra in the *Atrevida* surveyed in Alaskan waters (including Glacier Bay), as part of the work of this greatest of Spanish marine expeditions of the eighteenth century 1789–1794 (Fig. 15). Malaspina was accompanied by numerous scientists and artists, including the cartographer Felipe Bauzá and the mathematician-navigator José Espinosa y Tello. Two of Malaspina's officers, Dionisio Alcalá Galiano and Cayetano Valdés, were left in México to lead another expedition, in 1792, into northern latitudes in the schooners *Sutil* and *Mexicana*, and they were the first to circumnavigate Vancouver Island. More or less at the same time was the last Spanish exploratory expedition into these waters. Led by Jacinto Caamaño in the frigate *Aranzazú*, it carried out an extensive survey in the channels of the British Columbia coast.[79]

SPANISH MICRONESIA: 1668–1806

Although Spanish contacts with Micronesia began with Magellan in 1521 on Guam, and Espinosa who sighted Sonsorol in 1522, the Spaniards did not occupy, conquer, and convert the Ladrones (named Marianas in 1668) until 1668 to 1698. During the sixteenth and seventeenth centuries native boats from the northwestern Carolines were occasionally carried by wind and current to the Philippine Islands, especially Samar, and the Jesuits tried several times unsuccessfully to reach the Caroline Islands. After two native ships from Palau were blown to Samar in 1696, Faraulep Atoll was discovered by a ship piloted by Juan Rodríguez in that same year. After some Palau Islands natives drifted to the Philippines in 1708, the Jesuits searched for the Palaus unsuccessfully in 1709, but were successful in 1710. In that year the *Santísima Trinidad*, under Francisco Padilla with Josef Somera as pilot, located seven islands including Sonsorol and Palau (Babelthaup). This was the first definite European contact with Palau. In 1712, Bernardo de Egui (or de Guia) sailing in the *Santo Domingo de Guzmán* from Guam made the first firm discovery of Ulithi, which was called Los Garbanzos. These islands were revisited by Father Juan Antonio Cantova in 1722. After natives from the Carolines drifted onto the Marianas in 1721, 1722, and 1725, the Jesuits established a mission in the Palaus in 1531, but all the missionaries were dead when the islands were revisited in 1733. Most of our information of exploration in the Carolines in this period (1696 to 1733) is derived from Jesuit sources.[80]

There were a few more Spanish discoveries in the Carolines in the early nineteenth century. A Spanish naval officer, Juan de Ibargoitia, in the *Filipino* discovered Onon (Namonuito) and Pulusuk and made the first firm contact with Puluwat in the period 1799 to 1801. Juan Bautista Monteverde in the *Palas*, sailing from Manila to Perú in 1806, rediscovered Oroluk and discovered Nukuoro atoll. Although the Spaniards expressed little real interest in the Carolines, Spain formally re-proclaimed sovereignty over these islands in 1874. Spain was then involved in a dispute with Germany which terminated in 1899 with the sale of the Carolines and the northern Marianas to Germany.[81]

FINAL VOYAGES: 1789–1867

The great tour of the Pacific by the Malaspina expedition commenced in Cádiz in August of 1789, and ended there in September of 1794. This expedition made few discoveries in the Pacific, but it was the greatest scientific marine expedition sent out by Spain, and it acquired an enormous amount of hydrographic, ethnographic, and biologic data. Unfortunately, Malaspina was imprisoned upon his return to Spain, and very little of the information acquired has been published. Some of the highlights of the expedition included the first scientific survey of the Galápagos Islands, detailed surveys of various sectors of the North American coast (of which the British Admiralty availed itself through publishing charts made by Malaspina's cartographer Felipe Bauzá), a survey of the Philippines, visits to Australia and New Zealand, and a careful study of the Tongas.[82]

In 1795–96, Admiral Ignacio María de Alava y Navarrete, en route from Cádiz to Manila with the Spanish Asiatic Squadron, revised charts of the Cape Horn and Chile-Perú areas. While in the Philippines Alava improved the charts of those islands. Before returning to Cádiz (which was reached May 15, 1803, via the Cape of Good Hope), further chart improvements were made for the North Pacific.[83]

Not exactly a marine expedition, yet of considerable interest, is the Expedición de la Vacuna under Francisco Javier Balmis which left La Coruña November 30, 1803, on the *María de Pita*, and spent several years in introducing vaccination against smallpox in the Spanish possessions from México to South America and the Philippines. Balmis crossed México to Acapulco, whence he sailed February 7, 1805, on the *San Fernando de Magallanes* to Manila. He returned to Spain in 1806, using Portuguese ships from Manila to Macao and Lisbon.

From 1862 to 1865, a group of Spanish naturalists and other scientists (Comisión Científica del Pacífico, 1862–1865) used the ships *Nuestra Señora del Triunfo* and *Covadonga* as bases for terrestrial studies in South America and Central America.[84]

A fitting note on which to end is the voyage of the *Numancia* under Commodore Juan Antequera. In 1865, Spain declared war on Chile and her allies and sent a squadron to the Pacific, which bombarded Valparaíso and Callao. The squadron, which left Cádiz February 4, 1865, finished intimidating the South Americans and sailed away May 10, 1866. Among these ships was the first Spanish armored steam battleship, the *Numancia* built in Toulon in 1864. From Callao it steamed and sailed (because of coal shortage) via Tahiti, Manila, Cape of Good Hope, and Rio de Janeiro to Cádiz where it arrived September 20, 1867. The *Numanica* was the first armored steam battleship to circumnavigate the world.[85]

SUMMARY AND CONCLUSIONS

An impressive list of "firsts" must be credited to the Spaniards in the Pacific. Although the terms Polynesia, Micronesia, and Melanesia were not used, the Spaniards discovered these great assemblages of archipelagos. A minor exception must be made for Melanesia since the Portuguese were in western New Guinea and the Papuan islands between New Guinea and the Moluccas in the period 1512 to 1526. The Spaniards, however, made four voyages along the north coast of New Guinea, 1528 to 1545, covering altogether from the Kepulauan Schouten to Astrolabe Bay, and took possession and named New Guinea in 1545. Furthermore, the entire south side was coasted in 1606, resulting in the discovery of Torres Strait and demonstrating that New Guinea was an island. Among the chief island groups discovered in the Melanesian region were the Kepulauan Schouten, Admiralty Islands, Solomon Islands, Duff Islands, Santa Cruz Islands, Banks Islands, New Hebrides, and the Louisiade Archipelago.

The Spaniards discovered all of the islands in the Marianas, and they also were the first Europeans to visit the Gilberts, the Marshalls, and the Carolines—which constitute Micronesia. Probably the Spaniards discovered the majority of the islands in the extensive Caroline-Marshall region. In Polynesia the Spaniards discovered the Tuamotus, Marquesas, southern and northern Line Islands, northern Cook Islands, and the Ellice Islands. All of the oceanic islands in the Pacific east of longitude 130° W. were discovered by Spaniards with the possible exception of Clipperton, Easter Island (to which Spaniards made the second visit), and Pitcairn. However, Speilbergen in 1615, provided the first adequate description of Isla Clarión (Santa Rosa) in the Islas Revillagigedo. In the northwestern Pacific Spaniards discovered the Volcano Islands, Parece Vela, one or more islands in the Izu Shotō, Wake Island, and probably the Bonin Islands and Marcus Island. Isolated discoveries also were made by Spaniards in the Îles Australes, Bismarcks, and Tongas.

Vith the considerable exceptions of the southwestern quadrant and the far north, the Spaniards outlined the boundaries of the Oceanic basin. The entire Pacific coast of the Americas, from Tierra del Fuego to the Queen Charlotte Islands, was first explored and charted by Spaniards, and Tierra del Fuego and Vancouver Island were first circumnavigated by Spaniards. The first European survey of the Pacific coasts of the main Japanese islands was made by Spaniards. The Spaniards also were the first to circumnavigate and chart Luzón, Samar, and Mindanao, which—with their discovery of the Pulau-pulau Talaud, circumnavigation of Halmahera, and coasting of northern New Guinea—outlined the western Pacific from about latitude 40° N. to latitude 5° S.

The extent of the Spanish discoveries, however, has been minimized by the lack of publicity for the resultant logs and charts. As a consequence, only a small fraction of the names applied by the Spaniards exist on contemporary maps. Nevertheless, enough charts and accounts were published so that one can only attribute the renaming of many islands and coastal features of the mainlands to the studied ignorance and impudence of the British and other hydrographers. Outstanding examples of this attitude by non-Spanish navigators and cartographers will be found in the names given to places on the Pacific coast of México by British and American navigators in the *nineteenth century*, which names are current on British and American charts despite the fact that other names had been in existence on Spanish and Mexican charts for several centuries.

The Spaniards, through observation and trial-and-error, developed a number of the great sailing routes within and across the Pacific. If Krusenstern and Maury had had access to the charts and logs in the Spanish Depósito Hidrográfico de Madrid (which functioned under this name 1787 to 1862) they could have turned out better sailing directions and wind and current charts for various parts of the Pacific. From 1520 on, the Spaniards were much concerned with observations on declination of the magnetic needle, and nature and regime of the winds and currents and tides. Periodically these observations were studied and recommendations were made by many individuals from Santa Cruz, through Sarmiento, García de Palacio, Ríos Coronel, Porter y Casanate, Seijas y Lobera, Cabrero Bueno, Juan and Ulloa, to Malaspina and Espinosa y Tello, in the period from the sixteenth through the eighteenth centuries. Among the Spanish charts which exerted considerable influence in their time were those by Ribero 1529, Santa Cruz 1542, Cabot 1544, López de Velasco 1575/80, and scattered productions up to the charts of Bauzá and Espinosa y Tello in the early nineteenth century.

Two interesting developments in the determination of longitude or position in the Pacific, prior to the introduction of chronometers toward the end of the eighteenth century, were the use of observed magnetic declination (termed variation) in relation to latitude, to help a pilot spot his ship's position on the chart, and the so-called *señas* (certain kelp and other marine vegetation, "dirty" water, etc.) which denoted the position where a ship sailing eastward in the north Pacific should veer to the southeast.

Among other techniques used first in the Pacific by Spaniards was the distillation of fresh drinking water from sea water on board ship (first noted on the Quirós voyage of 1606), and the consistent use of lemon juice as an antiscorbutic beginning with Ulloa in 1758. Lead sheathing of ships was used by the Spaniards as early as the first half of the sixteenth century, but the most common protection against the teredo was the preferential use of ships constructed in Ecuador and the East Indies from certain local hardwoods.

Valuable ethnographic notes occupy an outstanding place among the nonhydrographic results of Spanish voyages in the Pacific. The first ethnographic records from Oceania were obtained by Spaniards, including the first data on Micronesian (Marianas, etc.), Melanesian (New Guinea, etc.), and Polynesian (Marquesas, etc.) peoples. Oceanic linguistics began with Vigo (the first beachcomber in the Pacific) who lived 1522–1526, in the Marianas and learned Chamorro. The formal work of linguistics in the Pacific area, however, was due principally to Roman Catholic missionaries (chiefly Jesuits) whose work began with the Portuguese in the Carolines in the 1530s, and was continued by Spanish Jesuits in the Marianas and Carolines in the seventeenth and eighteenth centuries, and missionaries from Perú in Tahiti in the 1770s. Miscellaneous scientific observations and collections ranged from those of trained botanists, such as F. Hernández on the Mexican coast in the 1570s and the botanists on the Malaspina expedition in the 1790s, to the observation of the aurora australis by Ulloa at the middle of the eighteenth century.

All in all, we must conclude that Spain was the greatest exploring and scientific nation in the Pacific region during the sixteenth and seventeenth centuries. Furthermore, the scientific expedition led by Malaspina at the end of the eighteenth century would compare favorably with any other of the period. However, it is indicated that a series of studies must be made of the unpublished and for the most part little-known Spanish documents in the archives of Spain and Mexico, the British Museum, and the Bibliothèque Nationale (as well as in lesser collections), before Spain can gain widespread recognition for more than the few voyages which have obtained wide publicity.

8

GEOGRAPHICAL EXPLORATION BY THE PORTUGUESE

DONALD D. BRAND*

Although the Portuguese were in the Pacific (as defined in the previous chapter) but a relatively short time, their role as European pioneers by sea was highly important. In order to circumvent the Venetian-Alexandrine monopoly of the spice trade, and also to eliminate a number of the middlemen in the trade with China, the Portuguese pioneered the sea route around the Cape of Good Hope to India which was reached in 1498, and Malacca which was attained in 1509 and conquered in 1511. The search for "Prester John" and other "lost" Christian kings and kingdoms also contributed to the drive eastward by the very Christian Portuguese nation. Malacca, the great emporium of the Indies, became the forward base from which Portugal sent out expeditions to explore, conquer, and trade.

The explorations and discoveries made by the Portuguese in the Indo-Chinese-Malayan world can be considered as such only in terms of activities carried out by a Christian western European nation operating mainly in its own ships. Certainly by the third century A.D. Persians and Arabs made trading trips by sea to Canton, and in the seventh and eighth centuries there were large colonies of Moslem Arabs and Persians in such cities as Canton and Hangchow. There were reciprocal movements as Chinese junks navigated from Canton to the Euphrates during the Tang Dynasty (618–907 A.D.). Making use of Arab, Indian, Javanese, Siamese, Cambodian, and Chinese vessels, a number of literate travelers from the West visited Indonesia and China during the seven centuries before the Portuguese incursion.[1]

Preliminary to Portuguese exploration in the open Pacific was the expedition sent out by Albuquerque, the Portuguese Viceroy of India, from recently conquered Malacca in November of 1511. The expedition consisted of three Portuguese ships, the *Santa Catarina* under Antonio de Abreu and the *Sabaia* under Francisco Serrão, and a caravel under Simão Afonso Bisagudo. Two native pilots accompanied the expedition, along with three Portuguese pilots including the pilot-cartographer Francisco Rodrigues. The ships coasted Sumatra, sailed along the northern coasts of Java, Bali, Lombok, and the Lesser Sunda Islands, and then turned north from the Pulau-pulau Barat Daja (Wetar, Roma, Damar) past the volcano of Pulau Gunungapi to Buru, Ambon (Amboina), and the port of Guli (Gulir) on Ceram (Fig. 16). The exact route in the Banda Sea has been the subject of much controversy, some modern writers insisting that the expedition went as far east as the Kepulauan Aru and that Abreu possibly sighted New Guinea while backtracking WNW to the southern Spice Islands (Moluccas). There seems to be no good reason to believe that the native pilots

---

*Dr. BRAND is professor of geography at the University of Texas, Austin, Texas.

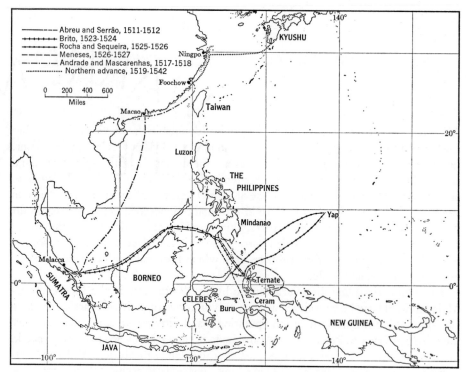

Fig. 16. Significant Portuguese voyages, 1511–1542.

would have taken the ships so far out of their way in getting to the Moluccas, the route to which was well known and much traversed by Malacca craft.[2]

After some time in the Ceram port of Guli (Gulir) because of bad weather, the expedition sailed to Banda (Pulau Bandalontar) where a junk was purchased to replace Serrão's ship which had been lost earlier. The ships were loaded with nutmeg, mace, and clove, and the fleet headed back towards Malacca. However, a storm soon separated Serrão's junk from the other vessels and this junk was wrecked on a reef of the Lucipara Islands. After numerous adventures, including capturing a piratical junk, Francisco Serrão and six to nine other surviving Portuguese arrived at the island of Ternate in the Moluccas proper—apparently some time in 1512. Antonio Galvão, who was Portuguese governor of the Moluccas, 1536–1540, states that after the wreck of the junk on the Luciparas, Serrão and his companions went to Mindanao whence they were invited by the king of the Moluccas to come to Ternate; this Serrão did, accompanied by four or five other Portuguese. If Galvão can be believed, this would make Serrão and his group the first Europeans known to have been in the Philippines. At any rate, the Serrão group were the first Europeans to be in the Moluccas north of the equator.[3] The main expedition under Abreu returned to Malacca in December 1512, and the resultant charts prepared by Francisco Rodrigues about 1513 (which incorporated data from the native pilots) were the first European charts to represent Indonesia from first-hand information.

THE MOLUCCAN PERIOD: 1512–1545

Francisco Serrão lived in the Moluccas, principally on Ternate, from about 1512 until his death in 1521. I have mentioned in the previous chapter how letters from Serrão in the Moluccas to Magellan contributed to Magellan's desire to reach the Moluccas. We know little about Serrão's activities while in the Moluccas, but we do know that he went out on trading trips in local seagoing craft. It is most probable that Serrão was the first European to see the open Pacific, in the sector between the Moluccas and the Philippines, but this is mere conjecture.

The first Portuguese ships from Malacca did not reach Ternate in the Moluccas until 1515, and definite occupation was not made until Antonio de Brito (first Portuguese governor of the Moluccas) arrived on Ternate May 13, 1522 and commenced the construction of a fortress. Some two years before this, a Portuguese fleet commanded by Tristão de Meneses sailed from Malacca to Ternate with orders from Portugal to intercept the Magellanic expedition should it appear in Moluccan waters. Due to the wanderings of the *Trinidad* and the *Victoria* in the Mindanao-Palawan-Borneo region after the death of Magellan, the Magellanic remnants did not appear in the Moluccas while Meneses was there. It is interesting to speculate as to what the fame of the Magellan-Elcano voyage would have been if the Spanish ships had been captured by Meneses.

While the Portuguese were strengthening their hold on the Moluccas, there occurred several Portuguese voyages from Malacca via Sumatra toward the southeast in search of some reported Ilhas do Ouro.[4] Cristovão de Mendonça in 1522 is supposed to have reached Australia. A number of writers have connected these voyages searching for Islands of Gold with the supposed representation of Australia on the so-called Dieppe maps of 1536–1566. It is outside of our province to enter this controversial field, but I am not convinced by the evidence. The interested reader might commence by consulting the references in Cortesão.[5] It is possible, of course, that the Dieppe maps do contain representations of Australia. If this is so, the data more likely were obtained from Malay sources than from Portuguese voyages. There seems to be good reason to believe that there was trade between Malaysia and Australia.[6]

In May of 1523 Antonio de Brito sent out his relative Simão de Brito from Ternate to open up a route to Malacca, going via the Basilan Strait and Balabac Strait and along the northwest coast of Borneo (Fig. 16). Brito accomplished the mission, reaching Malacca in November of 1524 via Singapore Strait, but the route between Brunei in Borneo and the Moluccas already had been traversed by Spanish ships in 1521.

The first voyage by Portuguese from the Moluccas into the open Pacific was an involuntary one. In June of 1525 a ship commanded by Diogo da Rocha, with Gomes de Sequeira as pilot, left Ternate for a trading trip to the Celebes. When headed back towards Ternate in August or September a great storm carried the ship 200 or 300 leagues to the northeast, where a large island was encountered in nine or ten degrees north latitude (Fig. 16). The island had a pleasant climate and was inhabited by a kindly people with straight hair and skin of a color more light than dark. Here the ship's crew stayed four months while recuperating and waiting for favorable winds; in January of 1526 the ship was back in Ternate. As the island was marked on a chart by the pilot, it became known as the Ilha de Gomes de Sequeira. Some writers have used their imagination and not the chronicles and the wind systems that obtain in this part of the world, and they would have the voyage resulting in a discovery of Australia. The more scholarly investigators of the subject are agreed that the island was in the Carolines and most probably was either the Palau or Yap islands.[7]

The next discovery by Portuguese in the Pacific also was involuntary. Jorge de Meneses, the governor-designate of the Moluccas, left Malacca in August of 1526 and sailed for the Moluccas via the route north of Borneo (Fig. 16). While south of Mindanao, wind and current carried the ship past Halmahera an estimated 200 leagues east of the Moluccas to a land of kinky-haired dark-skinned people (Os Papuas). Meneses spent several months in a port on the "island of Versiga," south of the equator, waiting for the seasonal shift in winds. He apparently returned via Salat Dampier (strait) and around the south side of Halmahera to Ternate, where he arrived in May of 1527. There is no log extant of this voyage, but gleanings from the Portuguese chroniclers of the sixteenth century would indicate that Meneses probably "wintered" near the present Kaap de Goede Hoop (Tandjoeng Jamoersba) on the north side of the Vogelkop of western New Guinea. This discovery had little general effect, although it is probable that Saavedra knew of this discovery of land to the east of the Moluccas when he made his voyage of 1528.

While Antonio Galvão (The Apostle of the Moluccas) was governor of the Moluccas, he sent Francisco de Castro out in 1538 with two priests to convert the natives of Mindanao and other islands in the region. Galvão himself identifies some of these islands as being the same as those where natives greeted the Villalobos expedition in Spanish saying "Buenos días, matalotes," which natives had Christian crosses. These islands apparently were Fais and Yap or Ulithi. Galvão was apparently reasoning from the presence of the crosses. It is not explained why the natives should have spoken in Spanish rather than in Portuguese. A possibility is that contact with the officers and crew of the Rocha-Sequeira ship for four months produced some acculturation. This new "cult and its cant" might have been carried from one island group to several others in the region. It does not seem probable that Castro would have wandered out to the Carolines when he had such a rich field for missionary work in Mindanao alone.[8]

The last "discovery" of note by the Portuguese in the Pacific borderlands of Indonesia was that by Pero Fidalgo. In June of 1545 Fidalgo sailed from Brunei, Borneo, in a native junk. He is credited with "discovering" the island of Luzón and coasting its western side for a considerable distance. Actually, Luzón was well known by hearsay to both Spaniards and Portuguese beginning in 1521 or earlier, and Bernardo de la Torre in 1543 was the first European to see Luzón when he used the San Bernardino Strait.[9]

ADVANCE UP THE CHINA SEAS

With the conquest of Malacca in 1511, the Portuguese were in control of an emporium to which came junks and other craft from Siam, Cambodia, Tonkin, China,

Part of Linschoten's chart of southeast Asia in 1595, reproduced in R. A. Skelton: see Note 11, Fig. 13 on page 18. (Courtesy of R. A. Skelton.)

PLATE 23

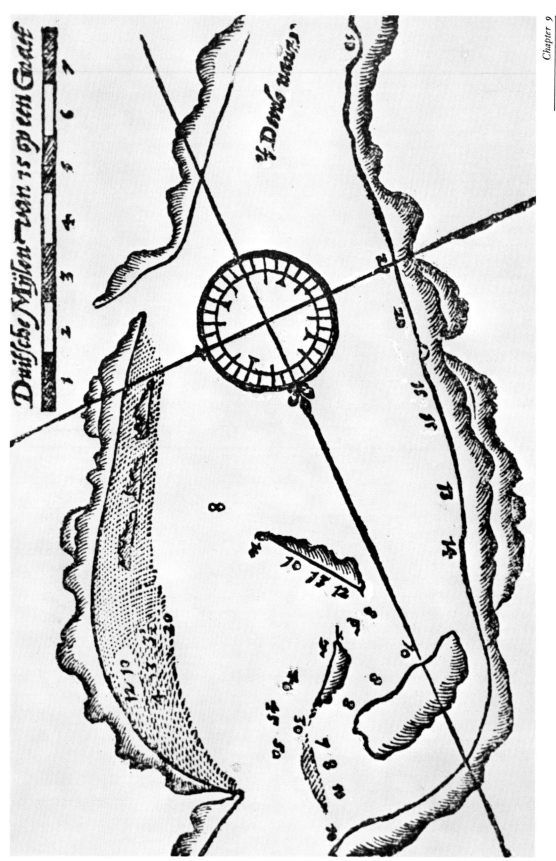

Sketch map by Jan Outghersz of the Strait of Magellan, at the third narrows ("'t Derde nauwte," to the right of the compass rose), observed in 1599

PLATE 24

Borneo, Luzón, and many other lands. The first Portuguese to reach China was Jorge Alvares, a trader, who went in a junk from Malacca to Tunmen Island (Nei-ling-ting) in the delta of the River of Canton (Chu Chiang) in 1513. Alvares returned to Malacca in 1514 with first-hand information concerning the trade and wealth of the Canton area.[10]

After several Portuguese traders in junks had made the voyage between Malacca and Canton, an official Portuguese fleet, consisting of four ships and four junks under the command of Ferñao Peres de Andrade, sailed from Malacca in June of 1517 and reached Canton in August. These were the first Portuguese ships to get as far north in the China seas as Canton. The fleet carried the first Portuguese embassy to the Emperor of China, which embassy was headed by Tomé Pires. Earlier, while living in Malacca (1512–1515), Pires had written the *Suma Oriental*. Although small portions of this work were published by Ramusio and others, the complete work was not available until 1944. Despite being based principally on second-hand information obtained from Malay, Chinese, and other sources, the *Suma Oriental* contained the best available description of Indonesia for more than a century, and in it is the first European mention of the Philippine Islands (Luzones).[11]

Although the embassy ended in failure, the Portuguese did become acquainted with a further stretch of the Chinese coast. Peres de Andrade sent Jorge de Mascarenhas in the *Santiago* with instructions to reach the Lequeos (Ryukyu) Islands. Mascarenhas did make profitable contacts on the Fukien coast, apparently at one or more points in the Amoy region which harbored the fabulous Zaytun of Marco Polo (Fig. 16). He had reached the mouth of the river which flows past Foochow when he was told to return with the fleet to Malacca, which was reached late in 1518.

Briefly the Portuguese had good relations with the official Chinese, but Portuguese impatience with Chinese customs and Chinese disdain for the "western barbarians" soon resulted in such bad relations that the Portuguese were forbidden the ports of China in 1522. The prohibition was applied most rigorously in the Canton area, 1522 to 1551, but the Portuguese-Chinese trade was so profitable to both Chinese and Portuguese that a great deal of smuggling or contraband trade went on every year in the islands and waters off the coasts of Fukien and Chekiang provinces. It was during this period that the Portuguese made their first direct contacts with Japan.

Although there may have been an anonymous Portuguese contact with Japan in 1534 or 1539, the first definitely recorded visit by Europeans was in 1542. The sources differ somewhat both as to the details of the event and as to the names of the Portuguese. I follow Armando Cortesão and other Portuguese writers in believing that Fernão Mendes Pinto was one of the three Portuguese who were on a Chinese junk in 1542 heading for Ningpo, which junk was carried by storms to Tanega-shima just south of Kyushu. Several months were spent on Tanega-shima and Kyushu by Mendes Pinto, Diogo Zeimoto, and Simão or Christovão Borralho. About 1544, Portuguese trading ships began to frequent the harbors of Kyushu. The Portuguese maintained trade relations with the Japanese for about a century, until the Portuguese were expelled in 1639/40. Much of our information concerning the Portuguese in Japan is derived from the accounts of the Jesuits who began work in Japan with (Saint) Francis Xavier, who was in Japan 1549–1552.[12]

By the 1550s the Portuguese had acquired a permanent foothold at Macao (Macau) and colonies of Portuguese traders were in such Chinese ports as Canton and Ningpo. Furthermore, Portuguese trading ships were frequently visiting the Ryukyu Islands and Japan. The arterial route for the Nao de Macau ran from Goa via Malacca to Macao and thence to ports in Kyushu (1571–1615 to Nagasaki). Although Portuguese activities in the China seas and Japan represented neither actual discovery nor territorial conquest, it was through the first-hand knowledge of the Portuguese that the sailing routes and recognizable geography of this portion of western Pacific lands came into the ken of western Europeans.

The oldest known European rutter for the Malacca to Canton route is that provided by Francisco Rodrigues. More detailed information for Far Eastern waters is contained in the sixteenth century *Livro de Marinharia* (Plate 22, *facing page 113*). A number of sailing routes used by the Portuguese in the Far East about 1550–1588 were collected by Linschoten in Goa about 1583 to 1592, and were published by Linschoten in 1596 (Plate 23, *facing page 148*). The cartographic information acquired by Francisco Rodrigues about 1512–1513, and by later Portuguese pilots, was employed by better-known European cartographers such as Pedro and Jorge Reinel in their maps 1517–1519, Lopo Homem in his map of 1519, and Nuño García de Toreno and Diego Ribero in the 1520s. Of especial importance for Japan were the maps by Fernão Vaz Dourado, beginning in 1568, and by Luiz Teixeira in the second half of the sixteenth century. In a very real sense the Portuguese were the European discoverers of the navigation and initiators of the cartography of the Pacific seas that front the coasts of China and Japan.[13]

The work of the Portuguese in the Pacific is not adequately depicted unless we mention some of the leading individuals among the many Portuguese who sailed the Pacific under the Spanish flag or who made maps and charts for Spain. The list must be headed by Ferdinand Magellan (and the numerous Portuguese who sailed with Magellan including especially Duarte Barbosa) who made the pioneer voyage across the Pacific 1520–1521. Juan Rodríguez Cabrillo, 1542–1543, and Sebastián Rodríguez Cermeño, 1595, outlined much of the California coast. A Portuguese, Lope Martín, was the pilot of the *San Lucas*, the first ship to cross the Pacific from west to east. Pedro Fernández de Quirós was the pilot-major of the 1595 Mendaña expedition which discovered the Marquesas and the Santa Cruz Islands, and it was Quirós who (after the death of Mendaña) managed to get most of the survivors to Manila. Later, in 1605–1606, Quirós headed his own expedition, which discovered the New Hebrides; another Portuguese, Luis Vaez de Torres, who had been the *almirante* in this expedition, discovered the strait between New Guinea and Australia and proved that New Guinea was an island. Among the leading Portuguese cosmographers and cartographers who worked for Spain in connection with Pacific voyages were the Faleiro brothers, the Reinels (father and son), and Diego Ribero.

Altogether, the Portuguese as individuals and as a nation during a century (1511 to 1606) made contributions to the knowledge of the Pacific that were only a little less than those made by Spaniards. The outstanding contribution of the Portuguese, however, was the opening of south and east Asia to European trade and culture.

GEOGRAPHICAL EXPLORATION BY THE DUTCH

Jan O. M. Broek*

The struggle of the Dutch for independence from Spain led them to seek direct trade relations with the newly discovered lands. Attempts to find an alternate sea route to China and the East Indies along the north coast of Asia (1594 and following years) proved fruitless. Success came with the expedition of Cornelis de Houtman, which followed the Portuguese wake around Africa and reached Java in 1596. Its return to Holland the following year sparked an outburst of commercial enterprise which, within fifty years, was to make the Dutch masters of the Malay Archipelago and formidable rivals in all other African and Asian ports.

Compared to the stream of vessels plying the route around the Cape of Good Hope, the Dutch tracks across the Pacific have been relatively few (Fig. 17). Nevertheless, they left their mark on the map, from Cape Horn to Easter Island, and from Quelpart Island to Tasmania. As the Dutch came to the East Indies a century after the Portuguese, their contributions to the knowledge of this archipelago were more in the nature of filling in details than in making major discoveries. Within the framework of this book it seems best to leave the East Indies aside and concentrate on three topics: (1) Dutch voyages through the Strait of Magellan and around Cape Horn, (2) the discoveries of Australia and New Zealand, and (3) explorations in the northern Pacific (Fig. 17).

There is a rich literature on all these voyages, including original journals and charts as well as modern annotated editions.[1] In preparing this chapter I have consulted as much as possible early editions, and in some cases manuscripts, but I owe a large debt to the scholarship of the editors of the publications of the Linschoten Vereeniging, the Dutch counterpart of the Hakluyt Society in Britain.[2]

EARLY VOYAGES THROUGH THE STRAIT OF MAGELLAN

Among the several companies formed in 1598 to trade in distant lands there were two, both at Rotterdam, that chose to take the westward route through the Strait of Magellan. Their purpose, following the examples of Francis Drake and Thomas Cavendish, was to combine raids on Spanish territories and silver galleons with trading ventures in east Asia. One expedition was organized by a north Netherlands group, and put under the command of Olivier van Noort.[3] He reached the Strait of Magellan in November 1599. Over and again gales whipped the ships back into the Atlantic, currents led them astray, and Indians on the heights pelted them with penguins. When, after more than four months, they emerged into the Pacific a violent storm separated the vessels. The *Hendrick Frederick* raided Spanish ships as far north

---

*Dr. Broek is professor of geography at the University of Minnesota, Minneapolis, Minnesota.

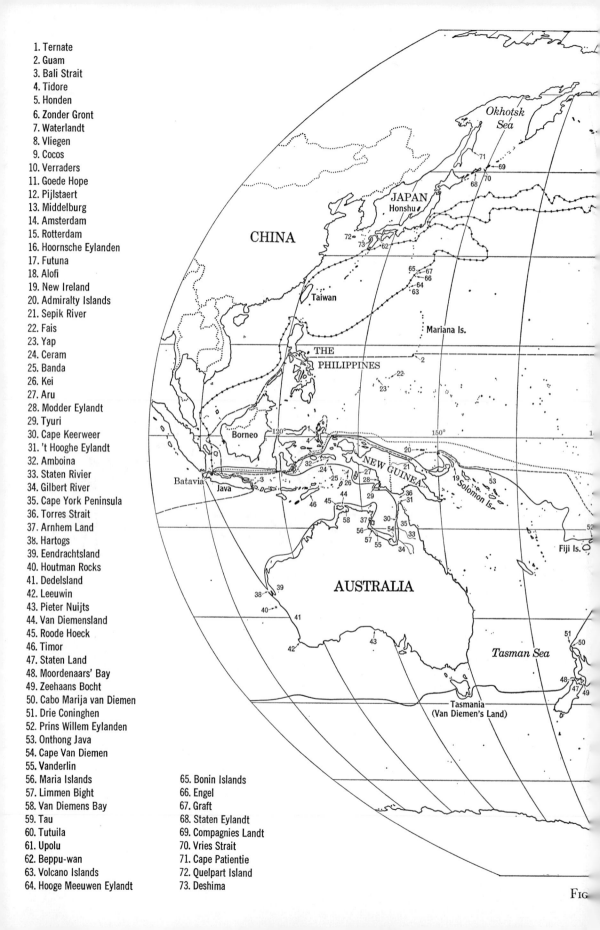

1. Ternate
2. Guam
3. Bali Strait
4. Tidore
5. Honden
6. Zonder Gront
7. Waterlandt
8. Vliegen
9. Cocos
10. Verraders
11. Goede Hope
12. Pijlstaert
13. Middelburg
14. Amsterdam
15. Rotterdam
16. Hoornsche Eylanden
17. Futuna
18. Alofi
19. New Ireland
20. Admiralty Islands
21. Sepik River
22. Fais
23. Yap
24. Ceram
25. Banda
26. Kei
27. Aru
28. Modder Eylandt
29. Tyuri
30. Cape Keerweer
31. 't Hooghe Eylandt
32. Amboina
33. Staten Rivier
34. Gilbert River
35. Cape York Peninsula
36. Torres Strait
37. Arnhem Land
38. Hartogs
39. Eendrachtsland
40. Houtman Rocks
41. Dedelsland
42. Leeuwin
43. Pieter Nuijts
44. Van Diemensland
45. Roode Hoeck
46. Timor
47. Staten Land
48. Moordenaars' Bay
49. Zeehaans Bocht
50. Cabo Marija van Diemen
51. Drie Coninghen
52. Prins Willem Eylanden
53. Onthong Java
54. Cape Van Diemen
55. Vanderlin
56. Maria Islands
57. Limmen Bight
58. Van Diemens Bay
59. Tau
60. Tutuila
61. Upolu
62. Beppu-wan
63. Volcano Islands
64. Hooge Meeuwen Eylandt

65. Bonin Islands
66. Engel
67. Graft
68. Staten Eylandt
69. Compagnies Landt
70. Vries Strait
71. Cape Patientie
72. Quelpart Island
73. Deshima

Fɪɢ

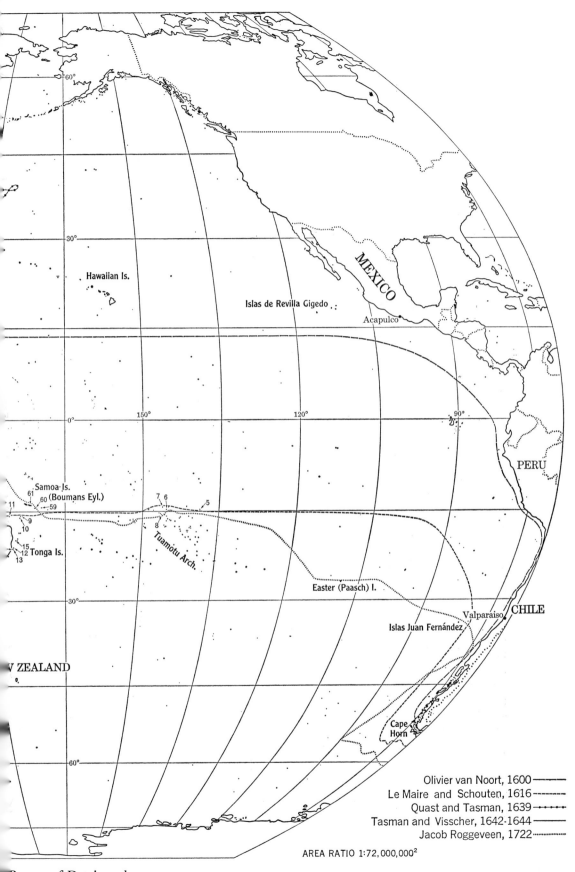

60°

30°

Hawaiian Is.

MEXICO

Islas de Revilla Gigedo

Acapulco

150°   120°   90°

0°

PERU

Samoa Is.
61
60 (Boumans Eyl.)
59
11
9
10
15
12 Tonga Is.
13

7 6
5
8
Tuamotu Arch.

Easter (Paasch) I.

30°

Valparaiso CHILE

Islas Juan Fernández

W ZEALAND

Cape
Horn

60°

Olivier van Noort, 1600 ——————
Le Maire and Schouten, 1616 --------
Quast and Tasman, 1639 +·+·+·+·+
Tasman and Visscher, 1642-1644 ——————
Jacob Roggeveen, 1722 ·················

AREA RATIO 1:72,000,000²

Routes of Dutch explorers.

as the coast of Nicaragua, and eventually reached Ternate in the Moluccas where, after stranding, it was sold to the Sultan. The flagship *Mauritius*, accompanied by a yacht, made some unsuccessful raids along the coast of South America. It then crossed the Pacific to Guam, without apparently seeing any islands on the way. From here van Noort went to the Philippines, and from there southward, leaving the Malay Archipelago through Bali Strait. He returned to Rotterdam via the Cape of Good Hope with only one ship, no cargo, and a mere 45 men of the 248 who had set out on the adventure. Nevertheless, he and his companions earned the distinction of having been the first Netherlanders (and the fourth expedition, after Magellan-Elcano, Drake, and Cavendish) "to embrace the round waist of vast Mother Earth," to borrow a phrase from Samuel Purchas (Fig. 17).

The other Rotterdam company was organized by refugees from Spanish-occupied Antwerp. Their fleet of five ships sailed from Rotterdam in June 1598, under the command of Jacques Mahu, and after his death under that of Simon de Cordes.[4] It took almost five months of misadventure (April 6–September 4, 1599) to pass through the Strait of Magellan, and hardly had the fleet entered the Pacific Ocean when a severe storm scattered the ships. One ship, the *Geloof* (Faith) under Captain Sebald de Weert, was swept back into the Strait, and returned to Holland.[5] Another surrendered to the Spaniards at Valparaiso, Chile. A third reached the Indies, but fell into the hands of the Portuguese at Tidore. The other two ships boldly set sail for Japan. One of these, *De Liefde* (Charity) reached its destination, as will be seen later, but the *Hope* disappeared.

These voyages, in spite of the many disasters of "taking, drowning, firing, trechery and hostilitie" (Purchas), were valuable lessons to the Dutch. Their most significant contribution to general geographic knowledge was a new survey of the Strait of Magellan by Jan Outghersz, mate on board of Sebald de Weert's ship, which returned to Holland after spending nine months in the Strait (Plate 24, *facing page 149*). De Cordes and his officers had in their possession copies of a chart of the Strait made by Cavendish or one of his companions. They also had Plancius' world map of *ca.* 1593, which contains an inset chart of the Strait, mainly derived from Cavendish. The merit of Outghersz is that he drew, albeit crudely, the entire passage in considerable detail on a number of sketches. He depicted the elevations of the shores, noted the soundings, described special features, and alerted the reader to lurking dangers. This pictorial guide, consisting of the series of sketches and a brief text, was published in Amsterdam, presumably in 1600.[6] Wieder, who made an intensive study of this booklet, considers it likely that Outghersz composed a unified chart from his sketches, such as the one published in reduced form in de Bry's 1601 edition of the voyage, and/or the map in the Jodocus Hondius edition of the Mercator Atlas of 1606. At any rate, his observations on the Strait of Magellan remained for a long time the standard presentation. According to Wieder, neither Narbrough in 1670, nor the officers of the Spanish frigate *Santa Maria de la Cabeza* in 1788 surpassed Outghersz' work.[7]

The third and last Dutch expedition to make its way through the Strait of Magellan was a small fleet of the East India Company under command of Joris van Spilbergen.[8] The enterprise had a double purpose: first, to reiterate and demonstrate the Company's interest in this route in the face of demands for exploration rights by rival merchants (see Le Maire's voyage, below); secondly, to attack Spanish settlements and ships along the west coast of South America. In comparison with his Dutch predecessors, van Spilbergen passed through the Strait rather swiftly (thirty-four days), doubtless aided by Outghersz' pilot guide and the presence of some officers who had previous experience of this formidable passage. He entered the Pacific in May 1615, and followed the west coast northward as far as Acapulco, but failed in his goal to catch some richly laden Spanish galleons. After having forced the Spanish governor of Acapulco to be a generous host and provider of the fleet, the Hollanders set out across the ocean. On December 3 they saw the Islas de Revilla Gigedo (Isla San Benedicto and Isla Socorra), on December 4 Isla Roca Partida, and on December 6 another island (identified as Isla Clarión) "having five little hills, each of which appeared as if it were a separate islet."[9] From here they crossed the Pacific to Guam in seven weeks without meeting any land or making any other significant observations.

The value of van Spilbergen's account for the Pacific lies mainly in giving an outsider's view on the Spanish-controlled coast of Latin America. It also contains a detailed order of battle which van Spilbergen drew up in anticipation of Spanish attack —a most interesting document for the study of naval warfare in those days.

THE VOYAGE OF LE MAIRE AND SCHOUTEN AROUND CAPE HORN

When the Dutch East India Company was organized in 1602 it had obtained the exclusive rights, for twenty-one years, of exploration and trade east of the Cape of Good Hope "or through Magellan Strait." Apparently the framers of the clause had fully accepted the prevailing geographic concept of a single passage between South America and the great Terra Incognita. Actually, observations by several navigators had already suggested that there was an open sea south of Tierra del Fuego, but these experiences were ignored or rejected by the theorists at home. The significance of Le Maire and Schouten's voyage is above all that they purposefully searched for the new route, and found it in January 1616.[10]

The effort originated in the antagonism between the East India Company and Isaac Le Maire, father of the explorer. Isaac, who had been forced out of the Company, was bent on revenge and sought a loophole to evade the monopoly clause. Taking a second look at the nautical record in the Tierra del Fuego region from Magellan to Drake, he became virtually convinced that there was an open sea between the two oceans.[11] The name of the Company which Isaac founded in 1614 in Hoorn indicated the purpose of the venture: The Australian Company. After finding the new highway into the Pacific the expedition should search for Terra Australis and, if found, investigate its commercial potential. Since Isaac was too old to undertake such an adventure he placed his son Jacob, a young man of great talents, in charge of the two vessels that were to make the voyage. Captain of the ship *Eendracht* (Concord) was Willem Cornelisz Schouten, an experienced navigator. The other vessel, which was under command of a younger brother of Schouten, burned at Port Desire (Puerto Deseado), the last stopping place before rounding the continent.

From this point they set their course southeastward to the vicinity of the Falkland Islands, and then steered southwest in the hope of clearing the south point of the continent. To their dismay there loomed up before them the high coast of eastern Tierra del Fuego. Anxiously Le Maire and his companions followed this coast eastward, till suddenly there appeared a channel in which there ran a strong northerly current, and to the east of which there was another tract of land. On the 25th of January 1616 "we sailed with great joy through the royal passage, thanking God that He had given us what we had sought" (Plate 25, *following page 158*). The land to the east, which they thought to be part of a large land mass, was called Staten Land (Isla de los Estados). The passage itself was named after Jacob Le Maire. It was so full of whales that the ship had to maneuver with great caution to avoid collisions. On the 29th of January, after some delay because of a storm, "we saw land north northwest, very high and white with snow and saw two high mountains in the west. Surmising that there the high land terminated, since we could see the ends in clear weather, our President (Le Maire) called it Cape Hoorn in honor of the city of Hoorn; lying at latitude fifty seven degrees, forty eight minutes."[12]

Le Maire, having accomplished the first objective, now turned to the second: the discovery of the Southland. He knew of Quirós' voyage of 1606, when this navigator had sighted, as he thought, a part of the fabulous continent.[13] Following Quirós' description, Le Maire went north to latitude 15° S. and then set his course westward. In the middle of April the *Eendracht* skirted the Tuamotu Archipelago on its north side, meeting first Honden (Dogs) Eylandt (Pukapuka atoll), then Zonder Gront (Bottomless, Takaroa?), Waterlandt (Manihi?) and Vliegen (Flies) Eylandt (Rangiroa).[14] On this stretch the sea showed no long swells, from which they inferred that Terra Australis might be close. Some weeks later they came upon the northern Tonga group, among them some high islands which they named Cocos (Boscawen; native name: Tafahi), Verraders (Traitors; Keppel; Niuatoputapu), and Goede Hope (Good Hope, Niuafoo). The journals tell about the appearance of the local people, their canoes and foodstuffs (including pigs, fowl, bananas, coconuts, and "oubas" roots), but the contacts had been too fleeting for detailed descriptions.[15] A very different experience awaited the explorers at two high islands which they called the Hoornsche Eylanden, now known as the Îles des Horne or by their native names of Futuna and Alofi. Here they anchored in a bay of the former island and stayed for almost a fortnight. After some initial violence—the Hollanders were generous with beads, old nails, and knives, but opposed the natives pulling nails from the ship's hull and shirts from the line—friendship prevailed and there was much entertaining back and forth. Jacob Le Maire wrote down the vocabulary, as he had also done at Tafahi. Among the foodstuffs mentioned here were "calabassen en patattes." The men also observed the preparation of kava from "Acona" (Yanggona) roots.

After this idyllic interlude the *Eendracht* moved northwest. There had been an argument between Le Maire and Schouten. The former, eager to find Terra Australis, wanted to continue the westward course, but Schouten, who had never shown much faith in the existence of the Southland, feared to end up on the southside of New Guinea, from where it would be hard to extricate the ship under the prevailing winds, or so he thought. As skipper responsible for the ship, his judgment prevailed, much to the disappointment of Le Maire who had the real explorer's spirit. So the ship set course for the north coast of New Guinea. They passed north of the main row of the Solomons, seeing only clusters of islets. On June 25 they reached "a very high, beautiful land" which they thought to be New Guinea. Actually it was the east coast of New Ireland, and the Hollanders were the first Europeans to see this. Then they passed south of the Admiralty Islands, some of which had already been discovered by Saavedra in 1528, and reached the coast of New Guinea south of the mouth of the Sepik River. Following this shore they reached the Moluccas in September 1616. There is no need here to describe the unhappy aftermath: the arrest of officers and crew on Java by the East India Company, the death of the thirty-year-old Jacob Le Maire on the home voyage, the court squabbles over claims and counterclaims. As G. Arnold Wood has said, this voyage through the Pacific is memorable as the Dutch link between Quirós and Cook in the quest for Terra Australis.

The Nassau Fleet

The next Netherlands expedition to take the route around Cape Horn was the so-called Nassau fleet of ten ships under Jacques l'Hermite. The express purpose of the enterprise was to attack Spanish possessions on the west coast of South America, and in this respect it accomplished very little. On this voyage, however, it was observed that Cape Horn was actually part of an island group (1624). After leaving the coast of New Spain the fleet, now under command of Gheen Huyghen Schapenham, crossed the Pacific to the Marianas, and went from there to the Moluccas. At about latitude 10° N., in February 1625, they encountered two islands, the first one being Fais or Ulithi, the second Yap. Whether the Dutch can be considered the discoverers of Yap is a moot point.[16]

APPROACHES TO THE SOUTHLAND FROM THE NORTH

How and when Europeans gained their first knowledge of Australia remains the subject of controversy. To some scholars the addition of fragments of textual and cartographic reference amounts to virtual certainty that Australia was known, or even visited, by the Portuguese—or perhaps the French—in the sixteenth century. Others dismiss the construction as a house of cards supported by figments of imagination.[17] Leaving speculation aside we will turn to the well-documented explorations by Netherlanders of Terra Australis.[18]

At the time that the Hollanders started their own travels to Asia their knowledge of these distant lands was what Jan Huijghen van Linschoten had gathered in his *Itinerario* (1595–1596). Speaking of Java he said "of its breadth nothing is known up to now, since it has not yet been explored, nor is this known to the inhabitants themselves. Some suppose it to be a mainland, [forming part] of the land called Terra Incognita, which would extend hitherward from beyond the C. de Boa Esperança, but of this there is no certitude hitherto, so that it is usually accounted an island. . . ."

When the Dutch reached the Moluccas they questioned the inhabitants of Ceram and Banda (Pulau-pulau Banda) about the lands to the east and south. In the journal of the ship *Gelderlant* it is recorded under date of Banda, May 15, 1602: "They can say nothing certain respecting the island of Nova Guinea, but say that there are white people living on the southside, inhabited by Portuguese but [they of Ceram] had never seen any Portuguese ships. They can give no information about their dealings and commodities." To gain first-hand information the Dutch authorities in Bantam, Java, toward the end of 1605, sent out the pinnace *Duyfken* (also *Duifien*, little Dove), under command of Willem Jansz. The journal of this voyage is lost, but references to it in other documents give an idea of the main results. Above all, a map made during the enterprise by the subcargo Jan Lodewijs van Rosingijn, depicting the route, has fortunately been preserved.[19]

After visits to the Kei (Kepulauan Kai) and Aru islands (Kepulauan Aru) the ship reached the southwest coast of New Guinea at about latitude 5° S. and, early in 1606, sailed southeastward along this coast. The north point of Prinses Marianne Straat was thought to be an island and named Modder (Mud) Eylandt. After rounding "Tyuri" (the later Frederik Hendrik-Eiland, now Pulau Kolepom) the ship continued along the coast until about longitude 141° E. Here Jansz, perhaps discouraged by reefs and shoals, changed course to the southeast. After awhile he encountered land again—the eastern shore of the Gulf of Carpentaria, as it was later called— and followed it south till latitude 13°45' S. Here they turned north again, whence this point was marked as Cape Keerweer (Turnagain). The map of Rosingijn has several names on this stretch of the Cape York Peninsula. Still moving north they saw, and perhaps visited, 't Hooghe Eylandt (Prince of Wales Island), skirted the west side of Banks, Mulgrave, and Jervis islands, and reached again the coast of New Guinea, from where they went back to their base. Thus, the men of the *Duyfken* had crossed the very entrance to the strait between New Guinea and Australia and had seen part of the Southland without realizing that it was a separate land. By coincidence—and with a touch of historic irony—Torres passed through the strait a few months later, but did not realize that he was in a passage, and that to the south of it lay Terra Australis.

Rosingijn's map left open the possibility of the existence of a strait. The accomplishment of Torres did not become public knowledge until 1762, although rumors of some such voyage may have reached the Dutch.[20] In subsequent years there were deliberations on further exploration, in particular after Dutch ships had sighted the west coast of Australia in 1616 and following years (see below). Finally, in 1623, two small vessels were dispatched from Amboina. The *Pera* was under command of Jan Carstensz, the *Arnhem* under that of Willem J. van Colster (or van Coolsteerdt). Only the journal of Carstensz remains. Sailing east along the south coast of New Guinea, Carstensz observed inland, when at about latitude 5° S., "a very high mountain range in many places white with snow, which we thought a very singular sight, being so near the line equinoctial." They slowly made their way eastward, taking soundings and naming various points along the coast.[21] They tried to make contacts with the Papuans, but were met with suspicion if not outright hostility. Even so, Carstensz' journal contains interesting remarks on their appearance ("curly hair, like the Caffres"), their boats and weapons.

When the Dutch reached the west entrance of Torres Strait they got trapped in the shoals. They extricated themselves by taking advantage of the westward ebbing

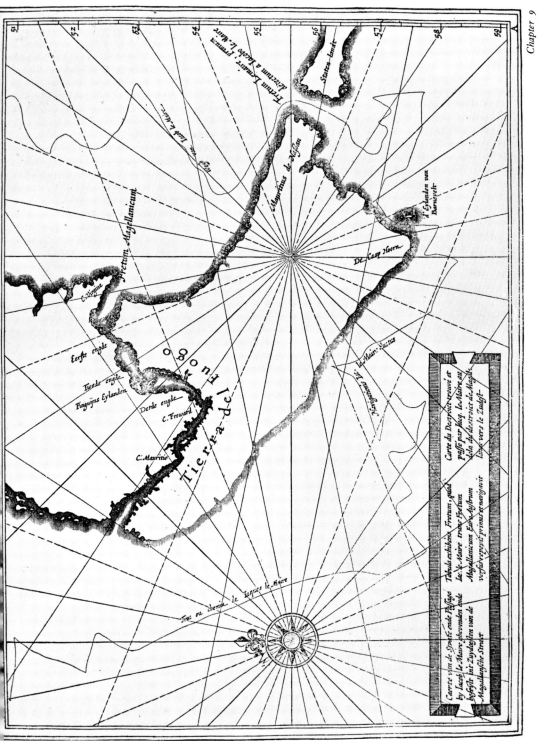

The route of Jacob Le Maire, according to his journal, around Tierra del Fuego, through the strait ("Fretum Lemaire"), and past Cape Horn in January 1616 [see Note 10, W. A. Engelbrecht and P. J. van Herwerden (eds.): op. p. 38]. (Courtesy of the Linschoten Vereeniging.)

PLATE 25

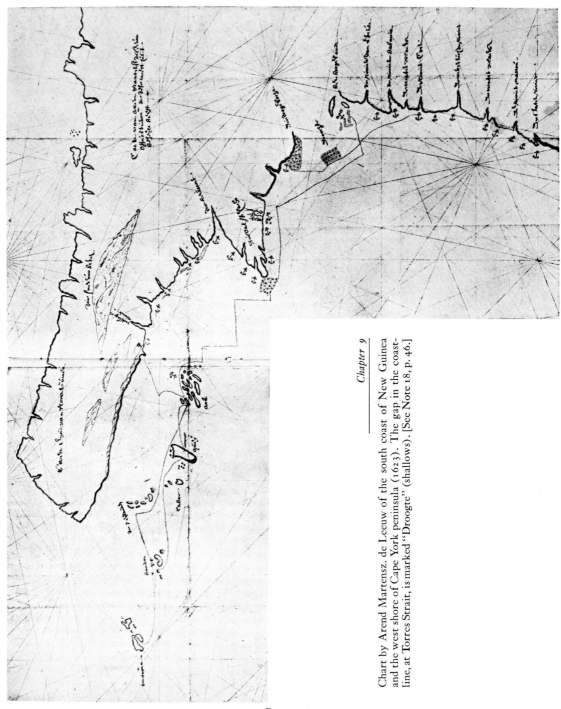

Chapter 9

Chart by Arend Martensz. de Leeuw of the south coast of New Guinea and the west shore of Cape York peninsula (1623). The gap in the coast-line, at Torres Strait, is marked "Droogte" (shallows). [See Note 18, p. 46.]

PLATE 26

of the tide and, having reached open water again, set course to the south. On this experience Carstensz writes under date of March 31, 1623:

> After hearing the aforesaid reports [from boats sent out to reconnoiter] of the shallows sounded to the eastward, we are sufficiently assured that it will prove impossible any longer to follow the coastline which we have so long skirted in an eastward direction, and that we shall, to our great regret, be compelled to return the same way we have come, seeing that we have been caught in the shallows as in a trap; . . . we were here in 9°6′ S. Lat., about 125 miles east of Aru, and according to the chart we had with us and the estimation of the skippers and steersmen, no more than 2 miles from Nova Guinea, so that the space between us and Nova Guinea seems to be a bight to which on account of its shallows we have given the name of shallow bight ("drooge bocht") in the new chart. . . .[22]

On April 12th they reached, like their predecessors, the west shore of Cape York Peninsula, but they followed it further south, to latitude 17°8′ S. according to their reckoning (Plate 26, *facing this page*). The most southern river they saw was named Staten Rivier. This may not have been the river that bears this name on modern maps, but the Gilbert River instead. On the 18th of April they encountered the first aborigines. Since Carstensz' notes give the first extant account of these people it is worth quoting some of the observations:

> . . . these blacks showed no fear and were so bold as to touch the muskets of our men and to try to take the same off their shoulders. . . . These natives are coal-black, with lean bodies and stark naked, having twisted baskets or nets round their heads; in head and figure they are like the blacks of the Coromandel coast. . . .

This first encounter was marred by the Dutch boatmen carrying off one of the Australians as a sample to take home. From then on they met hostility everywhere, which prevented them from going inland. But what they saw from the shoreline did not look inviting:

> The land appeared very dry and barren . . . we have not seen one fruit-bearing tree, nor anything that man could make use of; there are no mountains or even hills, so that it may be safely concluded that the land contains no metals, nor yields any precious woods. . . . In our judgment this is the most arid and barren region that could be found anywhere on the earth; the inhabitants, too, are the most wretched and poorest creatures that I have ever seen in my age or time. . . .

From the Staten Rivier the *Pera* returned to Amboina by much the same route as she had come. Skipper van Colster of the *Arnhem* took a more direct route back and sighted a section of the land bulge on the west side of the Gulf of Carpentaria, which became known as Arnhem Land. Some Dutch documents mention van der Lijns or van Speults land. These may refer to Groote Eylandt in the Gulf of Carpentaria, which lies fairly well on the route the *Arnhem* must have taken.

DISCOVERY OF THE WEST COAST OF AUSTRALIA

Initially, Dutch ships crossing the Indian Ocean followed the Portuguese sea route to India, sailing past Madagascar before aiming for Java. There were many perils along this route, however, and prevailing winds and currents made it a slow voyage. In 1611 Hendrik Brouwer, commander of an Indies-bound fleet, decided to try a more southern route to take advantage of the westerlies. He sailed straight east along the 36th parallel until he had gone far enough to catch the Southeast Trades for a northerly course to Java. The route, although somewhat longer, proved to be much faster. From 1613 onward this course (or even further south along latitude 40° S.) was apparently followed by many ships, and soon was officially authorized as the prescribed sailing route.

In an age when the determination of longitude was still very inadequate it was bound to happen that a ship would continue its course too far eastward and unexpectedly come upon the Australian coast.[23] The first vessel to do so was the *Eendracht* under Dirck Hartogs, which, in October 1616, encountered some offshore islands in latitude 26° S. The one behind which Hartogs anchored still carries the name of its first European visitor. The officers recorded their discovery on a flattened pewter dish which they nailed to a pole on the northwest end of the island (Cape Inscription on modern maps).[24] The coastal area at this latitude, later to include much of the southern west coast, became known as Eendrachtsland; it kept that name until well into the nineteenth century. In the framework of this book it will suffice to review only briefly further discoveries along this coast. In 1618 the *Seewolff* and the *Mauritius*, on separate voyages, came upon the coast at about 21 to 22 degrees. In 1619 the *Dordrecht* and the *Amsterdam*, under command of Frederik de Houtman and supercargo Jacob Dedel reached "Zuytland Beach" (Southland Beach, an echo of Marco Polo's nomenclature) at *ca.* latitude 33° S. Surf and heavy seas forced them to seek the open sea, but as the ships moved north the sailors repeatedly sighted stretches of land as far as 26 degrees. The "Houtman Rocks" and "Dedelsland" were their contributions to the cartography of Australia. The name of the ship *Leeuwin* (Lioness) remains attached to the southwest cape of Australia, which was sighted from this ship in 1622. Another ship, in 1627, sailed much farther east before going north, and struck the south coast in the Great Australian Bight, which it then followed eastward for some distance. The coast as well as an island group at longitude 133°30′ E. were named for Pieter Nuijts, a high functionary of the Company who traveled on this ship.[25]

All these discoveries on the west and south coasts had been accidental and piecemeal, thus leaving unanswered many questions regarding size and shape of the Southland as well as its commercial value. The Directors of the East India Company had from time to time suggested expeditions to solve these questions. It remained for Governor-General Antonio van Diemen (1636–1645), a man with genuine interest in exploration, to carry out these wishes. The instructions for the various expeditions sent out during his administration have been preserved. They contain valuable references to earlier ventures, present the contemporary image of the "Southern Regions," suggest routes, spell out the nautical, geographic, ethnographic, and commercial data to be gathered, and prescribe the conduct of the crews in the lands to be discovered.[26]

In 1636 van Diemen sent Pieter Pietersz with the *Cleen* (that is, small) *Amsterdam*, and *Wesel* to investigate the northwest side of the Southland. Pietersz sighted the present Melville Island, but thought it to be part of the mainland, and called it Van Diemensland. He also saw Dundas Strait, but considered it a bay rather than a sea channel. He sailed westward along Melville Island and called its northwest point

Roode Hoeck (Red Hook), the present Cape Van Diemen. From here on the land stretched to the southwest, but since the wind came from that direction the skipper saw little use in further effort and returned to Timor.

THE EXPLORATIONS BY TASMAN AND VISSCHER[27]

In planning his second expedition the Governor-General asked the advice of Franchoys Jacobsz, alias Visscher, a pilot-major with wide experience in east Asia and highly regarded for his hydrographic surveys and pilot guides. Visscher developed a project that went well beyond the direct interests of the East India Company, outlining in bold strokes the various routes that not only would determine what lands lay east and south of the East Indies, but also would solve the mystery for all other parts of the southern hemisphere, "whether it be land, sea or icebergs, whatever God has ordained."[28] If this well-conceived series of voyages had been carried out in its entirety it would have settled the question of the southern continent more than a century before Cook.

Van Diemen selected the first part of the proposals: the expedition was to use the island of Mauritius as the staging point for a voyage in search of the Southland as far south as latitude 52° or even 54° S. If no land were found, the ships should sail east until they reached the longitude of the Solomons or New Guinea's east end, and then turn north. Van Diemen wanted to know if there was a good passage from the Indian Ocean to the Pacific Ocean because he had an eye on the coast of Chile— neglected by Spain—as a potential trade area for the Company. The expedition should return to Batavia along the north side of New Guinea. As an alternate route van Diemen suggested that the ships might go east only as far as the longitude of Van Nuyts Islands (Nuyts Archipelago), about the limit of the known south coast, and then go north to find the east coast of the continent. Although official opinion now inclined to the view that New Guinea was connected with the Southland, this alternate route might settle the matter.[29]

Although van Diemen had relied primarily on the scientific competence of Visscher for planning the expedition, he appointed Abel Janszoon Tasman its commander, probably because of the latter's experience as captain and his executive abilities. Visscher became the chief pilot. Both of them sailed on the *Heemskerck;* the other ship was the *Zeehaen* under skipper Gerrit Jansz. The ships had provisions for twelve months, "and rice for eighteen months"; also a cargo of everything that might be useful to win friends and influence savages, from Coromandel cottons and Chinese silks to knives, needles, mirrors, combs, tinsel, and nutmeg.[30]

The ships left Batavia August 14, 1642, for Mauritius. From here, on October 8, Tasman sailed south, but, as the vessels approached latitude 50° S., the continuous storms made them retreat to 44 degrees, from where they followed an eastward course. This they maintained well beyond the longitude of the Nuyts Archipelago, although they drifted gradually north to 42 degrees. Thus the explorers had followed neither of the alternate routes laid down in the Instruction. However, luck was with them, because it led them to the landfall of Tasmania. They sighted its southwest coast on November 24; it was "a very high country" with three lofty mountains to the ESE and two lesser ones to the NE. The latter were named Mt. Heemskerck

(Mount Heemskirk) and Mt. Zeehaan (Mount Zeehan) by Flinders on his circum-navigation of Tasmania in 1798. Tasman was not aware of its island nature and named it Anthony van Diemen's Land. The ships rounded the south point and moved north along the east coast, naming various islets in honor of members of the East India Council.[31] They went briefly on shore on the southeast coast and although they saw signs of human occupation they met no one. The strong northwesterly winds discouraged Tasman from following the coast where it bends in that direction, and he decided to turn east. From December 5 to 13 the ships crossed what is now called the Tasman Sea. Then, in about latitude 42° S., they saw "a large land of high eleva-tion." This was the range of the Southern Alps of New Zealand; their landfall was a bit southwest from the present Cape Foulwind. The ships followed the coast north-ward, rounded the northwest point of South Island (Cape Farewell, as Cook called it) and anchored in a fine bay. Regarding this second discovery Tasman noted on the 19th of December, 1642: "We have given this land the name of Staten Land . . . since it could well be that this land is connected with the Staten Land [of Le Maire] but this is not certain. It seems a very beautiful country, and we trust this to be the coast of the unknown Southland."[32]

Here they saw the first inhabitants: "their color was between brown and yellow, with black hair tied in a top knot, in which there is a large white feather; their ves-sels consisted of two long narrow prahus over which were laid some boards." The attempt to make peaceful contact failed miserably. Several Maori canoes attacked a small boat and killed four Dutch sailors (Plate 27, *following page 164*). The ship council sadly concluded that they could not befriend these folk, called the spot Moordenaars' Bay (Massacre, now Golden Bay), and ordered the anchor to be lifted.[33]

Since Tasman had taken Cape Farewell to be land's end, one might have thought that he would pursue the coast eastward beyond this point for some distance; had he done so he would have found the strait between North Island and South Island. Tasman did explore this area and began to suspect a sea strait, all the more so when he observed the strong tidal current from the south. However, unfavorable winds and high seas caused him to abandon the search and turn northwestward when he was only six miles from the entrance of the channel. It is puzzling that Tasman's map shows an enclosed bay (Zeehaans Bocht) although observations had not proven the existence of a coastline; Visscher stayed closer to the truth and left on his map a gap in the coastline where later it indeed proved to be.[34]

The voyage now continued along the west coast of North Island. On January 4, 1643, they saw a cape (the northwest tip of the island) which they called Cabo Marija van Diemen. The next day they visited a small island which appropriately re-ceived the name of Drie Coninghen (Three Kings) Island; both names still are in use today. At this point it was decided to make a wide swing east, but the trade winds pushed the ships northward, to the Tonga group. First they saw little Pijlstaert (Ata) and then some larger ones, among them Middelburg (Eua), Amsterdam (Tongatapu), and Rotterdam (Nomuka). They stopped at the latter two islands for some ten days because of the friendly reception. The account of the visit provides the first information on life on the Tonga Islands.

The ships went north to latitude 14°40′ S., at which point the course was set to the west. Thus they remained south of Le Maire's Hoorn Island (Îles des Horne), which they had hoped to find; instead, they came upon the east coast of Vanua Levu in the Fiji group. They thought it to be an island cluster and called it the Prins Willem Islands. Their ships were in great danger among the reefs, and to escape these perils, and also to avoid striking the east coast of New Guinea (where, according to Visscher, the winds might drive them onshore), the course was set northwest. After a slow voyage they reached some islets inside a reef which they dubbed Onthong Java, the present Ontong Java islands (or Lord Howe Islands). From here the expedition followed approximately the route of Le Maire.

Tasman's instructions had ordered him to look for a passage between New Guinea and the Southland. Thus, when he had passed New Ireland and New Hanover (which he conceived to be the north coast of New Guinea), he was intrigued by the sea that opened up to the south. He sailed in that direction (hoping to reach Cape Keerweer in the Gulf of Carpentaria) until he sighted the north coast of New Britain, which convinced him that he was in a landlocked bay. Sailing northwestward he passed within a few miles of the strait between New Britain and New Guinea, later to be called in honor of Dampier, its discoverer. From here the ships followed the actual coast of New Guinea, but well offshore. They passed the Schouten islands and Waigeo island on the north side, thus missing their chance to find Geelvink Bay (Teluk Sarera) as well as the other Dampier strait. By this time of the year (June), because of the southeast monsoon, it was too late to attempt a new search in the Gulf of Carpentaria so they went on to Batavia, where they arrived on the 15th of June 1643.

Governor-General van Diemen and his Council received the report with mixed feelings. True, Tasman had sighted some new lands and had safely brought back his ships from a perilous voyage on which only ten men had died from illness in addition to the four massacred in New Zealand. However, the question of a strait or no strait between New Guinea and the Southland was still not answered. By not going far enough southward Tasman had left open the problem of whether another landmass existed in the higher latitudes, nor had he gained definite proof of a sea route across the southern Pacific to Chile. Furthermore, they were of the opinion that the explorers had not shown much perseverance in investigating the nature and opportunities of those lands which they actually had discovered, "leaving in the main everything open for a more curious successor."[35]

Although van Diemen obviously had some reservations about Tasman's qualities as an explorer, he appointed him early in 1644 as commander of a new expedition to the Gulf of Carpentaria for the purpose of searching once more for a passage.[36] Visscher was to accompany Tasman again, now as pilot-major as well as skipper of the yacht Limmen. Together with the Zeemeeuw (Sea Gull) and the "quel" (or galiot) Bracq, they left Batavia the 29th of January 1644, and proceeded to New Guinea's south coast, which they followed to approximately the present Indonesian-Australian boundary. Now came the critical stretch where the answer had to be found regarding the presence or absence of a strait. Since Tasman's journal is lost, it is not known what circumstances or motives guided his course. Apparently he went south across the western entrance of Torres Strait to the north tip of the Cape York Peninsula, probably where the Jardine River flows into Endeavour Strait. For the

164 THE PACIFIC BASIN

third time the strait was missed.[37] The little fleet sailed past Carstensz' point of return to the very end of the Gulf of Carpentaria, and thus established that here was no sea passage to the south.[38] A number of rivers and "capes" (actually offshore islands) were sighted, named and charted. Some of these names survive, such as Cape Van Diemen on Mornington Island, Vanderlin (from Dutch van der Lijn) and Maria islands, with the Limmen Bight near the latter. Along the north coast of Australia Tasman entered the sea strait between Melville Island and the mainland (now Dundas Strait) but mistook it for an enclosed bay, and called it Van Diemens Bay. The voyage extended southwestward to about latitude 23°30' S. and thus closed the gap between the known coasts of north and west Australia.[39] It was, however, only a generalized sketch, because Tasman remained too far offshore to observe the many river mouths and the insular character of the coast. From here the ships returned home.

Understandably, the managers of the Company in Batavia were disappointed. No sea strait had been found, nor its absence fully substantiated, nor had any riches been discovered—"only poor naked beach runners." However, as they hastened to point out to the Directors in Holland, Tasman had circumnavigated on his two voyages the great and so far unknown Southland, stretching from latitude 43° (Van Diemen's Land, now Tasmania) to 2½° S. (the north coast of New Guinea). Surely, they went on, such a vast land must contain profitable resources. And the Directors could rest assured that all this would be explored in good time "by more vigilant and more courageous persons than have been used so far. Exploration is not everyone's business."[40]

To a later generation, viewing Tasman's accomplishments in the perspective of time, the judgment by his superiors seems harsh. However, their opinions were not wholly unjustified. Repeatedly Tasman quickly backed off from spots where pertinent information might have been obtained with more perseverance: the island nature of Tasmania, Cook Strait, the shape of New Zealand, the two Dampier straits, Torres and Dundas straits, to mention the most critical places. Posthumus Meyjes advances two reasons for the course of events,[41] one being the broad-hull construction of Dutch ships at the time. The broad hull gave them great buoyancy, and this made them an easy prey of winds and waves. Sailing against the wind was very difficult, and sailing before the wind toward an unknown coast was perilous because the vessel might be swept on shore. The other reason lay in Tasman's personality. He was an excellent sailor, but not an ardent explorer. Rather than take chances, or delay the voyage by poking into narrow waters, Tasman played it safe. In spite of whatever shortcomings one may detect, he and his chief, van Diemen, belong to the group of men who defined the shape of the Pacific. The Southland which Tasman had helped to discover was at first called "Compagnies Nieuw-Nederlandt," but soon received the name of Hollandia Nova or Nieuw Holland. His name of Statenland was changed to Nieuw Zeeland, apparently because Hendrik Brouwer in 1643 had established that Le Maire's Statenland was not part of a great southern continent.[42]

THE VOYAGE OF JACOB ROGGEVEEN, 1721–1722[43]

Nothing came of further Southland expeditions by the East India Company, although the hope of finding Terra Incognita lived on. The mathematician-geographer

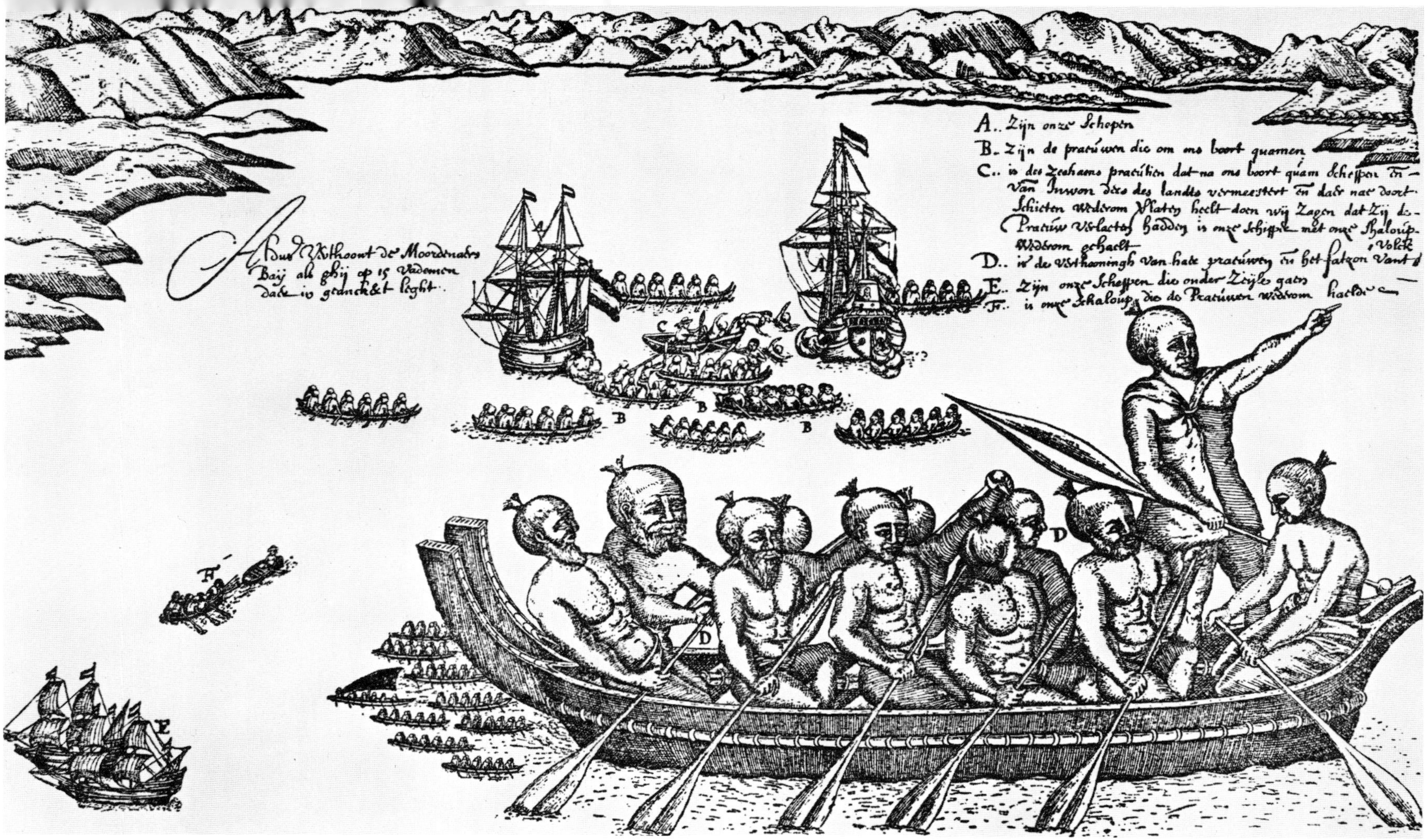

Sketch of the events at Massacre Bay, New Zealand, where Maoris attacked a sloop of the Tasman expedition in December 1642 [see Note 27, R. Post-humus Meyjes (ed.): p. 47]. (Courtesy of the Linschoten Vereeniging.)

PLATE 27

PLATE 28

Chapter 11

"Icy Bay and Mount St. Elias [Alaska]," in Gilbert Chinard: *Le voyage de La Pérouse sur les cotes de l'Alaska et de la Californie (1786)*, Baltimore, 1937, 144 pp. illus. op. p. 6. (Courtesy of the Institut Français de Washington). Icy Bay, an arm of the Gulf of Alaska, is some seventy miles west-northwest of

Arend Roggeveen made plans, in 1671, for a new search, quite independent from either the East or the West India Company.[44] Nothing came of this, but his son Jacob revived the project. The West India Company, fearing that rivals in France, England, and the Southern (Austrian) Netherlands might pre-empt new lands in the southern Pacific, listened to his plans and made available three ships for an exploration of the South Seas, the *Arend* (Eagle), the *Tienhoven*, and the *Afrikaansche Galei*. They left Holland on August 1, 1721, rounded Cape Horn on January 14, 1722, and reached Islas Juan Fernández (latitude 33° 52' S.) on February 25. Following their instructions they now set their course WNW until 27 degrees, which latitude they were to follow for some distance. The reason for this was to investigate the report of the buccaneer Edward Davis who, in 1687, had seen in this latitude a small sandy island and to the west of it "a long tract of pretty high land, tending away toward the North-West out of sight. This might probably be the coast of Terra Australis incognita."[45]

Sailing along this parallel they sighted on Easter Day (Paaschdag), the 5th of April, a low island which they thought at first to be the small island Davis had encountered. They soon realized that they were in error. It was not sandy, not really small, and, having several hills, could hardly be called flat. They checked this further afterwards by sailing some distance west without finding any "high land." Thus they felt sure that they were the first European visitors to this place, which they called in honor of the day Paasch Eylandt (Easter Island).

For the first days the initiative for making contact was left to the inhabitants, who came on reed bundles and in small canoes and swarmed over the ships with the greatest curiosity. They appropriated everything that their hands could grasp, from the sailors' caps to the captain's tablecloth, and jumped joyfully overboard with their loot. A few days later 134 Hollanders landed with great show, for a formal visit. They were only one day on the island, and the landing was marred by the shooting of some natives by nervous, trigger-happy sailors. Considering the circumstances the amount of information gathered is quite remarkable, even though sketchy. In the journal we read about the canoes, made of small pieces of driftwood, the low long houses like upside-down kayaks and the crops (including sugar cane, bananas, coconuts, "ubas roots" and/or yams).[46] Chickens are mentioned as the only domesticates. Bark cloth and body decoration are described as well as the preparation of food in pits with hot stones. Of special interest are the remarks on the now well-known statues. The Dutch first could not understand how these people, without any heavy timber or strong ropes, could have constructed the gear to erect these large monoliths, "but the amazement ceased with the discovery, on removing a piece of stone, that they were formed out of clay or some kind of rich earth, and that small smooth pebbles had been stuck into the surface, which, placed closely and neatly together, made it look like a human figure; . . . all statues were shaped as if a long robe was draped from neck to foot. They have on the head a basket piled full of cobbles painted white."[47] Unless the statue he had examined was an exception, Roggeveen had raised the right question but found the wrong answer, because the statues are commonly made from volcanic rock. His baskets with white stones are also puzzling. Later observations always speak of cylinders, crowns or wigs, of red stone.

After this adventure the expedition sailed WNW to get on the track of Le Maire

and Schouten. On their voyage along the northern edge of the Tuamotu Archipelago
these earlier explorers had observed that no swell came from the south, which they
had interpreted as a possible indication of a large land in that direction. Roggeveen
failed to find Le Maire's Honden Eylandt (Pukapuka), but did sight some of the
other islands in this group. By now, June 3, they concluded that the calm sea was
caused by the presence of the archipelago. Next, on June 6, they came upon what
they mistook for Cocos and Verraders islands of Le Maire (actually some 20 degrees
further west) and thus gave no names. These were Bora-Bora and Maupiti, and
Roggeveen was probably the first to note them. A week later they saw, beyond a
low little island (Vuyle—that is, Foul, because of rocks—the present Rose Island)
a high, well-forested bigger island. They had reached the Samoa Islands, which they
named, in honor of the captain of the *Tienhoven*, the Boumans Eylanden. They also
sighted Tau, Tutuila, Upolu, and several lesser isles, and must have passed Savai'i
in the night. The crew, suffering severely from scurvy, needed fresh vegetables,
fruits and water, but the ships could find no anchorage and so the voyage continued.
The course now was set to the northwest, so as to reach the East Indies around New
Guinea. This latter part of the trip was miserable because of disease and death stalk-
ing the ships. It yielded no discoveries.[48]

EXPLORATIONS IN THE NORTH PACIFIC

The first Hollander to visit Japan was Dirck Gerritsz (Pomp, alias China), who
made two journeys to that country from Goa, where he served in the Portuguese
establishment. His second trip, especially, when he spent eight months of 1585–1586
in Japan, gave him a good opportunity for observation. After his return to Holland
in 1590, a summary of his experiences was published in L.Jz. Waghenaer's *Tresoor
der Zeevaert* . . . (Leiden, 1592). A more elaborate account of Japan appeared in van
Linschoten's *Itinerario* . . . (Amsterdam, 1595), based for a good deal on what this
author had heard from his friend Dirck Gerritsz when both were in Goa.[49]

The first Dutch ship to reach Japan was the *Liefde* of the ill-fated Mahu and de
Cordes expedition.[50] The organizers of this voyage, when planning the route through
the Strait of Magellan, had in mind to exchange the merchandise for silver in Chile
or Péru, and then to sail to the Moluccas to buy spices. If no business deal could be
made in South America the ships should go to Japan, also famous for its silver, and
from there to the Moluccas. For the latter eventuality they engaged Dirck Gerritsz.
He came no farther than Valparaiso, but two ships, the *Hope* and the *Liefde*, set out
from the Chilean coast for Japan. Only fragments of the crossing are known. At
latitude 16° N. they saw islands, and eight men made off in a sloop.[51] No longitude
is given for this event. At latitude 27° or 28° the *Hope* disappeared in a storm.
Finally the *Liefde* with its exhausted survivors reached land in Beppu-wan on the
northeast coast of Kyushu. The men were allowed to stay in the country, and some
of them were to serve as valuable intermediaries in 1609 when the Dutch East India
Company sent a delegation to Japan to initiate commerce with the Empire.

There is a footnote to the story of the eight men who deserted near some islands
"at 16° N. Lat." In 1922 Bishop Restarick, in Hawaii, told of a native tradition

which relates that, long before Cook, seven men arrived at Kealakekua Bay "in a painted boat with an awning over the stern." They were all dressed "in white or yellow" and one of them had a sword. These men remained in Hawaii, married local women, and were made chiefs. Bishop Restarick linked this account to the (eight, not seven) men who jumped ship. There is no need to give his further arguments in support of this thesis. It is an intriguing story which probably never can be proven one way or another.[52]

VOYAGES NORTH AND EAST OF JAPAN

As the survivors of the *Liefde* settled down to business in Japan they must have heard rumors of the Silver and Gold islands which were thought to lie in the ocean somewhere east of Japan. The arrival of Vizcaino in 1611 to undertake a search for Rica de Plata and Rica de Oro brought the matter to general attention. It was, however, not until 1635 that Willem Versteghen, subcargo of the East India Company in Nagasaki, made a formal proposal to look for the fabled islands.

The Governor-General and Council took the matter under study. Plans ripened to combine the search for these islands with exploration of the coasts of Tartary and Korea. On June 1, 1639, they drew up the instructions for the voyage.[53] The preamble says: "Experience has taught that the principal and richest treasures of the earth are found under the latitude of 31, 32 to 40 and 42 degrees, of which the rich silver, gold and copper mines of northern Japan are living examples. Thus, the discovery of the islands east of Japan, lying in the same zone, will bring the East India Company not only respect and honor, but to all appearance great benefits." The expedition, consisting of two ships, the *Engel* and the *Graft* (also called *Graff* or *Gracht*) had Mathijs Hendricksz Quast as commander. One of the captains serving under him was Abel Tasman, in charge of the *Graft*. The ships sailed from Batavia through the South China Sea, rounded the north end of Luzón to about latitude 16° N. and then sailed eastward into the Pacific. After a few days they set the course NE, which brought them to the Volcano and Bonin islands. First they sighted, on July 20, 1639, "a very high and steep island," which they named Hooge Meeuwen (High Gull) Eylandt. This may have been either Arzobispo or Alessundio, among the northern Volcano Islands. The next day they saw two more hilly islands which they named Engel (Angel) and Graft. These have been identified, respectively, as Bayly or Coffin Island (Haha-jima) in the southern, and Peel (Chichi-shima) in the central Bonins. While it is possible that Spanish seamen had seen some of these islands a century earlier, the Dutch report is the first well-documented account.[54]

The further voyage yielded no results. First a thrust was made eastward at the thirtieth parallel as far as longitude 157° E. Then the ships turned northwest to within sight of the coast of Honshu, and set out again for a long cruise eastward along latitude 37½° N. as far as longitude 175° W. The return was along the 40th parallel and to the north of it. Widespread illness on board made it unwise to undertake exploration of the mainland coast, and so the vessels sailed along the east coast of Japan to Formosa, where they arrived at the Company's base in November 1639.

Governor-General van Diemen was not the man to abandon unfinished business.

In 1643 Maarten Gerritsz Vries (also de Vries) was sent out with two small ships —the *Castricum* and the *Breskens*—to investigate the coasts of Tartary and make another search for the fabled islands.[55] Vries, on the *Castricum*, lost contact with the *Breskens* and, after waiting at the agreed rendezvous at the north tip of Hokkaido, went on alone. Much of the voyage was shrouded in fog. Vries saw Ostrov Iturup, in the Kurils, which he called Staten Eylandt. He sailed through the strait between this island and the one to the north of it (Ostrov Urup), but mistook the latter to be part of the mainland of North America. Taking possession of it for the East India Company he called it Compagnies Landt. Passing through the strait, which received his name, Vries came into the Sea of Okhotsk and continued to about latitude 48° N., where strong winds pushed him back to the north coast of Hokkaido. From here he set out again into the Sea of Okhotsk, and reached the east coast of Sakhalin which he reconnoitered as far as latitude 49° N. He observed the eastern point of the island and called it Cape Patientie (Mys Terpeniya). He then went back to the coast of Japan and sailed some distance east to find Rica de Oro, in which he failed, of course, as had all his precursors. This was the last attempt of the Dutch to find the treasure islands. Although the search had failed in its primary purpose, the voyages had yielded new geographic knowledge of the little-known northern Pacific.

KOREA

"A little above Japan . . . not far from the Coast of China lies another great Island, called Insula de Core of which till so far there is no certain knowledge regarding size, people and products." Thus wrote van Linschoten in his *Itinerario*. Dutch maps of the middle of the seventeenth century still showed Korea as an island. What little the Europeans knew they heard from the Japanese who, in 1592, had forced the Koreans to accept a trading post at Fusan (Pusan). Any foreign ship that approached Korea's shores was forcibly driven off. Shipwrecked sailors were not allowed to leave the country. Under these circumstances the experience of Dutch survivors of a shipwreck, who lived thirteen years in Korea and escaped to tell the tale, deserves mention.[56]

The yacht *Sperwer*, on its way from Formosa to Nagasaki, lost its way and, in August 1653, ran ashore on Cheju-do, or Quelpart Island, south of Korea. The thirty-six survivors were taken to Seoul, and later moved to other parts of the country. In 1666 eight of them succeeded in escaping to Japan and joining the Dutch colony in Deshima. Among them was the bookkeeper (subcargo) Hendrik Hamel who, while in Deshima, wrote down their experiences. His account, soon published in several European languages, gave the West its first direct knowledge of Korea's government, social institutions, and way of life.

Quelpart Island (Saishuto), where the *Sperwer* ran ashore, had received from the Portuguese the epithet of Ilha de Ladrones, but was also known by the Chinese name of Fungma. In the 1640s the name Quelpaert came in use among Dutch navigators and gained popularity after publication of Hamel's story. Hamel writes that, after the shipwreck, the pilot made his observations and "found that the Quelpaerts Island lies on 33 degrees 32 minutes." In other words, the pilot knew the island by name, but now checked its position. B. Hoetink, who edited Hamel's account for the Linschoten Society, proved that the appellation was in use in 1648. Why the island received that name remains uncertain.[57] "Quel" or "quelpaert" was another term for a galiot, a fast light-draft packet or dispatch vessel. The first ship of this type, the *Quel de Brack* arrived in the Indies in 1640, and was here simply referred to as "the Quelpaert," or even as "galiot 't Quelpaert." In 1642 it made a trip from Formosa to Japan, the only visit by a quel to these waters. Nothing is known of an incident that might explain the tacking of its name to the island. The term Quelpaert is fading from modern maps as unobtrusively as it once appeared. A minor matter, to be sure, but like so many other names it is a symbol of the passing of the European era in the western Pacific.

GEOGRAPHICAL EXPLORATION BY THE RUSSIANS

Dimitri M. Lebedev and Vadim I. Grekov*

THE SEVENTEENTH CENTURY

Exploration of eastern Asia by the Russians was extended to the Pacific coast during the late thirties and early forties of the seventeenth century.[1] This was a consequence of a mass eastward movement beyond the Ural Mountains, mainly in a search for new lands and greater amounts of fur, and resulted in the addition of vast territories of Siberia and the Far East to Russia. In the sphere of geography it led to most important discoveries and research both in the interior areas of northeastern Asia and along its seacoasts, despite the extremely difficult conditions of this unexplored country.[2]

The leaders of the exploring parties sometimes were given very detailed instruction on the nature and population of the places visited, and maps. The primitive hand-made sketch maps were compiled without the benefit of scientific methods. Numerous geographical features plotted on these maps served as a basis for several general maps of Siberia that are of outstanding importance in the history of the cartography of northeastern Asia.

Initial Exploration of Northeastern Asia

The first Russian to reach the coast of the Pacific Ocean was Cossack I. Y. Moscvitin. With his detachment he left the Aldan River in 1639 and traveled down the Ul'ya River to the Sea of Okhotsk. Later the Cossacks sailed for about two years along its coasts to the Okhota River in the north and beyond the Aldoma River in the south, and, apparently, sailed close to the mouth of the Amur River or obtained information about it. Moscvitin was the first to submit data, partly based on inquiries, regarding the rivers, coasts, and population of this vast area.[3] V. Poiarkov's near-shore sailings in 1645–1646 from the mouth of the Amur up to the Ul'ya, as well as other sources obtained in the 1640s, provided information on the entire western coast of the Sea of Okhotsk and adjacent regions.

During this period a historic voyage was made in the extreme northeastern part of Asia by Fedot Alexeev and Semen Dezhnev (Fig. 18), who sailed eastwards from the mouth of the Kolyma in the summer of 1648. The group consisted of ninety men on several small ships (kochas), the majority of whom either perished or disappeared. The ships commanded by Alexeev and Dezhnev, however, rounded East Cape and they were the first Europeans to pass through and actually discover Bering Strait. Very soon the two ships lost sight of each other. Alexeev subsequently reached Kamchatka but his further fate is not clear.[4] Dezhnev, with his companions, passed the Diomede Islands and landed south of Anadyr' River. His communication about

---

*Professors Lebedev and Grekov are staff members of the Institute of Geography, The Academy of Sciences, Moscow, USSR.

his voyage was lost in the archives until it was discovered in the eighteenth century by Gerhard F. Müller.[5] Nevertheless, word about his exploits was common knowledge in Siberia and found its way into western European literature.[6] The passage by the Russians from the Arctic Ocean into the Pacific through Bering Strait subsequently attracted great attention and the accomplishment is indisputable.

During the second half of the seventeenth century there were many non-government sailings near the coasts and numerous land traverses between separate portions of the western margins of Bering Sea and the Sea of Okhotsk. One of the most inaccessible regions was Kamchatka. Apparently, Russians began to visit the peninsula about 1690,[7] although rumors about its existence were current even earlier. Kamchatka was visited by Luka Morozko and his Cossacks about 1696. However, the first, and for its time brilliant, description of Kamchatka's nature and population was given by V. Atlasov as a result of his trip in 1697–1699.[8] Some time prior to 1700–1701, Ivan Golygin and his companions reached Ostrov Karaginskiy, and in 1712 A. I. Bykov and A. Krestianinov visited Shantarskiye Ostrova.[9]

Individual reports and certain brief manuscript descriptions of Siberia, apparently written during the second half of the seventeenth century, contain geographical data on the coasts of, and on the rivers that flow into, the Pacific Ocean.[10] Some of them mention the legendary "Stone Nose" that allegedly barred the route from the "Lena Sea" (i.e., Arctic Ocean) to the "Amur Sea" (i.e., Pacific Ocean). Sometimes it is referred to on sketch maps as "impassable" and other times it is represented as a promontory protruding beyond the frames of the sketch. Thus, throughout the seventeenth century and even later the question of a free sea passage from the Arctic into the Pacific Ocean remained unclear, despite Fedot Alexeev and Dezhnev's cruise.

INITIAL CARTOGRAPHICAL REPRESENTATION

On the basis of these and other data the first generalized sketch maps of all of Siberia and the Far East were compiled. Though their content and the technique used in their compilation are imperfect, these maps nevertheless were the first information supplied to science giving a realistic representation of many millions of square kilometers of terrain in northeastern Asia and of the drainage systems discharging into the Arctic and Pacific oceans. Among the maps that reached us are the well-known sketch of Siberia in 1667 (Fig. 19), compiled by P. Godunov, which enjoyed popularity in western Europe;[11] the so-called sketch of Siberia in 1672, compiled not later than 1674;[12] the sketch map of 1678 by Spatharios;[13] a sketch map of Siberia in 1684–1685;[14] and some sketch maps by S. U. Remezov (Fig. 20), the best Russian cartographer of the late seventeenth and early eighteenth centuries,[15] which include a wealth of detail. All these maps were compiled without the benefit of scientific methods; they have no grid or regular projection; north is at the bottom of the map; boundaries are conventionally rectangular and the outlines of the coasts are indistinct. There is no exact division of the oceans and the Arctic coast from about the Lena extends beyond to the eastern side where the Pacific Ocean coast is represented.

More detailed and perfect outlines of the northwestern coasts of the Pacific Ocean are given on three extant maps (Fig. 21) of eastern Siberia and Kamchatka compiled

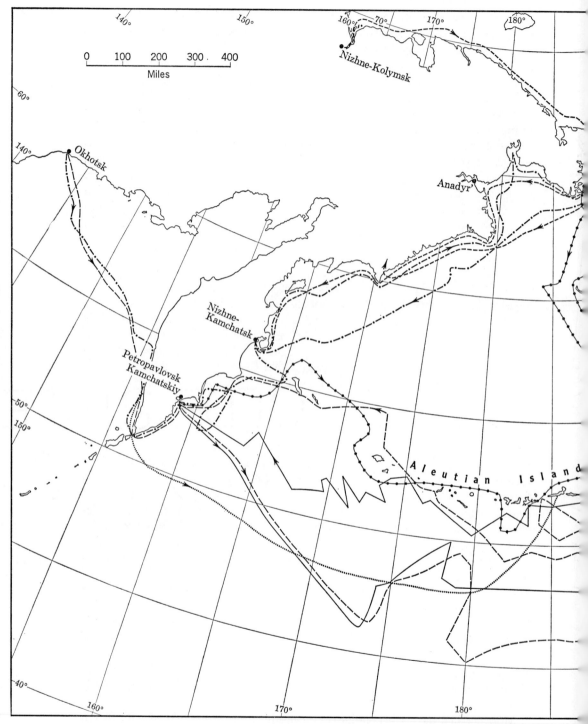

FIG. 18. Routes of the most important Russian cruises

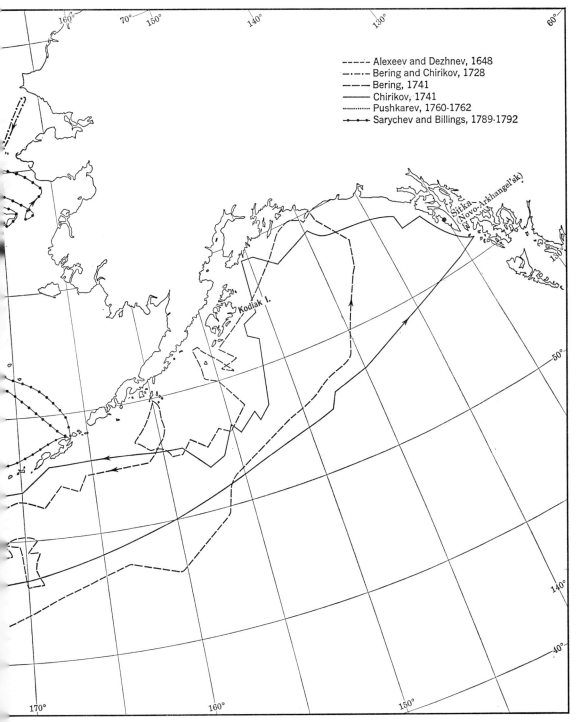

North Pacific Ocean prior to the nineteenth century.

Legend (within figure):
----- Alexeev and Dezhnev, 1648
-·-·- Bering and Chirikov, 1728
-- -- Bering, 1741
——— Chirikov, 1741
·········· Pushkarev, 1760-1762
•—•—• Sarychev and Billings, 1789-1792

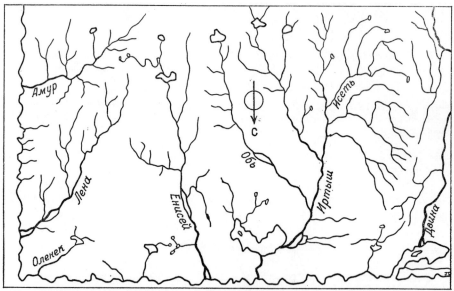

FIG. 19. Northeastern Asia as shown on the "chertezh" (draft) by P. Godunov, 1667. After A. V. Yefimov (ed.): [Note 11].

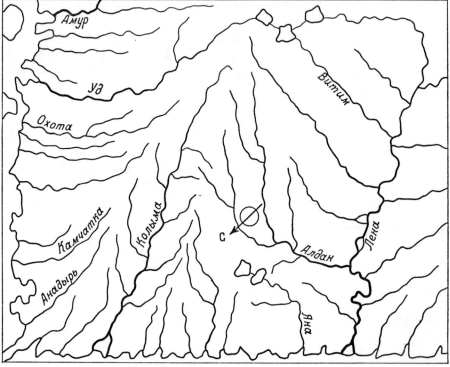

FIG. 20. Northeastern Asia as shown on the "chertezh" (draft) by S. U. Remezov, 1701. After A. V. Yefimov (ed.): [Note 11].

at the end of the seventeenth and the beginning of the eighteenth centuries.[16] Several of these maps include a reference to the "Impassable Nose." We note distinct outlines, even if in a somewhat distorted form, of Chukotskiy Poluostrov, Kamchatka, the Gulf of Anadyr', the Sea of Okhotsk, the first Kuril Islands, some of the islands of Japan, and other locations.[17] Despite the inevitable defects of these early maps, Russian information, including the cartographic representation of northeastern Asia and of its coasts along the Pacific Ocean, exerted great influence upon the maps compiled by outstanding cartographers of western Europe. Examples are the maps of Nicoloas C. Witsen (1691), Philip J. T. von Stralenberg (1730), and Goman (1725).[18]

THE EIGHTEENTH CENTURY

Reforms effected in Russia during the first quarter of the eighteenth century resulted in a rapid development of science. This was especially true with respect to geography and cartography, which acquired a state character. The establishment of the Russians on the coasts of the Pacific Ocean opened great vistas for the state and necessitated the gathering of more information about this remote periphery where so much, including the relations between the continents of Asia and America, still remained uncertain. From Petersburg (now Leningrad) Peter I sent well-equipped expeditions across the entire country. Even after his death expeditions continued to be sent to the Pacific coast at intervals throughout the eighteenth century. Overcoming tremendous difficulties, on horse and by boat, the expeditions covered thousands of kilometers of uninhabited expanse. With these expeditions were sailors, geodesists and other scientists, craftsmen, and sometimes a large part of the equipment for the ships which would have to be built in Okhotsk and on Kamchatka.

The first expedition sent by Peter I in 1719 was directed by geodesists I. Evreinov and F. Luzhin and was less carefully organized than those that followed. They crossed Kamchatka from the west to the east and returned. In 1721 they made a dangerous voyage from Bol'sheretsk on the west coast of Kamchatka to the sixteenth of the Kuril Islands (according to their calculations). Evreinov's map (Fig. 22) of the trip was the first to show plausible outlines of Kamchatka, and from its southern extremity he extended in a southwestern direction fourteen Kuril Islands of arbitrary outlines and gave latitudinal determinations with approximate precision. The determinations of longitudes are incorrect. This map, compiled by geodesists, was not published but has been used in subsequent cartographic work.[19]

THE FIRST KAMCHATKA EXPEDITION

The next expedition, more recently called the "First Kamchatka Expedition" (Fig. 18), was directed by Captain of the First Rank Vitus Bering,[20] a Dane who enlisted in the Russian fleet in 1703 when he was slightly over twenty. He remained in this service until his death in 1741. His assistants were Lieutenants A. I. Chirikov and M. Spanberg. On July 25, 1728, the expedition sailed from Nizhne-Kamchatsk at the mouth of the Kamchatka River in the ship *St. Gabriel*, which was built there. Keeping as close to the shore as possible, on August 26th they reached latitude 67°18'48" N. and about longitude 168° W., thus being the first after Dezhnev to pass through Bering Strait. From this point the expedition turned back and in Sep-

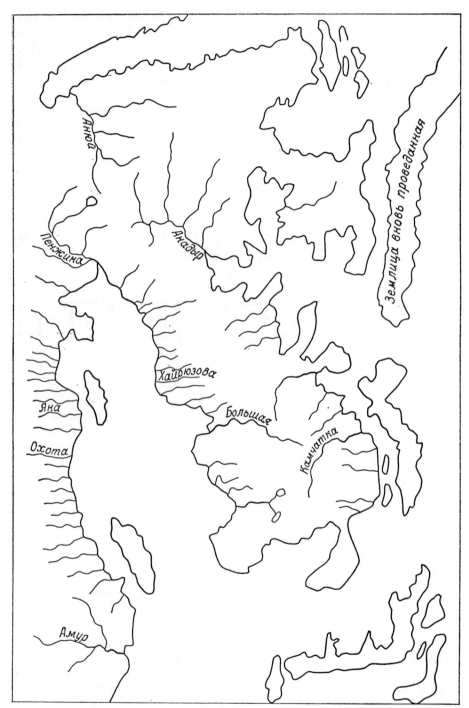

FIG. 21. Kamchatka as shown on a "chertezh" (draft) about 1700. After A. V. Yefimov (ed.): [Note 16].

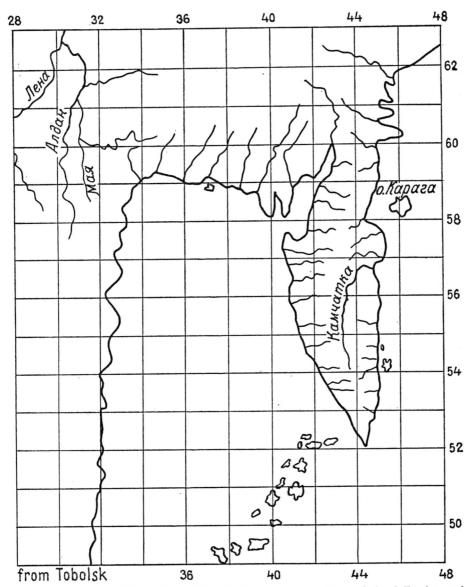

Fig. 22. Map of the Okhotsk Sea and Kamchatka region prepared by geodesists I. Evreinov and F. Luzhin in 1722. After O. A. Yevteyev: [Notes 11 and 19].

tember arrived at Kamchatka. After an unsuccessful voyage toward America in 1729, Bering with his companions returned to Petersburg in March, 1730. His trip through Bering Strait was recognized by the government as insufficient to prove there was no connection between the continents, inasmuch as the coast between the Kolyma River and East Cape remained unexplored.

The main results of this expedition were a very exact determination (for that period) of the position of different points on the Pacific Ocean coasts from East Cape to Mys Lopatka on Kamchatka,[21] and the compilation of a general map (Fig. 23), by warrant officer P. A. Chaplin in 1729, showing these coasts, and one of the Diomede Islands and St. Lawrence Island.[22] This information made it possible to de-lineate for the first time the position of the Asiatic coasts of the North Pacific on a world map and to give an idea of their outline. The discoveries of the expedition were widely used in scientific circles. A few days after the expedition's return a brief communication was published in Russia about the results of the voyage[23] and in 1735[24] and 1737[25] Chaplin's general map was published in France, the first publica-tion accompanied by a detailed account of Vitus Bering's report. Foreigners living in Russia sent hand-made copies of Chaplin's map abroad. These copies have been found in the archives of Sweden, France, Denmark, and England. The influence of this map can be seen on many of the general maps of the time, including some maps in the *Academy Atlas* of 1745, which was very popular in Russia and abroad and at that time was considered to be one of the greatest achievements in cartography.[26]

Exploration by Fedorov and Gvozdev

In August of 1732 a group led by subnavigator I. Fedorov and geodesist M. Gvozdev, participants in a big expedition organized in Siberia by D. Pavlutski and A. Shestakov for the investigation of northeastern Asia, sailed in the ship *St. Gabriel* from the mouth of the Kamchatka River in the direction of Anadyr' River and the "Big Land" (America). No log or navigation chart of this voyage have been pre-served, but they were known to their contemporaries. From other documents[27] it is possible to establish that the group crossed Bering Strait in its northern part, sailed past Diomede Islands, and made a landing on Big Diomede Island. Apparently, the participants of the expedition were the first Europeans to see all three islands of this group (including Fairway Rock). In September they approached the "Big Land" south of Cape Prince of Wales and from a native of King Island, who came out to the ship by boat, obtained some information regarding the nature of this land. The trip of Fedorov and Gvozdev gave a correct orientation of the American coast along the east side of Bering Strait which was included on general maps compiled in the middle of the eighteenth century in France as well as in Russia.[28] Some inscriptions on these maps include incorrect dates of the cruise.

The Second Kamchatka Expedition

Exploration of the Pacific Ocean was continued during the period 1733–1743 by the famous Second Kamchatka Expedition, generally referred to in literature as "The Great Northern Expedition." It was directed by Bering and his assistants on the first expedition (Fig. 18). In addition to making a study of the Northern Sea Route from the White Sea to Bering Strait and the nature and population of Siberia, the expedition intended to build ships in Okhotsk in which to make a trip to the coasts of northwestern America and Japan. The expedition left Petersburg in 1733 but, owing to organizational difficulties, the cruise in the Pacific did not get under way until July 26, 1738, when Martin Spanberg sailed from Okhotsk at the head of three ships and began the first of his three voyages to Japan. Fog prevented his making an

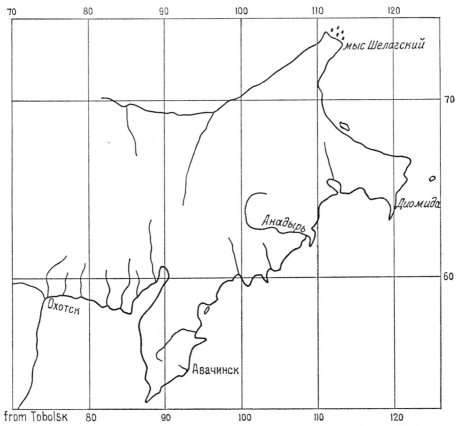

Fig. 23. Map of northeastern Asia by P. A. Chaplin of the First Kamchatka Expedition, 1729. After A. V. Yefimov (ed.): [Note 22].

accurate count of the Kuril Islands and he sailed only as far south as latitude 45° N. Lieutenant W. Walton, who lost him, explored south to latitude 43°20′ N. During the second voyage they approached Honshu. Spanberg cruised south along it to latitude 37°30′ N. and Walton to latitude 33°30′ N.[29] On his return to Okhotsk Spanberg cruised near the southern Kuril Islands and Hokkaido. The third trip (1742) did not bring any substantial results.

The maps of the cruises of 1738–1739 compiled by Spanberg and Walton, delineating the Kuril Islands, the coasts of Japan, and the route of the expeditions,[30] were not published at that time. Their results, however, together with those of Bering and Chirikov's voyage of 1741 were used in the preparation of the maps in the *Academy Atlas* published in 1745 and in Gerhard F. Müller's map. This was of very great importance because it provided a completely new and generally correct idea of the area between Kamchatka and Honshu and the regions east of them. On contemporary maps, fantastic islands and lands were shown in these regions: for example, Eso Island, Company Land, Island of the States, and De Gama Land[31] which, it was sometimes thought, were tied to America. On these Russian maps the Kuril Islands were shown for the first time on the basis of actual observations. These new delineations by Spanberg and Walton did not, however, receive immediate general recognition. Philippe Buache in his book of 1753 reproduced the Asiatic coasts of the Pacific Ocean as delineated on the maps published in the *Academy Atlas* of 1745, but he retained the Kuril Islands and questionable islands and lands shown on earlier maps.[32]

Outstanding discoveries were made by Bering in his ship *St. Peter* and by Chirikov in his ship *St. Paul* during their voyage to northwestern America (Fig. 18). They left Avachinskaya Guba on June 15, 1741, in a southeastern direction in a search of De Gama land, as directed by Joseph Nicolas de L'Isle, Professor of the Academy of Sciences in Petersburg, who subscribed to the views of French geographers (Fig. 24). They soon were separated and each on his own rounded the Aleutian Islands without noticing them. The coasts of America were seen from the *St. Paul* on July 26 in latitude 55°11' N. and longitude 133°57' W. and from the *St. Peter* on July 27 in latitude 58°17' N. and longitude 142°10' W.

A very brief landing on Kayak Island was made only from the *St. Peter*. The *St. Paul*, having lost both of its boats, could not land a party and consequently had no chance to replenish its water reserves. On their way back, owing to dramatic events which have been repeatedly described in the literature, the explorers were almost unable to carry out any researches. Moving farther north than on their way to America, they often came close to an unknown land. As we now know, they had discovered a part of the Aleutian Islands arc and some other islands, including Afognak Island, Kodiak Island, Chirikof Island, Semidi Islands, Shumagin Islands, Umnak Island, Unalaska Island, Atka Island, Adak Island, Kiska Island, Buldir Island, Semichi Islands, Attu Island, Agattu Island, and others. In the majority of cases the explorers could not determine whether these were islands or part of a continent. Chirikov, having lost some of his men, and with his remaining crew exhausted by thirst and scurvy, returned to Kamchatka on October 22nd. In 1742 he made another trip, but established only that Attu is an island and not a part of the continent. The *St. Peter* had suffered badly from a storm. All hands were forced to land and winter over on Ostrov Beringa. Those who survived the winter returned to Kamchatka in the autumn of 1742.[33] Chirikov and the officers of the *St. Peter*, S. Waxell and S. Khitzov, came to the conclusion that the lands seen on their trip were mostly the coast of America protruding westwards and consequently represented them as such on their maps.[34] Despite this mistake their maps gave a correct idea of the relationship between Kamchatka and the northwestern part of America lying on the other side of the ocean that was discovered by them. Their maps gave a correct indication of the existence of some lands in the area of the Aleutian Islands.

A description of the cruises made by the groups of the Second Kamchatka Expedition was first published by Gerhard F. Müller in Russian and German.[35] The discoveries of the First Kamchatka Expedition, the cruises of Fedorov and Gvozdev, and the definitive explorations of the Pacific groups of the Second Kamchatka Expedition made it possible to delineate the Pacific Ocean north of Japan with reasonable approximation, especially that part which had been unexplored up to that time. Correct representations were made on the Marine Academy map of 1746[36] and on

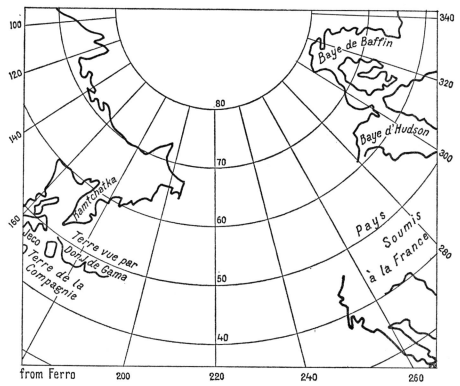

FIG. 24. Map of the region between northeastern Asia and northwestern North America, by Joseph Nicolas de L'Isle, *ca*. 1741. in Frank A. Golder: [Note 31].

Müller's map of 1754–1758 (Fig. 25). Unfortunately, the Marine Academy map was only recently published. Müller's map was published during the eighteenth century in French, English, and German editions.[37] Completely new material on the nature and people of the coasts of America, the Aleutian Islands, Ostrov Beringa and Kamchatka was included in a paper by naturalist Georg Wilhelm Steller, who made a voyage on the *St. Peter*.[38] Extensive and exact information on the nature and population of Kamchatka is given in Stepan P. Krasheninnikov's book, although he did not take part in the trip to America.[39]

EXPLORING EXPEDITIONS AFTER BERING

Soon after these discoveries, the islands between Asia and America were visited with increased frequency by merchants and *promyshlenniki* (people engaged in hunting, fishing, etc.). They were attracted to the region by information brought back by the participants in the Second Kamchatka Expedition and by the stories of valuable furs of sea otters and fur seals that were so abundant on Ostrov Beringa. Sergeant E. S. Bassov, in the ship *Peter* in 1743–1744, was the first to make a trip to Ostrov Beringa. Soon a fleet of small ships owned and equipped mostly by merchants sailed to the east in search of new islands and unexplored reserves of sea

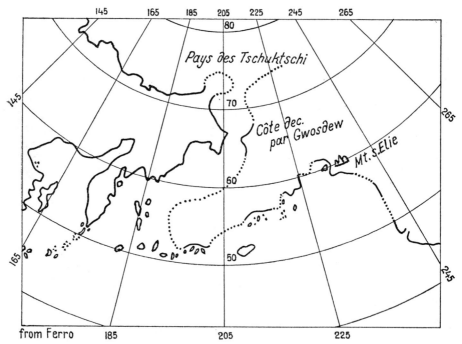

FIG. 25. Map of the North Pacific Ocean, by Gerhard Müller, 1754–1758. After V. I. Grekov: [Note 23].

animals. These cruises, especially during the first decade, often were undertaken by people completely inexperienced in navigation, and in very primitive ships that were built without nails and were referred to as "sewn-up ships." This resulted in a great number of accidents and shipwrecks.[40] In 1745, Bassov discovered Ostrov Mednyy in Komandorskiye Ostrova and navigator M. Nevotchikov explored the islands of Attu, Agattu, and Semichi from the group of Near Islands.

At the beginning of the 1750s a considerable decrease in the number of sea animals and an improvement in the technique of shipbuilding induced the *promyshlenniki* to undertake more distant voyages. It is rather difficult to find on our current maps the islands which they visited during their first distant travels. Reliable evidence appears to indicate that in 1757 a landing by seaman P. Bashmakov was made on Kagalaska Island in the Andreanof Islands, where thirteen islands were discovered in 1757–1758. In 1759 seaman S. Glotov discovered the islands of Umnak and Unalaska among the Fox Islands; and in 1761 Paikov discovered Unimak Island, the last big island before Alaska. During this year Alaska was reached by G. Pushkarev, who thought it to be an island (Fig. 18). In 1763 Glotov landed on the large Kodiak Island which subsequently played so important a role in the Russian advance eastwards. During the voyage of S. Novikov and I. Bakhov in 1748 from the mouth of the Anadyr' to Kamchatka, Saint Matthew Island was discovered.[41]

Some authorities, including Lev. S. Berg, have thought that it was discovered by I. Sindt in 1766.[42]

This is a very brief review, up to the middle of the eighteenth century, of the Russian advance to the east along the Aleutian Islands, toward Alaska and Kodiak Island. It does not give a complete picture of all the discoveries of some forty expeditions by *promyshlenniki*, whose voyages during the period 1743–1763 sometimes lasted several years and included lengthy landings and numerous adventures. The reports of the *promyshlenniki*, who had no scientific background but did have a lot of common sense and ability to observe, contain abundant information on the nature and population of these areas. Their ethnographic material has been repeatedly studied by scientists. Especially interesting are communications of several trips by Andrian Tolstykh prepared by his companions M. Lazarev and P. Vasiutinsky; by the brave navigator S. G. Glotov, whose notes have been discussed by the government and by the Academy of Sciences; and by S. Cherepanov, who described the Near Islands.[43]

Plotting the discoveries made by *promyshlenniki* was difficult because they did not give exact determinations of location. For example, the Aleutian Islands plotted on their charts are not accurate because they have a northern direction.[44] This has made it difficult to correlate their data with the more accurate discoveries of the Second Kamchatka Expedition. On generalized manuscript maps of that time we find an indiscriminate scattering of islands and outlines of lands taken from the maps of both expeditions but no conjectured protrusion of Alaska.[45] Between the middle and the end of the eighteenth century there were more than forty cruises to the Aleutian Islands by *promyshlenniki* and merchants.[46]

From this point on, the big Russian trading companies began to acquire a dominant role in the organization of these cruises. By the end of the eighteenth century their representatives organized the Russian-American Company which, during the nineteenth century, initiated numerous expeditions and much research. Navigators and seamen were better trained and more modern technical equipment was used. The Russian government took a greater interest in the voyages of the *promyshlenniki* and even organized its own expeditions for the study of the Aleutian Islands. The first of the government expeditions was a cruise of the Aleutian Islands by Captains P. K. Krenitzin and M. D. Levashov, who left Petersburg in 1764.[47] Information (Fig. 26) that they brought back about these islands was published with a map in 1780, by William Coxe.[48] Having determined rather exactly the latitude of Unalaska, but not its longitude, Krenitzin initiated precise determinations of the Aleutian Islands.[49] With Levashov, he was the first to discover Isanotski Strait (in 1768) and to prove that Unimak is an island and not a continuation of Alaska. Despite this fact, a map by Arrowsmith in 1820 shows it as a part of the continent, although on all Russian maps made after 1768 it is shown as an island.[50] After this expedition the voyages of the *promyshlenniki* lasted for a long time.

Some of these expeditions (noted in A. V. Yefimov's work) were of substantial importance. Navigator P. Zaikov, in 1774–1779 cruised among the Aleutian Islands and landed on some of them. Zaikov's description and map is the first reasonably

FIG. 26. Map compiled from the results of the cruise of Captains P. K. Krenitzin and M. D. Levashov in the North Pacific, 1767. After A. P. Sokolov: [Note 47].

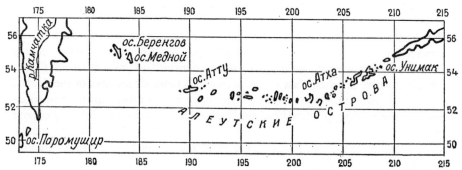

FIG. 27. Map of the Aleutian Islands compiled by P. Zaikov, 1779. After A. V. Yefimov (Note 11), map 161.

accurate record of this entire chain between Attu Island and Alaska proper (Fig. 27). The explorations of G. I. Shelekhov and his navigators G. Izmailov and D. Bocharov, after 1783, resulted in additional geographical information on the Russian possessions in northwestern North America, and on some of the Kuril Islands. In 1786–1787, navigator G. L. Pribilof discovered St. George and St. Paul islands, named for him Pribilof Islands.

Gavrul A. Sarychev occupies an important place in the history of exploration of the North Pacific. He and I. Billings were leaders of a government expedition in 1785–1793, with far-reaching scientific objectives. Sarychev's published paper contains detailed physico-geographical, economic, and ethnographic data on the extensive areas he investigated.[51] His voyages, independently and with Billings, took him into the Sea of Okhotsk, Bering Sea, some of the Kuril Islands, Bering Strait, the area near the islands adjacent to Alaska, and especially around and between the Aleutian Islands (Fig. 18). Carrying out repeated and systematic research during 1789–1792, Sarychev made numerous astronomical determinations of coordinates for many of the islands in the North Pacific, and plotted on a map (Fig. 28) not only all of the large Aleutian Islands between Attu and the peninsula of Alaska but also numerous small islands. The book he published is illustrated with a collection of

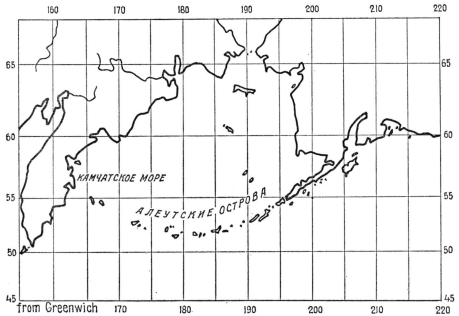

FIG. 28. Map of the North Pacific Ocean, by Gavrul A. Sarychev, 1802. [Note 51].

maps and drawings, and contains extensive oceanographic information such as currents, tidal phenomena, depths, character of the sea floor, etc., necessary for sailing across the ocean and between the islands. This book has been translated into several languages. On the basis of personal investigations and a critical use of numerous textual and cartographic sources, Sarychev in 1826 published an atlas of the northern part of the Eastern Ocean,[52] which became very well known. Both the book and the atlas have been highly praised by many Russian[53] and foreign[54] scientists.

THE NINETEENTH CENTURY

During the eighteenth century, Russian studies and explorations of the Pacific Ocean proceeded only in its northern part, but during the nineteenth century emphasis shifted to other parts of the ocean. An expansion of the economic development of Russian Far Eastern maritime areas and of the Russian-American colonies, as well as problems of their defense, were among the reasons for the organization and active support by the Russian government of a number of around-the-world and shorter voyages, especially into the Pacific Ocean. Most of these voyages originated from Kronshtadt.[55] They proved to be much more economical than a thousand-kilometer transport of freight across the land and then by water to the Russian possessions "beyond the seas."

Before the Russian-American colonies were sold to the United States of America in 1867, more than forty such voyages had been undertaken,[56] the overwhelming majority of which took place during the first half of the nineteenth century.[57] Despite their fundamentally practical purpose, each of them (with a few exceptions) carried out meteorological, magnetic, and hydrographic observations, and made studies and kept records of currents, surface temperature of the water, sometimes also temperature at depth, and water gravity determinations. During many cruises an even wider scope of scientific research was carried out, including detailed descriptions and instrument observations of a geographical, oceanographic, and natural-historical character. All ships were equipped with varying numbers and kinds of scientific instruments,[58] and we should emphasize that ships of the Russian navy at that time already had chronometers. According to Debenham, chronometers had been officially introduced into the British navy only as early as 1826.[59]

The commanders were supplied with the essential Russian and foreign maps, atlases, books about former voyages, and various handbooks. Larger expeditions were provided with detailed instructions, including routes to be followed (usually laid out to cover the least explored areas), methods and techniques of investigation, and the scope of their programs. The methods and techniques of astronomical, hydrographic, and magnetic observations were in terms of the best standards of world science at the time; consequently, we mention them only when something new and more advanced has been used. As will become evident later, the scientific quality of their application was very high, especially astronomical observation, terrain description, and mapping of numerous geographic features. In addition to erasing from the maps certain non-existent islands, some voyages resulted in discoveries of new islands[60] and in research that lead to important theoretical summarizations. All the major papers of the participants of expeditions published during the nineteenth century not only provide information about their progress and results, but also give very valuable data and description of the native population of the islands visited and of the coastal areas.[61] Space does not permit us to give even a brief review of the accomplishments of all the separate voyages. We shall, however, discuss those which are significant because of the considerable scientific results described by their leaders in extensive published papers.[62]

THE KRUZENSHTERN AND LISYANSKI EXPEDITION, 1803–1806

The first among them was the expedition of 1803–1806, commanded and lead by Ivan F. Kruzenshtern on the *Nadezhda*, and commander Y. F. Lisyanski on the *Neva*. The participants included some scientists: I. Horner, astronomer, W. Tilezius, Adjunct of Petersburg Academy, and K. Espenberg, Doctor of Medicine. The description of the voyage, published by Kruzenshtern in three volumes,[63] was almost immediately translated into a number of foreign languages, notably English, French, Dutch, and Swedish. Leaving Kronshtadt on August 7, 1803, the ships rounded Cape Horn. After visiting the Hawaiian Islands, they proceeded independently along different routes, which widened the sphere of observation (Fig. 29). The *Neva* returned to Kronshtadt on August 5 and the *Nadezhda* on August 19, 1806.

The main results of Kruzenshtern's geographical discovery, description, and mapping cover the northwestern part of the Pacific, where lengthy cruises were made, mainly out from a base at Kamchatka, into the area of the Kuril Islands, Sakhalin Island, and Japan. Most important were the investigations near the coasts of Japan. Despite the explorations and studies by such persons as Maarten G. Vries, Jean F.

de G. de La Pérouse, William R. Broughton, and others, part of its coasts, especially the western periphery, remained virtually unexplored. Kruzenshtern made detailed studies of the southern coasts of Honshu (Hondo), the western coasts of Ezo (Hokkaido), and portions of some smaller islands (Tsu-shima, Gotō-rettō, etc.). His group made about sixty-five new astronomical determinations, and described the Eastern Channel (Tsugaru-kaikyō) and Osumi-kaikyō. Information about the latter on British and French maps were contradictory and inexact.[64] Valuable meteorological and hydrographic data were obtained in coastal waters.

As a result of these investigations and his critical analysis of previously available stray data, Kruzenshtern published a report of his explorations and an atlas (in Russian and German) of 105 plates and fifteen maps.[65] The maps and profiles of the coasts of Japan introduced substantial improvements in and made available more detailed hydrographic information about the coastal waters of Japan up to that time. These results were highly praised.[66] The coastal outlines of Kamchatka and especially of the northern Kuril Islands up to Proliv Nadezhdy (Strait) were defined with greater clarity and detail. Small Ostrova Lovushki were discovered. Unfortunately, Kruzenshtern shared the mistake of La Pérouse and Broughton and considered Sakhalin Island to be a peninsula, despite his valuable work on the mapping of its coasts.[67]

In addition to the usual surface water temperature measurements taken at twenty-one stations (seventeen of them in the Pacific and in its adjacent seas), the *Nadezhda* took temperatures at different depths by a Six's thermometer, the readings of which were compared with a checked mercury thermometer.[68] It is especially valuable that at seven points, including one at Cape Horn and four in the Pacific Ocean, the first observations were made on the vertical series of temperatures.[69] With a stipulation of the small number of tests, Horner, who collaborated with Kruzenshtern in this work, noted "that at first the warmth diminishes imperceptibly, then more rapidly; further on at great depth it drops more slowly again and, finally remains constant."[70] The depths at which the temperature goes down rapidly vary in different parts of the ocean. These problems, correctly stated by Horner, are of interest to oceanographers and oceanologists at the present time.[71] At forty-eight stations, thirty-three of them in the Pacific and surrounding seas, Horner made determinations of the specific weight of the water. His conclusions that water salinity is not the same in the tropics and at higher latitudes; that in marginal seas, such as the Sea of Okhotsk, the Sea of Japan, and the South China Sea, the specific weight is lower than in the open ocean; and, especially, that the water of the Atlantic Ocean is more saline than the water of the Pacific,[72] have been confirmed by later research.

During 1804–1805, 340 observations on the direction and velocity of currents were made in the Pacific Ocean,[73] thus adding considerably to the information then available. Apparently, Kruzenshtern and the British seaman Hunter simultaneously discovered the eastern part of the current now called "the equatorial countercurrent."[74] Considerably fuller information on the meteorology of the Pacific Ocean was provided by systematic and careful observations carried out during the entire voyage of the *Nadezhda*, which were summarized in 127 pages of tables. Observations of barometric fluctuations of temperature, wind, and weather conditions within the tropics were analyzed by Horner,[75] who clearly established the presence of two

Petropavlovsk-Kamchatskiy

Macao

Philippine Is.

Marshall Is.

120°   150°   180°

Sydney

———— Kruzenshtern and Lisyanski, 1803-1806
+—+—+ Kotzebue, 1815-1818
················· Golovnin, 1817-1819
—○—○— Bellinsgausen and Lazarev, 1819-1821
- - - - Kotzebue, 1823-1826
—·—·— Lütke, 1826-1829

FIG. 29. Routes of the most important Russian

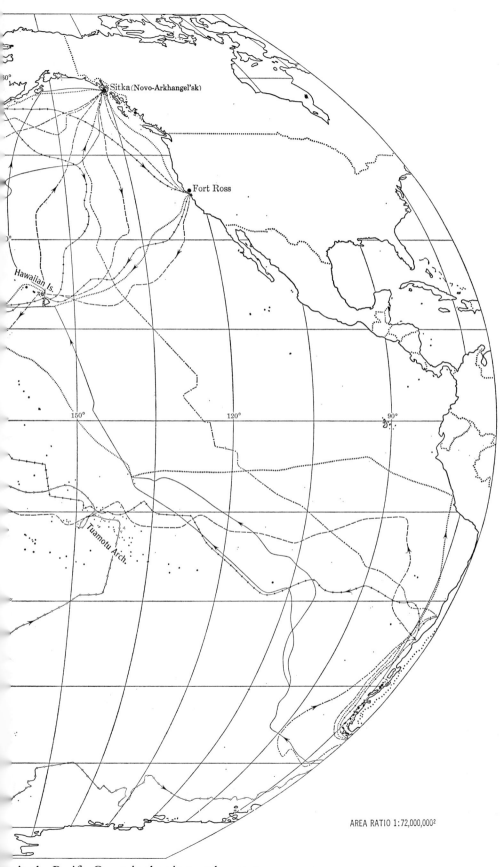

in the Pacific Ocean in the nineteenth century.

Sitka (Novo-Arkhangel'sk)

Fort Ross

Hawaiian Is.

Tuamotu Arch.

150°   120°   90°

AREA RATIO 1:72,000,000²

daily minima and two daily maxima, now a widely known phenomenon, but quite unclear before his discovery.

Kruzenshtern's voyage served as the basis for the compilation of his famous *Atlas de l'océan Pacifique*,[76] which is accompanied by a separately published explanatory text. In addition to maps, the thirty-four plates comprising the atlas include a great number of large-scale plans of straits, ports, bays, etc. Three volumes of explanatory text[77] contain factual information about the objectives of the atlas, a description of the methods used in its compilation, and a reference list with a very careful historical-geographical analysis of the extensive Russian and foreign material that was known at that time on the hydrography and cartography of the Pacific Ocean. Treating with great respect the work of his predecessors such as John Purdy, Aaron Arrowsmith, and others, Kruzenshtern introduced substantial changes and amendments which corrected numerous mistakes in previous textual and cartographic data. These widely known publications were a major contribution to the study of the Pacific Ocean. They were used for many decades by Russian and foreign scientists and won high praise.[78] Researchers consult them even now.

Having parted with Kruzenshtern, Lisyanski in the *Neva* went directly to Kodiak Island and for over a year cruised the northwestern coasts of America, which then belonged to Russia.[79] Astronomical observations added greatly to the data on these vast areas. Lisyanski established that among the numerous islands comprising the Alexander Archipelago near Chatham Strait four were the most important. He gave them the names Chichagof, Yakobi, Kruzof, and Baranof.[80] On the way back in October 1805, one island was discovered by and named for Lisyanski. The co-ordinates given for this island are almost precisely identical with those of today's determination. Lisyanski's book contains a detailed description of the natural conditions and population of the places visited by the *Neva*, not only in the northern Pacific but also in its more southern parts; for example, Easter Island, the Hawaiian Islands, and Marquesas Islands. The atlas that was published with the Russian edition of the book contains twelve maps, many drawings, and tables of ethnographic material.[81]

GOLOVNIN'S CIRCUMNAVIGATIONS, 1807–1819

The first voyage around the world by V. M. Golovnin, in 1807–1809 in the ship *Diana*, did not yield substantial scientific results; it reached Kamchatka and remained there. In 1810, Golovnin made a trip from Kamchatka to the northwestern coasts of America and back. During his voyage of 1811, Golovnin and his navigators, Khlebnikov and Novitzky, described and compiled a map of the Kuril Islands from Proliv Nadezhdya as far as the eastern coasts of Ostrov Iturup and Ostrov Kunashir.[82] Latitudes and longitudes of thirty sites were determined astronomically. A careful comparison of local names with those given by Europeans resulted in a clarification of the number of islands, their position, etc. The book which Golovnin published is supplied with a map, and his studies of the Kuril chain of islands, representing one of the most complicated problems, were highly appreciated by Russian and foreign scientists.[83]

The track of Golovnin's around-the-world cruise in the *Kamchatka* during 1817–1819 (Fig. 29) took him past Cape Horn on his way to the Pacific and Cape of Good

Hope on his return.[84] In addition to the usual practical purpose, his expedition had scientific aims: to make additional astronomical determinations and descriptions of Russian possessions in the North Pacific and the largely unexplored northwestern coasts of America. Golovnin determined the position of Chiniak Bay and established that the Trinity Islands were not a single island, as Cook had thought, but were two islands, Sitkinak and Tugidak. Golovnin also visited more southern islands such as the Hawaiian Islands, the Marianas, and the Philippines. His book contains abundant material about the Pacific Ocean, as, for example, the inclination of the magnetic needle in a number of regions, hydrography of coastal waters, winds, and currents.

KOTZEBUE'S EXPEDITIONS, 1815–1818 AND 1823–1826

Two around-the-world voyages were commanded by Lieutenant Otto Ye. Kotzebue, one in 1815–1818 in the brig *Riurik*,[85] and the second in 1823–1826 (Fig. 29) in the sloop *Predpriatie*.[86] The results of these voyages were published in several European languages, especially German and French. Both voyages produced very big scientific results. The first had precisely stipulated scientific aims which included the search for a sea route from Bering Sea along the coast of North America into the Atlantic Ocean, and geographical research in the Pacific Ocean. The second voyage had practical aims, although Kotzebue had permission to carry out scientific researches. The scientists who took part in the voyage of the *Riurik* included I. Eschscholtz, Doctor of Medicine, and naturalists A. Chamisso, and a Mr. Wormskjold (who left the ship upon arrival in Kamchatka). On the *Predpriatie* were E. Lenz, physicist, W. Preus, astronomer, and E. Hoffman, mineralogist. Both ships left Kronshtadt, rounded Cape Horn, and on their return home rounded the Cape of Good Hope.

Let us first review the results of these two voyages in respect to the discovery and study of the Marshall Islands and the Tuamotu Archipelago. Both groups of islands had been discovered and rediscovered in part by explorers of several countries. Of special importance to the history of discoveries of the first group of islands was J. Marshall, whose name was given to the archipelago at the suggestion of Kruzenshtern. He was right to indicate[87] that only as a result of Kotzebue's first cruise among these islands, on the *Riurik* during several months of 1816–1817, was the real position of the archipelago actually established. Kotzebue determined that it consists of two parallel series (Fig. 30): the eastern Ratak Chain, which he studied in detail and mapped; and the western Ralik Chain, which he only traversed, having obtained factual information about it from the local population.[88]

During his second voyage (Fig. 29), on the *Predpriatie*, Kotzebue again visited the Marshall Islands and made additional astronomical observations verifying his previous data.[89] In the Tuamotu Archipelago the researches he carried out in 1816 and 1824 resulted in the discovery of some new islands and in more detailed information about the entire group of islands.[90] During both his trips Kotzebue discovered and mapped eleven islands in the Marshall Islands, four in the Tuamotu Archipelago, and one in the Society Islands.[91]

Though Kotzebue did not achieve any success in his search for a sea route from the Pacific Ocean into the Atlantic Ocean, his cruise in northern waters resulted in

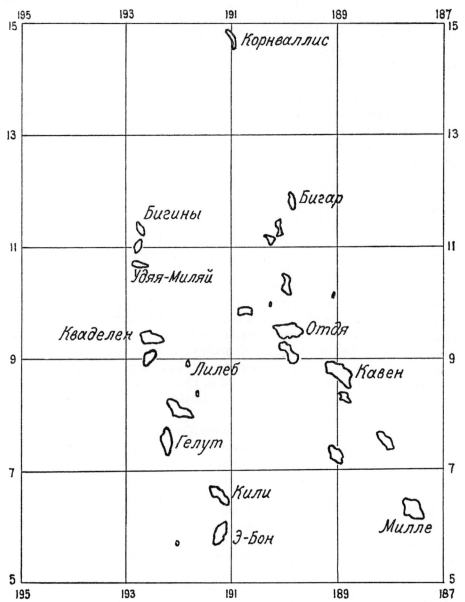

FIG. 30. Map of the Ralik Islands in the Pacific Ocean. Redrawn from Otto Ye. Kotzebue's *Atlas*, 1821–23: [Note 85].

a substantial increase in detailed information regarding many islands and especially those on the northwestern coast of America. In addition, Kotzebue Sound was discovered in 1816, and rather fully described.[92] When coral islands were studied in 1815–1818, they were described in detail, and interesting views, valuable for that time, were expressed as to their origin.[93] Subsequently, some of these views were favorably accepted by Charles R. Darwin.[94] During the voyages of the *Riurik* and *Predpriatie*, important scientific results were obtained in the study of temperature and of the specific weight of water. On the first voyage, 116 temperature measurements were taken with the help of Six's thermometer at different depths, about half of which took place in the Pacific Ocean and its marginal seas.[95] At eight stations, vertical series of temperatures were determined.[96]

Although these researches by Kotzebue greatly extended available information, their precision was very low, owing to the lack of refinement of the instruments used and of the method of research. E. Lenz, later a member of the Academy of Sciences in Petersburg and a world-reknowned physicist, studied this problem and made its solution his goal during his trip on the *Predpriatie*. For this purpose he and Professor Parrot designed a very efficient instrument, a bathometer, for sampling water at various depths, and a depth gauge (a winch) for lowering the instrument to the selected depth for a sounding. These two inventions can well be regarded as the beginning of an exact oceanographic technique. At seven stations Lenz made fifteen temperature observations and eleven determinations of specific weight. This included four stations, eleven observations, and six determinations in the Pacific. Despite a small number of observations, the results have passed the test of time. They have been confirmed, for instance, by M. Rykachev in respect to the temperatures when compared with the data obtained on the *Challenger* Expedition.[97] After his well-known voyage in 1886–1889 oceanographer Stefan O. Makarov ranked these observations by Lenz higher than his own observations and the data obtained on *Challenger* in 1875.[98] At the beginning of the twentieth century O. Krümmel wrote that temperature measurements at depth made by Lenz still remained among the best.[99] Lenz was successful in obtaining low temperatures of $+2°$ C and $+3°$ C in depths not heretofore measured.

Lenz came to a correct conclusion about a continuous but constantly smaller drop in temperature up to a depth of 1950 meters in the world ocean between latitude $45°$ N. and the equator.[100] A theory of oceanic water circulation formulated by him as an explanation of the appearance of lower temperatures at great depth was based on factual data observed on the *Riurik* and on his own tests on the *Predpriatie*.[101] According to his theory, water is warmed in the tropics and moves toward the poles at the surface, while cold water moves toward the tropics, at depth. The theory was reviewed in detail by Sir Joseph Prestwich who, in his extensive paper of 1876, introduced quite substantial changes.[102] On the basis of very exact observations over a vast area on the distribution of specific weights of sea water on the surface, Lenz was the first to establish the existence in the Atlantic and Pacific oceans of a salinity maximum north and south of the equator and a minimum in between, in the area of the equator. He correctly explained this phenomenon as a more intense evaporation in the area of the trades and a calm in the near-equatorial belt.

LÜTKE'S EXPEDITION, 1826–1829

In 1826–1829 Captain Fedor P. Lütke, with the participation of naturalists Karl H. Martens and Aleksandr F. Postels and ornithologist Friedrich H. de Kitlitz, made an around-the-world cruise (Fig. 29) in the sloop *Senyavin*.[103] In addition to prescribed practical objectives, they were to conduct scientific observations in the Pacific Ocean. Their primary results in the tropical zone were limited to a study of the Caroline Islands, which had been discovered at different times by many explorers and especially by Duperrey, though information about the islands had remained scanty and inexact. From November 1827 to the end of 1828 Lütke conducted numerous voyages between these islands, investigating them scientifically according to a definite plan, and systematically describing many of them from the north southwards and from the east westwards, with the exception of those which had been plotted on the map by Duperrey. Some of them, including a group that he called Senyavin Islands, were absolutely unknown. Lütke personally thought that of the twenty-six groups and separate islands he described he had discovered twelve.[104] In addition to geodetic work he gave detailed descriptions of natural conditions on the archipelago and of its population. He left a detailed map of the Caroline Islands which, Russian and foreign scientists acknowledged,[105] became known primarily because of Lütke's researches.

Astronomical determinations had been made of many points of importance on Kamchatka in the northern part of the Pacific Ocean. Proliv Senyavina had been discovered north of Avachinskaya Guba, and for the first time a scientific description was made of Ostrov Karaginskiy and the Pacific coast of Chukotskiy Poluostrov. Taking advantage of his personal investigations, plus the material obtained from the Russian-American Company and from other sources, Lütke compiled a detailed summary of the western and eastern coasts of Bering Sea with their peninsulas, capes, bays, orography, distances between points, depth of coastal waters, climatic and some other natural conditions, as well as of the separate islands of Komandorskiye Ostrova, Pribilof Islands, Saint Matthew Island, and the Aleutian Islands, and of part of the coast of Alaska and its adjoining islands.[106] This monograph, one of the most important physico-geographic studies of the Bering Sea, was highly praised both in Russia and abroad.[107]

On the basis of data obtained mainly during his voyage on the *Senyavin*, and from Russian and foreign cartographic sources, Lütke published a navigation atlas containing over fifty tables, maps, plans, and pictures of coasts and islands in the Bering Sea and Caroline Islands.[108] Lütke discovered the western part of the equatorial countercurrent[109] and added a good deal to our meteorological data on the Pacific Ocean, in particular on barometric fluctuations between latitude 30° N. and latitude 30° S.[110] Water temperatures were measured daily on the surface.

THE BELLINSGAUSEN-LAZAREV EXPEDITIONS, 1819–1821

In 1819 the Russian government organized two expeditions or divisions, as they have been officially called (Fig. 29). They were independent from each other, but were parts of one enterprise carried out according to a plan and pursuing ambitious scientific aims. The leader of the first expedition was Captain Faddey F. Bellinsgausen, commander of the sloop *Vostok*. His assistant, Lieutenant M. P. Lazarev, whose skill in ship management played a big role in the success of the expedition, was commander of the sloop *Mirny*. The second expedition was lead by Lieutenant-

Captain M. N. Vassiliev, in command of the sloop *Otkrytie*. His assistant was Lieutenant-Captain G. S. Shishmarev, commander of the sloop *Blagonamerenny*.

Both expeditions were well supplied with necessary instruments, books about previous voyages, charts, handbooks, and Russian and foreign atlases and maps. The leaders of the expeditions received nearly identical detailed instructions, except the route each was to follow and his final objective. In addition to the details of organization, the instructions contained very detailed scientific guidance on the methods of carrying out an extremely wide and complex plan of astronomical, physico-geographical and magnetic observations, and the manner of collecting ethnographic, historical, and economic information about the population.

Special mention should first be made of the expedition of 1819–1821 directed by Bellinsgausen and Lazarev,[111] which played an outstanding role in Russian and world geographical researches.[112] The main instruction received by Bellinsgausen required his expedition to achieve a maximum penetration to the south in order to discover unknown lands ". . . in the greatest possible proximity to the Antarctic pole." The expedition was also ordered to carry out research in the equatorial and tropical zones of the Pacific Ocean, to discover new islands, and to verify information about already known points.[113]

The important and highly praised voyage of James Cook to the Antarctic in 1772–1775 had been acclaimed by Bellinsgausen and other Russian and later Soviet explorers. Cook proved that there is no southern continent in temperate latitudes, but his confidence that it could be only near the South Pole, in places inaccessible and useless to humanity, halted further search. The voyage of Bellinsgausen and Lazarev was the first expedition after Cook's that was scientifically organized for achieving the specific goal of discovering land as near as possible to the South Pole. In addition to leaders of outstanding quality and volunteer officers and sailors, the expedition included I. M. Simonov, astronomer, and P. Mihailov, painter.

The sloops left Kronshtadt on July 15, 1819, and returned there on August 5, 1821; an absence of some 750 days. In accordance with instructions, explorations were made in both low and high latitudes of the Pacific Ocean (Fig. 29). The work in low latitudes resulted in a discovery of new groups of islands and a substantial amplification of data on lands already known. In his book, Bellinsgausen describes these researches in detail, giving exact information on the position of the islands[114] and abundant other data about them and the waters washing their shores. The atlas of the voyage gives schematic cartographic representations of fourteen discovered island groups in Tuamotu Archipelago and five in other places.[115] He united the majority of them under the name "Islands of Russians."

Those portions of the voyages in search of the Southern Continent or Antarctica that took place in the Atlantic Ocean are beyond our subject. We should, however, mention briefly that within the Atlantic Ocean the Russian expedition discovered some islands and added much to the detailed information available on South Georgia, Sandwich, and South Shetland islands, and on January 16 (Old Style, 28th), 1820, discovered the Antarctic continent[116] and briefly described its coasts seen on that day, on January 21 (O. S., February 2nd),[117] and on February 5 and 6 (O. S., 17th and 18th).[118] In his report to the Minister of the Navy,[119] Bellinsgausen called these coasts "a continent of ice," and in a private letter Lazarev called them "an ice continent."[120] These terms indicate that both explorers clearly realized the specific features of the landscape they had seen and definitely distinguished it from an "ice field." Russian discovery of the Antarctic continent has been fully proven by Soviet scientists and it is beginning to be recognized beyond the USSR.[121]

During a cruise in the Pacific Ocean near the coasts of the Antarctic continent the expedition, on January 10 (O. S., 22nd), 1821, discovered Peter I Island, described it in detail, and precisely plotted it on a map.[122] Jean B. Charcot, in 1910, located it in a fog by reference to the record of its position as determined by Russian seamen nearly ninety years earlier.[123] In summarizing the observations of Antarctica accumulated during 1820 and the early part of 1821, Bellinsgausen wrote that ". . . tremendous ice masses, which rise into sloping mountains upon the approach to the South pole, are called matyoroy[124] by me on the assumption that inasmuch as during the best summer day the frost is 4° C. and further south the cold is not diminishing, this ice stretches across the pole and must be immobile, touching locally upon shallow water or islands similar to Peter I Island."[125] On January 17 (O. S., 29th) 1821, Alexander I coast was discovered and mapped. After having seen land exposed free from ice and snow, Bellinsgausen spoke about this wonderful discovery very carefully: "I call this find a coast because the distance of the other end southwards disappeared beyond the range of our sight. This coast is covered by snow, *but talus on the mountains and steep rocks had no snow* on them . . ." (italics by the authors).[126] Until the last decades of the nineteenth century it was generally thought that this coast was part of the continent. This remarkable description well fits present concepts of the Antarctic continent.

Not denying the great value of the results achieved by Cook's voyage of 1772–1775, Yu. M. Shokal'skii indicates that a greater stay of the Russians, as compared with Cook's cruise south of latitude 60° (Bellinsgausen 122 days and Cook 75 days), and especially the greater length of the route covered south of latitude 60° (Bellinsgausen crossed 242 meridians of which 41 were south of the Antarctic Circle, while Cook crossed 125 meridians of which 24 were south of the Antarctic Circle) permitted Bellinsgausen to present a really complete picture of ice conditions in the southern latitudes of the Atlantic and Pacific oceans. This was something Cook did not do.[127]

The Bellinsgausen-Lazarev expeditions as a whole made a big contribution to physico-geographical studies of Antarctica and the low latitudes of the Pacific Ocean. From the point of view of cartography, a great number of islands were mapped. These were mostly those that are a part of groups, both newly discovered and previously known but whose position and outlines were verified and described in detail. A vast number of astronomical observations of latitude and longitude and numerous carefully compiled descriptions resulted in a high quality of cartographic representation. Very exact determinations of individual points were made along the route of the ships, especially in Antarctic waters.

An important contribution by Bellinsgausen in the physical geography of the Pacific Ocean was his characterization of the natural conditions in extensive oceanic areas, both in polar and low latitudes, and some theoretical summarizations of his observations and those of his companions. Numerous oceanographic researches produced new information on the temperature and specific weight of the water at different depths, and on the currents in the Pacific and Atlantic oceans. The structure of sea ice was studied and an attempt was made to classify Antarctic ice. Astronomer Simonov carried out systematic observations; in the tropics alone he made over 4300 observations.[128] In 1825, he summarized the results of his studies in a paper entitled "On Temperature Differences in the Southern and Northern Hemispheres." Terrestrial magnetism deviation determinations were made all along the route and at coastal points the angle of inclination was determined by an inclinometer.

Bellinsgausen (after Kotzebue and his companions) expressed very interesting views on the origin and structure of coral islands[129] which were close to these formulated by John Murray, the English oceanographer, half a century later. Inasmuch as even now there is no single generally accepted theory on the origin of coral reefs the views of Bellinsgausen, stipulated before Darwin, are of great interest. Finally, the *Atlas*[130] containing maps of Alexander I Coast, groups and individual islands in the Pacific (including Peter I Island) and in the Atlantic, and a great number of skillful drawings representing the Pacific flora, fauna, and native inhabitants, is important even at the present time.

THE VASSILIEV-SHISHMAREV EXPEDITION, 1819–1822

The Vassiliev-Shishmarev expedition left Kronshtadt in July, 1819, and returned in August 1822, having rounded the Cape of Good Hope on the way to the Pacific and Cape Horn on the way back. Its main purpose was to seek a sea route from the Pacific eastwards into the Atlantic, past the northern coasts of North America, or a route along Eurasia, westwards.[131] This aim, however, could not be achieved at that time. The trip was accompanied by the usual observations concerning the nature and the inhabitants of the Pacific Ocean and of its coasts which amplified available information, mainly about the northern part. During the voyage of 1820–1821, from Unalaska to Norton Bay, "Otkrytie Island" (Nunivak Island) was discovered. Detailed descriptions and data were prepared for some islands and especially for considerable stretches along the coasts of northeastern Asia and northwestern America, including part of Bristol Bay much farther north, as well as in some areas of Chukchi Sea between Cape Lisburne and Cape Krusenshtern. Vassiliev and Shishmarev established more exactly the geographical position of these extreme northern areas of the two continents.

EXPLORATIONS DURING THE PERIOD 1825–1867

Quite a special place belongs to the trip, in 1848–1849, of the officer G. I. Nevelsky, who was sent with a military cargo aboard the *Baikal* from Kronshtadt to Petropavlovsk-Kamchatskiy. Prior to his voyage the question as to the existence of a strait between Sakhalin and the continent, and the accessibility of Amurskiy Liman (estuary) for big ships without rounding Sakhalin from the north, had been decided in the negative. Despite the opinion of La Pérouse, Broughton, and Kruzenshtern (confirmed by officer Gavrilov on his voyage of 1846), Nevelsky overcame tremendous difficulties of an official nature, carried out exceedingly strenuous researches, and finally proved the insular character of Sakhalin and the complete accessibility of Amurskiy Liman and the river mouth for big ships.[132] Solution of this problem was of great practical and considerable scientific importance to the development of the Russian Far East.

A few of the world voyages during the first half of the nineteenth century which made contributions, even if smaller ones, to the study of the Pacific Ocean are:

1. Ferdinand P. Vrangel, in the transport *Krotky* in 1825–1827,[133] did not discover any new lands, but carried out detailed and careful surface temperature observations in the Pacific Ocean. The precision of these observations was a big contribution to this field of studies.[134]

2. M. N. Stanuikovich, in the sloop *Moller* in 1826–1829, passed near the Hawaiian Islands for hundreds of miles, inspected and astronomically established the position of some of them, and then made a careful description of some Aleutian islands and the Alaska peninsula from Isanotski Strait to Bristol Bay.[135]

3. L. V. Hagemeister, in the transport *Krotky* in 1828–1830, discovered and described two chains of small islands in the Marshall Islands, naming them Prince Menshikov Islands (Apataki Atoll), as well as several others previously known. Together with Professor Ermann of Berlin he carried out interesting magnetic observations.[136]

4. V. S. Khromchenko made two voyages, one in 1828–1830, in the ship *Elena*, and the other in 1831–1833, in the transport *America*. During his explorations Khromchenko obtained information on and compiled detailed descriptions of some of the Marshall Islands.[137]

5. I. I. Schantz, in the transport *America* in 1834–1836, discovered thirteen mostly uninhabited islands in the Ralik Chain of Marshall Islands. These were subsequently called Schantz Islands (Wotho Atoll).[138]

In addition to world cruises, Russian ships, most of which were commanded by officers of the Navy, made over 225 voyages within the North Pacific during the nineteenth century, mainly north of Japan. In sum, they embraced extremely large coastal stretches of the Asiatic and American continents and adjacent islands, Bering Sea, and the marginal seas. During each of them physico-geographical and magnetic observations were made. These numerous voyages thus resulted in a considerable amplification of hydrographic information about many areas and the compilation of more detailed and exact maps.[139]

Before the Russian possessions were sold to the United States of America in 1867, considerable attention was paid to scientific research carried out during operations of the Russian-American Company in the northeast portions of the Pacific Ocean, on the coasts of Alaska with its adjacent islands, and on the Aleutian chain. They were especially numerous up to the middle of the 1850s, including, for example, descriptions by Hagemeister in 1817–1818, by Ustiugov in 1818–1819, by Khromchenko and Etolin in 1821, and by Tebenkov personally or on his behalf by several seamen, 1843–1850.

The most interesting scientific results in the northwest Pacific were obtained by the following expeditions that took place before 1867: Shakhovsky's numerous descriptions and a more perfect map of the northern part of the Sea of Okhotsk in 1816–1819;[140] Kozmin's preparation of the first description of Shantarskiye Ostrova and the "Uda coast" according to modern methods and the compilation of an exact map of each in 1829–1831;[141] and descriptions of separate parts of Kamchatka by naval officers during the period 1836 to 1853. In 1850–1855 Nevelsky directed a number of researches for the verification of oceanographic information of Sakhalin Island, and the straits and Asiatic coasts lying to the westward.

During these years two general atlases were compiled on the basis of personal investigations and all available Russian and partly foreign materials. These were the *Atlas of the Eastern Ocean* (*north of Japan*) by navigator Kashevarov (Koshevarov), published in 1850; and a much more detailed and perfect atlas by M. D. Tebenkov, published in 1852.[142] The latter atlas, covering the northwestern coast of America, the Aleutian Islands, and part of the northeastern coast of Asia, includes very valuable hydrographic notes,[143] many separate plans, and thirty-eight sheets of maps, compiled mainly on the basis of hitherto unknown facts. The atlas was regarded as a most important contribution to the geography of Alaska up to the beginning of the 1870s.[144]

EXPLORATIONS DURING THE PERIOD 1867–1899

After 1867, Russian explorations in the northeastern Pacific Ocean were discontinued, but proceeded with intensity in its western part. The beginning was laid by K. S. Staritzky, whose outstanding researches lasted for six years (1865–1871).[145] The total length of his routes, which included the Sea of Japan, East China Sea, Yellow Sea, Sea of Okhotsk, the coasts of Kamchatka, and the coasts of the Kuril Islands, was 65,000 miles. He determined astronomically the coordinates of thirty-seven points from latitudes 15° N. to 62° N.,[146] with a total of 350 astronomic observations. In the Sea of Okhotsk alone he made twenty magnetic observations and sixteen depth measurements. Staritzky made many surveys and surveying measurements for his descriptions and cartographic work, and compiled plans and maps. During the period 1874–1877 M. Onatzevich and his officers effected extensive observations, mostly meteorological, hydrographic, and magnetic, in the Sea of Okhotsk, Sea of Japan, East China Sea, and in the open ocean in the waters east of Japan. The results were summarized and published.[147] In addition to the work of Staritzky and Onatzevich, much new data obtained personally or under their direction by officers Elagin, in 1872–1874, and Maydell, in 1874–1878. Academician L. I. Schrenk, who cruised the Sea of Japan in 1854 and repeatedly visited its coasts, published in 1869 a review of the physical geography of the region that was based on his personal observations and on published materials.[148] In 1874, he published an extensive work on the currents in the Sea of Japan, the Sea of Okhotsk, and in adjacent seas that was based on the observations of the ships of the Russian navy.[149] Schrenk's papers were the first scientific generalization of scattered information on the hydrography of these seas.[150] Finally, it should be stressed that in addition to the above-mentioned expeditions many exceptionally detailed descriptions were made of smaller areas during the second half of the nineteenth century (mostly after 1867). Most of these were concentrated in Amurskiy Liman, in the mouth of the Amur and in its lower reaches, and in Zaliv Petra Velikogo (Peter the Great Bay).[151]

Among other Russian researchers in the Pacific Ocean, after 1867, mention should be made of N. N. Miklukho-Maklai. He sailed on the corvette *Vitiaz* in 1871 on a world voyage, stopping for ethnographic researches on New Guinea. He earned his

world fame mainly by his ethnographic and anthropological researches, especially in
the west central Pacific. (In 1950–1954 the Academy of Sciences of the USSR published a collection of his papers in five volumes.) His hydrometeorological observations in the Pacific were also very valuable.[152]

Quite a special place in the history of oceanographic research during the nine-
teenth century belongs to Stefan O. Makarov's cruise from Kronshtadt in 1886–
1889, in the corvette *Vitiaz*. The principal route points were the Strait of Magellan,
Marquesas Islands, Hawaiian Islands, Yokohama, the Sea of Japan, the Sea of
Okhotsk, the Philippine Islands, the Indian Ocean, the Suez Canal, and thence to
Kronshtadt. Makarov published a two-volume monograph, the subject of which is
Vitiaz and the Pacific Ocean.[153] His scientific work consisted mainly of systematic,
very exact hydrological and meteorological observations of temperature and of specific weights of the water on the surface and at depth, and a determination of the
velocity of currents. Altogether there were 261 deep-water stations, including 166
in the Pacific Ocean. Water samples were taken from depths of 25, 50, 100, 200,
400, and 800 meters.[154] Having at his disposal areometer, bathometer, thermometer,
fluctometer, depth gauge, and other instruments, Makarov scrupulously studied their
behavior and employed a careful method of using the instruments and processing the
data obtained. He made improvements in Lenz's bathometer[155] and worked out corrections in the areometer readings which gave him a reputation as an outstanding
specialist in this field.[156] These accomplishments are discussed in the first volume of
his monograph.

On the basis of special researches Makarov compiled tables for measuring the
specific weight of sea water which were thought to be the best up to the appearance
in 1901 of the international oceanographic tables.[157] Makarov's numerous deductions
about specific hydrological and meteorological features of the Pacific Ocean were
based on his personal observations and on carefully analyzed and summarized extensive observations obtained in seventy-eight voyages in the North Pacific during
the long span of years 1804–1890. Sixty-three of the voyages were by Russians.
Most of the material used by Makarov was previously unpublished.[158] His two volumes clarify many theoretical problems of hydrology and meteorology in areas of
the North Pacific and its marginal seas[159] and contain a number of valuable discoveries; for example, that the equatorial current involves a water layer up to 200 meters
deep, while the countercurrent extends to an even lesser depth.[160] His concepts of
the Antarctic origin of the lower cold layers of water in the northern part of the
ocean, and of the direction of currents in all inland seas of the north against apparent
sun movement are in agreement with scientific information in the twentieth century.[161]

The book *Vitiaz and the Pacific Ocean* has long occupied a place of honor in oceanographic science because of its exceptionally rich and reliable data.[162] It was the first
to give an oceanographic description of an important and interesting part of the
Pacific Ocean, and greatly aided the progress of oceanography.

11

GEOGRAPHICAL EXPLORATION BY THE FRENCH

Robert J. Garry*

Exploration of the Pacific Basin by the French was begun perhaps as early as the second quarter of the seventeenth century. Prior to about the mid-eighteenth century, geographical exploration was almost always secondary to commercial and trading interests and to missionary activities. Apparently no important geographical discoveries were made, although several islands were discovered in the southern hemisphere.

Planned French geographical exploration of the Pacific Basin was initiated in 1766 by Louis Antoine de Bougainville; subsequent exploring expeditions included scientists and other professional men who made collections in natural history, recorded observations in the physical sciences, and described the landscape. The collections were added to the museums and laboratories in France, scientific results were discussed at professional meetings and in publications and official reports, and a large fund of new cartographical information appeared in maps and atlases. By the beginning of the nineteenth century French exploration of the Pacific Basin was competing favorably with that of England.[1]

The first French navigators to approach the Pacific Basin were the Parmentier brothers, Jean and Raoul, who arrived as far back as 1529 to engage in the pepper traffic in the Sunda Islands on behalf of a Dieppe shipbuilder. Though their mission was primarily trade, Jean Parmentier did leave a brief account of their stay in the Pacific, especially on Sumatra.[2]

In 1709 a navigator named Frondat sailed on the brig *Saint-Antoine* from Japan to California and on his way observed certain small islands in southern Japan, and the Île de la Passion (Clipperton Island). Between 1714 and 1716 Forgeais de Laugerie, on the frigate *Comtesse de Pontchartrain*, made the return journey from the Far East via Formosa, Paita, and Valparaíso. In his wake several Frenchmen, on their way back from China to Europe, followed the route of the Manila galleons.[3] Somewhat later, the French geographer Delisle de la Croyère was chosen by the St. Petersburg Academy of Sciences to accompany Vitus Bering's expedition (see Chapter 10). He died on Komandorski Ostrova in 1742.[4] The French also pressed the search for the southern continent and twice thought they had discovered it. The first time was in 1739, when Bouvet de Lozier discovered the island bearing his name south of the African continent in latitude 54°5′S.;[5] the second was in 1772, when Yves J. de Kerguelen-Tremarec discovered an island of the archipelago which has received his name bestowing upon it the lofty name "France Australe" (Southern France).[6]

It was quite obvious that France could not quickly aspire to play the same role in the Pacific as Spain and the Netherlands, which for quite some time had been powers bordering on the great ocean. This position changed only when scientific expeditions

---

*Dr. Garry is professor of geography at both the University of Montreal and Laval University, Quebec, Canada.

were organized by the French government. Publication of the celebrated *Terra australis incognita: or, Voyages to the Terra australis* . . . by Charles de Brosses, in 1766–1768,[7] was responsible for this rather considerable change of attitude on the part of the French authorities. The end of the Seven Years' War was followed by a fruitful rivalry between France and Britain in the methodical and scientific exploration of the Pacific generally and of Oceania particularly.

SIGNIFICANT EXPLORATION DURING THE EIGHTEENTH CENTURY

France established a colony at the Îles Malouines (the Falkland Islands) in 1764. Spain claimed that these islands were part of the mainland and demanded their cession on payment of an indemnity. In 1766 Louis Antoine de Bougainville was authorized to use the money France obtained from the cession to explore the Pacific lands between the Tropic of Capricorn and the Tropic of Cancer and to take possession of of "such as might be of some use for commerce and navigation."[8]

He sailed from Brest on December 5, 1766, on the frigate *La Boudeuse*, added the store ship *L'Etoile* while on his way to Rio de Janeiro, and cleared the Strait of Magellan on January 26, 1768. Bougainville's track in the Pacific is shown in Figure 31. He was the first navigator before James Cook to make systematic observations of longitude at sea. In the name of France he took possession of the seven groups of islands which constitute his discoveries and of which France did not trouble to avail herself: the Archipel Dangereux (Tuamotu Archipelago), the Archipel de Bourbon (Society Islands), the Îles des Navigateurs (Samoa Islands), the Grandes Cyclades (New Hebrides), the Louisiade Archipelago, Choiseul and Bougainville (in the Solomons), and La Nouvelle Irlande (New Ireland).[9] Bougainville did not realize that some of his discoveries had already been made by Samuel Wallis and Jacob Roggeveen, but he was the first navigator to sail directly through the Tuamotu Archipelago and to identify the Grandes Cyclades and the "Southern Lands of the Holy Ghost" that had been discovered by Quirós. He proved that they were joined neither to New Guinea nor to New Holland (Australia).[10] Starvation and scurvy, and syphilis contracted by his crew at Tahiti, prevented the continuation of his voyage and the completion of his discoveries. He sailed through Melanesia, retreated from the Great Barrier Reef, and, making a half-turn, traversed once more the Solomon Islands and New Britain, put in at Batavia, and arrived at Saint-Malo, where he cast anchor on March 16, 1776.

The success of Bougainville's voyage is perhaps more literary than geographical. It remains famous because of his account of his stay from April 6 to 15 at Hitiaa, on the east coast of Tahiti, which he had christened "the new Cythera." In forty pages of vivid, colorful narrative he brought to Europe an enchanting picture of the queen of the south seas. He forced Oceania on the attention of his fellow countrymen, who were never to forget those lands to which many French expeditions sailed from that time on.[11]

With Bougainville were two scientists, M. de Commercon, a naturalist, and M. Verron, an astronomer whose primary interest, apparently, was the problem of determining longitude at sea. Unfortunately, Verron's hope of taking a significant series of readings on Juan Fernandez Island as a kind of base in the eastern Pacific could not be made because winds carried the ship away from the island.

In Bougainville's report and that of others of his associates are vivid descriptions of the geographical landscape of most of the lands that were visited, particularly Tahiti. We note from these reports that longitude observations taken during May, 1722 showed that their ship was being carried westward by currents, which Bougainville believed explained why explorers reached New Guinea sooner than they had calculated. Astronomical and other observations were taken at convenient places. A pendulum and a quadrant were taken on shore when convenient in order to accurately determine the sun's altitude at noon. Using several different instruments, detailed observations were made of the eclipse of the sun while at New Britain; a marker noting this event was placed at the very spot where these observations had been made, now called Port Praslin. It was because of these detailed observations at several locations in the Pacific that Bougainville gave a more accurate value to the width of the ocean. Bougainville requested that each sailor receive ". . . a pint of lemonade prepared with a kind of powder called 'powder of faciot' " as an antiscorbutic agent. He also experimented with and made some use of Monsieur Poiffonier's water-distilling apparatus to ". . . make use of the seawater, which was by this means deprived of its salt."

In 1769 Jean F. M. de Surville left France for Pondicherry, India, on a mission about which there still is something of a mystery. At Pondicherry he took on cargo which presumably was to be delivered in Tahiti,[12] and then sailed on the *St. Jean Baptiste* to the Philippines. De Surville's probable track in the Pacific is shown in Figure 31. Thence he passed to the west of the New Britain Archipelago (Bismarck Archipelago) and New Caledonia, and dropped anchor in December, 1769 at Doubtless Bay, naming it Lauriston Bay (North Island of New Zealand). After revictualling and repairing his ship, he sailed eastwards, between latitudes 35° and 41° S., without sighting the Polynesian archipelago. He was drowned on the voyage home, while landing at Callao in Peru, and his voyage contributed relatively little new scientific information. Apparently a primary motive in sending this expedition was to anticipate Cook's reconaissance of Tahiti, but in this effort it failed by probably six weeks.

In 1771 Nicholas Thomas Marion de Fresnes received two ships, the *Mascarin* and the *Marquis de Castries*, from Monsieur Poivre, the Governor of Mauritius. He was given the responsibility for taking back to Tahiti a chief named Aoutourou who had been brought to France by Bougainville in 1769. Marion de Fresnes left Mauritius on October 18, and sailed southwards to latitude 46°. Shortly after the expedition was underway the chief died, presumably of smallpox, but De Fresnes decided to continue the voyage as planned. On January 24, 1772, he discovered two islands which he called Crozet Islands in honor of his first officer and of which he took possession in the name of the King of France. On July 11, 1772, two years after Cook's visit, he sighted Van Diemen's Land (Tasmania), to which he gave the name "France Australe," and then stopped at New Zealand where he and sixteen members of his crew were slain on July 14 by the Maoris.[13] De Fresnes' and Crozet's track is shown in Figure 31.

After avenging the death of De Fresnes and his companions, Crozet sailed north-

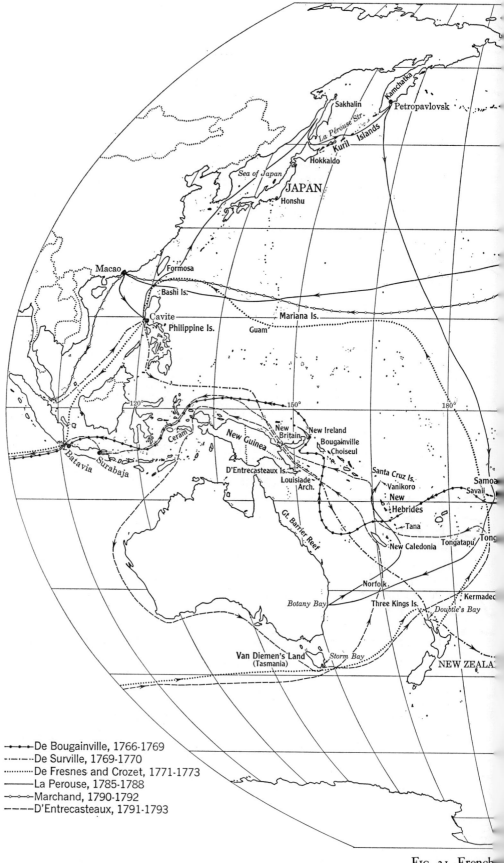

Kamchatka
Petropavlovsk
Sakhalin
La Pérouse Str.
Kuril Islands
Hokkaido
Sea of Japan
JAPAN
Honshu
Macao
Formosa
Bashi Is.
Cavite
Philippine Is.
Mariana Is.
Guam
120°
150°
180°
New Britain
New Ireland
New Guinea
Bougainville
Choiseul
Ceram
D'Entrecasteaux Is.
Louisiade Arch.
Santa Cruz Is.
Vanikoro
Samoa
Savaii
Batavia
Surabaja
New Hebrides
Tana
Tong
Tongatapu
Gt. Barrier Reef
New Caledonia
Norfolk
Kermadec
Botany Bay
Three Kings Is.
Double's Bay
Van Diemen's Land
(Tasmania)
Storm Bay
NEW ZEALA

●—●—● De Bougainville, 1766-1769
—·—·— De Surville, 1769-1770
··········· De Fresnes and Crozet, 1771-1773
———— La Perouse, 1785-1788
—○—○— Marchand, 1790-1792
— — — D'Entrecasteaux, 1791-1793

Fig. 31. French

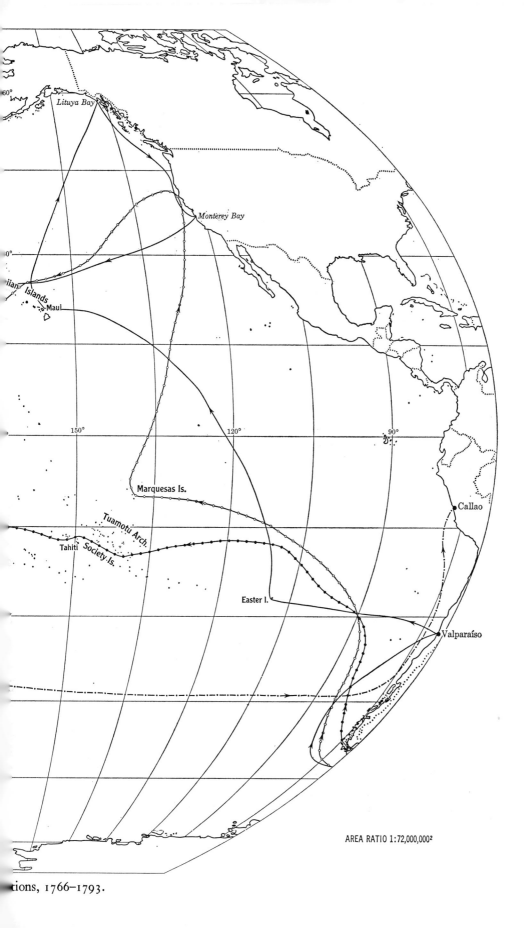

60

Lituya Bay

Montèrey Bay

150°   120°   90°

lian Islands

Maui

Marquesas Is.

Tuamotu Arch.

Tahiti Society Is.

Easter I.

Callao

Valparaíso

AREA RATIO 1:72,000,000²

eastwards and in the region of latitude 16°S., discovered an island which he called the Île du Point du Jour (Daybreak Island). Crossing the equator he reached Guam on September 25 and the Philippines in December, and subsequently returned to Mauritius.[14] This expedition contributed little to the general geography of the Pacific, other than the discovery of the Crozet Islands (in the Indian Ocean) and Île du Point du Jour.

In 1785 the French government entrusted Jean-Francois Galaup de la Pérouse with the mission of searching for "all the lands which had escaped the vigilance of Cook,"[15] and to check previous discoveries (Fig. 31). For the first time in history a scientifically manned and outfitted expedition was organized. All of the details were subject to minute preparation. A veritable mobilization of scientists and artists took place, and they were provided with the finest scientific instruments and a full library of published scientific literature, including books, maps, and charts.

La Pérouse sailed from Brest on August 1, 1785, with the two frigates L'Astrolabe and La Boussole, passed through the Estrecho de Le Maire on January 25, 1786, put in at Valparaíso, and arrived at Easter Island on April 8, where he landed, stayed two days, studied the inhabitants, and obtained an excellent series of observations. Avoiding Tahiti, which he considered too well known, La Pérouse followed a route through unknown waters 800 miles westward of the parallel route taken by Cook a few years before. He sighted the peaks of Maui in the Hawaiian Islands on May 28, and, sailing northwards, steered for Alaska where he lost twenty-one men in the wreck of a ship's boat in Lituya Bay. Then he sailed south to Monterey Bay, California, spent four months exploring and surveying the coast, and was the first to describe its general appearance and to produce a complete chart of the area surveyed (Plates 28, 29, *facing pages 165 and 212*). In October he set his course for Macao, sailing across an unknown sea between latitudes 19° and 20°N., and was nearly lost at night west of the Hawaiian Islands. On November 4 he discovered an uninhabited island which he named Île Necker, on which he found extremely interesting archaelogical remains. The next day he nearly ran aground on an unknown reef which he named Basse des Frégates françaises (French Frigate Shoals). On his way east he stopped at the Marianas and at the Bashi Islands, north of the Philippines, and cast anchor before Macao on January 3, 1777.

After a short rest at Macao La Pérouse steered for the Philippines, where he spent some time at Cavite in order to repair his ships and take on fresh supplies. On April 10 he sailed once more on a northerly course, following the east coast of the island of Formosa, and penetrated the Sea of Japan via Korea Strait. From field surveys he compiled the first accurate charts of the fog-bound coasts of the island of Hondo (Honshu), Tatary (Primorskiy Kray), the islands of Sakhalin and Hokkaido, and the northern straits of Japan (La Pérouse Strait and Tsugaru-kaikyó). Then he entered the Pacific and explored and mapped the Kuril Islands and on September 6, 1787, cast anchor at Petropavlovsk, Kamchatka.

From Kamchatka, La Pérouse steered southwards and crossed the western Pacific on December 6 at the island of Mauna (Tutuila) in the Archipel du Navigateur (Samoa Islands), where he made contact with the natives. While he was taking in fresh water on the shores of the island his second-in-command De Langle, the physician-naturalist De Lamanon, and ten of his sailors were killed by the natives.

La Pérouse explored two other islands which have not been definitely identified but which are thought to be Savai'i and Upolu, and then sailed for the Tonga Islands. The weather was so bad that he could not find a berth at Vavau in the northern group. He stopped at Tofua, already discovered by Cook, then explored two uninhabited atolls known today as Huonga Tonga and Huonga Haapai, and reached Tongatapu on December 31, 1787. He established relations with the natives (from whom he bought a few weapons) and has left us a vivid account of them. The next day he headed westwards but the winds drove him south and he sighted Pylstaart (Ata) Island. His course took him near Norfolk Island and, on January 26, he entered the roadstead of Botany Bay. Here the British, who had arrived before him on the east coast of Australia, undertook to transmit his letters and ship's logs to France.

From Botany Bay La Pérouse probably followed a northeasterly course. One night, during a storm, his frigates were cast on the reefs of Vanikoro in the Santa Cruz Islands. Neither he nor his companions escaped and their fate remains unknown, although traces of the wreck were found by Pierre Dillon in 1827.[16]

Despite the rapidity of his voyage La Pérouse made a great contribution to our knowledge of the Pacific. He contributed detailed geographical studies of the Japanese archipelago and its approaches, new and valuable information on Samoa, and the discovery of some islands, as, for example, Savai'i. La Pérouse was the first navigator to use marine chronometers for the determination of longitude by comparing local time with the time at the zero meridian. Fortunately, when La Pérouse arrived at Botany Bay and at the port of St. Peter and St. Paul (Petropavlovsk, Kamchatka) he sent a copy of his journal and other papers to the National Assembly of France. These documents were ordered published and are our primary source of La Pérouse's accomplishments up to this time. Among them is the excellent "Dissertation on the inhabitants of Easter Island and Mowee [Maui]," by M. Rollin, who was surgeon-naturalist aboard *La Boussole*. Had La Pérouse and his expedition survived there is little question that he would have made even more significant contributions to our knowledge of the Pacific, especially in the fields of surveying and mapping and in the natural sciences.

Despite the reopening of hostilities in Europe two French navigators, Étienne Marchand and Antoine R. J. de Bruni d'Entrecasteaux, each made an expedition into the Pacific during the closing ten years of the eighteenth century. Marchand left Marseille on the vessel *Le Solide* on December 14, 1790, doubled the Horn and steered for the Marquesas Islands, reaching them on June 12, 1790 (Fig. 31). The next day, while exploring the seas surrounding the archipelago, most of which had been discovered by Mendaña in 1595 and Cook in 1774, he sighted new islands of which he took possession in the name of France, calling them Île Marchand (Ua Pu), Île Baux (Nuku Hiva), les Deux Frères (Motuiti), Île Masse (Eiao), and Chanal (Hatutu). Then he headed for the northwest coast of America to pick up furs, recrossed the Pacific to the Hawaiian Islands and the Marianas, put into Macao on November 27, 1791, and cast anchor at Toulon on August 14, 1792. Though Marchand's expedition was essentially commercial he did explore and search for new islands and maintained a record of his discoveries (Fig. 31).[17]

The fate of La Pérouse was still a mystery. An expedition was organized under the command of Admiral D'Entrecasteaux to search for the commander of *L'Astro-*

labe and to learn of his fate. Two men-of-war, *La Recherche* and *L'Espérance*, were placed in his charge, and a naturalist, Jacques Julien de Labillardière, was attached to the expedition.[18] Admiral D'Entrecasteaux sailed on September 25, 1791, arrived at New Caledonia in June, 1792, and at the Louisiade Archipelago, in the southern tip of New Guinea, the following month (Fig. 31). The neighboring islands to the north are called the D'Entrecasteaux Islands in honor of the leader of the expedition. After following the eastern and northern coasts of New Guinea the expedition proceeded to the islands of Ceram and Amboina in the Moluccas. From Amboina D'Entrecasteaux steered for the west coast of Australia, which he explored during the months of November and December, 1792. Leaving the Australian coast and setting his course southeastwards the admiral arrived at Storm Bay in Tasmania on January 22, 1793. He established excellent relations with the inhabitants and made significant and revealing observations on their way of life. During his stay in Tasmania he explored the channel bearing his name and the two islands which separate it from the open sea.

On February 28, 1793, D'Entrecasteaux headed for Tonga Island. On the way, he touched at the Three Kings Islands north of the North Island of New Zealand, and made valuable observations on the Maoris and their canoes. On March 15 he sailed through a group of islands which had been discovered in 1788, identified two of them as Curtis and Macaulay, and named the third L'Espérance Rock, after one of his ships. The next day he discovered the largest island in the group, which he named the Île Raoul (Raoul Island). The archipelago as a whole was called Kermadec Islands, by which name it is known today. The ships of the expedition cast anchor at Tongatapu on March 24 and remained there two weeks, during which time the most cordial relations were maintained with the natives. This gave Julien de Labillardière, the expedition's naturalist, an opportunity to obtain valuable information on the Tongans. The expedition then traveled toward Tana and New Caledonia, reached the Santa Cruz Islands in May, and the Louisiade Archipelago in June. The expedition arrived at Surabaja on October 10, and because war had broken out between France and Holland the vessels were interned.

The primary purpose of the expedition had not been accomplished; D'Entrecasteaux had failed to secure any positive information about the fate of La Pérouse and his companions. From a scientific standpoint, however, the D'Entrecasteaux expedition had been a success, particularly the work done by Labillardière.[19] The description of the Tonga islanders by Labillardière is an ethnographical document of the highest value and is a major contribution to our early knowledge of these peoples.

SIGNIFICANT EXPLORATION DURING THE NINETEENTH CENTURY

Few seafaring expeditions are so little known as the voyages made by Captain Nicolas Baudin in Australian waters between 1800 and 1803.[20] The expedition, which was sponsored by the French government and the learned societies of France, was both scientific and political in its purpose. It was intended to "verify some doubtful points in geography," to "advance the study of the natural sciences," and to make collections of living or preserved animals for the Museum of Natural History in Paris.[21]

A large scientific general staff of zoologists, botanists, geologists, astronomers, engineers, and geographers, equipped with a generous amount of scientific instruments and material, was attached to the expedition. The French government and the learned bodies provided chronometers, sextants, an astronomical circle, and a large collection of literature, including narratives of voyages and works on geography and science. Captain Baudin's instructions required him to "make accurate charts, study the inhabitants, the animals and the natural products, collect those which it seems possible to preserve and the useful animals and plants which are foreign to our climates and might be naturalized in them."[22] According to the route set for it, the expedition was required to make an accurate and detailed survey of more than 3000 nautical miles of Australian coastline, together with a portion of Tasmania and New Guinea (Fig. 32). The French government placed at Captain Baudin's disposal a 30-gun corvette, *Le Géographe*, and a 10-gun frigate, *Le Naturaliste*. The expedition set sail from Le Havre on October 19, 1800, and came in sight of the southwestern tip of Australia on May 27 of the following year. Identifying Cape Leeuwin, they skirted a low, barren coast, doubled Cape Naturaliste, and on May 30 found an anchorage in the vast Géographe Bay, which has kept its name from the time that they passed through it.[23]

During their stay members of the expedition explored the shores of the bay, Rottnest Island, and the estuary of Swan River. The corvette, under Captain Baudin, and the frigate, under Lieutenant Hamelin, now parted company, agreeing to meet again at Rottnest Island. On June 9, 1801, the two ships were dispersed by a storm and were only to see each other again at Timor. Baudin sailed up the barren Australian coast, came in sight of Dirk Hartogs Island and explored the islands which close the entrance to Shark Bay, previously explored by Dampier, and visited in 1772 by Saint-Allouarn, lieutenant in De Kerguelen's expedition to the Indian Ocean, on his way back to France. Exact observations were taken on the shores of Shark Bay, observations which were completed by several subsequent French expeditions. A few weeks later, Hamelin corrected the position of the Abrolhos Islands or Houtman Rocks (the Dutch had placed them much too far out to sea) and between July 16 and September 4 completed a very detailed study of Shark Bay. The first accurate charts of the bay, which were to be completed by Louis de Freycinet in September, 1818, date from this methodical exploration by *Le Naturaliste*. The names of Hamelin's assistants, Faure and Saint-Cricq, have been given to an island and a cape in the bay. On September 4, *Le Naturaliste* lay off Kupang at Timor, beside *Le Géographe*, which had arrived there before her.

Meanwhile *Le Géographe*, which had stood out to sea since July 13, had surveyed the northwestern tip of Australia. She followed the shoreline of Eighty Mile Beach, where the Great Sandy Desert comes almost to the sea, and then coursed the terrible coast where "there is nothing but islands and perils and the navigation is difficult and dangerous." Since the charts of Tasman and Dampier were so hazy, Baudin made many observations and brought some order out of the chaos, giving French names to the capes, bays, and islands he surveyed. The names Monte Bello and Lacépède

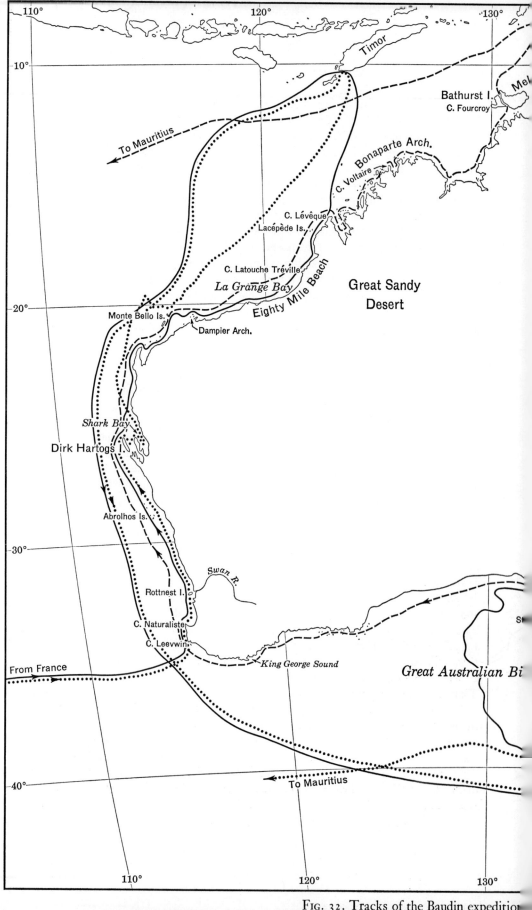

110°   120°   130°

Timor

Bathurst I.
C. Fourcroy

10°

To Mauritius

Bonaparte Arch.

C. Voltaire

C. Lévêque
Lacépède Is.

C. Latouche Tréville

La Grange Bay

Great Sandy
Desert

Eighty Mile Beach

20°

Monte Bello Is.

Dampier Arch.

Shark Bay

Dirk Hartogs I.

Abrolhos Is.

30°

Swan R.

Rottnest I.

C. Naturaliste

C. Leeuwin

From France

King George Sound

Great Australian Bi

40°

To Mauritius

110°   120°   130°

Fig. 32. Tracks of the Baudin expedition

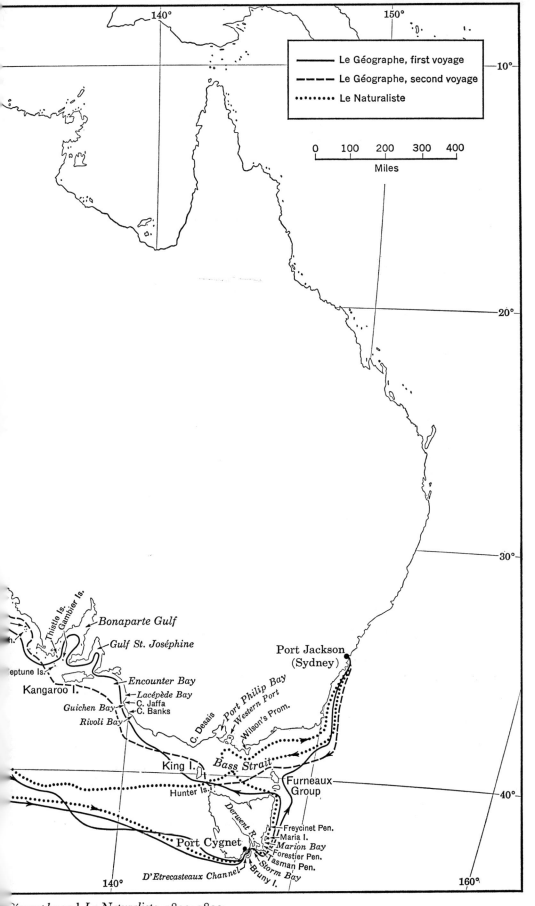

140°
150°
10°

Le Géographe, first voyage
Le Géographe, second voyage
Le Naturaliste

0   100   200   300   400
Miles

20°

30°

Thistle Is.
Gambier Is.
Bonaparte Gulf
Gulf St. Joséphine
eptune Is.
Kangaroo I.
Encounter Bay
Lacépède Bay
C. Jaffa
C. Banks
Guichen Bay
Rivoli Bay
C. Desais
Port Philip Bay
Western Port
Wilson's Prom.
Port Jackson
(Sydney)

King I.
Bass Strait
Hunter Is.
Furneaux
Group
40°

Derwent R.
Freycinet Pen.
Maria I.
Marion Bay
Port Cygnet
Forestier Pen.
Tasman Pen.
Storm Bay
D'Etrecasteaux Channel
Bruny I.

140°
160°

Géographe and *Le Naturaliste*, 1800–1803.

islands, Capes Latouche Tréville, Lévêque, and Voltaire, and La Grange Bay, are still in use. Only imperfect observations could be made from the corvette because of her deep draught. She put into Timor on August 22, 1801.

The arrival of the southern summer made it possible for the expedition to make a move southwards and, on November 13, 1801, Baudin sailed from Timor. Rounding the northwest tip of Australia, he was driven westwards into the Indian Ocean by the trade winds. On December 12, he set his course southwards; a few days later, with the help of the westerlies, he steered for Tasmania which he sighted on January 13, 1802. He entered the channel which had been overlooked by all navigators from Tasman to Bligh and which had received its name from the D'Entrecasteaux expedition. Passing between the southern point of Bruny Island and the mainland of Tasmania, the expedition explored the D'Entrecasteaux Channel on January 13, 1802. The following day De Freycinet, aboard *Le Naturaliste's* launch, was sent to the Derwent River, up which the canoes of D'Entrecasteaux had already traveled, and to Port Cygnet. Meanwhile, Baudin and Hamelin explored Partridge Island. The most important work was done to the north. Flinders and Bass had made superficial surveys of this region, but Freycinet, Faure, and Péron had been much more painstaking. On February 17, 1802, Baudin sailed from Storm Bay, rounded the Tasman Peninsula, and anchored in Oyster Bay near Maria Island. Like the coast, this island bristles with French names, as for example, Capes Bernier, Boulanger, Maurouard, and Péron, and Riedlé Bay. The coast and islands were carefully surveyed. The expedition discovered Marion Bay, the Forestier Peninsula which joins the Tasman Peninsula, hitherto believed to be an island, to Tasmania, the Freycinet Peninsula, and Schouten Passage (separating it from Schouten Island), the great Fleurieu Bay, and Oyster Bay. It was a splendid hydrographic survey.

On February 27 the expedition set out from Maria Island to explore the northeast coast of Tasmania, which had been imperfectly viewed by Furneaux in 1773 and by Flinders and Bass in 1799. The coast was followed very closely. The engineer-geographer Boulanger made a minute examination of Preservation, Clarke, and Waterhouse islands. After looking for *Le Naturaliste*, which had been driven away by a storm during the night of March 7–8, 1802, at Waterhouse Island and in the Furneaux Group, Baudin made for the Australian mainland. In the meantime Hamelin, after beating out to sea for six days and moving southwards to Maria Island, entered Bass Strait on April 1 and reached the Australian coast in the region of latitude 38°37′S. He explored Port Dalrymple, passed in sight of Wilson's Promontory, and put into Western Port and what would later be Port Phillip Bay at Melbourne. After reaching the Australian coast *Le Géographe* doubled Cape Desais (Cape Otway) and explored a depressing, barren shore where some French place names still remain, for example, Capes D'Estaing, Martin, and Buffon; Jaffa, Rivoli, Guichen, and Lacépede bays. After exploring 940 miles of coastline, Baudin met Captain Flinders in latitude 36°1′40″E., at a spot which has since been called Encounter Bay.

Pursuing his voyage westwards, Baudin discovered Kangaroo Island and rapidly explored its north coast, entered Gulf Saint Vincent and rechristened it Golfe Joséphine. He was unable to explore it completely because of the difficulties of navigation. A little later Péron carefully explored Port Champagny, subsequently

Plate 29

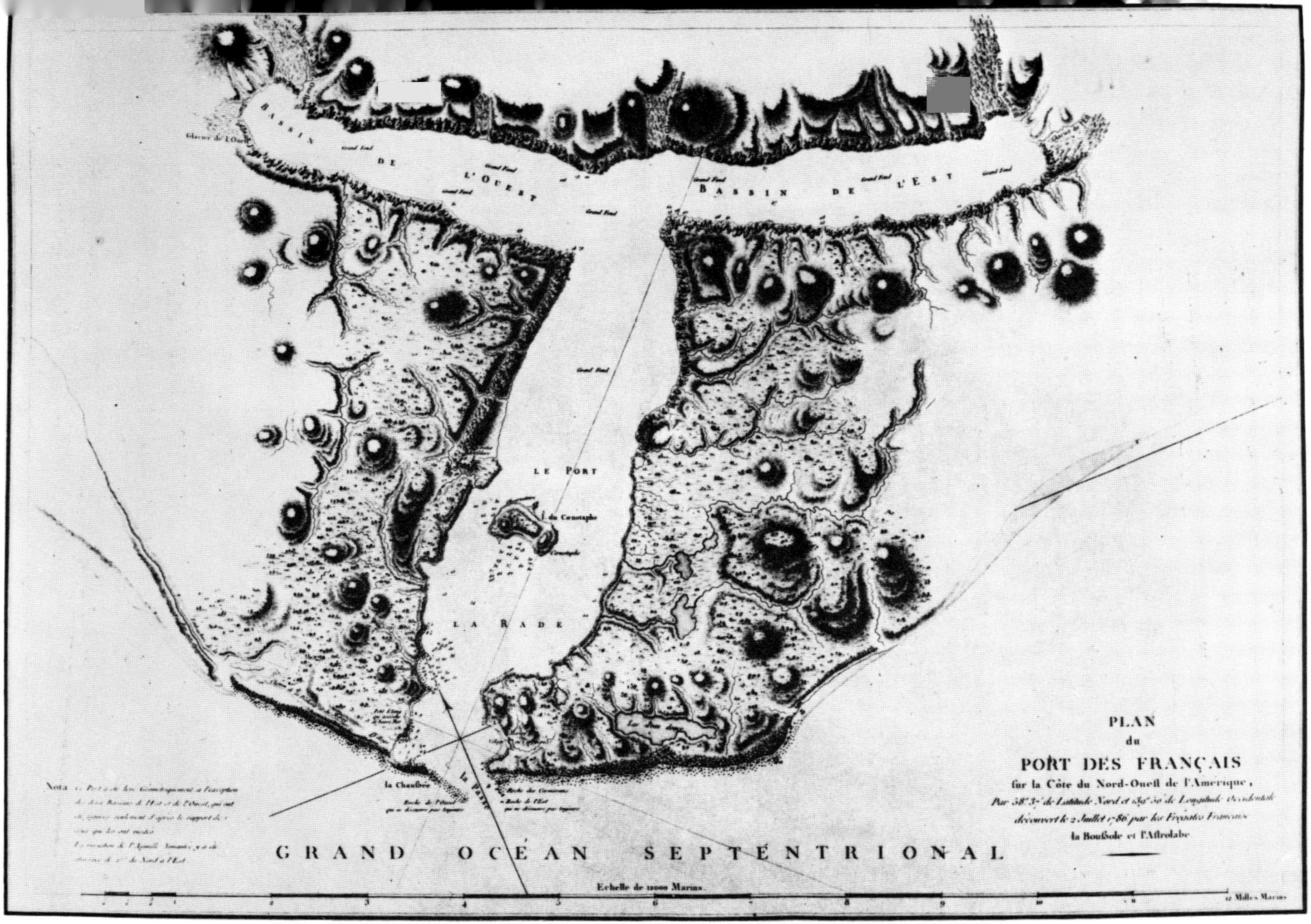

Chapter 11

"Plan du Port des Franaçis . . . ," in Gilbert Chinard: *Le voyage de La Pérouse sur les cotes de l'Alaska et de la Californie (1786)*, Baltimore, 1937, illus. op. p. 12. (Courtesy of the Institut Français de Washington). Named by La Pérouse when he discovered it in 1786, it is known today as Lituya Bay.

"Principal village de Bora Bora," in Dumont d'Urville: *Voyage pittoresque autour du monde* . . . Vol. 1, Paris, 1834, 574 pp., illus. op. p. 547. This is the most important island of the Leeward group of the Society Islands. This drawing probably represents the village of Vaitape and Taimanu mountain.

PLATE 30

called Port Lincoln by Flinders. Baudin explored Neptune Islands, Gambier Islands, and Thistle Island, entered Bonaparte Gulf (now Spencer Gulf) but could not sail up it because of the shallows. He set his course northwestwards, rounded Saint Peter Islands and the Isles of Saint Francis, and then returned to Tasmania to take in provisions. He anchored in Adventure Bay, below Bruny Island, and then headed for Sydney where he cast anchor on June 22, 1802, and spent the southern winter. On this first voyage the Baudin expedition had carried out a detailed survey of nearly 300 miles of coastline of southern Australia between Cape Banks and Encounter Bay, and had made accurate charts of the regions explored. On the remainder of the journey it had corrected the old English and Dutch charts, and further developed the work of Flinders and his predecessors in Tasmania.

After a six-months' stay in Sydney, Baudin and his companions set off again on November 18, 1802, stopping at King Island on December 7. The *Naturaliste* received orders to stand for Mauritius and return to France, where she arrived on June 7, 1803. Baudin continued his geographical work, using *Le Géographe* and *Le Casuarina*, a 30-ton schooner purchased in Sydney. He made a detailed exploration of the Hunter Islands and King Island. The first published account of these islands was based on his observations. On January 3, 1803, Baudin came to Kangaroo Island which, he thought, had been explored by Flinders, and made a detailed study of its south coast. The *Casuarina*, with her shallow draft, was able to explore Port Champagny (Port Lincoln) and hunted in vain for the strait supposed to lie behind the archipelago at the back of the Great Australian Bight. Baudin then passed on to Nuyts Archipelago and on the way explored many bays to which he gave French names, for example, Murat Bay and Tourville Bay. These explorations made possible the accurate charting of the south coast of Australia, which resulted in the opening of one of the busiest sea lanes on the globe to international commerce.

On February 12 *Le Géographe*, following a westerly course, arrived at King George Sound, discovered in 1791 by Vancouver, and the object of a quick visit by Flinders in 1802. Baudin spent eleven days here exploring and surveying various havens which make up the Sound. Despite adverse winds he explored the south-western coast in minute detail as far as Cape Leeuwin and Saint Alouarn Island, the exact position of which he determined. He then sailed up the coast to Shark Bay, Melville Island, and because of the shallow draft of the *Casuarina* was able to spend a month in detailed exploration and surveying of the labyrinth of channels and islands along the northwest coast. He corrected the charts of the Eighty Mile Beach coastline, checked the position of Holothuria Banks, Dampier Archipelago, Champagny Islands, and Bonaparte Archipelago, which he proved to be separate from the mainland. On July 17, 1803, Baudin followed the coast up to Cape Fourcroy, at the extreme western end of Bathurst Island, which is just west of Melville Island. Because none of the existing charts agreed with the observations he had made, Baudin drew up an accurate chart of the archipelago. Doubling Cape Leoben (Cape Van Diemen, the northern tip of Melville Island), Baudin stood out to sea, intending to survey Cape Walsh (Tandjung Vals) in the southwest of New Guinea, but the difficulties he encountered led him to put the ship about in latitude 8°26'N. and longitude 131°11'E. and to stand for Mauritius.

The scientific success of the voyage to the lands of the south was indisputable.

The voyage, especially the work of François Péron, the chief scientist, and the two artists Charles-Alexandre Lesueur and Nicolas-Martin Petit, greatly enriched French zoological and botanical collections. Anthropological and ethnographical collections, observations, and sketches brought back by the mission were the basis for the establishment in Paris of the Museum of Man and for the introduction of new disciplines. Thanks to the cooperation and the scientific interests of Baudin and under the direction of the scientists Georges L. L. de Buffon, Georges Cuvier, Jean B. P. A. de M. de Lamarck, Bernard G. E. Lacépède, and with the collections and notes that were obtained on the expeditions, especially Baudin's, the natural sciences flourished in France.

During Flinders' captivity in Mauritius (December 15, 1803 to May 27, 1810, *see* Chapter 12) the French obtained from him much valuable topographical information which made it possible for them to publish in 1807 the first complete map of Australia, showing the exact outline of the southern continent with the exact position of the south and northwest coasts of Tasmania. There were errors and approximations but they were mainly matters of specific and local detail. Many partial and detailed plans of Géographe Bay and Shark Bay appeared in these works. These cartographic and textual documents provided the primary source for the French marine charts of the Pacific Basin in the nineteenth century.[24]

After Baudin's voyage there was a lull in French maritime expeditions. We find almost nothing to be noted except the voyage of Captain César de Bourayne, who in 1807 escorted a Spanish galleon from Cavite to Acapulco.[25] He discovered the small island of Okino-Daitō, southeast of the Ryukyu Islands, christening it Île de la Canonnière.

In 1816 Lieutenant-Commander Camille de Roquefeuil left Bordeaux for the Pacific on a three-master of 200 tons fitted out by the shipbuilder Balguerie. He doubled the Horn, stopped at Valparaíso, Chile, Callao, Peru, and cast anchor at San Francisco on August 5, 1817 (Fig. 33). After a brief spell of fur trading at Nootka Sound (Vancouver Island) he proceeded to the Marquesas with a cargo of sandalwood, then sailed north toward Novo-Arkhangelsk (Sitka), traversed the channels between the islands of Alexander Archipelago and Queen Charlotte Islands, and returned to Nootka. He continued south along the American coast to San Francisco, put in at the Hawaiian Islands in January 1819, and on March 12 anchored at Macao, from where he returned to France via the Cape of Good Hope. Though essentially a commercial venture, the expedition returned with reports on the peoples of the Marquesas and the Hawaiian Islands, and the general geography of the American shores fronting the great ocean.[26]

The tradition of the great oceanic voyages was resumed by Louis C. D. de Freycinet on orders of the French government.[27] Freycinet had been cartographer on the Baudin expedition. On September 17, 1817, he left Toulon on the frigate *Uranie* to verify and to complete the discoveries of Baudin on the southwest coast of Australia, to explore Arnhem Land, and to engage in various scientific observations on the physics of the globe (Fig. 33).[28] Scientific observations were to include geography, magnetism, and meteorology. The artist Jacques Étienne V. Arago accompanied the staff as a draftsman and wrote an account of the explorations.[29] The *Uranie* spent three months at Mauritius and then steered for Australia. Between September 12 and 26 de Freycinet completed the exploration of Shark Bay that was begun by Baudin. He put into Timor and visited the easternmost of the Sunda Islands, Ombai (Palau Alor) and Pulau Pisang, and made observations on the earth's magnetism at Pulau Waigeo, below the equator and northwest of New Guinea. He took in supplies at Guam, stopped at Hawaii between August 1 and 5, then sailed for Sydney. On the way he discovered a reef east of the Samoa Islands which he christened Île Rose (Rose Island). From Sydney he set his course southwards to Campbell Island and determined its position. In latitude 59°S. he encountered floating ice and then steered eastwards. He doubled Cape Horn on February 5 and was wrecked the next week in the Falkland Islands. Subsequently he purchased an American vessel in the Falklands, named it *Physicienne*, and on it returned to France on November 13, 1820, having been gone three years and two months.[30]

On August 11, 1822, Captain Louis Isidore Duperrey, who had served as a lieutenant on Freycinet's cruise, left Toulon on the corvette *Coquille*, put in at Brazil and the Falkland Islands, took in supplies at Talcahuano in Chile and at Lima and Paita in Peru, and sailed for Tahiti by way of the Tuamotu Archipelago (Fig. 33).[31] He stayed there from May 3 to 22, 1823. His route then took him to Bora Bora (Plate 30, *facing page 213*), the Salvage Islands, Bougainville, Buka (Solomon Islands), New Ireland, New Guinea, and the Moluccas. Rounding Australia from the west, with stops at Sydney and the Bay of Islands (New Zealand), the *Coquille* sailed back again and between May and June traversed, and was the first ship to carry out a proper exploration of, the Gilbert and the Caroline islands. Duperrey reached Mauritius via New Guinea and Surabaja. His month's stay in the Falkland Islands gave Duperrey and his colleagues an opportunity to study and to report on the geography of the islands. Our principal sources of information about the accomplishments of this expedition are the publications of Pierre-Adolphe Lesson,[32] the scientist who accompanied the expedition, and René-P. Lesson, who published several accounts and interpretations of the scientific work that was done during the voyage aboard the *Coquille*.[33] Pierre-Adolphe Lesson published accounts of the work in the natural sciences, especially in biology, zoology, and botany;[34] René-P. Lesson also prepared a kind of journal account of the expedition.[35] Duperrey was responsible for obtaining a substantial amount of information from widely spaced observations of terrestrial magnetism, particularly as to magnetic variation.[36]

The two expeditions of Jules S. C. Dumont d'Urville[37] made a major contribution to our knowledge of the western Pacific.[38] Dumont d'Urville obtained his initial experience in the Pacific as an officer on Duperrey's expedition. The first (1826–1829) was made on the *Coquille*, the frigate of the Duperrey expedition, which had been completely refitted and rechristened the *L'Astrolabe*. It left France on April 25, 1826, on a mission to explore the western Pacific as far as the Tonga and Fiji islands, to complete Duperrey's work, and to explore the Carolines, the Palaus, and the approaches to New Guinea (Fig. 33). In the course of this first expedition

Petropavlovsk

Macao

Mariana Is.

Guam

Caroline Is.

Waigeo

Gilbert Is.

180°

150°

120°

New Britain

New Ireland

Bougainville

NEW GUINEA

Solomon Is.

Batavia

Vanikoro

Timor

Torres Strait

Louisiade Arch.

San

Santa Cruz Is.

Fiji Is.

Shark Bay

Loyalty Is.

Bay of Islands

Port Jackson (Sydney)

Tasman Bay

NEW Z

Hobart

Auckland Is.
Campbell I.

Adélie Coast

──○─○─○── De Roquefeuil, 1816-1819
──·─·─·── De Freycinet, 1817-1820
──•─•─•── Duperrey, 1822-1825
············ Dumont D'Urville, 1826-1829
── ── ── Du Petit-Thouars, 1836-1839
───────── Dumont D'Urville, 1837-1840

FIG. 33. Frenc

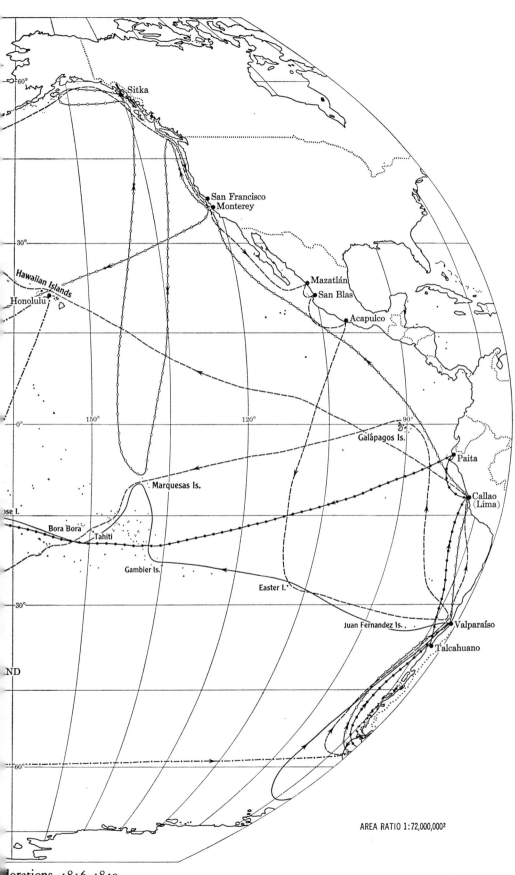

Sitka

San Francisco
Monterey

-30°

Hawaiian Islands
Honolulu

Mazatlán
San Blas

Acapulco

-0°   150°   120°   90°

Galápagos Is.

Paita

Marquesas Is.

Callao
(Lima)

ose I.

Bora Bora
Tahiti

Gambier Is.

Easter I.

-30°

Juan Fernandez Is.   Valparaíso

Talcahuano

ND

-60°

AREA RATIO 1:72,000,000²

lorations, 1816–1840.

Dumont d'Urville visited in succession the south of Australia, King George Sound and Western Port, and successfully explored and charted Tasman Bay (South Island, New Zealand) discovering a pass between its northern shore and an island in Cook Strait. The pass is named French Pass and the island D'Urville. His surveys of the coast carried him as far as North Island's Bay of Islands. One of his volumes is devoted entirely to the geography and ethnography of New Zealand. He followed the coast of North Island and then devoted twenty days to a geographical study of the Fiji Islands. Subsequently he explored the Loyalty Islands and observed that "their existence was equivocal, their position uncertain, and the delineation most inaccurate." Between June 15 and 20, 1827, Dumont d'Urville sailed to New Guinea by way of the Louisiade Archipelago and New Britain. He surveyed 350 leagues of unexplored New Guinea coastline and made his way back to Vanikoro in the Santa Cruz group, to continue the search for the remains of the La Pérouse expedition.[39] Here he obtained sufficient evidence to lead him to conclude that La Pérouse was indeed fatally wrecked on Vanikoro. It is of interest to note that this agreed rather substantially with the nearly simultaneous independent conclusion of a Captain Pierre Dillon.[40] A plan of the island was prepared and the channel was swept. He collected a few objects, erected a memorial, and then returned to France via Guam, the East Indies, and Mauritius, arriving in 1829.

The results of these several expeditions by the French were recorded in huge tomes (twenty-four octavo volumes for the voyage of *L'Astrolabe* alone, with an atlas containing reproductions of the original maps drawn by officers of the expedition). On the basis of these cartographic and journal records and other scientific observations the detailed geography of the Pacific was gradually given more precise and realistic form. On each voyage the officers studied the physics of the globe and the phenomena of terrestrial magnetism and increased the number and distribution of available observations of longitude. The expeditions also brought back vast quantities of ethnographic documents and many zoological specimens, thus finally placing the Pacific within the framework of the human sciences.

To these great voyages of circumnavigation may be added a few expeditions which, though primarily of a political or economic character nevertheless had scientific results that were not negligible. For example, during a voyage to the Far East in 1818, Captain Achille de Kergariou made a detailed examination of the coasts of the Indochinese peninsula and provided valuable geographical and economic information on these shores, with accompanying maps.[41] A few years later Post-Captain Henri de Villeneuve, under instructions to survey the almost unknown coastline of Central America, made accurate plans of the Gulf of Fonseca and the harbors of San Carlos (La Union) and Triunfo (Jiquilisco). He followed a coast which had been inaccurately surveyed by the Spaniards and entered harbors not previously shown on any chart.[42]

Jacques A. Moerenhout, a Dutchman acting as consul to France in Tahiti, made three trans-Pacific voyages over the years between 1828 and 1834. On one voyage from Valparaíso to Tahiti, Moerenhout visited the Tuamotu Archipelago (where he discovered Atoll Maria), the Society Islands, and Îsles Gambier. He resided for some years in Tahiti, learned the Tahitian dialect, and recorded valuable information about these much-admired Polynesians.[43] Moerenhout's accounts, written in French, were published in Paris. He later became United States consul in Polynesia.

Captain Abel A. du Petit-Thouars commanded a government expedition that sailed from Brest on the frigate *Vénus* on December 29, 1836, with a detailed itinerary prepared by the French Admiralty. He skirted Cape Horn and arrived at the Hawaiian Islands.[44] From Hawaii he headed to Kamchatka and anchored at Petropavlovsk on August 31, 1837 (Fig. 33). He departed on September 16, sailed eastward to the Aleutians and the northwest coast of the American continent, and cast anchor at Monterey, California. Throughout his voyage he explored the bays and roadsteads where whalers could establish bases. During the winter of 1837–1838 he carefully explored the coasts of Mexico, especially the harbors of Mazatlán, San Blas, and Acapulco. Driven by the winds to the west of the Galapágos Islands, he checked the position of Easter Island and surveyed its north coast, hitherto unseen by any navigator. Sailing past Juan Fernandez Island the *Vénus* reached Valparaiso, and from there in June, 1838, Du Petit-Thouars set out to explore the Galapágos Islands, still practically unexplored. He then sailed for the Marquesas, traversed the islands, and explored the northwestern group. Stopping at Tahiti and New Zealand, he returned in June, 1839 to France by way of Réunion and the Cape of Good Hope.

At the same time, Captain Jean B. T. M. Cécile, on the frigate *L'Héroine*, made a voyage through the southern Pacific. En route through the Indian Ocean, he carried out thorough surveys of Prince Edward, Crozet, and Saint Paul islands. East of New Zealand, he surveyed Chatham Island, and the Îlots de Bass, and mapped bays which would be suitable as ports of call for whalers.[45]

With the second voyage of Jules S. C. Dumont d'Urville (1837–1840), French explorers were to conclude the era of great voyages of discovery in the Pacific (Fig. 33).[46] Dumont d'Urville's instructions included specific requirements that he survey as much as possible of the South Polar regions, especially with a view to their potential for whaling, and to discover the extent of the new land which whalers were reporting. He was also requested to extend his explorations into Oceania to search for new islands. Under his command the corvettes *L'Astrolabe* and *La Zélée* left Toulon on September 7, 1837, explored the Strait of Magellan between December 13, 1837 and January 8, 1838, and then sailed southwards. Between January 15 and March 7, Dumont d'Urville skirted the vast ice barriers that appeared in front of the Antarctic continent. He discovered Louis Philippe Peninsula and Joinville Island in the Antarctic but was unable to penetrate southward beyond latitude 64° S. He sailed to Chile for a stay to restore the health of his men and then set out across Oceania, stopping at Îles Gambier, the Marquesas Islands, and at Tahiti. For over three months he accomplished important scientific work in the Samoa Islands and in Fiji, working out the detailed geography of the latter and surveying in the greatest detail more than 200 leagues of almost unknown coast. He visited the Solomons, the Carolines, and the Marianas, then sailed via the Moluccas and the Indies to Tasmania, reaching Hobart in December, 1839. Again advancing southwards from

Hobart, he discovered the Adélie Coast of Antarctica beyond latitude 65°S. on January 21, 1840, and noted that the coast was 1000 to 1200 meters high.

Heading northward again, Dumont d'Urville put in at the Auckland Islands, south of New Zealand. He next made a geographical survey of the Loyalty Islands and the Louisiade Archipelago, and then sailed to New Guinea, where he passed through Torres Strait. He returned to France via Timor, Réunion, and Saint Helena, arriving on November 6, 1840. Besides his Antarctic discoveries, Dumont d'Urville had carried out definitive surveys of the Solomon and Loyalty islands and gathered a vast quantity of new scientific data on other islands of Oceania. His report is covered in twenty-three volumes and an atlas of which there are variant editions.[47]

12

GEOGRAPHICAL EXPLORATION BY THE BRITISH

RICHARD I. RUGGLES*

Geographical knowledge of the general outline of the Pacific Basin was virtually complete by 1800. For the previous two centuries, the bulk of exploration had been undertaken by the British in the eighteenth, and the Dutch in the seventeenth century. These nations were, of course, beneficiaries of the magnificent achievements of Spain and of Portugal. The Dutch were interested particularly in the southwest Pacific, that is, in the reasonably precise delineation of the East Indies islands and the charting of the western and southern littorals of the continent of Australia. The British were concerned more with the open Pacific, to the knowledge of whose vastness they added by their systematic destruction of the imaginative concept of a great southern continent. They also discovered, or sited more accurately, the larger number of the myriad of islands in the open Pacific, and they framed the northeastern rim of the Pacific Basin with their remarkable hydrographic mapping of the northwest coast of North America.

This masterful sketching of broader forms on the Pacific canvas by the British was succeeded in the nineteenth century by the discovery and precise delineation of geographic detail, which was a natural concomitant of Britain's increased involvement in Pacific political and commercial affairs.[1] Settlers, traders, government servants, scientists, and the military were all involved, each for his own purposes, but all adding year by year to the store of geographical knowledge.

British exploration of the Pacific Basin may be subdivided into three general periods: from the 1570s to the 1760s; from the 1760s to 1800; and after 1800. For over a century and a half after 1570 those British seamen who entered the Ocean were privateers, intent upon voyages of personal aggrandizement, although national interests were at times involved. William Dampier alone was an exception, although only on his second voyage from 1699 to 1701 was interest in scientific exploration paramount. During this period there was little exploratory achievement, but at home in England speculation was rife in the form of schemes for the promotion of trade and in treatises on the hypothetical geography of the Pacific realm.

The four decades after 1760 were the climax of British exploration, culminating in the successes of Captain James Cook, and later, Captain George Vancouver. This period witnessed the demise of privateering and the entry of the British government and scientific institutions into all phases of exploration of this vast area. In addition, settlement projects were initiated in Australia and on many of the Pacific islands, and independent trading and fur-hunting groups were instrumental in adding to the known data. The English were able to reduce the dread disease of scurvy, a horror of long-distance sea travel, to relative insignificance in this period. This, therefore, was

---

*Dr. RUGGLES is professor of geography and head of the department of geography, Queen's University, Kingston, Ontario.

of great geographical value, for the lengthened journeys which were now possible allowed the volume of geographical research carried out by these later expeditions to be greatly increased.

British undertakings were many and varied in the nineteenth century. British naval patrols and expeditions, whose object it was to investigate, to pacify, and when necessary, to subdue, in the maintenance of *Pax Britannica*, provided the corollary benefit of considerable enhancement of hydrographic, nautical, and geographical information. Both physical and human geography were augmented by the observations gained on several notable journeys, undertaken almost exclusively in the interests of science, expeditions which were supported by the joint efforts of government and of scientific agencies. A multitude of individuals of diverse interests ranged the entire Pacific Ocean, and while engaging in commercial, educational, and governmental pursuits, or while searching for new areas of settlement, reached into most of the still-secret recesses of the Basin. Although only the most significant of men and voyages are discussed below, all performed roles of merit.

BRITISH PRIVATEERS AND INITIAL EXPLORATION: 1570-1760

BACKGROUND TO BRITISH ENTRY INTO THE PACIFIC

Generally, what was known of the Pacific realm by 1570, when Britain first entered the Pacific, was for the most part limited to a relatively narrow band of the open ocean flanking the equator, and the west-to-east return route to the Americas in the North Pacific, the American continental coastline north approximately to Cape Mendocino in North America, parts of the East Indies and some of the Melanesian and Polynesian islands, and the southern Asiatic mainland coast and offshore islands. This does not mean that such a geographical compendium was common knowledge among the populace of Western Europe. Rather, some definite information, coalesced with a bewildering variety of speculation, was the normal geographical fare at the time.

During the fifteenth and early sixteenth centuries the British were certainly not noted for geographical science, and were in fact far behind the standard reached on the European continent. Englishmen lacked curiosity about any regions in the world beyond those in which they had immediate contact. As one critic has stated, they were interested only in Protestant theology and Greek pronunciation.[2] Their scholars paid little attention to new information and to new speculations on distant geographic stirrings in Western Europe. In that continental area, on the other hand, geographic interest was both academic and practical. England's role in the growth of geographic studies was at first insignificant. There had been a few cosmographical productions published, dealing largely with mathematical geography. These writings were traditional in form, borrowing from a medley of classical and medieval writings.

The first English geographical treatise produced since the discovery of America was by Roger Barlow in 1540-41.[3] Barlow had accompanied Sebastian Cabot to the La Plata River in South America, and his *Geographia* reiterated concepts current during this early part of the century, mirrored in such writings as Sir Thomas More's

Utopia and John Rastell's play *A new interlude and a merry of the nature of the four elements*.[4] Rastell echoed More's ideas regarding the narrow ocean beyond America leading to Cathay (China). A southern continent, possibly civilized, was also suggested. In 1530–1531, Barlow and Roger Thorne prepared their *Declaration of the Indies*, a plan of English expansion to the Spice Islands (Moluccas). They believed that a great southern continent, Terra Australis Incognita,[5] existed, and these southern lands were the destiny of Britain. Their suggestion was that a route to this region could be found across the polar seas, south through the Strait of Anian[6] into the Pacific.

In the second half of the sixteenth century there was a significant change, and the first flourishing of a geographical *corpus* was observable in the writings and discussions of such men as John Dee, Richard Eden, Richard Willis, and the two Hakluyts. They were Elizabethan propagandists, and yet their output was still importantly cosmographical and mathematical. Theirs was the academic approach. They studied past records and reports of medieval travelers. Their reports clarified ideas on the general distribution of land masses, and showed increasing familiarity with the project of crossing the Pacific. But there were few descriptions or analyses of various regions, and none concerning the South Sea at this time. Although the tide of English interest in geographical science was rising there was little comprehensive training in the subject at the universities in England. The transfer of most geographical information occurred through personal contacts among the early geographers at home, and with their continental acquaintances of high repute, such as Gerardus Mercator, Gemma Frisius, Abraham Ortelius, and Johannes Finnaeus, or between them and persons in the high echelons of administration in England. There was considerable letter writing, brochure writing, and many memoranda produced upon geographical concepts of the world, and upon possible exploratory expeditions. Foreign books, globes, and maps were being included in libraries of the well-to-do. Humphrey Gilbert quoted thirteen of the best modern geographers in his library, but no English book or English map was among them. Frobisher's library contained nothing published by Englishmen by that date.

Other significant sources of information were more practical. French influence in the form of books was entering English libraries, and French pilots and mariners were in the royal service of Britain. The English merchant colony in south Spain was familiar with Spanish methods of discovery and colonization, for many had crossed the Atlantic and lived and traded in Spanish America. They were in close contact with some of the most recent Spanish and Portuguese data and were extremely useful, even though these nations were careful to keep as much information from foreign surveillance as was possible. Roger Bodenham corresponded with Walsingham, Francis Dwyer, Michael Lok, and the two Richard Hakluyts. Henry Hawks, living in Mexico City, heard of the discovery of the Solomon Islands when Alvaro Mendana de Neira landed in that country. Hawks brought the news to England in 1572, having escaped the Inquisition which wanted him on charges of heresy. Contacts were also growing with Flemish and Dutch businessmen passing to and fro between London and Antwerp. British sailors and navigators, principally centered at Bristol and other western ports, were becoming more adventurous. They also found it advisable to increase their contacts with London in order to be in closer touch with financial sources and government.

The geographical concept of the Pacific area current in the mid-sixteenth century and upon which the British based their plans for voyaging centered upon a supposedly enormous southern continent, pivoted upon the South Pole and projecting in vast peninsulas north into the tropical regions. Terra Australis Incognita, as it was called, was believed to be necessary as a structural balance to the northern continents, and its geographical extent indicated that it would include polar, temperate, and tropical climates. As most authors usually surmised, such a massive continent would include a great variety of natural resources, in particular, gold, silver, and precious stones. By this date, many sightings of the northern shores of this great southern land had been reported by Spanish and Portuguese seamen; in fact, a necklace of such locations festooned their Pacific maps from the Strait of Magellan northwest to the East Indies. Thus, the Pacific Ocean was estimated to be about one-half its true size. In the southwestern corner of this ocean there was said to be an archipelago of islands, lying north of the southern continent, which islands were the source of great wealth, particularly of spices. Into this great ocean there were considered to be four entries: one via the Cape of Good Hope and the Indian Ocean, which led into this extensive archipelago; the second through the Strait of Magellan, which according to contemporary thought separated South America from Terra Australis Incognita; and the other two being the supposed Arctic gateways from the northeast and northwest into the North Pacific, via the Strait of Anian.

Cosmographers and cartographers differed in their conceptions of the southern areas. One school of diminishing importance maintained that there was an open ocean in the south polar region; the more numerous group supported the existence of a great southern continent. References to Terra Australis Incognita had occurred in numbers of classical works including Pliny, Lucian, and Claudius Ptolemy. Ptolemy drew a line across the bottom of his world map, connecting Africa with Further India, and placed below this line in the open space the words, "Terra Incognita." By the first decades of the 1500s, maps of and discourses upon this area had connected the earlier imaginary Terra Incognita with Spanish and Portuguese sightings of southern smaller and larger islands of the South Pacific, and with the supposed land which Ferdinand Magellan saw south of Cape Horn. One family of maps depicted the southern land as having a serrated northern coast, gave names to the teeth as if they were capes, and showed rivers flowing into the gaps. The Dieppe school of cartography (1530–1550) included a rough northern outline to this southern mass and showed, south of an island named Java and separated from it by a narrow channel, a part of the great land mass designated as Java le Grande. This may have been Marco Polo's reference to Java Major,which was Java itself, inadvertently transferred south. Thus was illustrated, particularly on French maps, the controversy that the land mass of Australia had been sighted. Certainly, it is within the realm of possibility that Australia had in fact been discovered before the Dutch, by a Portuguese, Spanish, or French ship (or ships) wrecked there. Also, perhaps native peoples of the East

Indies had fished off the north and northwest coasts of this island continent and stories had circulated to the ears of Europeans by involved processes.

The problem of the Pacific, and its solution, may be summed up as the attempt to find Terra Australis Incognita, and growing skepticism as to its existence, antagonism between those who believed and those who disbelieved this continental hypothesis, and the gradual evolution of the true state of Pacific geography, voyage by voyage, until James Cook completed the task.

MOTIVES IMPELLING THE BRITISH TO ENTER THE PACIFIC

The center of gravity of European control was in the Americas and in the Atlantic during the sixteenth century and even in the seventeenth. To Spain and Portugal, the first inheritors of Pacific fame, conquest of Pacific Ocean space was not really central. It was the Asiatic area and the eastern islands which were important to Portugal, and the open ocean gradually lost any real political meaning. The Portuguese almost always approached the Far East from the Cape of Good Hope. To Spain the open Pacific was not of vital importance to their policy. The Philippines were "western isles" from America. Nevertheless, during this long period the Pacific remained more or less a Spanish sea, disturbed only by the intervention of adventurers, explorers, and pirates of other nations.

What motives impelled the English to enter the Pacific? Exploration was not the ruling motive; it was incidental to other factors. In the first place, there was the valid interest in the political and commercial advantages to be gained from Pacific holdings. Although territorial gains *per se* were not so important, it was hoped by overseas conquests to strengthen the British political and military position in Europe. Certainly, if a precedent was needed, the beguiling reports of riches carried yearly from the Pacific by the Spanish were sufficient to arouse English interest, if not cupidity.

Moreover, since the British were in schism from Rome, the Papal Bull[7] and ensuing Treaty[8] delineating Spanish and Portuguese territorial rights were not considered as governing principles in their actions. They, at least, did not conclude that they were heretical when invading the southern regions of the globe. Also, there was the sufficient safeguard that the papal delimitation did not juridicate the subdivision of the northern regions, and therefore the search for and expected discovery and consequent control of the Northwest and Northeast Passages were entirely free from any such stigma.

The later sixteenth century was also a time of swelling anti-Spanish sentiment, during which the best English brains were searching for means of breaking the Spanish monopoly of the riches of the New World. This animosity showed itself not only in the growing restraint between England and Spain, in many memoranda by high-placed Englishmen[9] on ways of strengthening Britain's position *vis-a-vis* Spain, but also in the very practical method of supporting, tacitly at least, the buccaneers raiding the Atlantic side of the Spanish New World possessions. English captains who had been denied access to the slave trade in the Caribbean by the Spanish, sought revenge by turning to buccaneering. They considered that they were securing redress for injuries suffered in the San Juan Treachery upon John Hawkins.[10] Francis Drake, for example, was sent out to retaliate in the Atlantic.

It was upon the foundations of buccaneering that English entry into and exploration of the Pacific were based.

BUCCANEERING FOUNDATIONS OF BRITISH PACIFIC EXPLORATION

Notwithstanding other valid reasons for exploration in the Pacific, the practical motive was the desire to interrupt the flow of specie to Spain and to direct some of it into the national income of England. In short, buccaneering provided the direct method.

British aims were essentially negative, and British interest in the Pacific was not continuous. Being privateers, the British remained close to the main Spanish track and therefore, in total, discovered little. However, there was also continuous promotion of Pacific possessions as a source of riches by such men as Richard Grenville and his associates, who vainly sought monopoly rights in parts of the Pacific region. At first, Queen Elizabeth declined these suggestions, not wishing to offend the Spanish because of England's European political relations.

Among the writers who helped to establish a climate of opinion which fostered the voyages and colonization of the latter half of the sixteenth and seventeenth centuries were the Hakluyts, John Dee, Richard Eden, and Richard Willis. Dee's compendium of discoveries[11] had as its purpose that of showing England how it might bring back to its shores the riches of the east. He suggested a voyage to latitudes 40° to 50° N. to settle the question of whether there was an entrance to the Pacific at that latitude from the Strait of Anian. He preferred access to the Pacific from the Arctic rather than through the Strait of Magellan, likely because it would lead past Cathay (China) and Cipangu (Japan). Dee's ideas on control of the North Pacific entrance were in concert with many others who proposed to find the Strait of Anian via either or both the Northeast and Northwest Passages, to claim this passage for Britain, to settle it, and thus to control an easy access into the Pacific.

There were many groups involved in this ferment of interest, some of them conflicting, and all vying for the Queen's ear, and for funds. In 1577, Queen Elizabeth changed her mind and put both her overt and secret weight behind English expansion into the Pacific and the sacking of Spanish wealth. By so doing, she changed the fashion in South Sea voyages for the next two centuries.

During this first phase of English entrance to the Pacific, from 1575 to 1594, there were four expeditions into the open Pacific: by John Oxenham, who was the pioneer; by Francis Drake, the illustrious circumnavigator of the globe; by Thomas Cavendish, who followed him; and, lastly, by Richard Hawkins, who reaped only "capture," as Spanish reaction to these incursions had taken the form of increased naval protection of the American west coastal waters.

The geographical results of the first phase were not excessive. Only Drake's voyage had considerable geographical significance. Yet, both Drake's and Hawkins' expeditions were essentially made under royal auspices, both were conducted in a most gentlemanly fashion, with humanity, with little loss of life as a result of violence, almost as if the initial plans called for a restrained approach to piracy.

The expedition led by John Oxenham in 1575 is not well known, being over-shadowed by the later voyages. In fact, it appears to have been something of an after-thought, as this group had been raiding in the Caribbean before deciding to walk across the Isthmus of Panama to launch out onto the South Sea. There was little if any geographical motivation involved, for they immediately built small craft and began marauding Spanish ships on the west side of the Isthmus. Their fate was to be captured and to be executed by the Spanish as pirates. The only geographical credit due to Oxenham and his followers, then, is that of primacy of English Pacific voyages.

Whereas the first British expedition into the Pacific apparently was an independent and to a degree a spur-of-the-moment act, the adventures of Drake from December 1577 to September 1580 were clearly premeditated and carefully organized. Drake had long wished to penetrate the Pacific. Very likely he was himself the chief author of the plans which were involved, but it is known that John Dee was of aid in their formulation, and the two Hakluyts were consultants on some matters.

Basically this was a royal, that is, national expedition, for the boat which was Drake's flagship was royal property and built at the Deptford naval yard, and for other reasons. One such reason was Queen Elizabeth's support of him against the ensuing Spanish denunciation of his pillaging and her recognition of his services by a knighthood.

The chief motives of his journey were three in number. Exploration must be given an important place, including the hope of finding some portions of the great southern continent, of discovering the Strait of Anian, and of learning much of the geography of the Pacific by passing across it on a voyage of global circumnavigation. The plans for the expedition clearly bear out this statement.[12] The initial plan stated that Drake was to enter and to return from the Pacific by the Strait of Magellan. The voyage was to extend over a period of thirteen months, during which unknown shores, not in the possession of any Christian prince, were to be visited. If it seemed advisable, Drake was urged to extend his voyages north to the thirtieth parallel. It seems most obvious that the chief expectation was to be the discovery of and extensive visitation of Terra Australis Incognita.

The main objective there was to be the landing upon several of the northern portions of this continent, likely Locach and Beach,[13] which were shown on the Ortelius map of 1570 in the *Theatrum Orbis Terrarum*, which was in the hands of every English cosmographer in the 1570s. The revised and enlarged plan was more specific. The voyage was to extend to the Moluccas, where it was to turn north, annexing any useful islands. When the expedition had reached Cathay (China) and Cipangu (Japan) it was to spend five months making friends of the countries' rulers, selling English cloth, making a headquarters for further sale of cloth, and investigating the possibilities of obtaining gold, silver, drugs, and spice. The southwestern winds would carry the expedition to the western extremity of the Pacific. It was expected that the Strait of Anian would be located, and the Passage breached and navigated. The timing was to be such that when the explorers had reached the Strait's most northerly position between Newfoundland and Greenland, it would be late summer, and there would be no danger anticipated from ice. It is obvious that such an extensive authority for action envisaged a very considerable expansion of geographical knowledge. Also, there was no authority for circumnavigation, except in the more limited sense of American circumnavigation.

The second reason, certainly, was the establishment of English control over some land areas which lay beyond Spanish authority, and the accompanying expansion of trade in these and other parts of the Pacific Ocean.

The third motive was that of wresting from Spain as much of her riches as was possible during the expedition. This was an aspect of the English desire to annoy the Spanish, and was also related to Drake's hope of recouping personal financial losses sustained earlier when the Spanish had seized an English expedition in the Caribbean, in which Drake had sizeable investments.[14] This latter consideration has always been given greatest attention because of the overpowering success of his marauding activities, and because of the audacity and skill which typified his command. Yet the results in the first two instances were considerable, though basically less exciting, and of less moment at that time.

Drake became the first Englishman to sail into the Pacific, and to use the Strait of Magellan, although only one among the five vessels in the flotilla, the *Golden Hind*, succeeded in entering the Ocean. After passing through the Strait the vessel was buffeted back and forth at the western entrance, and finally the explorers found themselves to the east of Tierra del Fuego among the island group located there. In fairer weather the ship coasted along the island shores until it reached the most southerly point of land, which Drake named "Cape Elizabeth," (Cape Horn). To the island mass he gave the title, "the Elizabeth Islands." He stated that he had set up a stone of commemoration on the "uttermost cape or hedland of all these Ilands . . . without which there is no maine nor Iland to be seene to the Southwards. . . ."[15] Drake discovered that Tierra del Fuego is an island group, rather than the northern projection of a great southern continent.

Upon issuing finally from the shelter of these islands, the expedition met such violent headwinds and storms in the Westerlies belt that it was not able to sail west at these latitudes to search further for the northern coasts of Terra Australis. Drake now had ample excuse for the formulation of plans which may have been nearer to his own desires. The decision was to prey upon Spanish ports and ships along the length of the American west coast, before passing north beyond the Spanish realms into the North Pacific. His ship reached approximately latitude 48° N., just to the south of Cape Flattery, in search of the Northwest Passage, and within a hairsbreadth of the Strait of Juan de Fuca, the first important break in the coastline north of Mexico. This point was the farthest north reached by Europeans on this coast at this time.

Returning south, the ship entered a bay in the San Francisco area, where Drake proclaimed English sovereignty over the land which lay north of Spanish, and beyond French control, to which unmeasured realm he gave the title "New Albion." The San Francisco Bay area was supported as a possible place of refreshment, a half-way house when the Strait of Anian would be found, and when either or both of the northern passages became shipping routes. Drake's concept of a vast "New England," occupying the bulk of North America was in truth the progenitor of the colonization projects which later secured British occupation of a large area of the continent. Drake's suggestion was based to an extent on the concept of Humphrey Gilbert of

1576,[16] wherein Gilbert proposed to plant a colony on the Pacific coast, near the Sierra Nevada, as a base for trade with the west. His idea was to reach this area via the supposed transcontinental waterway between the St. Lawrence and the Gulf of California.

The Spanish had by this time recovered from their consternation at the unexpected intrusion and costly depredations of the *Golden Hind*, and had strengthened their naval forces along the Peruvian and Chilean coasts to prevent Drake from escaping from the Pacific through the Strait of Magellan on his return to England. They were left without this revenge, for the vessel was turned west across the Pacific, reaching the Philippine Islands, turned south through the East Indian islands and out into the Sunda Sea, passing west into the Indian Ocean south of Java. In September of 1580, the first circumnavigation of the globe was completed by a vessel under the command of the original captain (Fig. 34). Although only a portion of the original planned program was completed, Drake's voyage was of both historic and geographic significance.

Drake enhanced the splendor of Elizabeth's reign with this historic circumnavigation. He discovered Cape Horn, reached the most southerly and northerly points in the Pacific attained by a European, showed that the Atlantic and Pacific oceans were undivided, and by accident removed Terra Australis Incognita from the map in this region. The *Golden Hind*'s buffeting against the westerly winds gave denial to reports that a perpetual easterly current and easterly winds would carry ships into the Pacific from the Cape Horn entrance, but barred their return. The belief in the Strait of Anian was not destroyed, it was simply pushed farther to the north than expected, although Drake's successful raids on the riches of the Spanish in the South Pacific contributed to the deferment of further search for the Strait for 150 years.[17] In the open Pacific, Drake's voyage was of lesser significance, for he missed the many intermediate island groups and made his first landfall somewhere near the Marshall Islands.

However, his expedition's North American contacts gave succor to further plans for colonization. He brought home news of an almost undefended Pacific Ocean, he discovered and claimed unknown territories both north and south of Portuguese and Spanish possessions, and he made known the California coast as a place of refreshment. To an extent, the geographical results were negative rather than positive, for Terra Australis was not discovered nor was it even partially charted. Instead, Drake had shown the insularity of the land southeast of the Strait of Magellan, and had seen a great expanse of open water to the south. This discovery has been proclaimed as "the first hole knocked in the edifice of the theory of a southern continent."[18]

Drake's original maps and journals have never been found, therefore the absolute details of this momentous voyage are to a large extent speculative. But the scientific results, particularly of coastal terrain and hydrographic characteristics might have been considerable had they been available, for a map of his was said to have been presented to the Archbishop of Canterbury, and Drake, and his nephew who accompanied him, were known to have spent considerable time in the captain's cabin sketching representations of items seen during the voyage. But, unfortunately, Drake's results did not enter geographical literature immediately, as they apparently

Canton

Philippine Is.

Guam

Marshall Is.

Caroline · Islands

Dampier Strait

150°

Gilbert Is.

180°

Sumatra

120°

New Guinea

New
Britain

New Ireland

Solomon Is.

Tokelau Is.

Batavia

Java

Timor

•—•—•Drake, 1577-1578
———Dampier, 1679-1691
··········Dampier, 1699-1700
—·—·—Woods-Rogers, 1708-1710
————Anson, 1741-1744
–o–o–o–Byron, 1764-1765
— — — Wallis, 1767-1768
—+—+—Carteret, 1767-1768

FIG. 34. Tracks of British navigators b

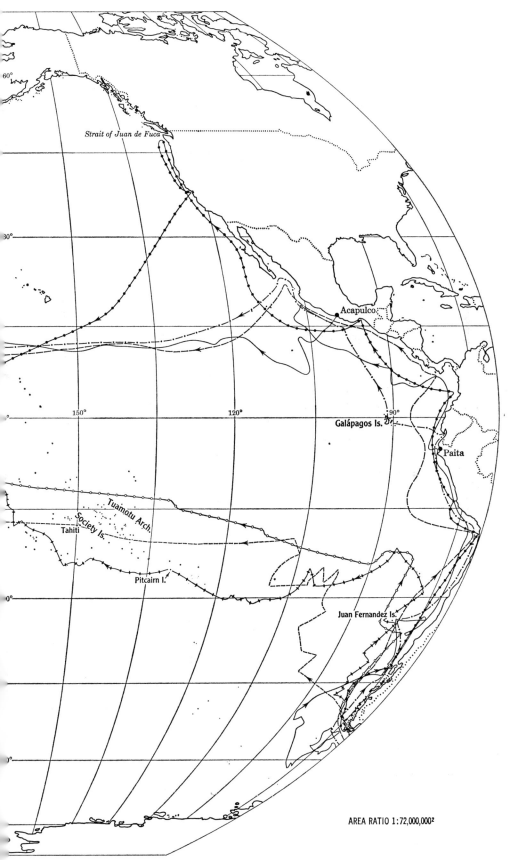

60°

30°

Strait of Juan de Fuca

Acapulco

0°   150°   120°   90°   Galápagos Is.

Paita

Tuamotu Arch.
Society Is.
Tahiti

Pitcairn I.

Juan Fernandez Is.

AREA RATIO 1:72,000,000²

Cook. Compiled by Richard I. Ruggles.

became state property when presented to the Queen. There is considerable mystery about many of the exploratory findings of Drake, particularly of Cape Horn. It would appear that these new discoveries were suppressed for political reasons, and that Drake was speaking about them only to the Council of State and to the promoters of his voyage. Some of the details were to become known later through reports of the Spanish ambassador in London to the Spanish court, and via reports of the Venetian ambassador in Spain to Venice.

By 1582, the secret of the southern Cape was known in Spain and Venice, the same year that the map which apparently first showed Drake's voyage was printed by Michael Lok. Before 1600, four other maps of the discoveries had appeared: one engraved on a silver plaque, a second prefixed to Hakluyt's edition of Peter Martyr in 1587, the map by Hondius published about 1595, and a new map adopted by Hakluyt for the second edition of his voyages.[19]

The last two English seamen in the Pacific during this initial period were primarily interested in treasure. Thomas Cavendish, in 1586, completed the second English circumnavigation, having followed Drake's path across the Pacific fairly closely. He proved to be most successful at his primary task of intercepting the bullion ships, but nothing of geographical value was forthcoming.

By 1594, when Richard Hawkins led a force into the Pacific, the Spanish had so strengthened their forces that they quickly interrupted his sweep up the coast, capturing the expedition. Upon his release from captivity Hawkins wrote a book[20] about his Pacific interlude, valuable for its discussion of New Spain and the west coast of South America. It included also a considerable note on the character of scurvy, and on aids to its eradication. This was the last English book of Pacific exploration and adventure produced for nearly a century. There was, in fact, also a hiatus of nearly the same length of time before the return of English seamen to the open Pacific. This century was occupied importantly by the Dutch involvement in the southwest Pacific (Chapter 9).

WILLIAM DAMPIER, THE VANGUARD OF BRITISH SCIENTIFIC EXPLORATION IN THE PACIFIC

The Dutch, like the English, entered the Pacific arena basically as an act of defiance of the Spanish and Portuguese who had denied the entry of Netherlands merchants to the European home trade after this new nation had declared its independence in 1581. Partially, also, Dutch concern with overseas trade resulted from intellectual ferment which was engendered by the struggle for freedom from Spanish control. Geographical and cartographical efflorescence was part of this expansionist trend. The Dutch, determined to outflank their former master, first attempted to reach the Pacific Basin via the Northeast Passage north of Siberia but, failing to do so, approached the region via the ancient route round the Cape of Good Hope and the Indian Ocean.[21] In fact, outside of a few trans-Pacific voyages which gained access to the Pacific from the east, the Dutch were never interested in that ocean as a highway to and from their areas of occupation in the East Indies.

The English entered the island empire of the southwest Pacific simultaneously with the Dutch, and, in contest with the Spanish and Portuguese, the struggle for trading supremacy in the East Indian Archipelago was joined. Actually, the first English flotilla, commanded by James Lancaster in 1591,[22] opened English trade in an area in which no English expedition had been since the passages of Cavendish and Drake. Lancaster returned in 1601 to 1603 via the normal Cape of Good Hope route and founded a trading factory in the Moluccas. Other English expeditions followed.[23] These included Henry Middleton[24] who led the second expedition, Keeling the third,[25] Sharpeigh and Rowles the fourth, David Middleton the fifth in 1610,[26] Henry Middleton the sixth,[27] Hippon the seventh,[28] and Saris the eighth from 1611–1613.[29] The last expedition was the first English approach to Japan. The trading results of these expeditions were none too successful, though those responsible were able to improve their navigation techniques in and knowledge of tropical seas, including information on currents, the monsoon, and typhoons, thus enabling them to improve their charts considerably.[30] Meanwhile, separate syndicates of Netherlands merchants initiated trading voyages after 1594.

Rapidly and extremely efficiently the Dutch infiltrated the islands of the East Indies, and established factories also on the Asiatic mainland and on Formosa. In 1602, all Dutch trading was incorporated under the monopoly privileges of a new company, the United East India Company, which provided concerted action in the struggle for trading control. By 1609, Holland had arranged a truce with Spain and Portugal and had superseded these nations in the East Indies. The English were able to maintain some portion of the trade there until 1623, when they were finally expelled, leaving the Dutch supreme in this vast region.

Dutch discovery and exploration were essentially by-products of trade. The addition of geographical information to maps and to literature was an incidental accompaniment to the search for articles of trade, and for customers. Yet, in the myriad wanderings of ships among the islands of the Indies a detailed knowledge of waterways, of ports, coastlines, and to some extent of the regional natural environment and human societies, was forthcoming.

By the end of the Tasman period (by 1650) the great highways of intercourse between the continents were becoming better known, and for the most part the navigators after this kept to the beaten tracks. For about a century there was only a small amount of positive discovery. This was a barren exploratory period when additions to knowledge were due more to accident than to the purposeful solution of obscure geographical problems. Britain and France were too absorbed in continental rivalry and in West Indian trade problems to devote much attention to this great oceanic region. Most of the late seventeenth and early eighteenth century English voyages were of a piratical or privateering nature, but there were some intelligent observers among them who preserved narratives. The supreme example was William Dampier.[31]

The true distinction of Dampier is that he was a century ahead of his confreres in his intense devotion to the gathering, assessment, and recording of the natural and social phenomena of those regions of the world to which his seafaring brought him. His major contribution was to bring into the homes, libraries, and offices of the literate world, honest, factual, yet exciting accounts of the South Sea region, and into the offices of public officials and mariners a reliable assessment and delineation of the hydrography, weather conditions, and nautical problems of the Pacific, which stood the test of increasing use. No other man of his period could equal his accumulated personal knowledge of this vast region. His contribution is more remarkable for other reasons than his singular position as a pioneer of rational observation of this area.

Dampier had had no formal training for this role. He was self-taught. He had an insatiable curiosity, which in his early twenties was channeled into regular and copious note-taking. This was ubiquitous in that every aspect of nature, peoples, society, and events was recorded. The acquisition of new knowledge was his sole ambition. He wearied of the scene when he had exhausted the information which it afforded him, and he drifted as the tide of events passed him. Yet, in his published writings he had developed such style, richness of detail, and credibility that they were accepted as being worthy of Royal Society patronage.

Moreover, this unusual man persisted under the most difficult and discouraging circumstances of place and company to record the passing scene: as common crew-man fulfilling his duties on both commercial and piratical vessels, in rough camps, on forced marches, and as commander of motley and disinterested crews and of ailing vessels. He studiously recorded his observations, aloof from comrades who drank and brawled, taking infinite pains to preserve his notes and collections to the journey's end.

After about 1670, Spanish possessions on the Pacific coast of the Americas and their vessels in these waters became increasingly the victims of British privateers operating individually or in packs. Such buccaneers as Sawkins, Basil Ringrose, Davis, Coxon, Bartholomew Sharp, and Harris, among others, had become accustomed to cut across the Isthmus of Panama, to build their own small vessels, or to capture their means of transport, and to search for further prey.[32] In a few cases they entered the Pacific via either the Strait of Magellan or the Estrecho de Le Maire. Several such expeditions crossed the Pacific Ocean in the course of their meanderings, and on one of these Dampier was a member of the crew. This was his first circumnavigation and, although followed over the next quarter century of his career by three further such voyages, of them all it was the most unusual. Extending from 1684 until 1691, this was not a purposeful voyage on a single ship but a circumglobal adventure employing over a dozen ships, apart from canoes and other small craft. Dampier entered the Pacific in 1683 and after taking part in the pillaging both on and off the American coast, joined a vessel which in 1684 headed across the Pacific from the coast of Lower California, reached Guam, and eventually the Philippines in 1686. Internal conflict among the crew caused them to split up, and Dampier joined a group which eventually wove its way south through the islands of the East Indies to touch down in 1688 upon the north coast of Australia, the first Englishmen to do so. They sailed on to the Nicobar Islands, where Dampier left the vessel and, with several other men, scudded in a light canoe on a remarkable, terrifying, and debilitating journey to Sumatra. Then, after serving both individual traders and the English East India Company in four voyages along the Asiatic coast and in the Indies until 1691, he was able to reach England in September of that year (Fig. 34).

Up to this time, Dampier was an unknown sailor. It was during the following few years that his unusual talents became known through the publication in 1697 of his first volume, *A New Voyage Round the World*.[33] Dampier's star rose precipitously, so much so that three editions of his book were run off within the first few months, and he set about to prepare a second publication, *Voyages and Discoveries*,[34] which was just as enthusiastically received in 1699. This volume was a miscellany of enlarged portions of his adventures on two continents, of personal narratives, and particularly of great significance, a discourse on the physical geography of winds, currents, tides, and climatological phenomena of the tropical regions.

No new geographical discoveries were forthcoming from his first extended voyage, although his two books were of great significance in the increase of geographical knowledge of this region. Dampier's writings indicate that he was more a recorder of his own observations than a theorist, much more interested in the local scene than in the broader nature of land and water arrangements. It is not until approximately half way through his first volume that a theoretical discussion is introduced, in which he suggests that his approach to the search for the Northwest Passage and the Northeast Passage would be via the Cape Horn entrance to the Pacific Ocean, progressing either north along the American coast, thence through the Strait of Anian and eastward, or north along the Asiatic coast, through this supposed strait and westward.[35] Coupled with this is his assertion that the Cape Horn entrance to the Pacific should be used by English trading ventures planning to reach the Orient, rather than that of the Cape of Good Hope, for in this way contacts with the Dutch would be minimized, and both on the way out and on the return voyage vessels could touch upon the eastern shores of New Holland and thereby add much to the knowledge of Terra Australis Incognita.[36] This assertion as to the mutuality of New Holland and Terra Australis was, however, not as clearly stated in other portions of his book because he confesses to the thought that New Holland may be a large island and not a continent, though he is certain that it does not connect with Asia, Africa, or America.[37]

In these first volumes, Dampier shows his remarkable proclivity, enlarged upon in later voyages, to make valuable navigational and hydrographic studies. Careful accounting of westerly transoceanic movement brought him to the conclusion that the width of the Pacific Ocean was normally underestimated by most travelers and that of the Indian Ocean overestimated.[38] He also discussed the factor of time change in trans-Pacific travel.[39]

During his sojourn in England while preparing his books Dampier became, to some extent, a much sought after man, a friend and protege of Admiralty officials, of leaders of the Royal Society, and of geographers. Also during this time, when he must have had considerable discussion with geographers and others interested in the character of the Pacific region, he indicated a strong desire to return there, to search for areas suitable for settlement and trade and, as he proposed, to engage in solving some of the major geographical enigmas related to Terra Australis.

His petition for leadership of an expedition was granted by the Admiralty, and a ship, the *Roebuck*, and crew were provided. The Royal Society also supported the enterprise. It is unfortunate for two reasons that Dampier was given command. Although an accomplished navigator and a veteran sailor, it became obvious that he was not a strong commander; both the ship, because of its dilapidated condition, and crew because of its motley nature and inexperience, required a strong helmsman.

Secondly, he would have been of far greater value as an independent geographical observer, shorn of the tasks and worries of a commander.

This first scientific expedition to leave the shores of Britain sailed on January 14, 1699. It was originally slated to strike from Cape Horn for the unknown eastern shores of New Holland, in conformity with his printed suggestion. Instead, for reasons which were not too convincing, the ship approached its task across the Indian Ocean. Well over five weeks were spent investigating the west coast of Australia, already reasonably known through the Dutch. Although valuable, and indeed to the public, fascinating details of the regional geography were gathered, he had thereby lost his chance of the greater prestige which fell later to Cook, due to his discovery and exploration of eastern Australia.

Certain discoveries were made by the *Roebuck*, however, and much valuable descriptive material collected, particularly related to Australia and Melanesia, for the vessel sailed from the northwest coast of Australia, north of Timor, and from thence round the northwest cape (Tandjung Jamursba) of New Guinea. Traveling east, a complete loop was made from north to south around the islands of New Ireland and New Britain, and Dampier discovered the passage separating these islands from New Guinea. He gave the name New Britain to what he considered to be the one island, but which is in fact two, and the name Dampier Strait commemorates his finding of the separating waters.

Dampier reached England in 1701 after his ship finally sank from sheer rottenness in the Atlantic off Ascension Island (Fig. 34). The miracle is that it had been kept afloat so long in view of its desperate condition when first assigned to him. Dampier was himself discouraged with the results, and some disappointment was also expressed by his contemporaries who thought little of his discoveries. Yet, his reputation as an expert on the Pacific Basin was not impaired, and his third volume, *Voyage to New Holland*[40] was a further spectacular literary success as well as a most valuable regional geographical source. In spite of the loss of his ship, Dampier managed to save a fair share of his natural collections, map drafts, and journals. From this time on, Dampier recedes from the development of Pacific geographical knowledge, even though he twice again (in 1703 and 1708) circumnavigated the globe, on these occasions clothed in his former garb as privateer.

The maps included in his three books varied from delineations of small islands to several of the world as a whole or larger part. It is this latter group which is of great significance, for it includes two maps of the "General and Coasting Trade-Winds in the Atlantick and Indian Oceans," and in the Pacific.[41] These maps enlarged on the current knowledge of wind systems in the tropical and subtropical regions, including data not found in any other source. Correlative with this information were the fundamental discussions on tropical wind systems, ocean currents, storm phenomena, and other characteristics of the Pacific Ocean which were basic to scientific study of these regions and of phenomena for well over a century following.

Dampier is not significant as a discoverer but as an investigator and narrator, more truly a geographer than many others more noted for exploratory contributions. He occupies the unique position as a transition from the age of Drake to that of Sir

Joseph Banks, partaking of both, yet not being either fully a pirate, nor a trained scientist. He was a gifted amateur.

British Privateer Circumnavigators: A Sterile Exploratory Epoch

Dampier's writings helped to stimulate British interest in the Pacific, and over the following decades this was translated in four ways: financial schemes for the promotion of trade in this region were developed; many speculative treatises on Pacific geography, of volumes of navigational journals, and of travel accounts were published; the vast Pacific Basin provided the setting for such fanciful locales as Utopia, for Robinson Crusoe's lone adventure, and for the land of Lilliput; and there was an expansion of English privateering on a grander scale, involving extensive round-the-world voyaging. What it did not immediately effect was a significant enlargement of geographical knowledge. As has been precisely said, it was "a time of wide interest, wild speculation and little achievement in exploration."[42] There was in fact no new British discovery in the Pacific for some sixty years after Dampier found New Britain.

The wide interest which has been mentioned manifested itself, for example, in a rash of tales of adventure, in national plans for occupation of the South Seas, and in translations of accounts of voyage by other nationalities to this region. Wild speculation refers particularly to the fantastic South Sea Company which never did float a ship to trade in the area for which it had gained monopoly rights.

That there was little exploratory achievement is born witness to by the roster of circumnavigations. In 1703, Dampier, as master of two craft provided by merchants, traversed the globe from the east as a privateer, returning the following year to England. Nothing of significance was noted. From 1708 to 1710, Woodes Rogers, with Dampier as pilot, circumnavigated the earth from the east, carrying on a greatly successful pillaging operation.[43] Nothing of geographical importance was reported (Fig. 34). In 1718, John Clipperton[44] and George Shelvocke,[45] in separate voyages, marauded from east to west across the Pacific, adding nothing to the Pacific map. And finally in 1741, Commodore George Anson with six ships of the Royal Navy set out, to return in 1744 with only one vessel remaining, but with a cargo of some £400,000 of treasure.[46] But again, in spite of his cross-Pacific venture, no new discovery had been forthcoming (Fig. 34). Anson's foray was the last of the Elizabethan style voyages in this first general "period of privileged plunderers."[47]

THE CLIMAX OF BRITISH EXPLORATION: 1760-1800

British Circumnavigators and the Pacific as a Field for National Enterprise

The last four decades of the eighteenth century, 1760–1800, were of prime significance in the history of Pacific exploration and mapping, for the major geographical enigmas of the region were solved during this time. The normal expectation by the mid-1700s was that Terra Australis would be found to extend northeast from New Zealand toward the Tropic of Capricorn as a great projection, then receding somewhat, both to the east and west into the South Atlantic and south Indian oceans. The

Northwest Passage was expected to be found somewhere along New Albion's shores, most likely north of the latitude of 48°, and leading to the northeast into northern Hudson Bay or the northeastern Arctic shore of Canada. Therefore, the instructions usually directed the expedition leaders to try to sail west from Cape Horn in more southerly latitudes than had been attempted before, and to search the northwest coast of America for a strait north of Cape Mendocino.

The journeys of Captain James Cook, 1768–1780, were the climax of this period of national endeavor, were backed by government and science together, had the most explicit instructions of any previous British expedition, had the type of ship and gear best suited to the task, and followed the above basic instructions to their ultimate extent. They represented, therefore, the climax of this age of circumnavigation and of national endeavor.

In spite of the maintenance of interest in the Pacific area by Britain after Anson's journey, by the mid-eighteenth century international events had intruded to such an extent that all attention and effort had to be focused upon the struggle with France in North America and in Europe. But, with the successful conclusion of hostilities, England turned to the Pacific as an inviting field for national enterprise. However, in spite of the colonial schemes and theoretical geographical analyses prepared by such writers as Campbell, Astley,[48] Callendar, and Dalrymple,[49] which helped to stimulate the government and to form a climate of opinion for Pacific adventures, Britain's official interest was still basically commercial rather than colonial. The national ascendancy of Britain in this region was promoted in order to contact producing areas, to foster trade monopolies, and to develop access routes to the home markets. Colonial predilection was a characteristic of the nineteenth rather than the eighteenth century in this sector of the globe.

From 1764 to 1780 a series of circumnavigations was undertaken, but these all had a different spirit compared to those earlier in the century. In the first place, those concerned were not privateers. Secondly, they were essentially government expeditions, equipped and directed as part of a continuing national program. Thirdly, they were each given definite instructions for geographical exploration and these were oriented around the two major geographical enigmas, the possible existence of a great southern continent, and of a northwest passage. These instructions were sometimes ignored in whole or in part by the commanders. Fourthly, there was an increasingly scientific spirit evident in the expeditions. The Royal Society, in company with other scientific groups, gave both academic and financial support to some of the enterprises, and it was observable that the Admiralty was taking a more scientific approach to its tasks also. In addition, Royal interest and patronage were provided for the development of hydrography and the navigational arts.

Two expeditions were supported between 1764 and 1768, before those of Captain James Cook. The first was led by John Byron, 1764–1765.[50] The second, commanded by Samuel Wallis, 1767–1768,[51] was separated by storms at the Strait of Magellan into two distinct units, one ship under Philip Carteret[52] taking a completely different route from that of the expedition commander.

Byron's instructions called particularly for a search for the elusive passage across the North American continent, and if successful in finding it, he was to sail home

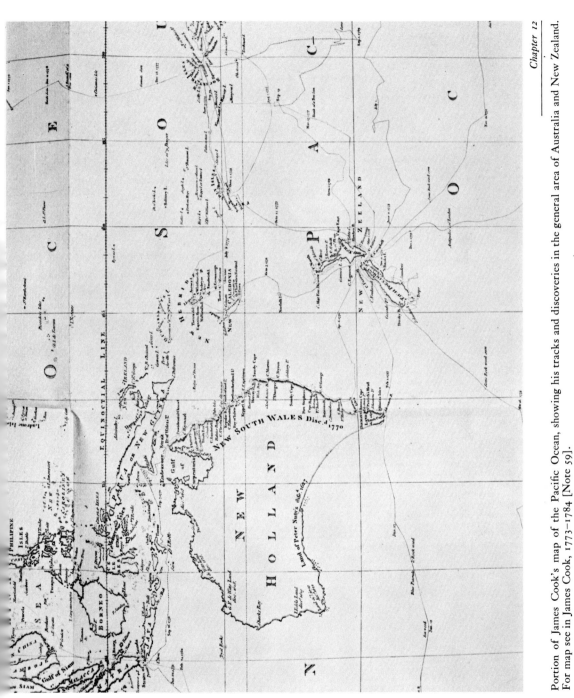

Portion of James Cook's map of the Pacific Ocean, showing his tracks and discoveries in the general area of Australia and New Zealand. For map see in James Cook, 1773–1784 [Note 59].

PLATE 31

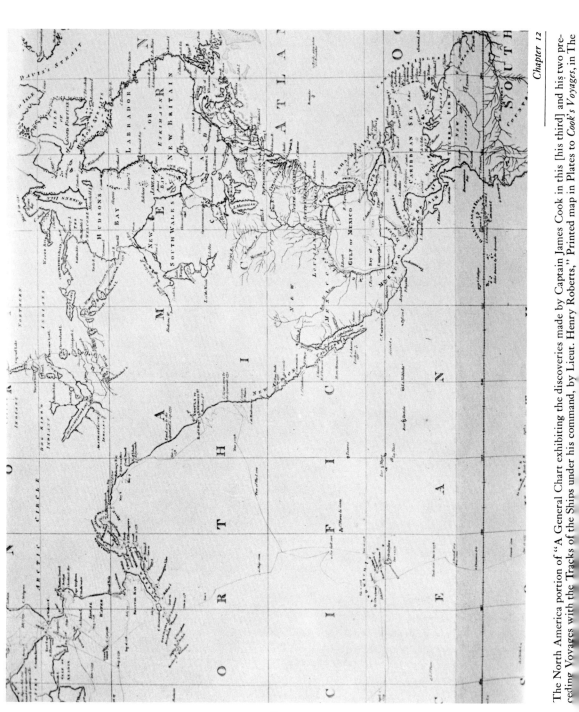

PLATE 32

Chapter 12

The North America portion of "A General Chart exhibiting the discoveries made by Captain James Cook in this [his third] and his two pre-ceding Voyages with the Tracks of the Ships under his command," by Lieut. Henry Roberts," Printed map in Plates to *Cook's Voyages*, in The through it. Failing this, he was to circumnavigate, searching for positive identification of some of the sightings of the southern continent reported by other seamen. He ignored completely the first part of his orders, attempting instead to cut west directly at latitude 27° S. into the supposed site of the southern continent. Impossible wind conditions prevented this, and instead he passed northwest in a shallow arc in the usual latitudes, during which he discovered some islands in the Tuamotu Archipelago, Tokelau Islands, and Gilbert Islands. From here, the ship moved on for refreshment in Batavia before completing its home run via the Cape of Good Hope (Fig. 34). The geographic results were relatively small, but positive; however, they had not negated the existence of any portion of the southern continent.

In 1767, the Wallis-Carteret expedition was authorized. On this occasion the directions made no reference to the Northwest Passage, but specifically instructed Wallis to search for Terra Australis. This was to be done by steering west in the Pacific, farther south than usual, to longitude 100° or 120° W. If the mission was successful, and if supplies were still available, the expedition was to retrace its track to Cape Horn, and to return to Britain. If they were unable to accomplish this task because of adverse winds, their route was to be that of a trans-Pacific navigation.

Philip Carteret, junior commander, adhered more closely to these orders than did the senior captain. Moreover, Carteret must be given high praise for his ability and courage in bringing his ship, the *Swallow*, back to port, for it was assigned to him in a most disreputable condition and no aid had been forthcoming from the government to improve it before departure. During what must have been one of the most difficult and lengthy passages in history through the Strait of Magellan, lasting four months, the two men were separated in a storm, Wallis believing that the *Swallow* had been sunk.

Wallis at first attempted to beat west at higher latitudes, and succeeded in reaching the one hundredth meridian at about latitude 35° S., a more southerly point than that attained by Carteret. After this, however, he steered for the tropics and like most others before him was carried by the trade winds northwest through the Tuamotu and Society islands toward the equator. In the process, he placed a number of these islands on the map for the first time, including the most important one, Tahiti. After adding several islands in the Marshall Islands to his list of discoveries, Wallis then moved on into the East Indies and from there past the African promontory (Fig. 34). Again, the positive results were valuable, but no further addition to the knowledge of Terra Australis was forthcoming.

After separating from Wallis, Carteret was forced north by storms and by the necessity of replenishing water supplies, heading for Juan Fernández Island (Isla Más a Tierra). Finding this island occupied by Spaniards, the boat was turned west to Isla Más Afuero. Some time was then spent searching for several reported islands north near the Tropic of Capricorn, before he turned his ship west by south and was carried across a corner of the ocean which was then conjectured to be dry land, to the south of the Tropic. During this section of the trip, Pitcairn Island was first sighted by a member of the crew, who thus had his name immortalized. From here the expedition returned into the normal cruising latitudes, passing through the southern Tuamotus, and on into the Solomons and the Carolines where several discoveries are accredited to it. The most important contribution of the expedition was the discovery, naming, and first use of the straits[53] separating New Britain from New Ireland, as Carteret named it, and this island from New Hanover. Carteret had thereby completed the delineation begun by Dampier. The expedition reached England via the normal passage from Java, in 1768 (Fig. 34).

A re-examination of these circumnavigations will indicate that they had contributed very little either to the clarification of the mystery of the great southern continent, or to the search for the Northwest Passage from its Pacific terminus. Their fullest contribution was provided by the discovery, re-discovery, exploration, and charting of many islands and waters of the south tropical zone of the Pacific. Little progress had been made beyond the Tasman journeys a century previous, in charting the unknown middle and high latitudes in the South Pacific.

THE CLIMAX OF ENGLISH PACIFIC EXPLORATION: COOK'S VOYAGES

Within about twelve years after these latest circumnavigations the situation had altered completely, due to the three expeditions commanded by James Cook. This is perhaps the most remarkably rapid reversal of a state of geographical knowledge ever recorded, for in this relatively short time practically all of the remaining major problems of Pacific configuration were precisely and brilliantly cleared.

The reason for such splendid success in exploration was due beyond all doubt to the personal qualities of Cook, and to the magnificent use of his training and experience.[54] There were other contributory factors, such as the manner in which the government and the Royal Society supported him with the vessel, equipment, and scientific personnel which he desired.[55] Too, the spirit of the time was to expand the knowledge of the Pacific Ocean without interference between nations.

James Cook was thoroughly prepared for the leadership of Britain's first extensive, nationally supported scientific maritime expedition in the Pacific, both by early training and later experience. Nursed as a mariner in the North Sea coal trade, hardened under fire in British naval actions in the Atlantic, and in the sieges of Louisburg and of Quebec, he had also been confirmed as a superlative marine surveyor along the shores of the St. Lawrence River, of Newfoundland, and of Nova Scotia.[56] Although a practical seaman, he had trained himself to some degree in astronomy and particularly in navigational theory. By this time he had come also to the notice of the Royal Society through the medium of a paper on the eclipse of the sun which he had presented to this august body.[57] This combination of talents favored his appointment to expedition leadership over the claims of other contenders. It was a fortuitous circumstance that Captain Cook was available for larger tasks just at that juncture when the rare celestial occurrence of a transit of Venus presented the necessity of Britain establishing an observation station in the mid-Pacific.[58] Cook was eminently suited to undertake these observations, which were the announced major purpose of the expedition. The secondary instructions stated, perhaps knowingly, the more important issue involved, which was no less than the discovery and exploration, or the abnegation, of the southern continent.

The first voyage from 1768 to 1771[59] followed the usual route from Cape Horn into the Tuamotu and Society islands, for Cook was aiming for Tahiti, which Wallis had described as an excellent base for refreshment. Here would be the base from which the transit of Venus was to be observed. Successfully completing this mission, the party moved on through the western islands of the Society Islands, south to the latitude 40° and then west to New Zealand, following the exact letter of the Admiralty instructions.[60] Six months were spent charting the entire circumference of the two islands, after which the ship sailed west to map in great detail the unknown east coast of Australia. This was the period of greatest danger to the expedition, for the ship became involved in the treacherous barrier reef off this newly discovered coast. After taking possession of this land as New Wales the expedition struck north and west through Torres Strait[61] and on south of New Guinea to Batavia, Cape of Good Hope, and to Britain (Fig. 35).

Until leaving for the south from the Society Islands Cook had not departed from normal practice, but after this his procedure was unique. By sailing south to latitude 40° at about longitude 145° W., Cook took a large area away from what would have been the northwest corner of the great northern projection of Terra Australis, and in fact threw considerable doubt on the continent's existence. His disclosure of an east side to New Zealand also eliminated the possibility of New Zealand being the west side of the southern continent, a thought which was a heritage of Tasman's discovery. Cook's wonderful navigational and surveying feat along the Australian coast added the final dimension to that continent, and framed the southwest border of the Pacific. His ship was the first also to follow that of Torres through the break between Australia and New Guinea, thereby proving for all to see the true character of this area and attesting to the veracity of the Torres' journey. The first major blow to the theory of a southern continent had been struck (Plate 31, *following page 238*).

A globe would be the best map to use to describe Cook's second voyage from 1772 to 1775, for he circumnavigated the earth from west to east and probed south on several occasions farther than anyone else before, even into the rim of the ice pack surrounding the true southern continent.[62] First, he cleared the south Indian Ocean of any possible large land mass by sailing south past latitude 50°, and finally beyond the Antarctic Circle to 67° S. Passing from here north to New Zealand, the expedition took a four-month circular cruise east and north through Polynesia before returning to New Zealand. In the course of this it again eliminated any possibility of a continent just east of New Zealand and discovered a number of islands in the by then fairly well-known island-strewn open Pacific. After approximately a month in New Zealand, Cook commenced an even larger loop into the South Pacific, determined to clear finally all question of the existence of land in this area. He reached latitude 71° 10' S. before turning almost due north for Easter Island, and from there in a large arc traveled north to the Marquesas and back to Tahiti. On the way to New Zealand the ship sailed west of about latitude 20° S. to the New Hebrides, then veered south where it discovered New Caledonia, and finally Norfolk Island as the expedition made for New Zealand. This most conclusive and valuable tour occupied almost a year. It was then October, 1774. The demise of the concept of Terra Australis Incognita was completed by the group when, after leaving for home in November, they cut across to Cape Horn through the mid-latitudes, and continued searching for the continent between latitudes 50° and 60° in the South Atlantic Ocean. Having

Aleutian Is.

Canton

Philippine Is. Guam Marshall Is.

Caroline Islands Gilbert Is.

120° 150° 180°

Batavia New Guinea Solomon Is. Tokelau Is.

Timor Torres Strait

New Hebrides Fiji Is.

New Caledonia Loyalty Is.

Cape Leevwin Norfolk I. Kermadec Is

Port Jackson (Sydney)

Bass Strait NEW ZEALA

Tasmania Chatha

------- Cook, 1768-1771
━━•━ Cook, 1772-1775
+━+━+ Cook, 1776-1780
━ ━ ━ Vancouver, 1791-1795
·········Flinders and Bass, 1798
━··━··Flinders, 1801-1802
━·━·━·Flinders, 1802-1803
━o━o━The *Beagle*, 1831-1836
━━━━The *Challenger*, 1872-1876

FIG. 35. British discovery and exploration by Co

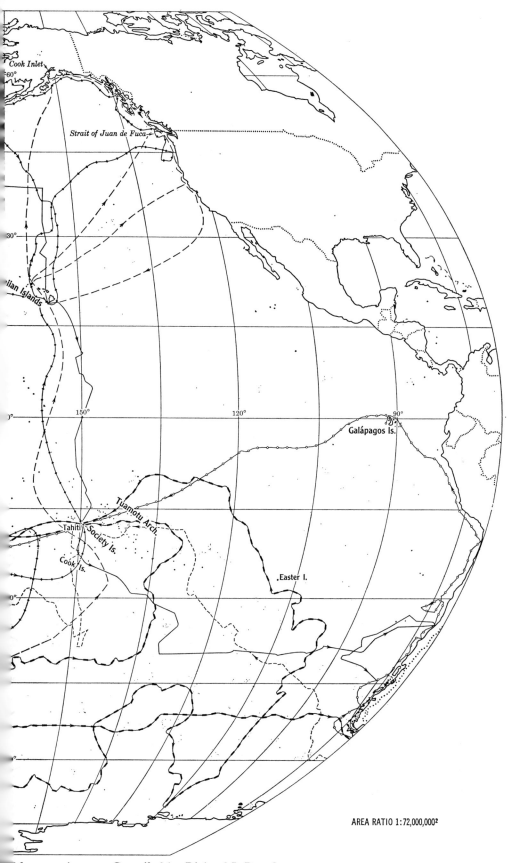

Cook Inlet
60°
Strait of Juan de Fuca
30°
lian Islands
150°   120°   90°
Galápagos Is.
Tuamotu Arch.
Tahiti Society Is.
Cook Is.
Easter I.
0°
0°
0°

AREA RATIO 1:72,000,000²

later navigators. Compiled by Richard I. Ruggles.

closed the world circuit finally south of Africa, the ship turned north and home to England (Fig. 35).

Of course the most significant feature of this extraordinary voyage was the cancellation of Terra Australis, even though Cook was quite correct when he hinted that if there was a great continent it must be closer to the South Pole than he was able to reach. The positive discoveries on this journey were considerable, exceeding twenty islands and being much more than those of any other English seaman (Fig. 36).

The third, and for Cook the fateful journey, from 1776 to 1780, was planned to clear up the mystery of the outline of the North Pacific.[63] Actually, much more than this was accomplished, for the vessels entered again from the west, revisited Tasmania, New Zealand, and the Polynesian islands, making several new discoveries there, and then struck north to bring Europeans for the first time to the Hawaiian Islands.[64] At this date, the west coast of North America was perhaps the least known of all the continental shorelines, except for the polar regions, and it was expected that somewhere along it was harbored the entrance to the long-sought strait.[65] Toward this coast Cook now turned his attention, and through the spring, summer, and early autumn of 1778 conducted the longest continuous coastal survey of his Pacific career. This included the shore from mid-Oregon, through the Bering Strait to latitude 70° 44' where the Arctic ice pack stayed his course. South again he surveyed part of the Siberian coast and some of the Aleutian Islands before heading back to Hawaii, or the Sandwich Islands, as he had named them. Here, Cook was killed as a result of a type of dispute which he had always been able to avoid or quieten during all his previous years in the Pacific. The expedition under a new leader, true to the training and example which Cook had given it, rather than retreating to Britain, instead returned north past Bering Strait searching again for a passage north of Siberia. Stopped once more by ice the vessel retreated south down the coast of Asia, and finally via the Cape of Good Hope reached its home port in Britain (Fig. 35).

This final voyage of Cook's was most important for its delineation of the American coast, though the survey did not undertake to chart more than the general form of the shoreline. Since its work was done by fixes taken on board ship standing offshore, the incredible complexity of island and inlet was ignored. Also missed was the mouth of the Columbia River, the Strait of Juan de Fuca and, therefore, the insularity of Vancouver Island. Cook reported negatively on the possibility of a strait along the coast, and of a way to east or west beyond Bering Strait. However, by leaving an incomplete end to Cook Inlet in Alaska, carte blanche was given to such men as Peter Pond to suggest that here lay the waterway into the interior. Also, it was quite logical that there was still hope that the generalized coastal survey masked an entrance somewhere deep in the recesses of the fiord and mountain-girt coast of America (Plate 32, facing page 239).

There were many other achievements of Cook's voyages which should be mentioned: the navigational charts, which in many areas stood the test of use for many decades; the very precise and clear exposition of his journals; and the care taken to describe the best places for replenishment for future voyaging in the Pacific. The most valuable aids to future travel, however, were the methods demonstrated by Cook to eliminate scurvy and other associated diseases from long-distance travel. This was based partly on the scrupulous cleanliness which he forced upon his men, their clothing, and their quarters. It was due also to his refusal to allow stale water to be drunk, to his provision of antiscorbutics, to have as much fresh fruit and vegetables provided at every opportunity, and to have as much room provided for each man as was possible below decks. The proof of the efficiency of his method lay in the very small handful of his men who either died of scurvy or even had a short bout with it.

In addition to these aspects, all of the expeditions had included several leading scientists of the time, particularly astronomer-mathematicians, and naturalists.[66] The most famous was Sir Joseph Banks, who accompanied the first tour. These men provided scientific materials of great value to posterity. Cook himself added a facet to the expedition journals which was somewhat unexpected. This was an unusually good ability as an anthropologist and as a psychologist, for he delighted in describing the native peoples, their material culture, and social customs; and he was able, except upon his last and fatal meeting, to maintain friendly contacts with them. Under his tutelage at least, the island peoples whom they met received excellent treatment and an acquaintanceship with some of the better qualities of European civilization.

Above all, Cook brought to the open Pacific the power of a nation which was becoming the mistress of the seas, and hence the increasing communication between the island groups gave to the Pacific islands a new unity which they had not had previously.

Tidying the Pacific Map to 1800

The unprecendented scope of the Cook expeditions was never matched in the Pacific area by other British seamen, or by the navigators of any other nation. The interest aroused by the expeditions' reports and the information made available were incentives for a variety of enterprises which blossomed in the Pacific realm; increased trading, fur-trading and hunting, establishment of a penal colony in Australia, and the migration of missionaries to some of the island groups. Either accidentally, as was often the case, or in some instances as a deliberate program of exploration, many of the remaining smaller archipelagos, individual islands within them, or the known island groups, separated islands in the open sea, or the details of continental coastlines, were added to the map by English seamen. It was a form of tidying operation.[67]

The recorded voyages into the Pacific after Cook to the end of the century are undoubtedly only a portion of the total which occurred. Voyages were yearly occurrences, and were sponsored by different organizations. One of the outstanding originating forces was the report of the immense wealth of sea furs to be obtained off the Pacific Northwest Coast. On the third voyage by Cook some furs had been taken and sold at great profit in Asia, and the reports brought back encouraged the outfitting of numerous vessels to engage in this trade. Soon there were several expeditions at a time making the round trip from England to the northwest coast and to the Asiatic side. Much valuable charting of the coasts was done by such seamen as Hanna in 1785–1787, Nathaniel Portlock and George Dixon, 1785–1788[68], John Meares and William Douglas, 1786–1789[69], George Mortimer[70], James Barclay[71] and others[72], many of whose names are now part of northwest coastal nomenclature.

The description of the coast and harbors of New South Wales in Australia, em-

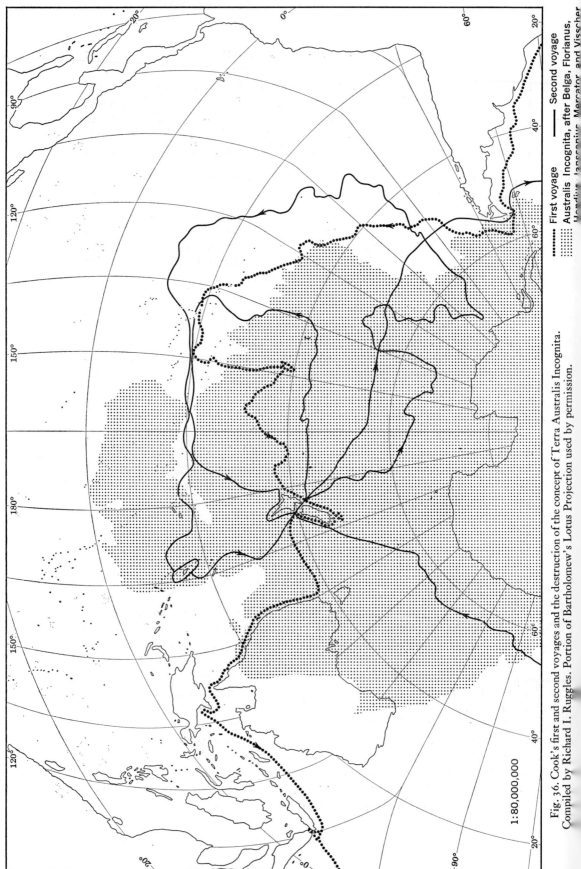

Fig. 36. Cook's first and second voyages and the destruction of the concept of Terra Australis Incognita. Compiled by Richard I. Ruggles. Portion of Bartholomew's Lotus Projection used by permission.

1:80,000,000

bodied in Cook's journal, suggested to some British government officials that this area would be most useful as the site of a penal settlement. In 1787, Captain Arthur Phillip was sent to this region in command of a fleet of eleven vessels, laden with convicts and supplies.[73] Some of these particular ships, and a number later, while returning from unloading at the penal colony founded at Port Jackson in New South Wales, came upon various unknown islands, particularly in Melanesia and in Micronesia, as they passed north either toward the Asiatic coast, or around New Guinea on the way to the East Indies. For example, after the founding fleet disbanded to return to Britain in their separate ways, Captains Gilbert and Marshall, in 1788[74], discovered portions of the island groups to which their names were later affixed. In the same year, Captain Watts discovered the Kermadec Islands northeast of New Zealand; Captain Lever noted the existence of several islands in the Kermadec Islands and in the northern Cooks; and Captain Shortland discovered the Russell Islands, the western members of the New Georgia group, and several independent islands in the Solomon Islands. Similarly at later dates, Captain John Hunter in 1791 noted the Stewart Islands, to the east of the Solomons; Captain Wilkinson in 1792 contacted two new islands south of the main Solomon Islands; in 1792, Captain Bond discovered two islets on the western fringe of the Marshalls; and Captain Musgrave reported in 1793 the finding of several unknown islands of the Caroline Islands. William Raven is given the honor of discovering the Loyalty Islands, between New Caledonia and the New Hebrides, on one of two voyages to Australia between 1793 and 1796; Captain Dennett in 1797 reported several new additions to the map of the western Marshall Islands; and in 1799, Captain Bishop added to the known total of islands in the Gilbert Islands. These represent only some of the discoveries which were noted upon the Pacific map by ships plying to and from Australia. Although these voyages were not individually of great importance, yet in aggregate they were of considerable significance.[75]

Continuous interest was displayed also by the new Australian colony in the configuration of the Pacific coast of this immense island continent. Among others, Bowen and Weatherhead coasted both north and south from Port Jackson for considerable distances. But most significant of them all, and prophetic of their further services during the early nineteenth century in the delineation of the continental outline, were the voyages undertaken by George Bass and Matthew Flinders in the last decade of the century.[76] Although they made many small-boat voyages north up-coast from Port Jackson, their initial interest centered upon the southern littoral, and particularly on the possibility of the separation of Tasmania from the mainland, a question left unsettled for over a century and a half following Tasman's charting of the southern promontory of this island.

In 1797, Bass and six companions sailed down coast in a whaleboat. Reaching Cape Howe, they rounded it, sailed southwest past Wilson's Promontory and on out into open water, approximately to latitude 40° S., before turning back. Convinced that this large expanse was not a great bight of the mainland coast but a wide separating channel, Bass and Flinders repeated much of this course the following year. Instead of turning west along the Victoria shore from Cape Howe, however, they continued south to the Furneaux Group and on to the Tasmanian north coast. From here they veered west following the shore to Cape Grim, its northwestern-

most projection. At this point, corroboration of their belief in the break between the
two land masses was first obtained, after which they confirmed the insularity of
Tasmania by continuing south down the west coast around the southern cape and
north along the island's Pacific shore. This important voyage was, in fact, another
important link in the chain of Australian configurative voyages, begun by Torres,
and continued by Tasman and Cook (Fig. 35).

Another interesting aspect of the exploration of the Pacific at this time was the
breadfruit mission under the command of Captain William Bligh.[77] A report by
Cook, as well as previous discussions by Dampier and Anson, of the value of breadfruit as a food among the Pacific islanders had encouraged West Indies merchants to
petition King George III to send an expedition into the Pacific to obtain cuttings for
the plant's introduction on the Caribbean islands. In 1787, William Bligh was given
command of the *Bounty*, which was outfitted for the task. Bligh reached Tahiti,
brought the breadfruit cargo on board, and sailed for home. In the Tonga Islands his
ship was taken from him by mutineers. Bligh and a loyal group were put off on the
ship's launch, and in this they traveled in an incredible journey of thousands of miles
to Timor, where they were picked up and returned to England.

Before the mutiny, the *Bounty* had touched down for the first time at a lonely series
of islands lying far out in the Pacific east of South Island, New Zealand, to which the
name of their ship, *Bounty*, was affixed. On the way west from Tahiti, heading for
Tonga, a small island in the southern Cook group was reached, and described for the
first time. The mutiny occurred a short time after this, and the epic open boat
journey commenced. Even in the extremity of the circumstances, Bligh kept a record
of all landfalls made by this unhappy crew, all of which were identified later to be
various islands in the Fiji and Banks islands.

Vhen reports of the mutiny reached England, the government dispatched a vessel,
under Captain Edward Edwards, in 1791[78], to search for and to apprehend the
mutineers. Some of these he captured and returned in irons to England for trial.
While searching the seas for the hiding place of that group of mutineers who reached
Pitcairn Island and were never taken into custody, islands in the Tuamotu Archipelago and Tokelau Islands, along with several others elsewhere were added to the
known roster.

Bligh himself returned again to the Pacific in 1792 to complete the breadfruit mission, and was successful also in discovering several more of the Fiji Islands.

In 1796, the newly founded London Missionary Society sent a party of missionaries to the Pacific under the aegis of Captain James Wilson, where they were
distributed in new mission fields in Tahiti, Tonga, and the Marquesas, thus founding
the mission colonies which became so important in the following century.[79] On this
voyage the Îles Gambier and several other atolls were discovered and named by
Wilson. In addition to these various, more-or-less-connected groups of voyages in
the Pacific, there were many which we might call, "independent," for they were
either private traders, or they were in the area for other reasons. Undiscovered
islands were found by such men as Douglas in Hawaii, 1798; Hunter in the Solomons,
1791; Butler in the Loyalty Islands, 1794; Mortlock in the Carolines, 1795; and
Fearn in the Loyalty and Gilbert Islands, 1798.

While these disparate voyages and discoveries were being recorded there was enacted, from 1791 to 1795, along the northwest coast of North America, a most complex and correlated program of hydrographic mapping, directed by Captain George Vancouver.[80] Vancouver was sent out by the British Admiralty in 1791 to supervise the orderly arrangement of affairs on the west coast of America which would result from the Nootka Sound Convention, and also to make a detailed survey of the west coast of North America into the Arctic. This was the only program which can be compared in scope with Cook's work, though it was much more thorough and detailed than this previous undertaking, albeit more restricted in area. In its own way, it was itself historic in nature, since it coincided with the final and culminating journey of Alexander Mackenzie across North America through the western mountains to the Pacific coast at Bella Coola, the end of the search for a route across North America to the Pacific Ocean.[81]

The Vancouver expedition occupied the time from April 1, 1791, to October 1795, but almost the entire first year was spent in crossing from England, via the Cape of Good Hope, to Australia, Tahiti, and Hawaii.[82] During this voyage the group discovered several islands, including Chatham Island east of New Zealand (Fig. 35). Vancouver's hydrographic charting was the most detailed and precise yet produced in the Pacific theater, for besides having the advantage of newer-model survey instruments, he and his associates worked for much of their time from the ship's launches which penetrated close to shore in practically every nook and cranny of this intricate coast. The Admiralty instructions specifically ordered the expedition to solve the problem of the possible existence of the entrance to a transcontinental strait on this coast. The two leading contenders were the Strait of Juan de Fuca and Cook Inlet. By this date the Spanish had already explored some of the complex of waterways which are reached through the Strait of Juan de Fuca, but Vancouver had no knowledge of or information on this, and the party completed its own task in these waters.[83] The result was that Vancouver Island was cartographically detached from the continental coastline, and the explorers were able to negate the possibility of a strait in this area.[84]

Cook Inlet was similarly nullified as the entrance to the transcontinental passage in 1794, when the ships were engaged in charting the coast north to the limit of latitude 60° which had been set for them in their orders. The result was the cancellation of all hope for a water passage across the continent, and thereby the solution of the second major enigma of Pacific geography (Plate 33, *following page 254*).

Although ships of the new Hydrographic Office,[85] founded in 1795, and of many other official and also private expeditions examined all parts of the Pacific in some detail after 1800, it can be said truly that it was in the eighteenth century that the British made their greatest contributions to the development of the Pacific map.

THE PERIOD OF GEOGRAPHIC ELABORATION: THE NINETEENTH CENTURY

Surveying for an Accurate Delineation of Australia and New Zealand

The advent of the new century witnessed no significant alteration of the British approach to the exploration and mapping of the Pacific Basin. The inauguration of a new phase had, in fact, occurred with the massive surveying assault by the Vancouver expedition upon the American northwest coast some years previously. This detailed enterprise, sponsored by the British government, was the forerunner of a series of surveying voyages by naval vessels during the following century. This continuing stress on surveying operations by the new Hydrographic Office was one of the two major facets of environmental exploration by the British. The second was the increasing scope of scientific investigation by combined government and private research interests. This had been heralded by Dampier's solitary research,[86] and was extended by Banks and his associates on board the *Discovery*, with Cook.[87] In the nineteenth century it was expanded by the voyage of the *Beagle* in the 1830s,[88] and culminated in the most complete research cruise of its time approximately a half-century later, that of the four-year cruise of the *Challenger*.[89]

The late eighteenth-century voyages of the British had won for this nation a primacy of influence in the Pacific, and this was maintained and enhanced without extensive military programs or operations. It was supported by her global position as Mistress of the Seas, and in this role it was usually sufficient for her to send warships from time to time to visit the Pacific islands, "to show the flag," and to investigate.[90]

New South Wales had become a secure base for trade, and Port Jackson (Sydney) a major port-of-call for vessels proceeding to or from the South Pacific, and a supply point for settlers in Melanesia and Polynesia. These settlers were, to a large extent, missionaries or traders, the former being of great importance in the socio-political orientation of the indigenous people of this region.

The nineteenth century held no great surprises for the world, in terms of Pacific shore configuration. This period may be characterized as one of elaboration, of the detailed charting of coastlines, of the inventory of archipelagic constellations, of the description of the natural and social environments of the area, and of the scientific analysis of the ocean basin. Description was the order of the day. Reams of books were written about travels in the South Seas,[91] concerning places, peoples, and events, by traders,[92] missionaries, naval officers, government officials,[93] and various independent travelers.[94] Many were of no great geographic significance but all fed a market in Britain and Western Europe, eager to hear of this still mysterious, vast region. No other nation could match the contributions of the British in the geographical investigation of the Pacific Basin.

In the first quarter of the nineteenth century, outside of normal trading, sea-hunting and missionary activities, and some marine surveying undertaken during the regular cruises of naval ships, exploratory activity was preponderantly that of Australian coastal delineation.[95] Matthew Flinders had set himself the task of completing the observation of the complete shoreline of Australia, in order to settle the question, still extant, whether this spacious land was indeed a continent, or a cluster of large islands.[96] With Bass, he had proved that Tasmania was detached from the continent by circumnavigating this island.[97] The task of verifying this assertion was given to Captain James Grant by the British government, which in 1800 ordered him to sail through the supposed Strait, named after Bass, on his way to Sydney from England, via the Cape of Good Hope.[98] He did this, and in addition touched upon the southern shore of the continent, being thereby credited with the discovery of the coast from near Cape Banks to near Cape Patton.[99] In 1801, John Murray sailed from Sydney, west through Bass Strait, examined its shores more carefully, and discovered, but did not fully explore, Port Phillip Bay, that large embayment upon which Melbourne was later founded.[100]

Matthew Flinders returned this same year to Australia as commander of the naval vessel *Investigator*, to spend over two years circumnavigating the continent.[101] His approach course lay across the Indian Ocean to Cape Leeuwin, the southwest promontory of the continent, from which point he explored much of the south coast, discovered Spencer Gulf and Gulf St. Vincent, and explored Port Phillip Bay. Having examined these three major re-entrants carefully, he was able to disprove the existence of a supposed strait, rifting Australia from south to north (Fig. 35).

After a short respite at Sydney, the *Investigator* was turned north on July 22, 1802, along the east coast. Flinders had based his actions upon a careful examination of Cook's charts and descriptions, in order to essay the difficult task of verifying the continuous nature of the coastline. He did this by clarifying coastal and offshore island details, by examining those portions of the littoral passed at night by Cook, and by sailing into all the major bays and on the leeward side of the major islands. Off the Queensland coast the *Investigator* searched for and found a safe, navigable gap in the Great Barrier Reef, which opening was carefully charted. Passing north, then, on the outside of the Reef, through Torres Strait, the crew charted the east and south coasts of the Gulf of Carpentaria, proved the insularity of the Wellesley Islands and Maria Island and the Sir Edward Pellew Group, searched the west shore, and thereby negated the possibility that a channel to the Southern Ocean would be found here. In effect, this had confirmed his south coastal deduction of the previous year.

Passing farther west, the *Investigator* traced the north continental coast to Cape Wessel, after which it repaired to Timor. Finding his vessel to be showing advanced signs of decay, Flinders decided to make for Sydney for the needed repairs, before tackling the detailed surveying of the west coast. He reached that port, via a straight run south out of sight of the west coast, around the cape, and through Bass Strait to his destination (Fig. 35).

Unfortunately, Flinders was not able to complete his appointed task, as he received orders to return to Britain. He reached home only after a shipwreck, accompanied by the loss of much data. In England he completed his book,[102] outlining his findings, and here he proposed the adoption of the name "Australia" for this now-proven continental island. Flinders rivals Cook in the scientific thoroughness of his surveying and in the breadth of his geographic interests.

Philip Parker King was appointed to complete the program carried on so splendidly by Flinders.[103] In December 1817, the Admiralty dispatched King from Sydney, and approximately five years later, after four extensive journeys, the mission was accomplished. The maps resulting remained the basic coastal delineation and navigational source for a considerable period of time.[104]

The first two voyages, undertaken in the *Mermaid*, extended from December 1817, to January 1820. First, sailing south and west, clockwise, King put his greatest emphasis on surveying the King George Sound coast, before coasting along the western margin of the continent to the Dampier Archipelago, Van Diemen Gulf, Melville Island, and Bathurst Island. These latter complicated and barren shores were studied and mapped in detail before the vessel, having been replenished in Timor, reversed its track on its return to Sydeny. In May 1819, the *Mermaid* was, on this occasion, turned north from home port, round Cape York, and over to the Wessel Islands off Arnhem Land, and eventually proceeded west along the north coast to overlap the area in which the ship had worked the previous year. Considerable time was consumed in defining the shores of Joseph Bonaparte Gulf, and in investigating the deep embayments in this large bight. King was back in Port Jackson in the first month of 1820.

King's third expedition in the *Mermaid* from July 12 until December 9, 1820, was again concerned with the east, north, and northwest coasts of the continent, but its chief result was to ascertain the safety of the entire eastern in-shore route in smooth water inside the reef.

The final contribution of King, as master of a different vessel, the *Bathurst*, was the preparation of accurate charts of the Australian west coast by the revision and correction of old Dutch maps. Upon his return to Sydney, after a voyage lasting from May 1821 to April 1822, King received instructions to report back to the Admiralty in London, in order to complete the final charts and journals resulting from these historic expeditions. On several occasions, King had included an Australian aborigine in his crew's complement, in order to interview native peoples whenever they were in contact. King's descriptions of the aborigines, their customs, and relationship to the harsh environment became significant sources of such information. Although many other individuals later investigated small segments of the shoreline, King may be correctly characterized as the last representative of the distinguished British explorer-delineators of the Pacific.

Throughout this century fragments of this island-and-atoll world were discovered, none of which could be called momentous, although all had significance.[105] For example, Bristow in the whaling vessel *Ocean* discovered Auckland Island in 1806,[106] and Hasselbrough in the *Perseverance* added Campbell Island in 1810,[107] both islands being south of New Zealand. A sandalwood trader, Lockerby, added several islands of the Fiji Islands to the map,[108] Ireland brought notice of another member of the Tuamotu Archipelago,[109] and Patrickson described his discoveries in the northern Cook Islands.[110]

MISSIONARY ACTIVITIES: A SOURCE OF GEOGRAPHICAL INFORMATION

Of far more consequence was the wealth of information of a diverse nature which became known through the settlement of missionaries under the aegis of various Protestant denominations. The London Missionary Society was the pioneer group, having entered this realm in 1796.[111] The advance of mission stations into most of the island groups during this century confirmed the primacy of influence of Britain in these regions.

Information about the Pacific region was brought home with returning or retiring missionaries, through reports of enquiry prepared for the religious governing bodies in Britain, through many personal accounts of lives spent in the mission fields, or through the biographies of distinguished missionaries.[112] None of these men were concerned primarily with this region as a geographic area to be analyzed, or even with native societies to be described or analyzed. Nevertheless, description and analysis resulted, which was of considerable consequence.

NAVAL SURVEYING VOYAGES

The Australian expeditions of Philip King were part of a continued series of British naval surveying voyages undertaken by the Hydrographic Office of the Admiralty.[113] Almost without exception, naval vessels on routine cruises also engaged in surveying, although there were several expeditions whose orders were almost completely oriented toward this purpose. British naval patrolling did not become normal or extensive until the first quarter-century had passed, and was a response, in part, to growing American influence in Hawaii and the North Pacific. In 1829 the Admiralty instructed the admirals of the East Indies and South American stations to arrange for warships to visit the Pacific islands from time to time as routine operations. As British missions and trade ties increased in this region there was an increasing necessity and a demand for the government to intervene, at times to show force, and at times to punish.[114]

In response to increasing government concern with Pacific activities and as a political act expressed as a gracious gesture, Captain Lord Byron was commissioned in 1824 to carry the bodies of the King and Queen of Hawaii back from England to their native land, after their deaths from measles, contracted while on a visit.[115] The ship, *Blonde*, returned to home port in 1826, after having discovered Malden Island south of Hawaii. Andrew Bloxam, a naturalist on board, provided further regional information in the written results of the journey.[116]

From 1825 to 1828, Captain Frederick Beechey in the *Blossom* completed a 73,000-mile trip, largely in the Pacific,[117] whose main purpose was to await the Parry and Franklin expeditions at their expected Bering Strait exit from their Northwest Passage journeys.[118] On the way to the rendezvous, the ship called in at Easter Island and Pitcairn Island and at the Îles Gambier, and an excellent account of the area and peoples was given. Three small islands in the Tuamotu Archipelago were discovered and others examined. While in the north in the summer of 1826, waiting as directed, Beechey spent some three months surveying the Kotzebue Sound coasts, before finally giving up hope for the Franklin expedition's arrival.[119] Turning south, they returned to Britain round the Horn.

In 1826 the naval ships *Adventure* and *Beagle*, under Captain Philip Parker King of Australian surveying fame, and Captain Robert Fitzroy, began a surveying cruise along the South American coast, which lasted until 1830.[120]

THE BEAGLE, CHALLENGER, AND OTHER CONTEMPORARY SCIENTIFIC SURVEYS

In the following year, 1831, the *Beagle* was recommissioned under Captain Fitzroy to intensify the hydrographic surveys on the American Pacific coasts, and to gather useful information on the natural environment of lands and seas visited.[121] Charles Darwin, a young biologist, was invited by Captain Fitzroy to accompany the expedition as scientist.[122] Although much valuable surveying was completed, the major significance of this voyage was the detailed scientific reports of the science cadre, and the field experience gained by Darwin in the Galapagos Islands particularly, which aided him substantially in the formulation of his epochal biological theories.[123] The cruise was far-ranging in regions visited,[124] as well as phenomena studied and reported upon. Although a considerable time was spent initially on the South American coast and offshore islands, the ship passed through the island-studded South Pacific, touching down in New Zealand and Australia before passing west around the Cape of Good Hope on the way home to England (Fig. 35). Excellent geographical description and analysis was produced, and included aspects of both the physical and social geography of lands visited, as well as such systematic physical aspects as winds, weather and cloud formations, and hydrographic data on tides and sea temperatures. In addition to the extensive biological materials,[125] two of the most valuable studies undertaken were those of the geology of Pacific South America,[126] and the structure and distribution of coral reefs.[127]

The *Beagle* expedition was not duplicated in scope for almost a half-century, until the momentous cruise of the *Challenger* initiated the era of massive scientific research programs. In the interim, naval surveying operations continued apace with such programs as that of the *Sulphur*, under Frederick W. Beechey and Henry Kellett along the South American shore from 1836 to 1838,[128] and after that under the command of Captain Sir Edward Belcher until 1842;[129] of the *Actaeon* under Lord Edward Russell in the Tuamotu Archipelago in 1836–1837; and the *Herald* under Kellett from 1845 to 1851.[130] At times, warships of the fleet, engaged in tours, included scientific personnel, or at least interested observers of the environment. For example, the cruise of the *Herald* included scientific personnel, interested primarily in zoological problems, but the naval cadre added nautical, meteorological, magnetical, and astronomical studies to their surveying tasks.[131] In 1865, the *Curaçao*, sent off to show the flag, included an ornithologist, a taxidermist, and a shell collector, whose extensive collections and detailed notes and drawings reached the British Museum and other scientific centers.[132]

During the latter half of the century, scientific analysis became more and more concerned with the open ocean, that is, with the character of the ocean basin and the water mass itself. Although considerable knowledge had been accumulated by this period about Pacific oceanography, initiated by Dampier in a descriptive way, and most vessels gathered soundings, and tidal and current data, no such single-purpose expedition had been organized by the British up to 1870.

In 1868 and 1869 the Royal Society succeeded in persuading the navy to place ships at their disposal to undertake the first systematic examination of the ocean's bed off Ireland and Scotland, and later in the vicinity of Portugal.[133] As a result of the great scientific and practical results of these voyages, the Society importuned the government for an extended cruise ". . . for the examination of the physical and biological conditions of the deep sea throughout the great ocean basins. . . ."[134] They succeeded, and had the *Challenger* seconded to this task. In collaboration, the ship was refurbished as a floating scientific laboratory, and a scientific staff gathered under the direction of Professor Sir Charles Wyville Thomson.[135] In addition to biological, chemical, and photographic laboratories, a large chart room was furnished to prepare the results of the proposed naval surveying program.[136] Overall command

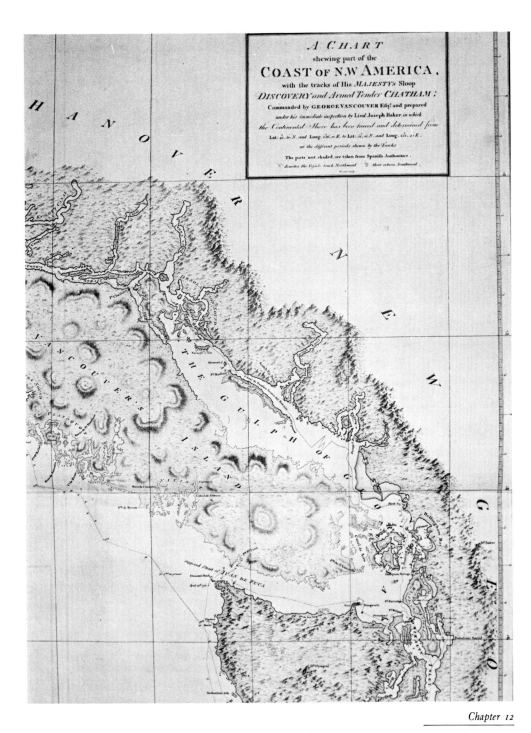

Portion of George Vancouver's "A Chart shewing part of the Coast of N.W. America . . . ," in his 1801 publication [see Note 82] vol. 4, in The Public Archives of Canada, Ottawa.

PLATE 33

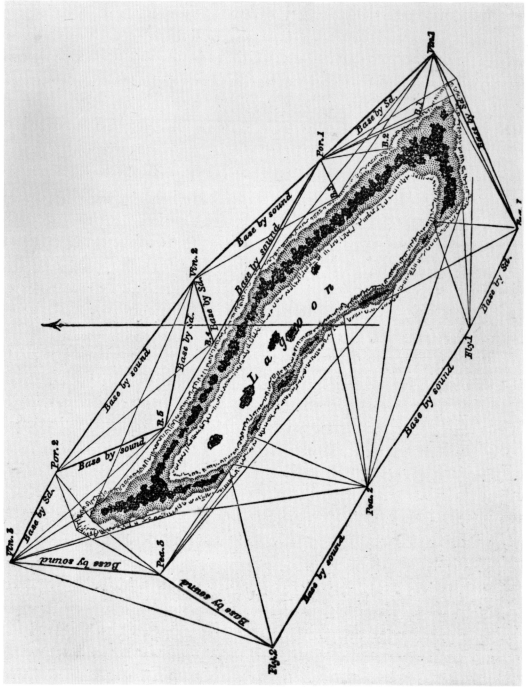

PLATE 34

of the expedition was given to Captain George S. Nares. This most important and pioneer scientific expedition left Britain on December 21, 1872.[137]

Their track was into the Pacific via the Cape of Good Hope, the Indian Ocean, south of Australia, and into Sydney. In order to gain a cross-section of the ocean bed for the possibility of laying a submarine cable, the ship crossed from that port east to Wellington, New Zealand. From here their course lay across to Fiji, west through the New Hebrides, south of New Guinea, and north to the Philippine Islands and Hong Kong. The return voyage brought them north of New Guinea, through the Caroline Islands and Mariana Islands, and thence to Japan. Following a journey to Hawaii, and south to Tahiti, the ship sailed east to Chile on its way round the Horn to England. Home port was gained in 1876 (Fig. 35).

Scientific results of the Expedition were published in the leading professional periodicals.[138] The most important publication that resulted from the expedition are the forty volumes of scientific results that are included in the *Report*.[139] Outstanding research was undertaken in this historic voyage, perhaps none more significant than that on bathymetry.[140] Next to ocean depths, the character of the bottom geology was of most general interest.[141] Considerable data on oceanic circulation was also gathered, but no agreement as to causes was reached. The discovery of a large and varied faunal population at lower ocean depths was perhaps more surprising to scientific persons than any other category of information derived.[142]

For two reasons, the *Challenger* expedition may be considered as the terminal voyage of the third period of British exploration of the Pacific. It was the end result of the spirit of enquiry first generated by Dampier, a gifted amateur, and nourished by scientific professionals through the following centuries. It was, finally, the pioneer model for scientific expeditions, opening the modern period of comprehensive international examination of the Pacific environment.

13

GEOGRAPHICAL EXPLORATION BY THE UNITED STATES

Kᴇɴɴᴇᴛʜ J. Bᴇʀᴛʀᴀɴᴅ*

Interest in the Pacific on the part of citizens of the United States and their national government is as old as the Republic itself (1783).[1] For more than a century a variety of maritime activities, such as the fur trade, whaling, surveys for trans-Pacific steamship lines, international telegraph communication via Bering Strait, the trans-Pacific submarine cable, the guano trade, and commerce in general provided a succession of stimuli for government-sponsored exploring and surveying expeditions. As commercial activity led to heightened political interest in the Pacific area, exploring and surveying expeditions created for specific purposes by acts of Congress or by executive orders were replaced by continuous mapping programs of established government agencies, such as the Depot of Charts and Instruments (after 1866, the Hydrographic Office) of the Navy and the Coast Survey (after 1878, the Coast and Geodetic Survey).

The rapid increase in the volume and frequency of maritime activities, especially in the Pacific Basin, emphasized the importance of having precise knowledge of the geographic position of islands and reefs, and a more accurate delineation of harbors and shorelines. There were, of course, large areas of the earth that were inadequately or little known in 1783 so that exploration and discovery were to continue even into the twentieth century, but detailed surveying and charting took precedence. During the first half of the nineteenth century, much in the spirit of the eighteenth, several countries, including the United States, dispatched naval exploring expeditions to the Pacific and especially to the polar regions. Most of these exploring expeditions in the Pacific Basin were superseded by surveying and charting expeditions and the explorations were incidental to surveying operations, or were made by commercially inspired voyages.

DISCOVERY AND EXPLORATION: 1783-1838

Tʜᴇ Fᴜʀ Tʀᴀᴅᴇ ᴀɴᴅ Iɴɪᴛɪᴀʟ Exᴘʟᴏʀᴀᴛɪᴏɴ

United States interest in the Pacific commenced with the China trade, initiated in 1784.[2] For approximately twenty years the most important commodity in this trade was furs: sea otter skins from the northwest coast of North America, and sealskins from sub-Antarctic and Antarctic islands. This trade was inspired by accounts of Captain James Cook's third voyage, 1776–1780, which noted that sea otter skins bartered from the Indians on the northwest coast for trifles were sold in China for fabulous prices.[3] Apparently the first word of this transaction was brought to America by John Ledyard[4] of Groton, Connecticut, who had been a corporal of marines on

*Dʀ. Bᴇʀᴛʀᴀɴᴅ is professor of geography and chairman of the department of geography at The Catholic University of America, Washington, D. C.

Cook's voyage. Upon his return to the United States he traveled between Boston and Philadelphia in a vain attempt to interest merchants and ship owners in sending a ship to the northwest coast to gather furs for sale in China.[5]

Robert Morris, a Philadelphia financier, was the only prominent American to listen with interest, but he concluded that such a voyage would be too risky.[6] Instead, on February 22, 1784, Morris and Daniel Parker of New York despatched from New York the 350-ton *Empress of China* on a voyage to Canton via the Cape of Good Hope with a small cargo of ginseng and furs. The furs, however, were from trading posts in eastern North America. When the *Empress of China* returned in May 1785 with a variety of goods from the Orient it brought news of the importance of the Siberian fur trade in China. Meanwhile Ledyard had published his journal, which gave further circulation to these ideas.[7]

The fur trade off the northwest coast was initiated by British sea captains in 1785. The Russians also engaged in it to some extent.[8] However, for a number of reasons such as the restrictive effect of the monopolies of the British East India Company and the South Sea Company, and Britain's involvement in the Napoleonic Wars, British trading on the coast soon dwindled. Thus, by the beginning of the nineteenth century the fur trade had become practically an American monopoly. In 1801, fifteen American ships were reported trading on the northwest coast.[9] The Yankee fur traders left comparatively little imprint on the geographic nomenclature of the region, having been preceded by Spanish, British, French, and Russian exploring expeditions, and by British fur traders. The major physical features of the coast had been discovered by these early mariners, and geographic names which they applied to the features commemorate their activity.

In the latter part of the eighteenth century Spain became concerned about English and Russian encroachments north of California. This rivalry resulted in a number of exploring voyages to gather information and to show the flag. As a consequence, the general trend of the coast and the details of its primary physical features were described and charted (for details see Chapters 7, 10, and 12). International rivalry was heightened by the rapid development of the fur trade, and by the Nootka Sound controversy in 1789, which focused the attention of the world on the northwest coast and the fur trade.

Captain James Hanna, who sailed from Macao in the *Sea Otter* in 1785, initiated the fur trade on the northwest coast. He returned in 1786 and was joined by seven other British vessels. In 1787, the year before the *Columbia* and the *Lady Washington* arrived, there were six British vessels trading on the coast.[10]

Joseph Barrell, a Boston merchant, and five associates were the first Americans to send a ship to the northwest coast. They outfitted two vessels, the 212-ton ship *Columbia*, commanded by Captain John Kendrick, and the 90-ton sloop *Lady Washington*, commanded by Captain Robert Gray.[11] They sailed from Boston on September 30, 1787.[12] By now Ledyard had given up hope of interesting anyone in his plan and had left for Europe and his fateful venture into Africa.

The *Columbia* was the first American vessel to sail around the world, and it set a pattern which was to develop into a flourishing trade dominated by Boston merchants. The voyage of the *Lady Washington* and especially the two voyages of the *Columbia* are important not only because of the role they played in opening New England's fur trade on the northwest coast but particularly because of the significant exploration that they did and discoveries that they made along the Pacific coast of the North American continent.[13] The following are highlights of these voyages.

While rounding Cape Horn on the first voyage in 1788 the *Columbia* and the sloop *Lady Washington* became separated in a storm and proceeded separately to the northwest coast.[14] Captain Gray in the sloop made his first landfall on August 4, north of Cape Mendocino on the California coast. Gray was well acquainted with Captain James Cook's report, and from remarks by Robert Haswell, second officer on the sloop, regarding statements made by Cook it appears probable that a copy of the report was on board.[15] From this first landfall Gray carefully examined the coast northward for a harbor. On September 16 he entered Friendly Cove in Nootka Sound, where he found and met with the English captains, John Meares and William Douglas. On September 23 he was joined by Captain John Kendrick in the *Columbia*.

After spending the winter in Friendly Cove Captain Gray, on March 16, 1789, sailed south to trade with the Indians and to examine and survey the harbors as far as the Strait of Juan de Fuca, which was entered for a distance of some fifteen miles. Haswell made "a tolerable accurate survey of the harbor" in Clayoquot Sound and sounded Barkley Sound.[16] On May 3 Gray sailed north on a trading mission through Queen Charlotte Sound, crossing the mouth of Clarence Strait and Dixon Entrance to Graham Island. On May 23 he was forced to return to Nootka Sound from the vicinity of Bucareli Bay, Alaska, because of damage to his ship. En route to Nootka Sound, where the ship was repaired, Haswell made a reconnaissance of Houston Stewart Channel.[17] On July 31, 1790, Gray was given command of the *Columbia* with orders to sail for Canton with a cargo of furs and then to return to the United States. Captain Kendrick, in the *Lady Washington*, cruised the Queen Charlotte Islands to trade for furs and then sailed to Canton and returned to the northwest coast.

The second voyage of the *Columbia* under Captain Gray began from Boston on October 2, 1790, and the ship arrived on the northwest coast on June 3, 1791. During the summer Captain Gray's trading cruise extended from the south shore of the Strait of Juan de Fuca to Revillagigedo Channel and the southern end of Clarence Strait, Alaska. On September 18 the *Columbia* entered Clayoquot Sound and Gray set up winter quarters. John Hoskins, the ship's clerk or supercargo, made a sketch map of the harbor.[18] During the winter a sloop, named *Adventure*, was constructed from timbers brought out from Boston and from lumber cut on the spot. The *Adventure*, launched on March 23, 1792, was placed in command of Robert Haswell, first officer of the *Columbia*.

On April 2, 1792, the *Columbia* and the *Adventure* sailed from Clayoquot Sound on trading cruises, the *Adventure* going north along the coast and the *Columbia* south. On April 28, off the mouth of the Quillayute River on the Washington coast, the *Columbia* met the English ships *Discovery* and *Chatham* commanded by Captain George Vancouver. Gray gave Vancouver valuable information about the coast, particularly the Strait of Juan de Fuca.[19]

On May 7 Gray discovered the harbor subsequently named for him. He sent a boat ahead to sound, but as the *Columbia* approached the bar stretching across the entrance to the bay a passage through the line of breakers was discovered from the masthead.[20] The Indians who came to barter apparently informed Gray of the mouth of the Columbia River and he sailed directly for it. In his logbook entry for May 11 he recorded:

At Four, A.M., saw the entrance of our desired port bearing east-south-east, distance six leagues; . . . At eight, A.M., being a little to windward of the entrance of the Harbor, bore away, and run in east-north-east between the breakers, having five to seven fathoms of water. When we were over the bar, we found this to be a large river of fresh water, up which we steered.[21]

John Boit, fifth officer on the *Columbia,* describes this important event in his entry for that date:

This day saw an appearance of a spacious harbour abrest the Ship, haul'd our wind for it, observ'd two sand bars making off, with a passage between them to a fine river. Out pinnace and sent her in ahead and followed with the Ship under short sail, carried in from ½ three to 7 f[atho]m, and when over the bar had 10 f[atho]m Water quite fresh. The River extended to the NE as far as eye cou'd reach, and the water fit to drink as far down as the Bars, at the entrance. we directed our course up this noble rive in search of a village . . .[22]

The *Columbia* ran aground at a point about seventeen miles above the mouth, and finally was worked free to sail downstream, crossing the bar and moving into the open sea on the afternoon of May 20. Captain Gray named the river "Columbia's River." His visit is the first record of a ship entering the river from the ocean, although the existence of a "River of the West" emptying into the Pacific Ocean had long been conjectured by geographers, explorers, travelers, and wishful thinkers. Conjecture became a proven fact in November 1805, when Captains Meriwether Lewis and William Clark descended the Columbia on their epic-making transect of the continent, observed the Columbia River mouth, and wintered over in their Fort Clatsop nearby. The mouth of the river apparently was discovered by Bruno Heceta, the Spanish navigator, in 1775, but he had been unable to put a boat into the water to examine it. The geographical importance of this discovery to the United States was considerable, especially in vindicating those who had believed in the existence of a "River of the West," and in stimulating an extensive exploration of the American West. In April, 1792, Captain George Vancouver viewed the same scene from some distance off shore. He concluded with Captain John Meares, who had been there in 1787, that no river existed.[23]

After leaving the Columbia River, Gray sailed north to join the *Adventure.* The two ships then sailed for and put in at Nootka Sound, where the *Columbia* was repaired and the *Adventure* was sold to the Spanish commander Don Francisco de la Bodega y Quadra. On October 3, the *Columbia* sailed for the Hawaiian Islands, then to Canton, and on July 29, 1793, arrived at Boston.

When Gray put into Nootka Sound on September 21 he met Vancouver there, reported his discovery of the mouth of the Columbia, and gave him a sketch map of it. As a result, Vancouver in the *Discovery* and Lieutenant William R. Broughton in the *Chatham* visited the mouth of the Columbia in October en route to San Francisco. Broughton succeeded in entering and surveying the river in boats. The river was then at a low stage, and conditions were quite different from the high water reported by Gray. Consequently, Vancouver disparaged Gray's report unjustly.[24]

Joseph Ingraham, who had been first mate on the *Columbia* during its first voyage to the northwest coast, was captain of the brigantine *Hope* on a similar voyage from 1790–1793. On this outward voyage, while sailing from Cape Horn to Hawaii, he reached the Marquesas Islands in April 1791, and discovered several islands not on Spanish charts or on Cook's map. He recorded the voyage in a journal of four volumes which contain many sketches and maps of coastal areas, islands, and reefs sighted on the voyage. Among them are sketch maps of the northwest coast, of the North Pacific Ocean, and of the Sandwich or Hawaiian Islands.[25]

These are but a few of the many voyages of American ships that searched the North Pacific Ocean for furs and returned to their Atlantic coast home ports with accounts in a journal, log, or diary. Many of these, unfortunately, have not survived although a surprisingly large number may be found in depositories and libraries, especially in New England, and were utilized by Matthew Fontaine Maury in compiling his remarkable collection of abstract logs in the 1840s and 1850s.[26]

EXPLORING THE SOUTHEASTERN GATEWAY TO THE PACIFIC

The fur seal trade was initiated by Francis Rotch of Nantucket who, in 1784, dispatched the ship *United States* in command of Captain Benjamin Hussey on a sealing voyage to the Falkland Islands.[27] Hussey returned in 1786 with a cargo of 13,000 sealskins which were sold at New York and shipped to Canton aboard the brig *Eleanora*, commanded by Captain Simon Metcalf.[28]

It was not long before other New England vessels were hunting for seals at the Falkland Islands, on the coast of South America, and on the island of South Georgia. Some sealing vessels returned home with their cargo, though most of them at this time sailed across the Pacific to sell the skins in Canton, returning home by way of the Cape of Good Hope.[29]

Competition among an increasing number of sealers led to near extinction of the seals, forcing skippers to search continually for new sealing grounds. In the 1790s they rounded Cape Horn and hunted up the west coast of South America and on offshore islands. The islands of Isla Mocha and Isla Más Afuera became favorite hunting grounds. Clark has estimated that "between the years 1793 and 1807, upwards of 3,500,000 fur-seal skins were obtained, and most of them taken to China from Más Afuera."[30] As many as fourteen vessels were reported at one time. One of these vessels, the brig *Betsy*, was commanded by Edmund Fanning who, while en route to Canton in June 1798, discovered Fanning Island, Washington Island, and Palmyra Island, lying north of the equator in the mid-Pacific.[31]

By its very nature the fur business, especially sealing, was a matter of boom or bust. It began to decline after 1810, and after 1815 furs no longer dominated the trans-Pacific trade; by 1830 the trade on the northwest coast had declined to insignificance. The fur seal business flourished briefly a second time after the discovery of the South Shetland Islands in 1819. The first American vessel to reach the South Shetlands was the brig *Hersilia* in January 1820.

Significant discoveries by American sealers in the Pacific Basin were made on its southeast or Antarctic threshold in 1820–1821.³² In that year there were thirty American vessels at the newly discovered South Shetland Islands. The exploits of Nathaniel B. Palmer of Stonington, Connecticut, have been widely publicized because of the controversy concerning his cruise in the sloop *Hero* to the shores of the Antarctic Peninsula in November 1820. In recent years, however, most significant information has come to light in the finding of two logbooks, one by John Davis, captain of the *Huron* of New Haven, and the other by Christopher Burdick, skipper of the schooner *Huntress* of Nantucket.³³ Interesting bits of related information are also recorded in the marine columns of New England newspapers of 1821 and 1822, and customhouse records provide additional information.

The logbook of the *Huron* documents the first landing on the Antarctic continent for which there is now such evidence. While the *Huron* was at anchor in Yankee Harbor in the South Shetlands, Captain Davis was aboard his shallop, the *Cecilia*, visiting the several camps on various beaches occupied by his men and those of Captain Burdick from the *Huntress*. On January 30, 1821, he decided to cruise in search of new lands, and sailed southwestward and then west to visit Smith Island. February 2 to 6 were spent on Low Island from whence he sailed south-southeast to "a large body of land." At 10 A.M., on February 7 he was close up with it and sent a boat on shore to look for seals. At noon he recorded his latitude as 64°01′S., where he "stood up a large bay, the Land high and intirely [sic] covered with snow . . . ," and concluded the entry with ". . . I think this southern land to be a continent."³⁴ By reconstructing Captain Davis' navigation, including his bearings to known points, it is obvious that his boat made a landing in the vicinity of Hughes Bay on the Antarctic Peninsula.

The logbooks of both Captain Davis and Captain Burdick record the return to Yankee Harbor, January 27, 1821, of Captain Robert Johnson from a twenty-two-day cruise to latitude 66° S., and longitude 70° W., where he "still found what he took to be land but appeared to be nothing but Sollid [sic] Islands of Ice and Snow."³⁵ Captain Johnson arrived in New York abroad the *Jane Maria* on May 11, 1821. On May 16 the *New-York Gazette & General Advertiser* reported that samples of eight different rocks and minerals had been brought home and were given to Dr. Samuel Latham Mitchill.³⁶ The same article also included this statement, "The manuscript chart made by Mr. Hampton Stewart is an instructive addition to geography, and ought to be incorporated into the charts of the globe." Unfortunately, nothing more is known of Mr. Stewart's map.³⁷

AMERICAN WHALERS IN THE PACIFIC

By 1792 a number of American whalers had rounded Cape Horn to hunt whales along the west coast of South America.³⁸ In 1804 the first American whaleship entered the Pacific from the Indian Ocean, looking for whales off New Zealand. Until about 1815 whaling in the Pacific was concentrated along the west coast of South America, the "on shore grounds," after which scarcity of whales caused the whalers to range farther out into the Pacific.³⁹ After 1818 the "off shore grounds," 1000 miles off the coast of Peru, was the favorite area, but whaleships were then beginning to range far over the Pacific, westward to the Society Islands and beyond, and northward to San Francisco Bay. In 1819 two American whaleships visited Honolulu which in a few years became the center for Pacific whaling. The *Maro* of Nantucket, commanded by Captain Joseph Allen, in 1820 was the first American whaleship on the "off Japan Grounds," a vast area midway between Hawaii and Japan. Within three years more than sixty New England whalers were cruising "off Japan."[40]

Whaling in the Pacific increased rapidly. In 1819 there were 119 American whaleships there; in 1840 there were 500. By 1838, whaleships were cruising along the northwest coast of North America, and by 1843 they were off Kamchatka and in the Sea of Ohkotsk. In 1848 Captain James Royce passed through Bering Strait in the bark *Superior* and sailed into the Arctic Ocean. American whaling reached its peak in 1846, and, after 1850, declined rapidly. The last great flourish was in the North Pacific Ocean and Bering Sea, which were visited by 148 American whaleships in 1849, 144 in 1850, and 145 in 1851.[41]

Without deprecating their work, it must be remembered that only a relatively small number of exploring expeditions had visited the Pacific in the seventeenth and eighteenth centuries. The Pacific is a vast ocean, and their ships were small. Their navigational instruments were crude and imperfect. Moreover, many Pacific islands are low-lying atolls not visible from a distance. It should not be surprising, therefore, that in the 1790s, when the whalers first entered the Pacific, there were several scores of islands still undiscovered.[42] By 1829 most of them had been sighted and many had been visited. The number actually discovered by American whalers who ranged so widely over the Pacific cannot be determined, but it is probably several score.[43] Many were reported as having been discovered more than once, and the reported positions were in many cases inaccurate.

BEGINNINGS OF OFFICIAL EXPLORING ACTIVITIES

Though the vessels engaged in sealing and in the fur trade were counted in the tens, the whaleships were counted in the scores, and their influence was proportionately greater. Sailing at night was extremely dangerous in the poorly charted Pacific during the first part of the nineteenth century, and many whalers came to grief on uncharted reefs and tiny atolls, even in daylight. For this reason New York and New England mariners were continually asking the government to provide them with better charts.

Prior to the establishment of the Depot of Charts and Instruments in the Navy Department in 1838, the Federal government did not have a central office from which hydrographic charts of the Pacific Ocean could be obtained. Ships of the Navy had frequented the Pacific on a variety of missions, some of which included scientific observations and making corrections and additions to extant available charts, but this was not of a systematic nature.[44] Perhaps the beginnings of American scientific approach to navigation of the Pacific were made by Nathaniel Bowditch, astronomer and mathematician of Salem, Massachusetts, who by 1802 compiled and published *The New American Practical Navigator* . . . , which became a standard work for maritime interests and ship captains.[45] Most of the published charts of the Pacific Ocean available in the United States prior to about the 1850s were obtained from the Blunts of Newburyport, Massachusetts and of New York City.[46] The Blunts in turn obtained their information from ship captains, from the Federal government, and from overseas sources. The Depot of Charts and Instruments during the period 1839–1866 became increasingly more of a chart publishing office, nearly all of which was accomplished under the direction of Matthew Fontaine Maury.[47] One of its first primary responsibilities was to provide accurate charts of the Pacific Ocean for whalers, but these charts were only as accurate as available information, and often that was open to question.

There were many demands that an exploring expedition be sent out, and in his message to Congress, December 6, 1825, President John Quincy Adams recommended an expedition to chart our own Pacific coast.[48] The shippers and whalers, however, had little success importuning officialdom until Jeremiah N. Reynolds entered the picture. Reynolds, an Ohioan, had the knack of arousing public interest. He was a popular lecturer who traveled about the country urging that the government send an exploring expedition to the Pacific and the Antarctic. At his instigation citizen groups and several state legislatures petitioned the Congress in favor of sending out a government expedition.[49]

Finally, in 1828, action began. In a resolution of May 21, the House of Representatives requested that one of the smaller vessels of the Navy be sent to conduct an examination of the coasts, islands, harbors, shoals, and reefs in the Pacific Ocean and the South Sea. Secretary of the Navy Samuel L. Southard took immediate action. He selected a ship, designated a commander, ordered Lieutenant Charles Wilkes, Superintendent of the Depot of Charts and Instruments to procure instruments, and authorized Reynolds to go to New England to gather information from conversations with sealers and whalers and from examinations of logbooks. Reynolds compiled a report which has become an important historical document.[50] Unfortunately, Southard found his appropriations could not cover the expedition and President Andrew Jackson cancelled the idea in 1829 in the interest of economy.[51]

Although the prospect of a government expedition was lost temporarily, enough interest had been generated to make possible a private expedition. Reynolds, working with Edmund Fanning, the veteran sealing captain, found sufficient support to send out two vessels on a combined sealing-exploring expedition in 1829–1830.[52] It was assumed that enough sealskins would be obtained to cover the costs and reimburse the crew, especially if islands with seal rookeries were discovered. The expedition consisted of the brig *Annawan*, commanded by Nathaniel B. Palmer, and the brig *Seraph*, commanded by Benjamin Pendleton, who was also leader of the expedition. Both men were part owners of their vessels. Although officially not a part of the expedition, the schooner *Penguin*, commanded by Alexander S. Palmer, also participated. The scientific corps of five included Reynolds and Dr. James Eights of Albany, New York, the only true scientist in the group.[53]

As an exploring venture the expedition was a failure. After sealing in the South Shetland Islands, where Dr. Eights made geological and biological investigations, the *Annawan* and the *Penguin* cruised westward in February and March in a vain search for the islands reported by Captains Swain, Macy, and Gardiner in about latitude 59° S. and longitude 90° W. After withstanding a succession of gales

between latitude 58° and 59° S. to about longitude 103° W. the men were suffering
from exposure, and some were unfit for duty. On March 23 the two vessels sailed
northward, to Isla Mocha on the coast of Chile, where they anchored on April 3.
Meanwhile Captain Pendleton sailed westward from the South Shetlands, and south
of latitude 60° S. to about longitude 101° W. without sighting land. He joined the
Annawan and the *Penguin* on the coast of Chile, where Reynolds and Watson made
contact with the Araucanian indians.[54]

Upon the expedition's return to the United States, thirteen chests of natural
history specimens were given to the Lyceum of Natural History in New York, which
had sponsored the scientific program. Two chests were sent to Philadelphia. Reynolds gave his personal collection to the Boston Society of Natural History, and
Eights' specimens went to the Albany Institute. Seven papers by Eights were
published,[55] his work on the South Shetlands being the first scientific work on the
Antarctic by an American.[56] Reynolds left the expedition in Chile and later became
private secretary to Commodore John Downes of the United States frigate *Potomac*
when that vessel arrived there from the East Indies. In this capacity Reynolds
became historiographer of the globe-circling voyage.[57]

SCIENTIFIC EXPLORATION AND SURVEYING: 1838-1860

The United States Exploring Expedition: 1838–1842

The interest in an exploring expedition that Jeremiah Reynolds had aroused in the
public continued, and he gained national stature with the publication of his account of
the voyage of the *Potomac*.[58] Fanning, in a quiet way, was busy among maritime
interests. He sent letters and memorials to members and committees of Congress
regarding the need for and the nature of an exploring expedition. Public interest was
furthered by the publication in 1833 of Fanning's *Voyages Round the World*.[59] Reynolds pursued his campaign with such vigor that he generated animosities which
ultimately kept him off the staff and probably contributed to the controversies
which accompanied the organization of the expedition.[60]

Complaints of ship owners and whalers concerning the dangers to navigation in
the Pacific grew louder as the number of vessels involved increased.[61] In 1836
Congress finally heeded the clamor by authorizing the President to "send out a
surveying and exploring expedition to the Pacific Ocean and the South Seas."[62]
Samuel L. Southard, former Secretary of the Navy and now Senator from New
Jersey and Chairman of the Senate Committee on Naval Affairs, played a large role
in the drive for favorable legislation. The expedition was given an appropriation of
$300,000.

From the very beginning the "United States Exploring Expedition," as it was
officially designated, was beset with controversy regarding its size, its function, the
kind of ships, and the personnel.[63] After many senior officers had refused it and
others had been passed over, command of the Expedition was finally given to
Lieutenant Wilkes, by whose name it is popularly known.[64] Although only a junior
officer, Wilkes was well qualified by training and experience for the position. He
had been head of the Depot of Charts and Instruments of the Navy and had con-

ducted the hydrographic survey of Georges Bank. By determined and persistent effort Wilkes managed to complete the organization of the expedition within five months after his appointment.[65]

It is important to point out that the American Philosophical Society of Philadelphia contributed information, scientific knowledge, and recommended scientists to the Expedition.[66] The Philadelphia Academy of Natural Sciences also played an important role in personnel recruitment and in supplying scientific information.[67] The East India Marine Society of Salem, Massachusetts, and the Naval Lyceum of New York were consulted, especially on subjects dealing with commerce and navigation.[68] The final size of the Expedition and the smallness of its ships restricted the number of scientists to a total below that originally planned by Wilkes. The scientists finally selected to accompany the Expedition as a kind of civilian scientific corps included James D. Dana, mineralogist; William Rich, botanist; William D. Brackenridge, horticulturalist and assistant botanist; Horatio Hale, philologist; Titian R. Peale and Charles Pickering, naturalists; John P. Couthouy, conchologist; and Alfred T. Agate and Joseph Drayton, draftsmen.[69] The fields of geography, terrestrial magnetism, hydrography, meteorology, and physics were assigned to qualified officers.

The instructions to the Expedition issued by Secretary of the Navy J. K. Paulding, and said to have been mostly the work of Wilkes, were specific, and far-reaching, and emphasized the scientific aspects. "Although the primary object of the Expedition is the promotion of the great interests of commerce and navigation, yet you will take all occasions to extend the bounds of Science and promote the acquisition of knowledge."[70]

Wilkes, a man of decisive action, was also a man with a fervent zeal in the interests of science. He made certain that he had with him a group of well-qualified scientists and that they were furnished the best instruments and equipment available. Indeed, Wilkes personally had selected and purchased many of these items during a stay in Europe and remarked that ". . . every expense that could be lavished on this equipment was incurred . . ."[71]

The Expedition consisted of the *Vincennes*, a sloop-of-war of 780 tons, the flagship; the *Peacock*, a sloop-of-war of 650 tons; the *Porpoise*, a brig of 230 tons; and the *Relief*, a store ship. These four vessels were augmented by two New York pilot boats renamed the *Sea Gull*, of 110 tons, and the *Flying Fish*, of 96 tons. The *Vincennes* and the *Porpoise* were the only ships to make the entire voyage. The three larger ships, being naval vessels, were not especially suited for exploration, particularly in high latitudes, and the questionable seaworthiness of the *Peacock* make the accomplishments the more remarkable.

The details of the tracks (Fig. 37) and of the work and scientific accomplishments of the Expedition are given in the official Narratives.[72] We shall give here only the highlights of the work in the Pacific Basin.[73]

The Expedition sailed from Norfolk, Virginia, on August 8, 1838. Exploration was begun in the Cape Horn region in February and March 1839. Two penetrations were made into the Antarctic. One was southwest from Cape Horn toward Captain Cook's farthest south.[74] Lieutenant William L. Hudson in the *Peacock* and Lieutenant

May 1841

December 1841

Philippine Is.

Sulu
Sea

Singapore

120°

150°

180°

Marshall Is.

Gilbert Is.

Ellice Is.

Phoenix

Sep

Samoa

Fiji Is.

Tong

1839

November

April 1840

Sydney

Bay of Islands

March 1840

Wilkes Land

——— Vincennes
– – – Peacock
·········· Porpoise

When two or more vessels sailed in
company only one track is shown

Fig. 37. Generalized tracks of the United States Exploring Expedition, 1830–

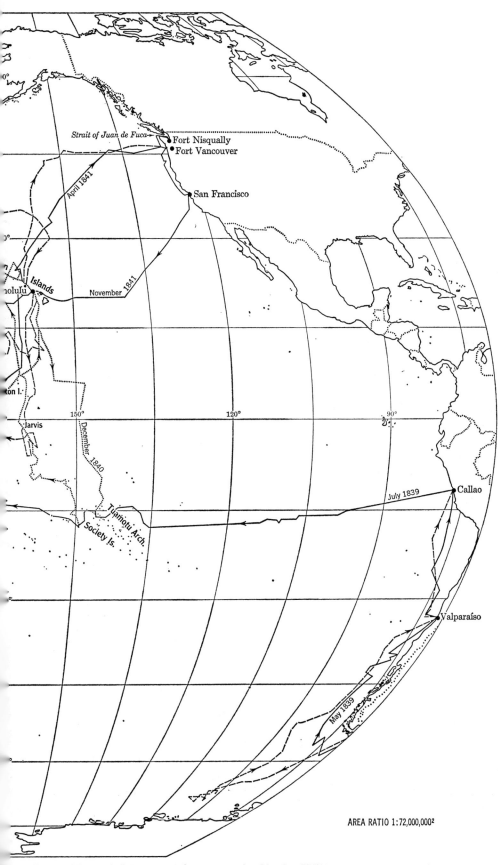

Strait of Juan de Fuca → ●Fort Nisqually
                         ●Fort Vancouver

●San Francisco

April 1841

November 1841

Islands
holulu
ton I.

150°   120°   90°

Jarvis

December 1840

Tuamotu Arch.

Society Is.

July 1839   ●Callao

●Valparaíso

May 1839

AREA RATIO 1:72,000,000²

ompiled by Kenneth J. Bertrand from maps in Charles Wilkes, 1844 (Note 72).

William M. Walker in the *Flying Fish* experienced very stormy weather and bad ice conditions, but Lieutenant Walker was able to maneuver the *Flying Fish* to latitude 70° S. and longitude 101°16′ W., about 110 nautical miles north of present-day Thurston Island.[75] Today this area is known to be the least accessible coast of Antarctica.[76]

The *Sea Gull* was lost in a storm off Cape Horn while en route to Valparaiso, where the expedition was ordered to rendezvous. At Callao the storeship *Relief* was detached from the squadron, and in July the remaining four ships proceeded to the South Pacific, where surveys were made of the Tuamotu Archipelago, Society Islands, and Samoa Islands. The loss of the *Sea Gull* was a serious handicap, for it and the *Flying Fish* had been included because of their shallow draft which made them especially suitable for work among the reefs and close inshore.

Wilkes devised a special method for surveying the islands (Plate 34, *facing page 255*). The larger vessels would take stations offshore to establish a baseline. At a given signal a shot would be fired and the sound timed to determine the distance between the ships. Bearings would then be made to and from boats on the beaches and to prominent features onshore, and the normal process of triangulation followed.[77]

From the Samoa Islands the squadron sailed for Sydney, Australia, to prepare for an Antarctic cruise. In January and February 1840, Wilkes accomplished one of the greatest feats of Antarctic exploration.[78] Although two of the ships were disabled and forced to retreat northward before completion of the cruise, Wilkes in the *Vincennes* and Lieutenant Cadwalader Ringgold in the *Porpoise* succeeded in sailing along the edge of the pack ice fringing the coast of Antarctica from 160° longitude E. to 100° E., a distance of approximately 1500 nautical miles, much of it fronting on the South Pacific. As a result of sighting land at many points during the cruise, Wilkes concluded that he had demonstrated the existence of an Antarctic continent.[79] He compiled a "Chart of the Antarctic Continent."[80]

Following the Antarctic cruise the expedition visited the Bay of Islands in New Zealand.[81] In April 1840, the expedition sailed for Tongatapu of the Tonga or Friendly Islands, but when surveying proved impracticable owing to troubles between two native factions Wilkes directed the ships to survey the Fiji Islands. Wilkes' instructions to Lieutenant Ringgold, commander of the *Porpoise*, whom he ordered to survey the eastern part of the Fijis, is typical of such orders and reveals much about Wilkes' methods (Plate 35, *following page 270*). The officers were expected to conciliate the native chiefs, to seek the cooperation of the missionaries, to make note of anything of scientific interest, to collect specimens of natural history, to observe the natives and their customs, to make sketches, and to determine the native names for islands. Great accuracy was urged in making observations for geographic position and in locating harbors, reefs, shoals, and passages. Magnetic observations were to be made regularly.[82]

On August 11, 1840, the expedition left the Fijis. The *Vincennes*, *Peacock*, and *Flying Fish* took separate courses for Hawaii to make a wider search for possible islands and reefs en route. The *Vincennes* visited the Phoenix Islands, and two of them, previously not on the chart, were named Hull Island and McKean Island.

Meanwhile, the *Porpoise* returned to the Tonga Islands to complete unfinished work, and visited the Samoa Islands before sailing for Hawaii.

During the northern winter of 1840–1841 several of the Hawaiian Islands were visited. This afforded the scientists an opportunity to make extensive collections.[83] The island of Hawaii was crossed, and Wilkes set up a magnetic observatory on Mauna Loa. Meanwhile the *Porpoise* was dispatched to the Tuamotu Archipelago to complete surveys there, and the *Peacock* and *Flying Fish*, after refitting at Honolulu, returned to Samoa. They searched for islands reported to exist in the central Pacific, and visited Washington, Jarvis, and the Phoenix islands. Bowditch Island (Fakaofu Atoll) was discovered and named. Returning northward from Samoa the two vessels visited the Ellice, Gilbert, and Marshall islands, making surveys and taking magnetic observations.

The surveys of the Pacific coast of North America from the Strait of Juan de Fuca to San Francisco Bay were made from May to November, 1841.[84] The *Vincennes* and the *Porpoise* arrived off the mouth of the Columbia River on April 28. The *Peacock* and *Flying Fish* had not arrived at Honolulu from Samoa at the time of Wilkes' departure. In the absence of the little schooner and not wishing to risk one of the larger vessels on the bar with a heavy sea running, Wilkes decided to sail for Puget Sound. At Fort Nisqually, a Hudson's Bay Company post at the mouth of the Nisqually River near the present site of Tacoma, Wilkes set up an observatory for magnetic observations and for determining accurately the geographic position. While crews in boats from the two vessels were surveying the waters in the Puget Sound area, two overland reconnaisance journeys were made. Wilkes led a party southward from Fort Nisqually to the Columbia River, which was followed to its mouth. From Astoria Wilkes proceeded upstream to Fort Vancouver, site of the present city of Vancouver, Washington, before returning to Fort Nisqually. Joseph Drayton, who had accompanied Wilkes, joined a Hudson's Bay Company party to travel up the Columbia as far as Fort Walla Walla at the mouth of the Snake River, where he joined Lieutenant Robert E. Johnson's party on its return to Fort Nisqually.

Lieutenant Johnson was given command of a party which explored the Columbia Plateau. Setting out from Fort Nisqually they crossed the Cascade Range and journeyed upstream on the Columbia to its junction with the Okanogan River. From there they traveled eastward across the Grand Coulee and up the Spokane River. Johnson traveled as far as Lake Coeur d'Alene while the main party traveled southward to the Snake River. The party was reunited at Fort Walla Walla and, on July 4, headed up the Columbia again to the Yakima and thence across the Cascades to Fort Nisqually.

Meanwhile, the *Peacock* and the *Flying Fish* arrived off the mouth of the Columbia River on July 18. Their work in the Pacific had put them two and a half months behind the deadline set by Wilkes for their arrival. In attempting to get across the bar the *Peacock* grounded, and each wave pushed the ship higher on the bar. Within a few hours she began to break up. The men and as much of the stores as possible were taken from the ship under hazardous conditions. Two days later little remained of the ship.

By this time the surveys of Puget Sound and adjacent waters had been completed, and the Strait of Juan de Fuca and Haro Strait were being surveyed. When word reached Wilkes of the wreck of the *Peacock*, plans were altered and the *Vincennes* and *Porpoise* proceeded to the Columbia. A land party was at the time proceeding from Fort Nisqually to the Columbia by way of the coast, with instructions to survey Grays Harbor.

Wilkes reorganized the expedition, and on August 9 the survey of the Columbia River was begun. To replace the *Peacock* he purchased the brig *Thomas H. Perkins* from Captain Varney at Astoria and renamed it *Oregon*. The *Porpoise*, *Oregon*, and *Flying Fish* proceeded up the river to Fort Vancouver where an observatory was set up for magnetic observations and to determine geographic position. While Wilkes took charge of the work on the Columbia, Lieutenant Ringgold was given command of the *Vincennes* and sent south to survey San Francisco Bay. Lieutenant George F. Emmons was assigned to lead a land party up the Willamette Valley and down the Sacramento River to San Francisco.

The expedition was reunited in San Francisco Bay in October, and in about two weeks remaining survey work was concluded and the observatory dismantled. After he arrived at San Francisco Bay, Ringgold surveyed the northern part of San Francisco Bay, San Pablo Bay, the lower part of the San Joaquin River, and the Sacramento River to a short distance beyond its junction with the Feather River.

On November 2, 1841, the four vessels sailed for Honolulu and thence to the Philippines, where the Sulu Sea was examined. At Singapore the *Flying Fish* was found to be in poor condition and was sold. The remaining three vessels sailed for home via the Cape of Good Hope, reaching New York in June, 1842. Of the six vessels originally comprising the expedition only the *Vincennes*[85] and the *Porpoise* completed the cruise, having sailed a distance of nearly 88,000 miles in three years and ten months. The total cost of the expedition while under Wilkes' direction amounted to $928,183.62.[86]

Among the areas visited were the Antarctic in 1839 (to a latitude of 70°14′ S.); the South Pacific islands, Australia, New Zealand, and Antarctica in 1839–1840; the Hawaiian Islands and other islands of the North Pacific Ocean in 1840; the northwest coast of North America in 1841; the South Pacific islands again in 1841; and the Philippine Islands, Singapore, the Cape of Good Hope, and Saint Helena on the return home in 1842.

Especially noteworthy among the accomplishments was the plotting of nearly 1500 miles of the coastline of the Antarctic continent, now identified as Wilkes Land, in January and February of 1840. Some 280 islands in the Pacific Ocean were surveyed and mapped, and the position of many of them was accurately fixed for the first time. Surveys of the west coast of North America covered 800 miles of coastal and inland waters, including Puget Sound, the lower Columbia River, the Willamette River, San Francisco Bay, the lower Sacramento River, and the lower San Joaquin River. Most of the nearly four years of exploring and surveying and mapping were in the Pacific Basin.

A primary purpose of the Expedition had been achieved, namely, to

... survey and explore the islands, reefs, and shoals of the Southern Pacific, particularly in those regions frequented by our vessels engaged in the whale fisheries and ocean commerce.[87]

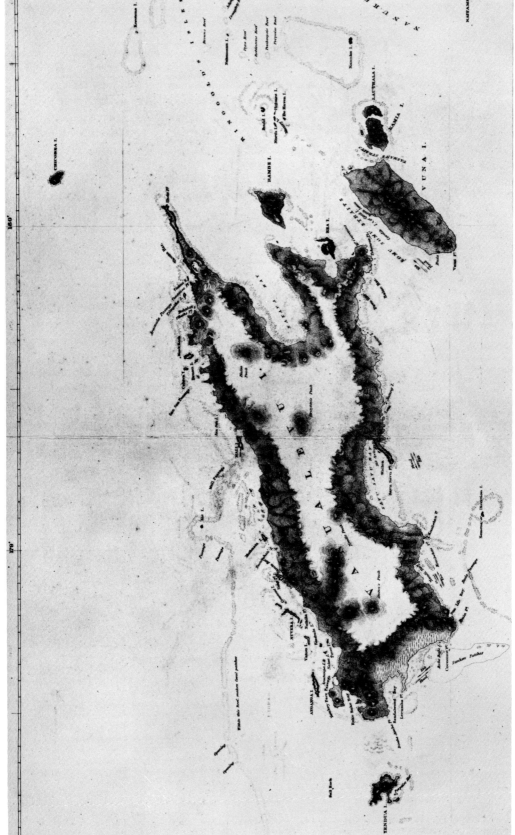

The Vanua Levu island part of a "Chart of the Viti Group or Feejee Islands by the U. S. Ex[ploring] Ex[pedition], Charles Wilkes Esq. Commander, 1840." Reduced from a published copy of the map in *Records of the Hydrographic Office* in the National Archives, Washington.

PLATE 35

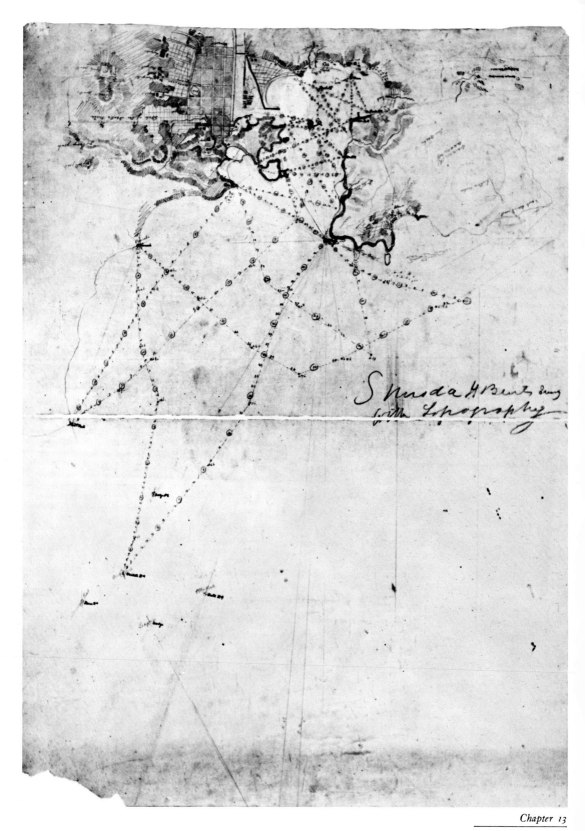

Boat sheet of "Simoda [Harbor, Japan] Lt. Bents Survey with Topography." The Perry Expedition, April 1854. Reduction of map in manuscript 451.36 in *Records of the Hydrographic Office* in the National Archives, Washington.

PLATE 36

Most of the surveys were to be made among the low coral islands of the Pacific, and Wilkes devised an effective procedure for accomplishing them . . .[88]

The scientific results of the expedition were published in twenty-two large quarto volumes and twelve atlases, and at least three additional volumes were prepared but never printed.[89] The natural history collections and observations of the scientists led to a wealth of new information about the natural landscape of many areas of the Pacific Basin. These and the published results were the basis upon which scientist members of the expedition, such as James Dwight Dana, William Dunlap Brackenridge, and Charles Pickering, built international and lasting professional reputations.[90]

The hydrographic work of the expedition was published in one volume written by Wilkes and in two atlases prepared under his direction. The 106 plates contain 220 maps, including insets showing detailed maps of harbors.[91] It is possible that even more were prepared than were published in the atlas, for in his *Synopsis of the Cruise of the U. S. Exploring Expedition,* . . . , he notes that ". . . we now have one hundred and eight charts nearly ready for the engraver; it is probable that we shall have as many more when all the islands, harbors, shoals, and reefs are plotted, that have been examined and surveyed . . ."[92]

The two volumes of charts, especially, were considered a major accomplishment. Nearly all of the charts were of areas in or bordering the Pacific Basin. The maps and charts of the Pacific coast of the United States were esteemed by the Secretary of the United States Navy in 1843 to have been worth the full cost of the expedition.[93] Perhaps the most important single contribution of the expedition was the wealth of geographical knowledge in chart form, in observations and terrestial fixes that were acquired, and in the improvement in the accuracy of most extant charts of the Pacific region published prior to the surveys.[94]

The scientific results of the expedition were large. In addition to the official reports, the scientists of the expedition and others published numerous articles and books which covered not only the specific results but also led to new theories and hypotheses in the physical sciences.[95] These accomplishments were perhaps best summarized by Harley H. Bartlett who in 1940 noted that

The Reports of the United States Exploring Expedition of 1838 to 1842, known as the Wilkes Expedition, are a monument in the record of American science. The inception of the Expedition in the first place marked America's assertion of its scientific coming of age and the publication of the narrative and the scientific reports, even though attended by difficulties and delays of all kinds, some of which were inevitable, and some quite unnecessary, was finally carried almost to completion in a manner entirely creditable to the authors.

. . . There were other and greater values that came about from the Expedition through the development of scientists themselves, and through the organization of scientific institutions to perpetuate the scientific work begun by the Expedition. The greatest value was that the enormous coordinated effort that the few scientists of a hundred years ago put forth enabled America to take a place with the leading European nations as a partner in the development of world science.[96]

Portions of the extensive collections of natural history specimens were placed in the custody of the National Institute (predecessor, to a large degree, of the present-day Smithsonian Institution) where they were arranged, described, and catalogued, and where some of the scientists upon their return from the expedition continued their research and publication.[97] Correlation, synthesis, and interpretation of the large mass of textual, cartographic, graphic, and other information obtained were undertaken even before the expedition returned.

One of the most valuable products of the expedition are the extant official and private records, which have been a mine of information for scholars. Wilkes issued strict orders to all members of the expedition ". . . that all papers of this sort [concerning the work of the expedition] should be surrendered to the captain of each ship prior to the return of the Expedition to the States. . . ."[98] These records nevertheless are widely scattered, although the principal body of official records is in the National Archives.[99]

Publication of the results extended over a period of some three decades[100] and included beautifully illustrated scholarly reports of far-reaching importance to the world of science specifically and to the public generally. George Brown Goode of the United States National Museum noted that ". . . although published in an extremely limited edition, the magnificent volumes of its reports are among the classics of scientific exploration."[101]

Role of the Depot of Charts and Instruments

As Superintendent of the Depot of Charts and Instruments and of the Naval Observatory and Hydrographical Office from 1842 to 1861, Matthew Fontaine Maury fathered the science of oceanography and made substantial contributions to geography and the other earth sciences.[102] His scientific career began perhaps on his first cruise as master of the *U. S. S. Falmouth*,[103] which in 1831–1835 surveyed in the South Atlantic and Pacific oceans. On this cruise Maury developed a concept in navigation, especially in the transit of Cape Horn and in the Pacific Ocean. Published in 1833 in the *American Journal of Science and Arts*, it perhaps led to his concept of wind and current charts.[104] Maury's voyages into the Pacific in the early 1830s gave him a substantial background for the publication of his definitive treatise on navigation in 1836.[105]

When Maury became Superintendent of the Depot of Charts and Instruments in 1842 he saw the potentialities of the rapidly growing but disordered accumulation of ships' logs, journals, and similar records of voyages in his charge. By August 1843, he had digested enough of the data in them to prepare and deliver before a meeting of scientists in the National Institute in Washington a paper on the Gulf Stream.[106] This paper was the first of his many cartographic, statistical, and descriptive studies pertaining to the geography of the sea and of the atmosphere.

Maury gained universal cooperation in his program of scientific research, and often referred to its international origins and application. His interests in the Pacific Ocean were based on his voyages there and on his early recognition of the need of the Federal government and of ship captains for sound cartographic and geographic information. He was among the foremost government officials to recognize the need for continuous scientific surveys of the Pacific Ocean area, and was responsible for some of them being undertaken.[107]

There can be little doubt that Maury was the instigator of many of the official

Navy issuances regarding mapping and scientific observations. One of his principal assignments as Superintendent of the Depot was to furnish the Navy and, as practicable, the merchant fleet with the best charts and maps available. He was ever on the watch for such materials and when authorized acted quickly to accept and to reproduce them. He carefully appraised foreign charts and those that passed his careful test he reproduced in quantity, he said because of the great need for them by American whalers cruising in the world's oceans, especially in the Pacific.[108]

Maury ceaselessly pressed for better and more charts. He proposed that expeditions should be outfitted to survey the Pacific. He further suggested that officers of all government vessels be requested to make scientific observations and report their findings to him.[109] In order to develop a systematic approach to the compilation of a wide variety of charts and maps he devised and distributed a set of reporting forms to be filled in by whalers and captains of ships at sea and returned to him.[110]

From these voluminous resources and the reports and observations of the ships of the Federal government Maury compiled a remarkable variety of maps that did much to revolutionize sailing and whaling. These maps included the so-called "Whale Chart of the World," "Wind and Current Charts," and "Pilot Charts" of the oceans, especially the Pacific.[111] Maury and his Depot also were directly involved in the preparation of maps resulting from the Wilkes Expedition.[112] His repeated correspondence with his superiors and friends emphasizing the lack of adequate maps of much of the Pacific Ocean was directly responsible for the sending of surveying and mapping expeditions to that area, beginning in the 1850s.[113]

During the 1840s and especially the 1850s Maury lectured extensively on a wide variety of subjects, one of the most frequent of which was navigation and mapping of the oceans, especially the Pacific.[114] Perhaps his most important scientific publication was his *Physical Geography of the Sea*.[115] In the introduction to the first edition, published in 1855, Maury notes that

The primary object of "The Wind and Current Charts," out of which has grown this Treatise on the Physical Geography of the Sea, was to collect the experience of every navigator as to the winds and currents of the ocean, to discuss his observations upon them, and then to present the world with the results on charts for the improvement of commerce and navigation.[116]

After Maury had established an international exchange of information on weather and climate he observed that an accurate knowledge and understanding of world climate could not be achieved without a full knowledge of the Antarctic continent.[117] He believed that all nations of the world should pool their resources and make a grand assult on the South Pole. His requests to the Secretary that the United States Navy adopt such a program fell on deaf ears. Realizing that a Civil War was imminent, Maury wrote to leading scientists of the principal nations of the world imploring them to carry out this program. Maury's plan was to approach the South Pole from the Ross Sea indentation of the Antarctic continent. It is of interest to point out that one hundred years later (1956–1958) the International Geophysical Year Program included a comprehensive study of Antarctica by many nations.[118]

Matthew Fontaine Maury's impact on the comprehensive planned scientific exploration of the Pacific Basin, especially by the United States, was far greater than has generally been recognized.[119]

EXPEDITION TO THE CHINA SEAS AND JAPAN: 1852–1854

By the mid-nineteenth century American whaleships were active in great numbers in the western Pacific.[120] Although furs were no longer important as a commodity, the value of commerce between the United States and China had greatly increased. To protect this commerce the United States Navy maintained an East India Squadron in the South China Sea.[121] Commercial treaties between the United States and China during the period 1842–1850 opened ports to American ships.[122] Rapidly increasing trade with the Orient was fostered by the beginning of settlement of the Pacific coast by citizens of the United States, by the construction of a railroad across the Isthmus of Panama, and by the surveys of routes for a transcontinental railroad in the United States. To handle this growing trade trans-Pacific steamship lines were being projected at mid-century, and the development of ports where ships could be coaled and provisioned was becoming increasingly important. The closed-door policy of Japan, which lay on the great circle route between the United States and China, was considered a hindrance to this development.[123] The ill-treatment shipwrecked sailors had been receiving at the hands of the Japanese and the efforts of the Japanese to prevent surveys of their coasts were generally resented by the leading maritime nations.

Prior to 1852, at least three attempts had been made by Americans to break the official Japanese policy of isolation which limited trade with foreigners to the Chinese and the Dutch, and which required that any ships coming within range of shore batteries be fired upon. In 1837 an American merchant, C. W. King, attempted to repatriate seven Japanese seamen who had been shipwrecked in various parts of the Pacific. His ship, the *Morrison*, was driven from Tokyo Bay and from Kagoshima. Commodore James Biddle with the *Columbus* and the *Vincennes* was sent to Tokyo Bay in 1846 to attempt to open negotiations with the Japanese, but failed. In February 1849 Commander Glynn in the United States ship *Preble* of the East India Squadron on a mission to Nagasaki succeeded, after five days of negotiations, in rescuing thirteen American seamen who were prisoners of the Japanese.[124]

In 1852 Commodore Matthew C. Perry[125] was appointed commander of the East India Squadron and was ordered to organize an expedition which was to proceed to Tokyo, then known as Yedo, to deliver a letter from President Millard Fillmore to the Emperor of Japan requesting that the two nations enter into a treaty of amity.[126] In carrying out these instructions Perry made two voyages to Japan, one in the summer of 1853 and another in the spring of 1854, and succeeded in negotiating a treaty which eventually opened Japan to world commerce.[127] The scarcity of charts of Japan at that time is indicated by the fact that the United States paid the Dutch $30,000 for copies of the only ones available.[128] Although Perry's primary purpose was to negotiate with the Japanese and to obtain a treaty which ostensibly would open Japan to world commerce he did recognize the opportunity that this voyage would offer for scientific and cartographic work. He wanted to have strict control of every member of the expedition so included no civilian scientists, but he did require qualified members of his staff to carry out these activities. In his General Order, dated at sea on December 23, 1852, he noted

... I have to request and to direct that each officer of the respective ships may employ such portions of his time as may be spared from his regular duties and proper hours of relaxation in contributing to the general mass of information which it is desirable to collect, and, in order to simplify and methodize these researches, a paper is subjoined particularizing the various departments, in reference to which information is more especially wanted, so that each officer may select that or those departments, which may seem most congenial to his tastes and inclinations.[129]

Perry arrived at Hong Kong in the steam frigate *Mississippi* in 1853.[130] Other vessels under his command included the steam frigate *Susquehanna*, the sloops-of-war *Plymouth* and *Saratoga*, and the storeship *Supply*. Making the *Susquehanna* his flagship, Perry sailed from Shanghai on May 17 for Naha, Okinawa, capital of the Ryukyu Islands, where he was joined by the other ships under his command. Permission having been granted for the men to go on shore, Perry stretched it a bit by ordering a party of twelve to make an inland excursion of Okinawa to study its geology, look for coal, and examine the economy. Various natural history specimens were collected.

In June the *Susquehanna* and the *Saratoga* visited the Bonin Islands (Ogasawara-guntō), where a survey was made of the largest of the group, including its harbor.

After six weeks in Okinawa the squadron sailed for Tokyo, leaving the storeship *Supply* at Naha. On July 8 the Americans arrived off Tokyo. Sounding as they went, they proceeded up the bay and came to anchor in Uraga Bay. While Perry carried on negotiations with Japanese authorities, the boat crews were out at every opportunity surveying the bay and harbor.[131] Although the Japanese put out boats to prevent this, the Americans managed to carry out the work. One boat got to within 100 yards of the shore on one occasion.

In Perry's *Narrative* . . . are references to the difficult problem of navigating and surveying in waters adjacent to Japan. He notes that

It is true that the Japanese have constructed charts, but they are on a plan peculiar to themselves, and of little benefit to the bold navigators, with their large vessels, of Europe and America. The Japanese charts, without meridian or scale, and totally destitute of any record of soundings, are hardly of any use, except in their own timid navigation. . . .[132]

The Japanese finally agreed to accept the letter from President Fillmore, which Perry delivered to them in a ceremony at Kurihama Bay on July 14. He stated he would return for an answer the following spring, and on July 17 the squadron sailed for Naha where a supply base had been established.

During the autumn, Commander Kelly, who remained at Okinawa with the *Plymouth* while the squadron returned to Chinese waters, explored the entire coast of Okinawa, correcting English and French surveys.[133] Kelly also visited the Bonin Islands where he surveyed and made a formal claim to the southern group in the name of Captain Coffin, the American whaler who landed there in 1823.[134]

In January 1854 Perry had ten vessels under his command.[135] The steam frigate *Powhatan*, the corvette *Macedonian*, the sloop-of-war *Vandalia*, and the storeships *Lexington* and *Southampton* had arrived from the United States during the latter part of 1853. All but the *Plymouth* assembled at Naha in preparation for the second visit to Tokyo. The *Plymouth* was sent to Shanghai to relieve the *Saratoga*. On February 11, 1854, the squadron was at the entrance to Tokyo Bay. In March, after the arrival of the *Saratoga* and the *Supply*, nine American ships, including three steam frigates, were in the bay.[136]

During negotiations leading up to the actual signing of a treaty the boats of the squadron continued the surveys begun the previous summer (Plate 36, *facing page 271*). In these operations in 1854 they sailed to within four miles of Tokyo.[137] Moreover, officers were able to copy a map of Tokyo Bay that one of the Japanese brought on board the *Powhatan*. When the Japanese agreed to open the port of Shimoda the *Southampton* and the *Vandalia* were sent to examine it to determine its suitability as an anchorage. By the treaty, which was concluded on March 31, Hakodate on the island of Hokkaido was also opened to American ships.[138]

After the treaty negotiations had reached the concluding stage one after another of the ships of the squadron were dispatched for other duties, the last two leaving on April 18. The *Susquehanna* was sent to Canton and the *Saratoga* sailed for the United States with copies of the treaty.[139] The survey of Tokyo Bay had been concluded. Many soundings had been made, and the western shoreline of the bay was well delineated.

From Tokyo Bay the *Powhatan* and the *Mississippi* sailed to Shimoda to join the other ships of the squadron remaining in Japan. Shimoda, by the treaty just concluded, had been designated as the residence for the American consul. The bay was surveyed and a general reconnaissance was made of the city and its surroundings.[140] When this was concluded the squadron proceeded to Hokkaido where a survey was made of the harbor of Hakodate. A reconnaissance was made of the surrounding area, and Uchiura Bay at the southeastern tip of Hokkaido was surveyed.[141] The squadron returned to China via Naha, but the *Macedonian* was dispatched to Formosa where a survey was made of the harbor of Chi-lung before the ship sailed for China.[142]

Perry's mission was diplomatic, but the expedition returned with a considerable amount of information gleaned from visits at Okinawa, Shimoda, and Hakodate.[143] While this was mere sampling, it had much significance in view of the policy of isolation which had restricted information about Japan from the rest of the world except for that obtained through Dutch and Chinese contacts.

Secretary of the Navy John P. Kennedy was emphatic in his request that all records of the expedition should be preserved. He requested that

... The journals and private notes of the officers and other persons in the expedition must be considered as belonging to the government, until permission shall be received from the Navy Department to publish them.[144]

In the Secretary of the Navy's letter of November 13, 1852, to Commodore Perry he emphasized that Perry's

... attention is particularly invited to the exploration of the coasts of Japan and of the adjacent continent and islands. You will cause linear or perspective views to be made of remarkable places, soundings to be taken at the entrances of harbors, rivers, &c., in and near shoals and collect all the hydrographical information necessary for the construction of charts. You will be careful to collect from every reliable source, and particularly from our consular and commercial agents, all the information you can of the social, political, and commercial condition of the countries and places you may visit, especially of new objects of commercial pursuits. . . .[145]

Perhaps the most significant scientific product of the expedition were the nautical charts and other hydrographic information.[146] Twelve charts were published with the official *Narrative*.[147]

In his introductory note to Papers on Natural History that appear in volume two of his *Narrative* Perry states that

> . . . With reference to the following papers upon the respective branches of Natural History of which they particularly treat, it should be borne in mind that, in the equipment of the Japan Expedition, scientific researches were to be considered of secondary importance, and consequently no special appropriations were made or any steps taken at the outset to employ civilians, as in other expeditions, for purposes purely scientific.
> Mr. William Heine contributed chiefly to the procurement of the birds. The collections of fishes and shells were made under my own supervision, and the botanical specimens were gathered and preserved by the chief interpreter, Mr. S. Wells Williams, and by Doctors Green, Fahs, and Morrow.
> The birds have been described by that well-known naturalist, Mr. John Cassin, of Philadelphia; and for the classification and description of the fishes and shells, I am entirely indebted to the gratuitous services of my personal friends, Messrs J. Carson Brevoort and J. C. Jay, of New York. . . .[148]

Volume two of Perry's *Narrative* is an excellent account of a variety of field observations by Daniel S. Green, James Morrow, Charles F. Fahs, George Jones, Bayard Taylor, Captain Joel Abbot, and several others on the expedition, and an analytical description of the natural history of specimens by John Cassin, James C. Brevoort, John C. Jay, Asa Gray, Francis Boott, Daniel C. Eaton, William H. Harvey, and William S. Sullivant.[149] These collections were reported on by these scientists in the leading scientific journals.[150] Wilhelm Heine was the delineator of many of the remarkable landscape views that illustrate the *Narrative*.[151]

NORTH PACIFIC EXPLORING EXPEDITION: 1853–1856

Aware of the increase in trade with the Orient, the considerable importance of whaling, and the great need of adequate maps, especially as they pertained to the North Pacific Ocean, the Congress of the United States in 1852 appropriated $125,000 for equipping and sending an official expedition into that region.[152] There is little doubt that Matthew Fontaine Maury played a major role in persuading government officials of the urgent need of such an expedition, and he was directly involved in the scientific activities that were related thereto.[153] The primary responsibility of the expedition was to survey and map and to implement the treaty that Perry had negotiated with Japan.[154]

On September 24, 1852, Secretary of the Navy John P. Kennedy informed the Chief of the Bureau of Ordnance and Hydrography of the scope of the expedition and directed him to render all necessary assistance. The letter was sent to Lieutenant Maury, who was in charge of the Depot of Charts and Instruments, for action. It noted that

> In preparing the Expedition, authorized by the Act of Congress of August 31st, 1852, for the reconnaissance and survey for Naval and commercial purposes of such parts of Behring's straits, of the North Pacific Ocean and of the China Seas as are frequented by American

whaleships and by trading vessels in their routes between the United States and China and for the purpose of facilitating the duties which will be required of it, you will be pleased to furnish all the information at the command of the Bureau in relation to the surveys and Hydrographical researches and examinations that have been made of the proposed field of operations, particularly of the China and Japan seas, Behrings Straits, the Kurile Islands, the Aleutian Isles, and the North Pacific Ocean which is embraced within the route to and from California, Oregon, China and Japan. Also in the relation to the sea frequented by whales in the vicinity of the Caroline and Rodick chains of Isles. You will also have skeleton charts prepared, on which the Islands, reefs, shoals and other difficulties to navigation with the attending circumstances and how determined, are carefully laid down and on which the Gaspar Straits and all the Eastern passages with the Sooloo and Mindoro Seas, also Mc-Elfield's Bank are particularly referred to.

As it is believed that Professors Henry and Agassiz, and the Geographical Society of New York would prepare papers and other suggestions likely to extend the bounds of useful science, . . . you will direct Lieut. Maury to address them accordingly on the subject. The Royal Geographical Society of London, so distinguished for its exertions in geodetic and geographic matters, would perhaps furnish interesting information which might add to the success of the Expedition . . .

You will furnish sets of charts of all the portions of the Earth named and of the most recent surveys (and you will, also, furnish a list of works of science on hand at the observatory, that may be useful) and a list of astronomical instruments that may be available.[155]

The five ships comprising the expedition were equipped in the most substantial manner and were supplied with the best instruments, maps, apparatus, and scientific library that was available. Richard Rathbun notes that it was the best equipped expedition that had taken to sea up to that time.[156] A number of civilian scientists were included with the personnel.[157] These were William Stimpson, zoologist; F. H. Storer, chemist and taxidermist; Edward M. Kern, photographer and artist; Charles Wright, botanist; and A. H. Ames, assistant naturalist.[158] It is fortunate that Lieutenant John M. Brooke, astronomer, was added as one of the officers because he played a significant role in scientific observations that were made.[159]

The expedition, commanded by Commander Cadwalader Ringgold,[160] sailed from Hampton Roads on June 11, 1853 (Fig. 38).[161] Five ships comprised the squadron. They were the sloop of war *Vincennes*, the brig *Porpoise*, the storeship *John P. Kennedy*, the bark-rigged steamer *John Hancock*, and the schooner *Fenimore Cooper*. The first two had been in Wilkes' squadron during his explorations of 1838–1842. At Simons Bay, at the Cape of Good Hope, the squadron separated. The *Vincennes* and *Porpoise* sailed separate but parallel courses to Australia, arriving on December 26;[162] the other three vessels proceeded to Batavia. From January to May the *Kennedy* and the *Hancock* surveyed Karimata Strait and the islands between Batavia and Singapore and the *Cooper* surveyed the island groups in the southern portion of the South China Sea. When the *Cooper* arrived at Hong Kong late in June the other four vessels were there. The *Porpoise* had passed through the Solomon and Bismarck seas and had visited the Carolines and Guam en route from Sydney. The *Vincennes* had taken a more easterly course to visit the Santa Cruz Islands.

At Hong Kong the *Kennedy* was transferred to the East India Squadron. Commander Ringgold became ill and was sent home in September, 1854. Lieutenant John Rodgers, second-in-command to Ringgold, assumed command of the expedition. Rodgers was well qualified by experience, having previously served as a naval officer with the Coast Survey.[163] In September the *Hancock* and the *Cooper* were dispatched to transport American diplomatic representatives from Shanghai to north China where, with French and British representatives, they were to ask for a revision of the commercial treaties of 1842 and 1844. The cruise afforded opportunities for sounding the mouths of five rivers, the Min Chiang, Huang-p'u Chiang, Yangtze, Huang-Ho, and Pei Chiang.[164] After returning their passengers to Shanghai the two vessels sailed for Formosa to survey parts of the east coast.

Meanwhile the *Vincennes* and the *Porpoise* sailed northwestward through Formosa Strait where the *Porpoise* was last seen; it apparently was lost some time later in a typhoon. Lieutenant Rodgers sailed eastward to the Bonin Islands and then returned to Okinawa to chart the Ryukyu Islands between Okinawa and Kyushu. In February 1855, the three remaining vessels of the squadron were again at Hong Kong.

From Hong Kong the expedition set out on its major objective (Fig. 38). The steamer *John Hancock*, commanded by Lieutenant H. K. Stevens, continued the survey of the east coast of Formosa before proceeding to Okinawa where it joined the *Cooper* and the *Vincennes* at Naha. The three vessels sailed from Naha on April 27, 1855, to examine both coasts of Japan.[165]

The *Vincennes* and the *Hancock* sailed northward along the Ryukyu Islands to Ō-shima, which was carefully surveyed. From Ō-shima they set a course for the treaty port of Shimoda, where they arrived on May 13.[166] Ignoring objections of the authorities at Shimoda, the two vessels visited the nearby port of Heda (Plate 37, *following page 284*), taking soundings and charting the coast of Izu-hantō and into Suruga Bay. Lieutenant Rodgers considered the coast north of Tokyo Bay too foggy to risk the two ships in surveying close to land. Therefore, fifteen men took to an open boat, the *Vincennes Junior*, to survey the coast at close range under the direction of Lieutenant John M. Brooke. Edward M. Kern, an artist, was responsible for contouring and sketching the topography.[167] Camping on shore as they worked northward, Lieutenant Brooke and his men completed the survey and extensive sounding by lead line of 450 miles of coast and reached Hakodate in June. This was probably the single most remarkable accomplishment of the expedition.[168]

Meanwhile Acting Lieutenant William Gibson, commanding the *Cooper*, sailed for Kyushu, charting rocks and parts of islands, en route. Setting a course along the west side of Kyushu, he mapped the Gotō-rettō and adjacent islands. The schooner continued through Korea Strait and northward along the coast, paying particular attention to the charting of Oki-guntō, Sado, and Noto-hantō. On June 6 the schooner joined the *Vincennes* and the *Hancock* at Hakodate. Surveys were made of Hakodate and vicinity during the three weeks the squadron remained there.[169]

Late in June the expedition sailed from Hakodate. The *Hancock* first completed the survey of Tsugaru Strait, then sailed along the west coast of Hokkaido to La Pérouse Strait. From there Lieutenant Stevens set a course which was essentially a circuit of the Sea of Okhotsk, including a penetration into Zaliv Shelikhova. Most of the time he steamed just off the coast so as to make a running reconnaissance, but often fog and heavy weather blotted the shoreline from sight. In September the *Hancock* terminated the circuit at the northern tip of Ostrov Sakhalin, and Lieutenant Stevens set a course for San Francisco, which was reached on October 19. Both the *Cooper*

Herald I.

Sea of
Okhotsk

Sakhalin   Kamchatka
            Petropavlovsk
Kuril Is.   Aleutian   Islan

Hakodate   Hokkaido

JAPAN
      Honshu
      Shimoda

Shanghai   Kyushu

                    Bonin Is.

Hong Kong
        Formosa
        Ryukyu Is.

                              Guam

                    Caroline   Islands

Singapore   120°   150°   180°

Batavia

                                        Santa
                                        Cruz Is.

                              Sydney

———— Vincennes
– – – John Hancock
············· Fenimore Cooper

FIG. 38. Generalized tracks of the North Pacific Exploring Expedition, 1853–18

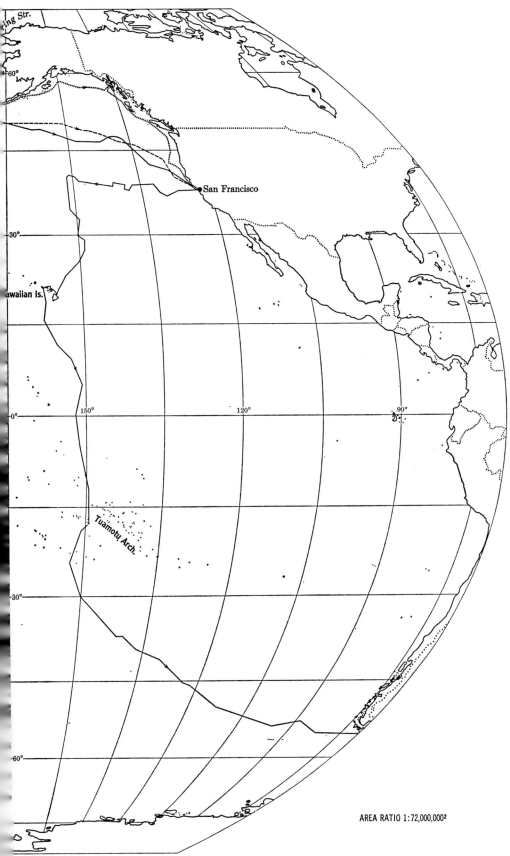

60°

San Francisco

30°

awaiian Is.

150°   120°   90°

0°

Tuamotu Arch.

30°

60°

AREA RATIO 1:72,000,000²

npiled by Kenneth J. Bertrand from a map in Allan B. Cole (ed.), 1947 (Note 152).

and the *Vincennes* were already there, having arrived on the 11th and 13th respectively.

From Hakodate the *Vincennes* and the *Cooper* had skirted the east coast of Hokkaido en route to Petropavlovsk, the flagship staying in close to the Kurils, the schooner sailing in the open sea.[170] On July 14 the *Vincennes* departed for the Arctic, passing between Komandorskiy Ostrova and Kamchatka. A boat's crew was put ashore on the west side of Bering Strait, and the *Vincennes* continued into the Arctic Ocean to Herald Island. Sailing as far north as latitude 72° 05', Lieutenant Rodgers searched in vain for Wrangel Island because he was east instead of west of Herald Island. Returning to Bering Strait, the shore party was picked up, and Lieutenant Rodgers set a course for San Francisco, making deep-sea soundings near the Aleutians en route.[171]

On July 16 the *Cooper* sailed from Petropavlovsk for the Aleutians, where positions were determined for all but one of the main islands and for most of the smaller ones.[172] The passages between the islands were carefully examined and other survey work carried out. The schooner called at Sitka on September 19 and then proceeded to San Francisco.

As a result of the surveys by the crews of the three vessels during 1855, Lieutenant Rodgers was able to report on October 19, 1855 that drawings for a total of thirty-two charts had been finished or were in various stages of preparation.[173] This was in addition to twelve charts of earlier work sent home from Hong Kong on April 2, 1855.[174] Most of the manuscript charts prepared by the expedition were turned over to the Depot of Charts and Instruments, but very few were published. Rodgers and Maury corresponded frequently about their publication, but funds were always lacking.[175] The charts of the North Pacific Surveying Expedition, however, were used extensively after 1866 by the newly established Hydrographic Office in the compilation of its charts.[176]

From the standpoint of the form of cartographic representation it is interesting to note that relief on the boat sheets and manuscript maps is shown by form lines, and where the details were known, by contours at an interval of 100 feet and sometimes at 300 feet. When the maps were published, however, hachures were used to show relief, except in the case of large-scale insets of harbors where contours could be shown in monochrome without confusion.[177]

In view of the fact that most of the 1855 surveys were done in areas where fog is common and where the ships could not wait for clear weather, there are stretches of the coasts of Japan and Siberia where the shoreline only is indicated on the maps, and is shown by a dashed line. In some instances Russian surveys were available to the members of the Expedition, and when a field check showed that they were reliable, they were incorporated into the charts of the expedition.[178]

The expedition returned to the United States with collections and field observations in the natural sciences that were of great magnitude, and included many new and rare species. The zoological collection alone comprised a total of 5211 different species divided into the following six principal groups:[179]

Vertebrates	846
Insects	400
Crustacea	980
Annelids	220

```
Mollusks . . . . . . . . . . . .  2359
Radiates  . . . . . . . . . . .    406
                                  ─────
                                   5211
```

Most of these were collected, arranged, and identified by Dr. William Stimpson, who was peculiarly well fitted for this activity. Shortly after his return to the United States Dr. Stimpson was made director of the Chicago Academy of Science and transferred to the Academy most of the invertebrate collections. Rathbun notes:

Considerable progress had been made in working up results, and several short papers briefly descriptive of the more interesting groups of animals had been issued, when the memorable conflagration of 1871, which destroyed so large a part of Chicago, completely annihilated the entire collection there, as well as all the MSS. and drawings which had been prepared for publication. The only collections of marine invertebrates which escaped were the corals and a few of the Crustacea, which had been left for study at the Smithsonian Institution, the Museum of Comparative Zoology, and Yale College.[180]

Apparently Dr. Stimpson prepared a comprehensive illustrated report of the 980 species of crustacea which, sometime after his death in 1872, was discovered in the Navy Department and subsequently was transferred to the Smithsonian Institution. In 1907 this remarkable report, with appropriate annotations, was published by Mary J. Rathbun.[181] The botanical specimens, in their original packages, occupied a bulk of more than 100 cubic feet.[182]

The status of publication of the scientific results was noted by Ferdinand V. Hayden in 1862 as follows:

. . . The [Civil] war has interfered with the completion of this report, as the Commander of the Expedition, with several of his officers, are in active service on the Southern coast, and the appropriations for the department of Natural Science have ceased. The narrative by Capt. Rodgers has not yet been written. Many charts of portions of the Chinese and Japanese seas, and also of parts of the N. E. Asiatic coast to the Aleutian Islands, are finished.

The following reports on the Natural History are in progress: On the Zoology, by Dr. Wm. Stimpson, assisted by Dr. A. A. Gould, Mr. John Cassin, Dr. Hallowell, Dr. Uhler, Mr. Barnard and Prof. Theo. Gill. The zoological portion will probably comprise about 3 vols. 4to, with an atlas of plates for each.

A Report on the Botany by Prof. Asa Gray and Charles Wright, is in progress. [183]

During the decade or more following the return of the expedition, scientists utilized the rich collections of specimens in natural history and prepared and published papers about and descriptive catalogues of selected species.[184] These scientists included the most notable and recognized authorities in the several fields of specialization. Articles of varying lengths and complexity were published in the leading scientific journals, especially in the United States.[185]

SURVEYS OF THE WEST COAST OF THE UNITED STATES

Acquisition of California in 1848 and of Oregon Territory (Washington and Oregon) in 1846 introduced the immediate need of accurate maps and nautical charts, especially of the harbors, of the entire shoreline. The first reasonably accurate map of this western region of the United States was compiled by Lieutenant Gouverneur K. Warren in 1857 in the office of the Topographical Bureau.[186] It was compiled primarily from the field work of surveys and explorations for determining the most practicable route for a railroad from the Mississippi River to the Pacific Ocean.[187] Included with these extensive surveys and explorations were several that were responsible for mapping the west coast. These were by Lieutenants Robert S. Williamson and John G. Parke in California and Oregon and Isaac I. Stevens in Washington and Oregon (1853–1856).[188]

Commander Cadwalader Ringgold, who had been responsible for a survey of San Francisco Bay for Wilkes in 1841, published in 1851 a five-sheet chart with accompanying sailing directions of San Francisco Bay and the Sacramento River to Sacramento. This chart was based on detailed field survey and exploration.[189]

During the 1850s the War Department increased its topographical surveys of the western territories, but, with very few exceptions, the surveys were restricted to inland areas, leaving surveying and mapping of the littoral fringe to the Coast Survey.[190]

The United States Coast Survey[191] began its surveys of the Pacific coast in 1849, in response to the urgent need for coastal and harbor charts by maritime interests, especially those that were intimately involved in the great rush to the gold fields in California in the late 1840s and in the 1850s.[192] For more orderly administration the Coast Survey divided the Pacific coast of the United States into two parts, sections IX and X. Survey of the west coast was begun by first establishing by precise observations a line of positions.[193] Hydrographic surveys were begun in California by Lieutenant Commander William P. McArthur in the schooner Ewing in 1849.[194] The following year McArthur was joined by George Davidson who initiated his brilliant career of many years of scientific work on the Pacific coast with the establishment of a geodetic and topographic survey.[195]

In 1852, six parties were employed in the field on the west coast.[196] One, using the schooner Ewing and the steamer Active, was engaged in hydrographic surveying; one was employed in astronomical and magnetic work; two were establishing triangulations; and two were doing topographical surveys. Fourteen army officers and fifty-nine naval officers were attached to the Coast Survey to assist in performing these assignments.[197] A chart of Point Pinos harbor at a scale of 1:20,000 was completed in 1851, and one of Monterey Bay at a scale of 1:40,000 was published in 1852.[198]

By 1853 a system of preliminary geographical positions for nearly every two degrees of latitude was completed from the southern border of California to the northern border of Oregon. Surveys of the principal ports and harbors of California and of the Columbia River were begun. In this work Lieutenant James Alden and George Davidson made significant contributions.[199] Triangulation was continued up the Columbia River a distance of thirty-five miles. A monochrome map of San Francisco Bay on a scale of 1:10,000, showing relief by contours, and reconnaissance charts of six other California ports were published in 1853.[200]

The following year a reconnaissance map of the west coast of the United States in three sheets was published to meet the urgent and immediate needs of the Federal government and maritime interests. This was the first reasonably accurate map of the west coast.[201] By 1854, systematic observation of the tides by means of permanent self-registering gauges at Astoria in Oregon and San Francisco and San Diego in California, and temporary gauges at a number of other positions revealed the large diurnal inequality of the tides and that in this respect the Pacific coast differed from

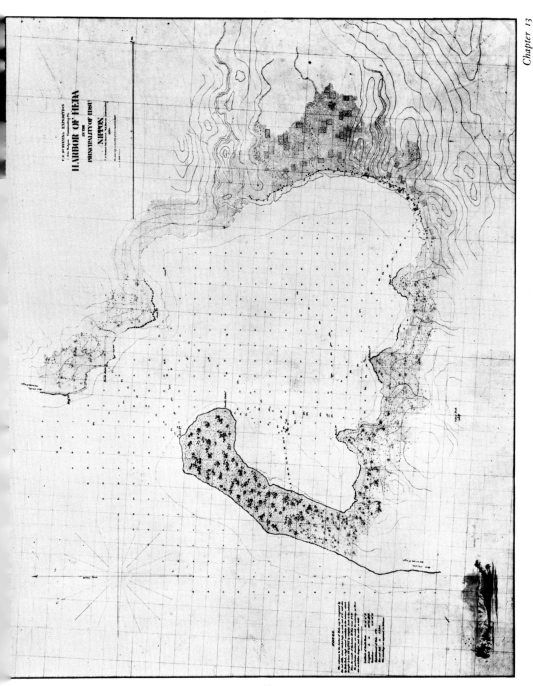

PLATE 37

Part of a map of the "Harbor of Heda . . . Nippon . . . 1855." North Pacific Exploring Expedition. Reduction of map in manuscript 451.36 in *Records of the Hydrographic Office* in the National Archives, Washington.

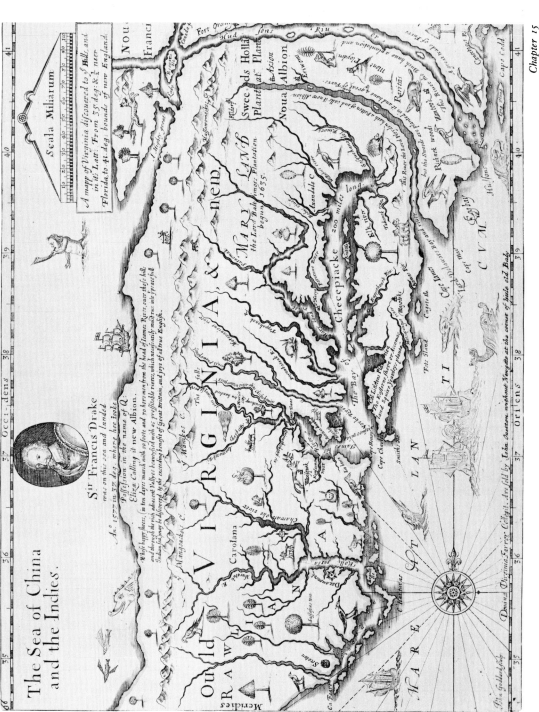

The Sea of China and the Indies.

Scala Miliarum

A mapp of Virginia discouered to y Hills, and in it's Latt: From 35 deg: & ½ neer Florida to 41 deg: bounds of new England.

Sir Francis Drake
was on his sea and landed
An.° 1577 in 37 deg: where hee tooke
Possession in the name of Q.
Eliza: Calling it new Albion.

Whose happy shore, (in ten dayes march with 50 foote and 30 horsmen from the head of Iames River, ouer those hills and through those rich adiacent Vallyes beautified with as profitable rivers, which necessarily muste run into y peacefull Indian Sea) may be discovered to the exceeding benefit of Great Britain, and ioye of all true English.

VIRGINIA &c. new.

MARYLAND
the Lord Baltimores Plantation begunn 1655.

Checepiacke 200 miles long

Ould RAWLEY

Carolana

Meridies

Nova Francia

Sweeds Holla Plantat
Nova Albion

ATLAN TI CVM

MARE

The Bay

Occi-dens 36 37 38 39 40 41

Orlens 36 37 38 39

PLATE 38

Chapter 15

Map of Virginia by Virginia Farrer, showing the hoped-for Pacific Ocean separated from Chesapeake Bay by a narrow peninsula. Originally published in Edward Williams's *Virginia Richly Valued*, London, 1651. The map is here reproduced from the copy, *ca.* 1670 in, and by courtesy of, the

the Atlantic coast.[202] From these beginnings in the early 1850s the United States Coast Survey expanded its scientific activities and issued reports that give some of the best, most comprehensive geographical information about this region.[203]

SURVEYS OF LESSER MAGNITUDE

There were voyages of many individual ships of the U. S. Navy in the Pacific Ocean during the period 1838–1860, but most of their contributions to the scientific knowledge of the area were either negligible or routine.[204] The following are examples of voyages that did make important contributions.

The North Pacific Surveying Expedition had not had time or funds with which to explore a safe route for steamships through the central Pacific from California to China by way of Honolulu, although this had been one of the original objectives. There were a number of islands, reportedly sighted by whalers and others in the South Pacific, whose existence had not been confirmed or whose position had not been accurately fixed. As a means of completing some of this unfinished business, Secretary of the Navy James C. Dobbin, in a letter of December 5, 1855, directed John Rodgers to

> . . . transfer her[the schooner *Fenimore Cooper's*] officers, crew and stores (if any) to the *Vincennes* and you will turn the vessel [the *Cooper*] over to the Yard [Mare Island Navy Yard]. You will then with the *Vincennes* proceed to New York by such route as you may deem advisable informing the Department by the course of mail of your intentions.[205]

Rodgers welcomed the Secretary's broad mandate, for he had definite ideas of what remained to be done. Leaving San Francisco on February 2, 1856, he sailed on a wide detour into the Pacific, carrying out surveys in the Hawaiian Islands and the Society Islands, before rounding the Horn en route to New York.

During the latter part of the 1850s Lieutenant William Gibson, commander of the *Fenimore Cooper*, Lieutenant Brooke, Lieutenant Rodgers, Commander Ringgold, Lieutenant Bent, and Lieutenant Maury were assigned to the Naval Observatory to compile and to draft the charts of the several recent expeditions.[206]

Lieutenant Brooke was ordered to plan and command a cruise to survey proposed steamship routes between California and China.[207] On September 26, 1858, he sailed in the *Cooper* from Mare Island Navy Yard at San Francisco. This was mainly a deep-sea sounding mission to verify the existence of reported reefs and shoals on the routes normally taken by steamers.[208] Six weeks were spent in deep-sea sounding and six weeks in surveying and correcting the charts of the islands and reefs northwest of the Hawaiian Islands. After a month in Honolulu the *Fenimore Cooper* sailed southwestward, sounding and surveying in the Marianas and in adjacent islands, en route to Hong Kong. In the summer of 1859 Lieutenant Brooke set a course for the Ryukyu Islands and Yokohama. Near the end of her assigned mission the schooner was wrecked off Japan in a typhoon on August 23, 1859 but the crew, instruments, and records were saved.

An Act of Congress, dated August 3, 1848, directed the United States Navy ". . . to set on foot an expedition to the most southern available position on the western continent, for the purpose of making observations on the planet Venus . . . ".[209] The United States Naval Astronomical Expedition, commanded by Lieutenant James M. Gilliss left New York on August 16, 1849, to carry out the provisions of

the Act. A narrative account of the expedition and of the scientific results was published as a Congressional Document in 1855–1856.[210] Though the expedition was
almost exclusively restricted to the special mission of observing the planet Venus,
and there were no professionally trained naturalists aboard, valuable collections of
botanical, zoological, and ethnological materials were made and geographical observations were recorded, especially about Chile.[211] Most of the natural history collections were given to the Smithsonian Institution. Published reports on these collections were prepared by Spencer F. Baird, William D. Brackenridge, John Cassin,
Timothy A. Conrad, Thomas Ewbank, Charles Girard, Augustus A. Gould, Asa Gray,
James L. Smith, and Jeffries Wyman.[212] A large quantity of valuable astronomical
observations were made in the extreme southeastern part of the Pacific Basin.[213]

During the 1850s commercial interest developed in the guano resources on islands
in the Pacific. Guano as a fertilizer was in demand by farmers in Maryland, Dela-
ware, and Virginia, but the price was prohibitively high due to a monopoly granted to
a British company by Peru, the chief source. Consequently, other sources were
sought among the Pacific islands reportedly discovered by American whalers and on
whose discovery a claim could be based. Thus Baker Island and Jarvis Island were
developed by the American Guano Company of New York. In August 1856, Congress passed a law by which discoverers of guano-bearing islands could register their
discovery and receive official recognition of their claims, providing no other nation
claimed the island.[214] The United States government supported the discover's
exclusive right to dig and sell guano from the island.

A number of private voyages were organized to visit, to make a landing if possible,
and to establish the proof of guano deposits on islands in the Pacific.[215] At least two
voyages were made by naval vessels to investigate guano islands on which claims
were being made. In 1856 Commodore William Mervine, commander of the Pacific
Squadron, visited the Hawaiian Islands and the Samoa Islands for this purpose. He
was unable to land on Baker Island. In the summer of 1857 Commander Charles H.
Davis was sent by the Navy in the ship *St. Marys* to take formal possession of Jarvis
and Baker islands and to map them.

Naval vessels also performed detailed special surveys for specific purposes in the
Pacific.[216] Some of these involved selecting sites for lighthouses. The vessels of the
East India Squadron made numerous surveys while cruising along the coast of China
on diplomatic missions.[217]

A good summary account of expeditions of the Federal government and of private
individuals to the Pacific usually was included in the Annual Report of the Secretary
of the Smithsonian Institution for the period 1846–1860.[218] These annual reports
often included a description of the natural history specimens collected and the observations made on the expeditions. Many of the collections and descriptive accounts
were added to and now comprise a part of the nucleus of the early collections in the
Smithsonian Insitution.[219]

SCIENTIFIC SURVEYING AND MAPPING: 1860-1899

American participation in the exploration and surveying and mapping of the Pacific
Basin during the period 1860–1899 was directed primarily to facilitating the safe

movement of the rapidly expanding maritime commerce and to the scientific examination of the physical characteristics of the sea.[220]

Ships of the United States Navy made innumerable tracks across much of the Pacific in search of dangers to shipping, measuring, describing, and pinpointing the precise location of islands, atolls, reefs, barriers, and other physical features that were obstacles to safe navigation.[221] Hydrographic Office ships made oceanographic surveys for information on winds and currents, bottom sediments, the profile of the ocean floor, plant and animal life, salinity of the water, and a host of other subjects, thereby carrying on much of the work of Matthew Fontaine Maury. Censuses were also taken of seal and walrus rookeries and of whaling grounds.

The United States government cooperated with other nations in a more accurate and systematic survey of coastal waters, harbor entrances, and river mouths.[222] Scientific information was exchanged and many large-scale and small-scale nautical charts and maps of these areas were compiled, published, and revised as more accurate and more recent hydrographic information was acquired. The Hydrographic Office was primarily responsible for the large amount of this work done by the United States government.

The west coast of the United States and of Alaska was surveyed, charted, and mapped in detail and with considerable accuracy, especially by the United States Coast Survey (after 1878 the Coast and Geodetic Survey). Toward the end of this period private academic and professional scientific institutions became interested in and actively supported oceanographic and other scientific cruises. The following sections consider representative highlights of these activities.

Hydrographic Surveys of the Pacific Ocean

In 1866 the Bureau of Ordnance and Hydrography of the Navy was reorganized. The former Depot of Charts and Instruments in the Naval Observatory became the United States Hydrographic Office, a separate agency of the Bureau of Navigation.[223] Three years earlier, the Navy had purchased the Edmund M. and George W. Blunt publishing firm of New York, thereby acquiring the charts and other records of that pioneer American company to combine with those produced by the former Depot of Charts and Instruments.[224] The Hydrographic Office was charged with the map- and chart-making activities of the Navy.

Significant among the cartographic products of the Hydrographic Office during the 1870s was the publication of a wind and current chart for the North Pacific Ocean from the coast of North America west to longitude 180°, compiled under the direction of Lieutenant T. A. Lyon.[225] Lieutenant J. E. Pillsbury compiled a list of 1302 reported dangers to shipping in the Pacific Ocean.[226] In 1878, a new map of the North Pacific Ocean in four sheets was published and in the following year an eight-sheet map of the South Pacific Ocean was issued. This marked the beginning of the publication of a series of charts which eventually covered all oceans on a scale of six-tenths of an inch to a degree of longitude.[227]

The best single source of published information on the extent of publication and the frequency of revision of the several different series of nautical charts and maps of selected areas in the Pacific Basin for the period since the birth of the Hydrographic Office in 1866 are various editions of the *Catalogue* published periodically by the Hydrographic Office.[228]

One product of cruises by United States Navy ships in the Pacific Ocean area was the wide variety of information recorded in logbooks and journals and on charts during each operation. This information was carefully evaluated and transcribed for use in compiling standard United States Hydrographic Office Charts, which have been published and made available to all navigators. Hydrographic surveying was conducted on a regular and continuing basis, replacing the occasional expedition.[229] Individual ships were dispatched on specific planned survey missions organized and directed by the Hydrographic Office as part of an overall program.[230] The duties included, especially, the survey for and preparation of nautical charts of harbors and anchorages in Korea, China, Japan, Mexico, Sea of Okhotsk, and Pacific islands.[231] The *Narragansett*, the *Portsmouth*, and the *Tuscarora* were three of the naval vessels which were almost continually engaged in survey operations in the Pacific for the decade or more following the Civil War.

In 1871 the Congress of the United States appropriated $50,000 for surveys in the Pacific Basin. The steamship *Narragansett*, considered to be most suitable for this purpose, was already on a cruise in the Pacific in command of Commander George Dewey.[232] In 1872 the *Narragansett* surveyed the harbor of Pago Pago in Samoa, and a band of the ocean from Honolulu to Sydney, Australia, including especially several of the Marshall and Gilbert islands. The *Portsmouth* also was equipped for survey work and in 1871, under Commander Joseph S. Skerrett, surveyed the area between the west coast of the United States and Hawaii for dangers to shipping. The following year Skerrett was directed to continue this work west from Hawaii.[233]

At the conclusion of the cruise of the *Narragansett* in 1872 Commander Dewey was ordered to make a running survey the following year of the coast from San Diego south to Corrientes, Mexico. Following this survey he was to initiate a survey of the Gulf of California. This marked the beginning of a program extending over a quarter of a century during which the coast of Latin America was surveyed in detail from California to northern Peru. The coast of Mexico was surveyed between 1873 and 1880 by the *Narragansett* under Commander Dewey and the *Tuscarora* under Commander Philip. Relatively few of the harbors on this coast had been accurately surveyed prior to these operations. Extensive offshore soundings were taken by the *Tuscarora*. These two ships were replaced in the early 1880s by the *Ranger*, the *Alert*, and the *Thetis*.

Closely related to these operations were special surveys of the west coast of Central America for a route for a canal connecting the Atlantic and Pacific oceans.[234] A succession of proposals and preliminary surveys had been made by private and government organizations during the nineteenth century but with no tangible initial results until the ill-fated attempt by the French, beginning in 1879, and the successful completion of this canal by the United States in 1914.[235]

The Darien Expedition of the U. S. Navy under Commander Thomas O. Selfridge in 1870 was the first of a succession of United States government undertakings to investigate the area for a canal route.[236] These surveys were continued through a period of nearly six years (1870–1875), and were concentrated on the lowland of the

Río Atrato which flows into the Golfo de Urabá. In 1875 Lieutenant Frederick Collins, a member of a Navy expedition, investigated the potentialities of the Atrato-Napipí route.[237]

In 1872 and 1873 Commander Edward P. Lull led a survey party into the Río San Juan-Lago de Nicaragua region to ascertain its potentialities in relation to a canal route.[238]

The large volume of graphic, descriptive, cartographic, and statistical information accumulated by the Hydrographic Office from the ever-increasing number of surveys and from other sources, comprises one of the most valuable bodies of archival scientific materials extant on the Pacific Basin.[239]

OCEANOGRAPHIC SURVEYS OF THE PACIFIC BASIN

The United States Navy was given the primary responsibility for making extensive oceanographic surveys of the Pacific Basin.[240] During the second half of the nineteenth century much of this responsibility was for deep-sea sounding.[241] Spurred by popular interest in submarine cables between the United States and countries in the Far East, Congress passed a resolution authorizing the use of a naval vessel to conduct a series of trans-Pacific deep-sea sounding and to compile profiles of related submarine relief.[242] In 1873, the *Tuscarora* under Commander George B. Belknap initiated this program.[243] The *Tuscarora* was equipped with a sounding machine using piano wire, invented in 1872 by William Thomson, the English scientist. Following several test runs off the California coast, Belknap, in 1873, was directed to run a line of soundings on a great-circle route from Cape Flattery at the south portal of the Strait of Juan de Fuca to the entrance of Tokyo Bay. He was instructed to return by way of the Ogasawara (Bonin) Islands and Honolulu to San Francisco or San Diego. This important survey was begun on January 6, 1874 from San Diego with stops at Honolulu, the Ogasawara Islands, and Yokohama. A total of 145 soundings were taken. The return cruise from Yokohama to Cape Flattery along a great-circle route was begun in June 1874. Depths of nearly 28,000 feet were taken. The *Tuscarora* discovered the Japan Trench, one of the great ocean deeps. During the summer the *Tuscarora* ran lines of soundings in the North Pacific, especially between Yokohama and the Kuril Islands, and from the Aleutian Islands to Cape Flattery, discovering the Aleutian Trench. This pioneering venture in deep-sea sounding in the Pacific accounted for nearly 500 soundings, discovered two primary submarine features, proved the reliability of wire sounding, recorded unsuspected depths, collected bottom specimens of considerable zoological interest, obtained records of surface and subsurface seawater and air temperatures and currents, and prepared detailed maps and profiles of the survey.

The *Tuscarora's* successful surveys stimulated an ever-increasing number of similar deep-sea sounding surveys by Navy ships,[244] such as the *Enterprise*[245] and the *Nero*.[246] The *Nero* in 1899 sounded a depth of 5160 fathoms (30,960 feet), the deepest known probe up to that date. One of the principal results of these wide-ranging surveys was the preparation of a variety of useful maps and charts showing such subjects as the course of the Japanese Current (Kuroshio), the air and surface temperature of the ocean, isothermal charts, wind and current charts, and of course cable-crossing charts. Significant by-products were the wide varieties of natural science specimens obtained, many of which were given to the Smithsonian Institution. Naturalists, especially from or responsible to the Smithsonian Institution accompanied these survey expeditions, or examined and described the collections, as for example those of the *Portsmouth* during its survey of the islands of the North Pacific Ocean in 1873–1874[247] and the *Palos* during its astronomical survey to Japan and China in 1881 and 1882.[248]

Surveying and Mapping the Western Littoral of North America

Acquisition of Alaska in 1867 and the subsequent discovery of gold in the Klondike, the rapid expansion of sealing and fishing along the Pacific coast, and the considerable increase in settlement of the west coast necessitated an acceleration in the surveying and mapping of this littoral area. The United States Coast Survey (after 1879 the United States Coast and Geodetic Survey) was responsible for establishing the geodetic framework, conducting the offshore observations, and the topographic surveying for the littoral and offshore features.[249] By 1871 the Coast Survey had outfitted its new steamer, the *Hassler*, for deep-sea collecting and for surveying and mapping on the west coast.[250] This was the extension of the pioneering scientific work begun in the 1850s. A succession of ships and well-trained scientific personnel completed the detailed mapping of the coast and in addition prepared and published accounts of their special studies in various fields of science.[251] Many of these reports are included in the annual reports of the Superintendent of the Survey and cover a wide range of subjects.[252] In addition to harbor charts, anchorage charts, and detailed topo-hydrographic maps of the coast the Survey also published coast pilots, notices to mariners, tables of depths for harbors, tide tables, and special publications on such subjects as gravity determination, deep-sea sounding and dredging, physical hydrography, geodetic observations, triangulation observations, and current and temperature observations of the Pacific coast of North America.[253]

George Davidson, a top scientist of the Coast Survey who had prepared remarkably accurate descriptive reports and detailed maps of the west coast during the 1850s and 1860s, was assigned to direct much of the exploration and surveying of the Pacific coast of Alaska in the 1870s.[254] He was responsible for establishing high standards for surveying and charting and for accurate accounts of the history of scientific work along the west coast during these decades.

The Coast Survey initiated its work in Alaska in 1867, the year the Territory was purchased from Russia. Until then charts of the Alaskan coast and offshore islands were compilations based on the work of Russian, British, Spanish, French, and United States exploring expeditions.[255] This work was spotty and for the most part accomplished without the benefit of precise survey. Much of the coast shown on maps was sketched in, and therefore was inadequate for the maritime requirements of the latter part of the nineteenth century. Nearly every summer from 1867 to 1880 one small survey ship and a shore party were engaged in determining latitude, longitude, and magnetic variations at selected sites along the coast in order to prepare the precise frame of reference for mapping. Some reconnaissance mapping of harbors was also carried out.[256] The first comprehensive surveying and mapping of Alaska was begun in 1882, beginning at the southern boundary and working up the "inside passage."[257] Sometimes as many as three survey ships were employed in this survey, but until gold was discovered in the Klondike in 1898 work progressed slowly because greater priority was given to surveying the west coast of continental United States.[258]

During the period 1867–1899 the United States Army carried out terrain reconnaissance surveys of the valleys of Alaskan rivers emptying into the Pacific Ocean. The resulting maps and topographic studies made possible the building of roads and other transport facilities to the interior, and safe movement through the treacherous coastal waters and associated river lowlands.[259] The Signal Office of the Army explored the littoral area and the Aleutian Islands and reported on the natural history.[260]

In the 1880s and 1890s the newly organized United States Geological Survey began the systematic topographical and geological survey of the west coast, although nearly all of its surveys were of the interior and of important ports and harbors such as San Francisco Bay and vicinity.[261]

The Bureau of Fisheries, which was established as an independent agency in 1871 had as one of its functions the exploration and survey of marine areas, which included especially the northeastern Pacific Ocean.[262] Prior to 1881, the Commission had the services of the U. S. Coast Survey steamer *Bache*. Beginning in 1881 it used its own ship, the steamer *Albatross*, for annual explorations and surveys in these waters and prepared scientific reports on the results.[263] Surveys included dredging, sounding, making a detailed record of animal life, meteorological observations, trawling, recording ocean temperatures and specific gravity measurements.[264]

THE ROLE OF SCIENTIFIC INSTITUTIONS AND ORGANIZATIONS

Nearly all of the activities of the United States in exploration of the Pacific Basin during this period were carried out by agencies of the Federal government. However, individual scientists with specialization in one or several fields of investigation pursued during or following the explorations made important contributions as members of the expedition or as interpreters and appraisers of the observations and collections. The role of the National Museum of the Smithsonian Institution in Washington in this endeavor was very large. The extent of this role is noted in the *Annual Report of the Secretary of the Smithsonian Institution* for the period 1860–1899.[265] The Institution often was invited to recommend and to furnish the expeditions with well-qualified scientists and to advise as to the fields and the scope of collecting, and to the nature and extent of taking observations. The Institution offered an outlet for publication of the scientific results.[266]

Other professional institutions that played an important role in supplying assistance to or in publishing comprehensive results of the expeditions were the California Academy of Sciences, Harvard University Museum of Comparative Zoology, Academy of Natural Science of Philadelphia, and the American Geographical Society of New York.

14

GEOGRAPHICAL EXPLORATION IN THE TWENTIETH CENTURY

H. Arnold Karo*

The general outline of the Pacific shores and the locations of most Pacific island groups were fairly well established early in the nineteenth century. However, little was known of the hydrographic and related geographical environment of the submarine landscape. This knowledge was gained as the application of scientific research to geographical investigation increased,[1] particularly with the sending of the first major scientific expeditions to the Pacific in the late nineteenth and early twentieth centuries. These expeditions, and those which followed, varied in purpose. Some were biological, others were geological and geophysical, and still others began observational studies of the Pacific Ocean, its characteristic physical properties, and its circulation patterns. This chapter is a summary of twentieth-century geographical exploration in the Pacific: oceanographic expeditions, marine biological exploration, marine geological exploration, geophysical investigations, weather observations, and the geographical aspects of new technological advances contributing to mapping and charting operations in the Pacific. Emphasis is placed on exploration before 1950, to provide better continuity with the preceding chapters and because the quickened pace of scientific exploration since the midpoint of this century can be alluded to only briefly at best. Geographical exploration on land and in coastal and shallow-sea areas is discussed only incidentally to related deep-sea exploration. Insofar as possible, a chronological sequence is followed within most sections.

OCEANOGRAPHIC EXPEDITIONS

The first major expedition devoted to the study of the Pacific Ocean itself, its physical features, the character of its floor, and the nature of its denizens, was that of the British vessel *Challenger* in 1873–1876 (Chapter 12). Other expeditions in the tradition of the *Challenger* followed, the more notable being the voyages of the *Dana* and *Carnegie* in 1929 and the *Albatross* and *Galathea* in 1947 and 1952[2]. These expeditions were primarily biological and geological in purpose and are considered under those points of view. Prior to the seventh cruise of the nonmagnetic ship *Carnegie* in 1928–1929[3] little was known of the physical oceanography in the Pacific deep-water areas. What was known was based on expeditions undertaken before 1910, many of them in the last decades of the nineteenth century. These expeditions were not equipped with accurate thermometers and did not determine salinity with the desired precision later regarded as necessary. Those expeditions that did obtain reliable information did not operate at great distances from land. Consequently, the oceano-

---

*Vice-Admiral Karo is deputy administrator, Environmental Science Services Administration, Department of Commerce, Rockville, Maryland. He has formerly served as Director of the United States Coast and Geodetic Survey, Washington.

graphic observations on the *Carnegie's* seventh cruise provided data for Pacific regions where few and sometimes no observations had been available and disclosed the character of the Pacific deep-water stratification and circulation in greater detail than was possible before this time. [4]

Early in the twentieth century, the United States Navy contributed to the study of the Pacific circulation by collecting current observation data from merchant vessels of many different nationalities. The Hydrographic Office served as the national repository for this information and for the data obtained from the release and recovery of drift bottles by many participating vessels. During the 1930s oceanographic stations were occupied over much of the eastern North Pacific in connection with the Navy's hydrographic surveying program to obtain temperature and salinity values that could be used in computing the speed of sound to correct sonic soundings. This data also yielded information about Pacific water masses and the circulation. During World War II, oceanographic investigations were directed toward studies of underwater sound, and, following the atomic bomb tests at Bikini in 1946, toward the prediction and tracing of movements of radioactive water. Much of this work was accomplished in cooperation with the Scripps Institution of Oceanography and the Oceanographic Laboratories of the University of Washington. The Navy has helped support operations of the research vessels of these institutions in addition to maintaining its own oceanographic unit at the U. S. Navy Electronics Laboratory in San Diego. Oceanographic surveys have been conducted by Navy vessels in the Bering Sea, the Antarctic, and throughout the Pacific. Cooperative surveys have been made with Canadian agencies and those of some South American countries.[5]

In 1931, the British research vessel *William Scoresby* carried out oceanographical investigations in the Peru Current, sometimes called the Humboldt Current, and as far into the ocean as circumstances would permit.[6] This survey along the Chilean and Peruvian coasts of South America was concerned with the layers between 400 meters and the surface, with special reference to their temperature and salinity, the effect of wind upon water movement, and the consequent effect on phosphate content and life in the sea.[7]

The United States Coast Guard's twentieth century activity in the Pacific stems from its ninety-seven-year operation of the Bering Sea Patrol—renamed Alaska Patrol in 1964.[8] Coast Guard ships, in addition to providing logistic support of military operations in both the Antarctic and Arctic, have patrolled the Bering Sea in the interests of law enforcement, search and rescue, the Alaskan Native Health Program, and, more recently, in the interest of meteorological and oceanographic investigations. Examples of the latter include the 1934 oceanographic investigation by the *Chelan* in the eastern North Pacific and the Bering Sea[9] and the 1962 oceanographic expedition of the *Northwind* in the western Bering Sea and Gulf of Anadyr.[10]

In the western Pacific, much oceanographic data was collected in the Kuroshio and South Seas region by the Hydrographic Department of the Imperial Japanese Navy after 1920, and in the seas adjacent to Japan with the beginning of oceanographic work by the Imperial Marine Observatory in 1927.[11] Reports by Japanese fishermen about 1935 indicated a displacement of the Kuroshio by a cold water mass off the

Fig. 7. Tracks of the Mid-Pacific, Northern Holiday, Shellback, Capricorn, and Trans-Pacific expeditions, 1950–1953. After W. S. Wooster, 1957

AREA RATIO 1:106,000,000²

Labels on map: San Diego, Aleutian Islands, Midway, Hawaiian Is., Marshall Is., Fiji Is., Tonga Is., Tahiti, Marquesas Is.

Legend:
——— Mid-Pacific, 1950
··········· Northern Holiday, 1951
—·—·— Shellback, 1952
— — — Capricorn, 1952-1953
——▶ Trans-Pacific, 1953

south coast of Honshu. Since then, oceanic observations have been obtained on a nearly continuous basis by many Japanese agencies to study changes in the Pacific deep-sea circulation.[12]

Southeast Asian waters—consisting of the South and East China seas, Java Sea, Sulu Sea, Philippine waters, Celebes Sea, Banda Sea, Flores Sea, Arafura Sea, and Timor Sea—have been studied during the *Snellius* Expedition of 1929–1930, during the *Dana* crossing of these waters in 1929, by Japanese research vessels between 1928 and 1941, by the U. S. Fish and Wildlife Service from 1947 to 1950 during its investigations of Philippine waters,[13] by the Indonesian research vessel *Samudera* in 1956–1957, and over a period of years by the investigations conducted by the Dutch Laboratories Zeeondersoek in Batavia (now Djakarta).[14]

Early exploration of Australian oceanic waters was confined largely to surveys by the British ships *Discovery II* and *Dana* during the course of their work in the Pacific and Indian oceans. In 1932, the University of Sydney commenced studies of the physical properties of coastal waters off Sydney, and in 1939 the Commonwealth Scientific and Industrial Research Organization (Fisheries Division) began a program of fisheries and oceanographic work in southeast Australian waters. Since 1959, the Royal Australian Navy has provided several vessels for oceanographic investigations. Studies include work in the Coral and Tasman seas, the detailed plotting of the East Australia Current, and investigations of the circulation within the deep basins of the New Guinea, Solomon, and New Hebrides Islands.[15]

Large-scale investigations of Pacific waters began in 1949 with expanding fisheries research programs by the United States (see section below, on Marine Biological Exploration).[16] Several other expeditions that contributed much to a knowledge of Pacific water types and major circulation features in the early 1950s require special mention. The Scripps Institution of Oceanography planned three expeditions to cross major current systems and to sample the principal water masses of selected areas. They were the Northern Holiday Expedition of 1951 in the eastern North Pacific, the Shellback Expedition of 1952 in the eastern equatorial Pacific, and the Trans-Pacific Expedition of 1953 in the deep Bering Sea and western and central North Pacific (Fig. 39).[17]

The discovery in 1952, during Pacific Oceanic Fishery Investigations, of the Pacific Equatorial Undercurrent (now known as the Cromwell Current) resulted in intensified observational programs to determine the geographic distribution of equatorial current systems.[18] Among the special studies carried out was a five-vessel simultaneous survey in 1955 of the central and eastern tropical Pacific known as Expedition Eastropic. Five research vessels participated, representing the Scripps Institution of Oceanography, Inter-American Tropical Tuna Commission, California Department of Fish and Game, Pacific Oceanic Fishery Investigations of the U. S. Fish and Wildlife Service, and the Peruvian Navy Hydrographic Office.[19]

The need to obtain oceanographic observations over a large area of the Pacific in a short period of time had been confirmed by 1953 from contiguous cruises on the part of scientific institutions and agencies in Canada, Japan, and the United States. To meet this need, the NORPAC Expeditions were carried out in 1955 by nineteen research vessels representing fourteen institutions from the three countries. These ships covered the Pacific Ocean between latitudes 20° and 60° N., occupied 1002 oceanographic stations, and collected more than 2000 plankton samples.[20] The *NORPAC Atlas* was an end-product of this cooperative effort.[21]

Expedition Downwind in 1957–1958 was the first of three cruises by Scripps research vessels comprising one phase of the University of California's deep-sea participation in the International Geophysical Year (IGY). This expedition extended from the central Pacific to the South American coast and from equatorial regions to nearly latitude 50° S. Areas of special investigation were the Tuamotu Archipelago, Albatross Cordillera (that part formerly known as the East Pacific Rise), and Peru-Chile Trench.[22] During the International Geophysical Year (1957–1958) and International Geophysical Cooperation (1959) twelve survey vessels from France, Japan, USSR, and the United States each made one or more oceanographic cruises in the intertropical Pacific between latitudes 20° N. and 20° S.[23]

The Japanese IGY oceanographic project[24] included five separate surveys in the western and northwestern Pacific, as follows: (1) a multiple-ship survey in the polar front region in June to July 1957, (2) the polar front survey of August to December 1957, (3) a multiple-ship survey in the equatorial region in January and February of 1958, (4) the polar front survey of June to September 1958, and (5) the deep-sea circulation study of 1958 and early 1959, extending into tropical waters east of the Philippines. The institutions participating in these surveys were the Japan Meteorological Agency; Hydrographic Office, Maritime Safety Board; Faculty of Fisheries, Hokkaido University; Tokyo University of Fisheries; and the Tokai Regional Fisheries Research Laboratory.

As part of the USSR IGY program, the research vessel *Vityaz* of the Institute of Oceanology, USSR Academy of Sciences, made four cruises in the central, northeast, and northwest Pacific. During these cruises, between June 1957 and March 1959, the *Vityaz* covered 73,700 nautical miles and occupied 618 comprehensive oceanological stations. Each expedition had a specific program based on the geographic area of the survey.[25] In addition to the *Vityaz*, the Russian research ships *A. I. Voyeikov*—which conducted its fourth routine voyage in 1960—and the *Yu. M. Shokal'skii* have made extensive hydrometeorological investigations in the Pacific Ocean.[26]

MARINE BIOLOGICAL EXPLORATION

At the beginning of the nineteenth century, leading maritime nations began sending out warships on combined surveying, exploring, and political-commercial cruises. Naturalists often accompanied these cruises but their research was confined mainly to shallow-water fauna, partly because of the belief that there was no life at greater depths. The first large-scale, deep-sea expedition to include biological investigations of such wide scope was that of the British naval vessel *Challenger* from 1872 to 1876. This expedition showed that a rich and varied fauna was present in the ocean and on the sea floor as far down as 6000 meters. Another significant development late in the nineteenth century was the growth of the fishing industry. This led to the founding of fisheries biology and, together with the continuing development of natural science, to the establishment of marine-biological and fishery-biological laboratories and research stations. The establishment in 1902 of the International Council for the

Exploration of the Sea at Copenhagen, Denmark, although principally to coordinate the work of fishery-research institutions in northwest Europe, has also contributed to international marine research on a global scale.[27]

Several world expeditions to study the deep-sea fauna merit special mention for their work in the Pacific Ocean: the Danish *Dana* World Expedition of 1928–1930, the Swedish Deep-Sea (*Albatross*) Expedition of 1947–1948, and the Danish *Galathea* Deep-Sea Expedition of 1950–1952. The former of the Danish expeditions was devoted mainly to studies of the uppermost 1000 meters and was a result of extensive work on the breeding biology and migrations of the fresh-water eel. The *Galathea* Expedition was carried out to complete the Danish collection of marine fauna, which lacked only a representative collection of the bottom fauna from the greatest depths. Many specimens were added to this collection from the extreme depths of the New Britain, Philippine, Kermadec, and Tonga trenches in the Pacific, and from the North and South Banda basins in the Indo-Pacific.[28]

Fishery-related biological oceanography in the Pacific has followed regional patterns of growth based on differences in fisheries and their needs, local cultural and economic differences, and other imparted regional characteristics. Only a few representative examples of this phase of Pacific exploration are cited below, and these can not adequately depict the geographical coverage, the chronological sequence, or the contributions of the many countries engaged in fisheries investigations in the Pacific.

In the southern Pacific, the British Discovery Committee was concerned with the Antarctic whaling industry and the investigation of the ecology, distribution, and fluctuation of planktonic organisms which make up the food of whales. Over a period of twenty-seven years, fourteen expeditions were sent to the Southern Ocean. The Royal Research Ship *Discovery* sailed in 1924, but was replaced by the *Discovery II* in 1929. The Royal Research Ship *William Scoresby* was built in 1926 and made six Antarctic voyages. The Committee was discontinued in 1949 but the investigations were continued by the National Oceanographic Council. Results of the work are published in the *Discovery Reports*—thirty-one volumes being published by 1961.[29]

In the early 1930s Russian oceanic exploration was intensified to develop its Far East fisheries and certain new branches of this industry, such as trawl fishery, crab fishery, and seal hunting. This led to hydrological, hydrobiological, and ichthyological research expeditions in the westernmost North Pacific formed by the Sea of Japan, Sea of Okhotsk, and Bering Sea. The investigations were directed by the Pacific Scientific Institute of Fisheries in Vladivostok, the State Hydrological Institute of Leningrad, and the State Oceanographical Institute in Moscow.[30] Soviet fishery investigations were further intensified and extended after World War II. As part of this effort, the *Vityaz* surveyed the far eastern seas of the USSR and northern Pacific between 1949 and 1956,[31] and both the *Vityaz* and the *Ob* investigated the distribution of deep-sea plankton in the Pacific region between latitudes 50° N. and 63° S. during the period 1953 to 1958.[32] Also in 1958, the whaling ship *Slaba* and the commercial fishing ships *Perbenetz* and *Shemtchug* carried out scientific investigations in the western part of the Bering Sea.

The exploration, investigation, and development of the high seas fisheries of the

territories and island possessions of the United States in the tropical and subtropical
Pacific Ocean and intervening seas was authorized by the United States Congress in
1947. This major investigation was begun in 1950 by a unit, called the Pacific Oceanic
Fishery Investigations, within the U. S. Fish and Wildlife Service. General features
of the program include exploratory fishing for various pelagic species by different
methods and observing oceanographic and biological conditions to obtain information
on particular ecological situations in which the fish are present or absent.[33]

The California Current has been surveyed nearly every month since 1949 as a result of the California Oceanic Fisheries Investigations. Participants in this program,
which was initiated in 1948 by the Marine Research Committee of the State of California, include the California Academy of Sciences, California Division of Fish and
Game, South Pacific Fishery Investigations of the U. S. Fish and Wildlife Service,
and Scripps Institution of Oceanography.[34]

Investigations in the subarctic Pacific region have been carried out since 1955 by
the International North Pacific Fisheries Commission through the agencies of the
three member nations—Canada, Japan, and United States.[35] As part of the Canadian
effort, the Pacific Oceanographic Group of the Fisheries Research Board of Canada
commenced synoptic surveys of oceanic and coastal waters west of Canada in 1961.
These surveys, at approximately six-week intervals, were initiated to provide information for the Canadian fishing interests and the Canadian Oceanographic Information Service.[36]

In the southwestern North Pacific, the Fisheries Research Unit of the University
of Hong Kong has conducted hydrological and plankton surveys in the waters of the
South China Sea off Hong Kong and on more distant fishing grounds, in support of
Hong Kong's fishing industry. A new vessel, acquired mainly for deep-sea research,
began operations early in 1960.[37]

More recent field investigations in biological oceanography have involved studies
of marine productivity in the Pacific, its variation with the standing crop of zooplank-
ton, light, and oceanic conditions north and south of Hawaii. These studies were made
in 1961 by the Botany Department of the University of Hawaii during multipurpose
cruises by the U. S. Navy vessel *Rehoboth* south of Hawaii and the U. S. Coast and
Geodetic Survey vessel *Pioneer* north of Hawaii.[38]

MARINE GEOLOGICAL EXPLORATION

Geological knowledge about the Pacific Basin was acquired slowly during the late
nineteenth and early twentieth century because only limited techniques were available
to explore the obscure depths of the ocean floor—its topography, sediments, and
crustal features. Nevertheless, significant results were obtained in the 1870s by the
British ship *Challenger* and the United States ship *Tuscarora* in the measurement of the
depths and in the dredging of the sea bottom. In the early twentieth century, wire
rope and faster sampling methods were introduced. Development of echo-sounding
and radio-acoustic position-finding devices in the 1920s, electronic and related engineering technology during World War II, and new and improved methods of sediment analysis and underwater exploration through the 1950s and 1960s, including

deep-sea photography, drilling, and submersible craft, have contributed greatly to geological exploration in the Pacific. The brief historical résumé which follows is confined mainly to depth soundings, bottom sampling, and special investigations of algal and coral reef structures.

SEA FLOOR SOUNDINGS

At the beginning of the twentieth century, only a few thousand deep soundings along widely spaced ship tracks were available for the Pacific area. From these, Sir John Murray of the *Challenger* expedition prepared generalized bathymetric charts that are still valid for the broad features of the Pacific Basin, though they lack topographic detail.[39] The first years of the twentieth century also were important for the intensified interest in the Pacific shown by the United States as newly acquired areas, including the Hawaiian Islands, Guam, and Philippine Islands, came under its sovereignty. Some of these areas had long been ports of call for ships of United States whalers, sealers, and merchantmen and for Navy expeditions, but their waters and the oceanic reaches between them were still poorly charted, at best.[40]

When Spain ceded the Philippines and other islands to the United States in 1898 the production of nautical charts became the official concern of the United States Coast and Geodetic Survey, whose charting jurisdiction, by law, covered not only the continental limits of the United States but its territories as well. The first official of the Coast Survey arrived at Manila in September 1900, to initiate a survey of the Philippine Islands which involved over 7000 islands and rocks above water and a tidal shoreline of 21,000 statute miles. The hydrography of shoal water was done by hand lead, the soundings in the deeper water were supplemented by wire-line casts and pressure tubes. Continuous profiles of the bottom were not obtained until the "fathometer" came into use in the 1930s. During the forty years[41] of active Coast and Geodetic Survey activity in the Philippines, twelve general sailing charts and 152 coast and harbor charts were prepared.[42] Hydrographic operations were begun by the Coast Survey in the Hawaiian Islands following their annexation, and charts of the harbors and bays were produced during the first two decades. In the late 1920s, with the installation of echo-sounding equipment, two ships began charting the waters extending 2000 miles from the Hawaiian Islands toward Midway.[43]

Development of automatic echo sounders in the 1920s increased the number of deep-sea soundings, but erroneous readings and uncertainties of positioning continued to limit the adequacy of sounding information in the Pacific. As a consequence, many of the bathymetric charts prepared between 1920 and 1940 were misleading and less useful than the earlier generalized but more reliable Pacific charts of Sir John Murray. A notable exception was the series of charts off western United States made by the U.S. Coast and Geodetic Survey; these showed submarine canyons, ridges, and troughs in great detail.[44]

Continuous echo sounding across the Gulf of Alaska was begun by the U. S. Coast and Geodetic Survey in 1925. At the end of 1939, over 30,000 nautical miles of sounding lines had been run. By 1941, the area had been surveyed with sounding lines spaced about twenty-five to thirty miles apart. From these soundings, and those of

U. S. Navy vessels, many individual submarine mountains were observed to rise from one to two miles above the surrounding sea floor. The term "seamount" was applied to each such feature by the United States Board on Geographic Names.[45]

The Hydrographic Department of the Imperial Japanese Navy also commenced extensive hydrographic surveys with echo-sounding apparatus in 1925. These surveys covered the western Pacific from the Bering Sea to the Antarctic.[46]

In 1935, the U. S. Navy, at the recommendation of the National Academy of Sciences, arranged to divert ships equipped with sonic-sounding apparatus from regular routes to survey unsounded areas.[47] To guide United States vessels and those of other countries in obtaining data for inadequately surveyed areas, the U. S. Navy Hydrographic Office prepared charts showing sounded and unsounded areas of the world ocean. Sounding information assembled by 1937 showed one of the largest areas of inadequate information to be that in the South Pacific between the equator and latitude 50° S. Noteworthy bathymetric charts already compiled by 1937 included those for the South China Sea by the Institut Oceanographique de l'Indochine; the seas adjacent to Japan, by the Hydrographic Department of the Imperial Japanese Navy; the Philippines, by the U. S. Coast and Geodetic Survey; and the Netherlands East Indies, by the *Snellius* Expedition.[48]

Flat-topped seamounts, or guyots, first attracted attention during World War II when these anomalous features were noted on echo-sounder traces of U. S. naval vessels in the mid-Pacific. Later more than 140 flat-topped seamounts were inferred from study of U. S. Navy Hydrographic Office charts.[49] In 1950, the Scripps Institution of Oceanography and U. S. Navy Electronics Laboratory (San Diego) sent a joint expedition to study the mountainous sea floor between the Hawaiian Islands and Wake Island. During this four-month Mid-Pacific Expedition (Fig. 39), about 12,000 nautical miles of echograms were obtained by the research vessel *Horizon* of Scripps and the *EPCE* (R) 857 of the Navy Electronics Laboratory. The findings of Mid-Pac showed for the first time that the Mid-Pacific Mountains form a major, well-defined, geomorphic feature of the earth's crust—a great underwater mountain chain surmounted by sharp peaks and ridges and by flat-topped seamounts or guyots. This expedition—along a route extending from San Diego to the equator and northward to Hawaii, then westward to Kwajalein and Bikini atolls in the Marshall Islands, and back to San Diego—also disclosed numerous other seamounts and three large escarpments, identified many smaller features of the Pacific Ocean floor, and provided profiles of the sea-floor structure around Midway and the Hawaiian Islands.[50]

In December 1952, during Expedition Capricorn (Fig. 39), the research vessels *Horizon* and *Spencer F. Baird* of the Scripps Institution of Oceanography carried out a special echo-sounding survey of the Melanesian Border Plateau south of the Central Pacific Basin. Much information was gained about the tectonic position of the Plateau area and the drowning of atolls.[51]

The submarine topography of the northeastern Pacific, particularly the Gulf of Alaska and adjacent Aleutians, is better known than any other large part of the Pacific Ocean floor. Detailed mapping of this area was made possible largely by hydrographic surveys of the U. S. Coast and Geodetic Survey, which by 1957 included ninety sounding lines across the gulf; sixty surveys of special seamounts, sea-knolls, and ridges; and 42,400 miles of graphically recorded profiles obtained between 1951 and 1957.[52] These soundings were supplemented by those taken by U.S. Navy ships and those obtained on the Northern Holiday Expedition in 1951, a joint exploration in the northeastern Pacific by the U. S. Navy Electronics Laboratory and Scripps Institution of Oceanography aboard the Laboratory's research vessel *EPCE (R) 857*.[53]

Knowledge of the deep areas off western South America dates back to 1875 and the first laying of submarine cables along parts of the west coast. A submarine feature of great interest paralleling this coast from Ecuador to Chile is the Peru-Chile Trench. Profiles across this trench by the *Horizon* during the Shellback Expedition of 1952 and by the Woods Hole Oceanographic Institution's cruise 221 of the *Atlantis* in in 1955 provided data to help determine the exact shape of the trench. One hundred coring stations were occupied on the *Atlantis* cruise to investigate the sediments of the trench.[54] The Middle America Trench, which extends from Isla Tres Marias off western Mexico to the Cocos Ridge southwest of Costa Rica, was surveyed in considerable detail from 1952 to 1959 during nine expeditions of the Scripps Institution of Oceanography and one by the U. S. Navy Electronics Laboratory. Research vessels of the two institutions recorded 31,950 miles of echo-sounding traverses in and adjacent to the Middle America Trench.[55]

In the southwest Pacific, three long sounding profiles of note were obtained by the Royal New Zealand Navy Survey Ship *Lachlan* in 1956. Constant-echo sounding was carried out by the *Lachlan* over 4,500 sea miles: Fiji to Christmas Island, Christmas Island to Tahiti, and Tahiti to Fiji.[56]

Surveys of the Pacific sector of Antarctica, from Palmer Peninsula to Wilkes Land, have been carried out by United States ships on the Byrd expeditions of 1929, 1933, and 1939, during the Navy's Operation Highjump in 1946–1947, and during Operation Deep Freeze in the 1950s. United States activities since 1955 have been directed primarily to establishing bases for geophysical investigations. Since 1962 the National Science Foundation's ship *Eltanin* has cruised in Antarctic and sub-Antarctic waters as a floating laboratory. Its mission includes a wide variety of scientific investigations such as marine biology, meteorology, marine geology, and various aspects of chemical and physical biology. This ship conducted its twentieth cruise in September 1965.[57] Marine geological and oceanographic work also were undertaken during the Soviet Antarctic Expedition of the *Ob*, 1955–1957, along the Antarctic coast and in the South Pacific between Antarctica and both New Zealand and Australia.[58]

SEA FLOOR DEPOSITS

Nearly all of the early Pacific expeditions collected samples of the sea bottom; many of these, however, were not critically studied or lacked published descriptions. The *Challenger* expedition, 1872–1876, and the reports of Sir John Murray who examined the samples of this and many other early expeditions laid the broad foundation for investigating marine sediments. Among the samples examined by Murray, those collected by the United States ship *Tuscarora* in 1874 led to the first knowledge of the belt of diatom ooze extending across the North Pacific. Other late nineteenth-century and early twentieth-century ship surveys contributing to knowledge of Pacific bottom deposits are summarized as follows:

British surveying ships: *Rambler*, 1888–1904; *Dart*, 1888–1902; *Britannia*, 1888–1907; and *Waterwitch*, 1894–1901.

Dutch steamer *Siboga*, 1899–1900, Dutch East Indies.

German ships *Edi*, *Stephan* (1905–1911), and *Planet* (1906–1914).

Many of these samples were collected by ships surveying for trans-Pacific cables.[59]

The U. S. Fish Commission Steamer *Albatross* collected many Pacific sea-floor samples between 1888 and 1897 off the west coasts of North and South America, in the Gulf of Alaska, the Bering Sea, the Sea of Okhotsk, and between California and Hawaii. Four of the *Albatross* expeditions, two in the late nineteenth century and two at the beginning of the twentieth century, were under the direction of Dr. Alexander Agassiz. The first of these expeditions, in 1891, consisted of three short cruises in the Panama region.[60] The second, in 1897, involved studies of coral reefs in the Fiji Islands.[61] The third, in 1899 and 1900, included the tropical Pacific from San Francisco to Tahiti, the Fiji, Gilbert, Marshall, and Caroline islands, and then to Japan.[62] The fourth expedition, 1904–1905, was along the following route: San Francisco—Panama—Galapagos Islands, Punta Aguja, Peru—over deepwater to Callao, Peru—Easter Island—Galapagos Islands—Mangareva in the Tuamotu Archipelago—Acapulco.[63]

The *Carnegie*,[64] on her seventh cruise in 1929, collected seventy-five bottom samples in the north and southeast Pacific, between latitudes 45°24′ N. and 40°24′ S. and from longitudes 141°15′ E. to 77°54′ W. The average depth of all samples was 4223 meters, and the extremes were 6008 meters and 1089 meters. These samples were described and compared with the nearest previously collected samples; subjected to chemical, mechanical, and x-ray analyses; and classified according to a revised and more detailed system of nomenclature in terms of their origin and history.[65] Twenty-eight of the samples, which contained sufficient bulk to permit other studies, were used for radium determinations.[66] Also in 1929, the *William Scoresby*, while on a voyage with the *Discovery* in Antarctic waters, collected 51 samples of sea-floor deposits along the west coast of South America between the equator and latitude 40° S.[67]

As part of the *Snellius* Expedition, 1929–1930, the geological investigations included studies of the sediments in the eastern part of the East Indian Archipelago. A large number of bottom samples were collected throughout the separate basins and troughs of the region to provide at least partial answers to such geologic problems as the distribution of volcanic materials, means of scattering on the sea floor, stratification of sediments, indications of submarine sliding, rate of sedimentation, organic content of the samples, and other relationships between oceanographical and sedimentary conditions.[68]

One of the main objects of the Swedish Deep-Sea Expedition, 1947–1948, was to investigate deep-sea deposits by means of the piston core sampler, a new sampling technique to obtain longer cores. Core samples having lengths of over 15 meters were obtained from the Pacific Ocean floor at depths greater than 5000 meters. Short cores also were collected with a conventional gravity corer at many Pacific locations.[69]

In the southwestern region of the North Pacific Ocean, samples of the sea floor were collected early in the twentieth century and stored by the Hydrographic Department of the Imperial Japanese Navy. However, many of these samples were destroyed by the fire of the great Japanese earthquake of September 1923. Between 1925 and 1928, about 700 bottom samples were collected in the same area by the Japanese survey ship *Manshu*.[70] Further investigations of deep-sea deposits in this area were made between April 1943 and August 1946 by staff members of the Institute of Geology and Paleontology, Tohoku Imperial University. The latter survey obtained dredged materials, predominantly from depths between 1000 meters and 7000 meters, with many from below 7000 meters.[71] Following World War II, a Japanese collection consisting of nearly 1000 small snapper samples from the Gulf of Chihli, Yellow Sea, Gulf of Tonkin, the inner shelf from Shanghai to Hainan, and outer continental shelf between Korea and Hainan, was studied at the University of Southern California. This study led to the first published report, based on modern analysis, of the sediments in the East China Sea and South China Sea regions.[72]

In October of 1962, the seaward extension of the east rift zone of Kilauea volcano, Hawaii, was dredged by a joint U. S. Geological Survey and U. S. Coast and Geodetic Survey team aboard the latter's ship *Pioneer*. Samples of fresh lavas were collected at intervals of about 1000 feet to depths of 17,000 feet, and deep-sea photographs were obtained of the environment from which the samples were dredged. Rock samples and bottom photographs also were obtained from Wini Seamount 75 miles southeast of Hawaii.[73]

Sampling of the Pacific sea floor has provided a great variety of scientific information, depending in part on the location and method of sampling and the type of sediment analyses. The Mid-Pacific Expedition in 1950 afforded an opportunity to investigate the kinds of bacteria in red clay and globigerina ooze.[74] The Trans-Pacific Expedition in 1953 (by the *Spencer F. Baird* of Scripps) dredged many rock fragments and pebbles, near Jimmu Seamount in the northwest Pacific, which were subjected to petrographic and chemical analyses at the Geological Institute of Tokyo University.[75] The research vessel *Brown Bear* of the Department of Oceanography, University of Washington, collected deep-sea cores containing ash layers in the Gulf of Alaska between 1953 and 1959. The ash samples were studied and correlated with other ash deposits and their origin determined.[76] From deep-sea samples collected by Russian ships in the Sea of Okhotsk, the distribution of pollen in cores was studied to provide information about climatic fluctuations, and from other sampling in the Bering Sea sedimentological maps were published.[77] From deep-sea drilling in some 4000 meters of water near Isla de Guadalupe off the west coast of Mexico during Project Mohole tests in 1961, core samples were obtained from depths greater than 500 feet in the ocean floor.[78] As a concluding example, cores collected in the Gulf of Alaska by a joint U. S. Geological Survey—U. S. Coast and Geodetic Survey team aboard the *Pioneer* in 1961 were studied to learn about differences in the geochemistry and biochemistry of environments of deep-sea sedimentation with respect to latitude.[79]

CORAL REEFS

Numerous investigations, both biological and geological, have been made of Pacific coral reefs and associated phenomena. These include studies of reef-forming organisms and their stratigraphic distribution, of the geologic history of different reef areas, and of reef development relative to the history of the Pacific Basin. Among the earlier twentieth-century field investigations of note were those of the U. S. Fish Commission Steamer *Albatross*, 1899–1900, in the tropical Pacific;[80] the British Great Barrier Reef Expedition, 1928–1929, along the north Queensland coast of Australia;[81] and the investigations conducted by Dutch scientists of the *Snellius* Expedition, 1929–1930, in the East Indian Archipelago.[82]

Between 1932 and 1943, the Japanese made detailed studies of the geology and physiography of the South Sea islands then under Japanese mandate, and the submarine topography of the ocean bottom. These studies were later condensed and brought together in one publication.[83]

World War II operations in the Pacific focused more attention on coral islands and such places as Eniwetok, Kwajalein, and other isolated atolls that rise thousands of feet above the Pacific Ocean floor. Although much was learned from field studies prior to 1946, the geographic remoteness of these atolls and the inadequacy of available tools of investigation combined to limit man's knowledge about most atolls to their surface features. Shortly after the United States' decision in 1945 to test nuclear-fission explosions at Bikini atoll, intensive oceanographic, geologic, and biologic studies of Bikini and neighboring Eniwetok, Kwajalein, Rongelap, Rongerik, and Ailinginae atolls were undertaken by teams of scientists participating in Operation Crossroads. As part of the investigations conducted from 1946 to 1952, several deep holes were drilled on Bikini Atoll (one to a depth of 2556 feet) to gain further knowledge of the subsurface structure.[84]

Between 1946 and 1957 the U. S. Geological Survey, in cooperation with several other agencies of the United States government, undertook intensive investigations of many islands, coral reefs, and adjacent marine areas within the Caroline, Mariana, Marshall, and Ryukyu islands. Emphasis of the coral reef studies was placed on their morphology, ecology, and structure.[85] The Northern Marshall Islands Expedition during 1951 and 1952, a project of special note, was carried out as part of the Pacific Geological Mapping Program by the Office of the Engineer, Headquarters, Army Forces Far East, and the U. S. Geological Survey.[86] A principal activity of the Pacific Science Board has been its coral atoll program.[87]

French expedition teams have studied the reefs and lagoon sediments of the New Caledonia and Loyalty Islands, from 1960 to 1962, and the Maupihaa (Mopelia) and Bora Bora reefs and lagoons in the Society Islands, during 1963.[88]

GEOPHYSICAL INVESTIGATIONS

Geophysical studies in the Pacific were initiated early in the twentieth century with the scientific expeditions of the *Galilee*, a wooden surface vessel of the Carnegie Institution of Washington, and the *K XIII*, a submarine of the Royal Netherlands

Navy. These expeditions, respectively, had as their objectives the determination of accurate values of the magnetic elements and of gravity at sea. The impetus to acquire more detailed and extensive geophysical information about the Pacific was provided by the onset of World War II, at which time the inadequacy of available data soon became apparent. Both the technological advances of wartime programs of geophysical research and the scientific observations made during wartime cruises and postwar military operations greatly accelerated Pacific exploration in the postwar years, particularly the study of the earth's crust beneath the ocean as determined by geophysical measurements at sea.[89]

Magnetic Field Measurements

Knowledge of the earth's magnetic field has been applied in navigation, mineral exploration, surveying, and other engineering activity, in a great variety of military applications, and in the investigation of terrestrial and extraterrestrial phenomena.[90]

The magnetic compass has been widely used for centuries, and throughout this interval there has been a growing study of the earth's magnetic field and recognition of its significance for both day-to-day needs and scientific ends. However, the comprehensive detailed registrations that form the backbone of the modern science of geomagnetism date back only a little more than a century, to about 1840.[91] At the beginning of the twentieth century there were wide gaps in the world magnetic data, partly because data were not available for the vast oceanic areas and, in part, because many measurements prior to 1900 were incidental to other expeditions and travels of interested scientists. Measurements at sea were further hampered by movements of the vessel and, particularly with the change from wooden to steel vessels during the latter part of the nineteenth century, by disturbance of the magnetic elements caused by the iron used in ship construction. In the Pacific region the problem of obtaining satisfactory magnetic data, especially of the annual magnetic changes, was even greater than for many other parts of the world.[92] This gap can be attributed to the comparatively recent exploration and occupation of the Pacific, the lack of regularly established travel routes between its distant islands, and the vast expanse of ocean between possible magnetic base stations.[93]

During early expeditions, the magnetic aspect of exploration was of primary concern to both explorers and seamen. Russian expeditions, from those of Bering's first voyage to explore the coast of Kamchatka in 1728–1729 through subsequent expeditions, determined the magnetic elements for points on the Russian coast and islands, for other islands of the northwest Pacific and Japan, and for points in the Sea of Japan, Sea of Okhotsk, and Bering Sea.[94] The great need for more information about magnetic complexities in polar regions led to cooperative efforts in collecting magnetic data as early as 1882–1883 in the north polar region (International Polar Year of 1882–1883). Similar efforts followed in the south polar region in 1902–1903, and supplementary data were collected in the north polar region at the same time.[95] Marine magnetic observations of note in the Pacific prior to the twentieth century were made by the British ships *Erebus* and *Terror* (1839–1843), chiefly in southern waters, the German vessel *Gazelle* (1874–1876), the Austrian frigate *Novara* (1857–1860), and the British ship *Challenger* (1872–1876).[96]

Existing magnetic observatories have never satisfied the uniform distribution needed to investigate the main features of the earth's magnetic field in its totality. Most of the observatories are in Europe, within an area comprising one-fiftieth of the earth's surface. This situation has long been recognized as a severe obstacle to progress. At the turn of the century there were three observatories in the southern hemisphere, none of them south of latitude 38°, and the immense surface of the Pacific was devoid of them.[97] Observations at stations bordering the Pacific were being made at Melbourne, Australia; Batavia, Netherlands East Indies; Manila, Philippine Islands; Hsü-chia-hui, China; Hong Kong; and Tokyo, Japan.

The beginning of the twentieth century witnessed further advances in the collection of magnetic data in the vast Pacific. In Japan, complete photographic registrations of variations of magnetic elements were being made continuously at the Central Meteorological Observatory and at four stations belonging to the Earthquake Investigation Committee by 1901.[98] In November 1901, registrations were begun at a new observatory at Christchurch, New Zealand.[99] In the Samoa Islands a magnetic observatory was established in 1901–1902 under the auspices of the Göttingen Academy of Science.[100] A temporary observatory was operated at Discovery Bay, southeast Australia, in 1902–1903. In the Antarctic, marine observations included those of the British ship *Discovery* (1902–1904) and the German ship *Gauss* (1902–1903).[101]

By July 1, 1902, the U. S. Coast and Geodetic Survey had established two of its four primary magnetic facilities in the circum-Pacific and Pacific regions—the Sitka Magnetic Observatory in Alaska and the Honolulu Magnetic Observatory in Hawaii.[102] At each observatory, continuous records of variations in the earth's magnetism were obtained by photographic means.

In 1904, the Carnegie Institution of Washington founded a Department of Terrestrial Magnetism[103] and initiated a project to complete a comprehensive world magnetic survey by filling the large gaps then existing in magnetic data by means of land and ocean expeditions. Prior to this, magnetic measurements in ocean areas were of varying degrees of accuracy set by available instruments and the magnetic character of the vessels while the distribution of the observations, in geographic position and time (epoch), was not such as to yield coordinated charts applying to definite periods. Much of the Department's effort was concentrated in the Pacific region, where magnetic observatories were established at Watheroo, Western Australia, in 1919, and at Huancayo, Peru, in 1922. Its first ocean surveys were made with a chartered, wooden sailing vessel, the *Galilee*, between 1905 and 1908; then by a specially constructed nonmagnetic vessel, the *Carnegie*, which made extensive surveys from 1909 to 1929. The world-wide data obtained by the three cruises of the *Galilee* (all in the Pacific) and seven cruises of the *Carnegie* (cruises 2, 4, 5, 6, and 7 having Pacific traverses) include declination at 3844 points, inclination and horizontal intensity at 2321 and 2322 points, respectively, and atmospheric-electric elements on 1913 days.[104] In addition to the Department's work at Pacific island localities and the cruises of the *Galilee* and *Carnegie*, instruments and equipment were provided to other organizations and expeditions, including the Australasian Antarctic Expedition of 1911 to 1913 and the *Maud* Expedition of Captain Roald Amundsen, begun in 1918.

After the destruction of the *Carnegie* by fire in 1929, at Apia, Western Samoa, no oceangoing nonmagnetic ship was in service until the Russian ship *Zarya* was commissioned in 1956.[105] Between 1929 and 1956, the Second International Polar Year (1932–1933) was carried out, but was largely confined to the Arctic Basin with many permanent observatories and temporary stations in lower latitudes cooperating to provide more detailed records of the transient magnetic fluctuations.[106] In 1950–1952 the Danish deep-sea expedition of the *Galathea* in the Pacific Ocean also made satisfactory measurements of the earth's magnetic force at depths between 3000 meters and 4000 meters by mounting special magnetic instruments in watertight spheres. These measurements were obtained in the Kermadec and Tonga trenches and in the Gulf of Panama. Although few in number, and disturbed by proximity of the bottom, the measurements demonstrated the technical possibility of making three-dimensional magnetic surveys in the sea.[107]

The development of magnetic airborne detectors during World War II to detect submarines made possible the first practical airborne magnetometers. Since then much progress has been made in aerial magnetic surveys over the oceans.[108] In 1951, the U. S. Navy Hydrographic Office (designated U. S. Naval Oceanographic Office in July 1962) initiated an Airborne Geomagnetic Survey Program, known as Project Magnet, to provide urgently needed magnetic data over the world's ocean areas. The Vector Airborne Magnetometer, which measures inclination, variation, and total magnetic intensity simultaneously, is used on these worldwide surveys.[109] Between 1955 and 1957 approximately 20,000 nautical miles of magnetic survey traverses were flown over the Pacific Ocean.[110] By 1965, completed Project Magnet flight line coverage in the Pacific exceeded 300,000 nautical miles. Most tracks were flown at altitudes between 8000 and 10,000 feet, but flight altitudes varied from 4000 feet to 20,000 feet, depending upon survey conditions. When the basic Project is completed, tracks will have been flown over the Pacific at approximately 200-mile intervals. In addition, Project Magnet has flown six special airborne magnetic surveys, at lower levels and along closely spaced tracks, to provide greater detail of selected areas.[111] To examine the spectrum of anomaly structures around the earth, a magnetic profile was pieced together from segments of flight paths on Project Magnet. The Pacific segment of this profile extended from Bangkok to Manila, Tokyo, Adak, and Portland.[112] Airborne magnetic traverses also have been flown over the Pacific by the Dominion Observatory of Canada in cooperation with the Royal Canadian Air Force.[113]

Magnetic surveys by aircraft and by ship are complementary rather than mutually exclusive. Hence the need for surveys at sea has continued and even increased. Surveys by ship also have the additional advantage, in geophysical exploration, of being able to record the topographic features of the ocean bottom simultaneously with the magnetic observations. Until about 1945, however, magnetic measurements at sea were made aboard ship with instruments requiring special, tedious techniques and careful maneuvering. The development of a magnetometer that could be towed from a ship led to improved methods of exploring the ocean bottom and its underlying structure.[114] By the late 1950s and early 1960s, detailed magnetic surveys of total magnetic field intensity along closely spaced tracklines were completed off the west

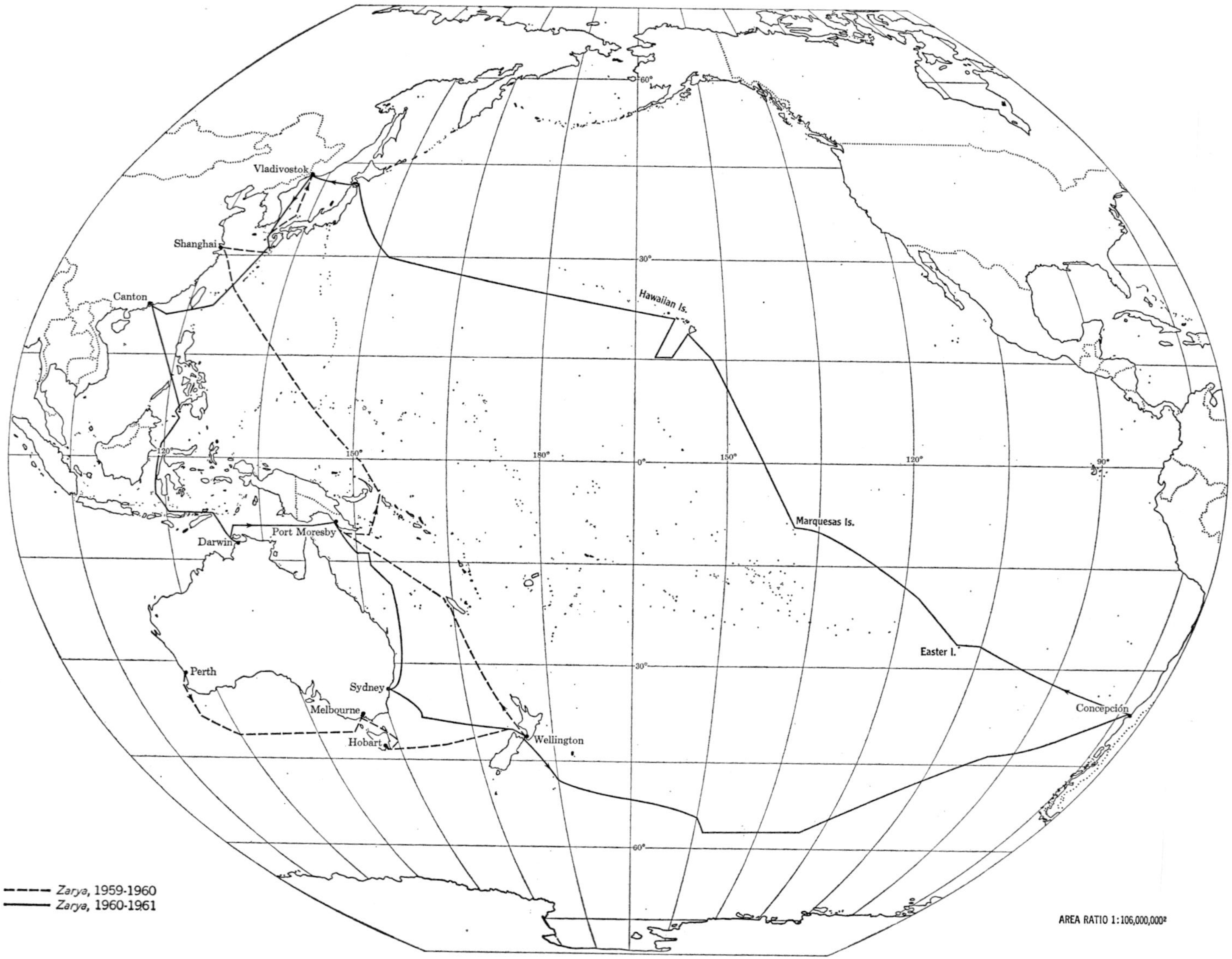

FIG. 1.—Tracks of the *Zarya* expeditions of 1959–1960 and 1960–1961. After M. M. Ivanov, 1962 [Note 118].

AREA RATIO 1:106,000,000²

----- *Zarya*, 1959-1960
——— *Zarya*, 1960-1961

Conceptión

Easter I.

Marquesas Is.

Hawaiian Is.

Wellington

Vladivostok

Shanghai

Canton

Darwin

Port Moresby

Perth

Melbourne

Hobart

Sydney

coast of North America and in the northeast Pacific Ocean by the Scripps Institution of Oceanography and the U. S. Coast and Geodetic Survey.[115]

The *Rehoboth* of the U. S. Navy completed similar, detailed, marine magnetic surveys, using towed magnetometers,[116] in a 56,000-square mile area south of the Hawaiian Islands in 1961 and in two North Pacific areas totaling 32,520-square miles in 1962. The Navy also obtained continuous magnetic profiles along more than 70,000 nautical miles of en-route tracks in the Pacific, including an equatorial Pacific survey by the *Rehoboth* in 1961, work in the Antarctic region and between United States and New Zealand by the *Staten Island* as part of Operation Deep Freeze 1961, and surveys by the *Burton Island* during Deep Freeze 1962.[117]

The work of the Russian nonmagnetic vessel *Zarya* during the International Geophysical Year, 1957–1958, was extended into the Pacific Ocean and adjacent seas in 1959–1960 (Fig. 40). The expedition worked in the western Pacific at the beginning of 1960 along the following route: Perth—Melbourne—Hobart—Wellington—Port Moresby—Shanghai—Vladivostok. Continuous magnetic sections were obtained across the Tasman Basin and the ridge dividing the Tasman Sea from the North and South Fiji basins, the deep to the south of the Solomon Islands, and the Mariana Ridge and Mariana Trench. The next expedition followed a course from Vladivostok —Canton—Darwin—Port Moresby—Sydney—Wellington—Concepción—Easter Island—the Marquesas Islands—the Hawaiian Islands—Vladivostok. This voyage of over 24,000 sea miles was completed in May 1961 and provided measurements over the Campbell Plateau, the southern part of the southwestern Pacific basin, the Albatross Cordillera (that part formerly known as the Pacific Antarctic Ridge) at two latitudes, the San Felix-Juan Fernandez Ridge off the Chilean coast, the Aracena Trench, the Peru-Chile Trench, and the regions of Easter Island and the Marquesas and Hawaiian islands.[118]

The most significant stimulus to geomagnetism in recent years has been that provided by the International Geophysical Year (IGY) and the ensuing space exploration effort. In geomagnetism, the IGY comprised a world-wide coordinated program comparable with those of the First and Second Polar Years, but greatly expanded in scope and areal coverage, with special emphasis on observatory work and related research activity, including investigations of configurations of current in the ionosphere, the phenomenon of the equatorial electrojet, the character of transient fluctuations such as solar and lunar daily variations, magnetic storms, bays, solar flare effects, and pulsations.[119] In the Pacific area, the following magnetic observatories cooperated in the international program (some being newly established for the IGY): Sitka, Barrow, College, Healy, and Big Delta, Alaska; Victoria, British Columbia; Fuquene, Colombia; Teoloyucan, Mexico; Huancayo, Peru; Honolulu, Hawaii; Apia, Guam, Koror, and Easter Island, Oceania; Watheroo, Toolangi, Macquarie Island, Australia; Amberley, New Zealand; Pulau Tjipir, Indonesia; Muntinlupa, Philippines; Kakioka, Memambetsu, Asō, Onagawa, and Shimosato, Japan; Uelen, USSR; and some dozen Antarctic stations set up by several nations. In addition, many temporary recording stations with limited objectives were operated during portions of the IGY.

A considerable part of the IGY program was continued for another calendar year under the International Geophysical Cooperation. More recently, a new and more modest effort was devoted specifically to those aspects of geophysics which can best be examined when the sun is relatively quiescent; this was the program of the International Quiet Sun Years of 1964–1965 or IQSY. Magnetic stations operated especially for this interval include Koror, Midway, Majuro, and Adak.

A related coordination of spatial survey work has been a continuing project since 1957 under the designation World Magnetic Survey.[120] This has stimulated the collection of data and the improvement of magnetic charts by promoting standards of accuracy, spacing of survey lines, and uniformity in the reporting of results. Instrumental developments such as the flux-gate magnetometers, the various nuclear precession magnetometers using protons, metastable helium and alkali vapor, special telemetry transmitters, automatic observatories, and instrumented satellites to explore the magnetosphere,[121] have contributed profoundly to modern studies in geomagnetism.

GRAVITY MEASUREMENTS

The determination of gravity on land and at sea has both geodetic and geophysical implications, that is, it is important in measuring the size and shape of the earth, and in interpreting the composition and density of the earth's outermost layers as well as the tectonic movements that take place therein. Although the first known observations of gravitational force were by the Italian scientist Galileo[122] in the sixteenth century (1590), the only practical method perfected for measuring gravity until about the middle of the twentieth century was that based on observation of a freely swinging pendulum. This method was used to make both absolute and relative determinations of gravitational force over the earth's land areas and to establish networks of gravity base stations, but was not suited for measuring gravity from surface ships at sea because of the ship's movement.

In 1923, F. A. Vening-Meinesz of the Netherlands Geodetic Commission devised a pendulum technique for measuring gravity in a submarine. In that year, the Dutch submarine *K II* made gravimetric observations from the Netherlands to Java via the Suez Canal. In 1926, the Dutch submarine *K XIII* also made gravity measurements from the Netherlands to Java but via the Panama Canal along a route that covered more than 20,000 miles and partly over long unbroken stretches of the Pacific Ocean. Measurements were obtained over the continental shelf between Panama and San Francisco, the Hawaiian Ridge and nearby Hawaiian Trough, the Nero Deep near Guam, Yap Trench, Philippine Trench, and in the eastern part of the East Indies Archipelago. The harbors visited in the Pacific included Colon (Panama), Mazatlan (west coast of Mexico), San Francisco, Honolulu, Guam, Yap, Manila, Ambon and Kepulauan Banda (Moluccas), Bima (Sumbawa), and Surabaja (Java). This trip resulted in 128 gravity stations, fifteen in the harbors mentioned, and terminated in February of 1927 with two trips to investigate the Java Trench south of Java, during which twenty-six stations were observed at sea besides observations in the harbors of Surabaja and Batavia.[123]

Between June 1929 and February 1930, the Dutch submarine *K XIII* made three expeditions through the East Indies Archipelago, together covering nearly 16,000 miles and providing gravity data for 233 stations. The significance of this work perhaps is best indicated by the following account:

> The conviction, that the clearing up of the relation between gravity and tectonic activity would be of primary importance for both sides of gravity research: the geodetic problem of the Figure of the Earth and the geophysical problem of the investigation of the condition of the Earth's crust, gave rise to plan a further expedition, i.e., a complete gravimetric survey of the seas in the Netherlands East Indies and the adjoining parts of the Indian and Pacific Oceans. This part of the Earth's surface is especially appropriate for the elucidation of these problems, because it is tectonically very active, as it is shown by the great number of earthquake-centres and volcanoes and by the geological data, and it has the advantage of being well investigated geologically, seismically and topographically. The submarine topography is likewise known in detail; prior to 1929 a great many soundings have already been made, but since then, the hydrographic expedition of Hr. Ms. Willebrord Snellius under leadership of Mr. Van Riel has added more than 30,000 echo-soundings over the whole Eastern part of the Archipelago, thereby giving us a detailed knowledge of the sea-floor.[124]

The 233 gravity stations obtained during these expeditions, in combination with those already observed in 1923, 1926, and 1927, form a network of very complete gravity data over the marine areas of the East Indies Archipelago and the adjoining oceans.

The second period of Netherlands Geodetic Commission gravity expeditions at sea, 1933–1940, began in November 1934, with the voyage of the submarine *K XVIII* from the Netherlands to Java via the Atlantic and Indian oceans. This eight-month trip terminated in July 1935 after obtaining a coastal profile of gravity near the northwest cape of the Australian continent and a continuous series of observations from there to the port of Banjuwangi in Java.[125]

In 1934 and 1935, the Japanese used submarines and the Vening-Meinesz pendulum apparatus to obtain gravity measurements over the Japan Trench and adjacent areas of the western Pacific.[126] In 1956, the Lamont Geological Observatory, in cooperation with the Commonwealth of Australia, made similar measurements in the southwest Pacific aboard the submarine *Telemachus*, the latter measurements being in the general area of the Tonga and Kermadec trenches, and the Tonga, Kermadec, and Lau ridge structure.[127]

Following World War II, the Netherlands Geodetic Commission resumed its gravity determinations at sea and on land. In 1957 the Royal Netherlands Navy submarine *Walrus* made sixty-four gravity observations in the Pacific area west and south of Panama (Fig. 41), mainly for geophysical reasons. Objectives of this survey included study of the gravimetric features over submarine ridges southwest of Costa Rica and Panama, and over the Pacific area contiguous to the Andes between Panama and Ecuador.[128]

The application of gravity observations to subsurface exploration by the oil industry following World War II gave considerable impetus to the development of gravity instruments having high precision, portability, and speed of operation. As instruments for measuring gravity differences, these gravity meters had many advantages in both accuracy and efficiency over the pendulum method. In 1948, an improved gravity meter, which provided greater range of measurement, a higher degree of accuracy, lower drift, and a means for maintaining constant temperature of the instrument was used for a special around-the-world survey to: (1) check the

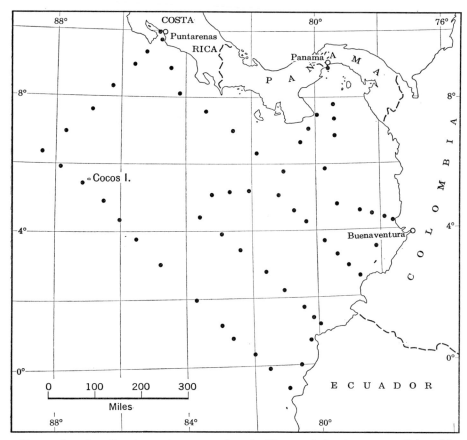

FIG. 41. Location of gravity stations west and south of Panama during the 1957 expedition of the Royal Netherlands Navy submarine *Walrus*. After G. J. Bruins (ed.), 1960 [Note 128].

accuracy of existing national gravity bases, (2) establish new bases where none existed, (3) tie the bases of absolute gravity determination together so that their relative accuracy and that of the Potsdam system[129] could be determined, and (4) establish an integrated network of stations whose relative values would be reliable to better than 1 mgal. This survey, which was accomplished by the Woods Hole Oceanographic Institution in cooperation with the U. S. Navy, covered over 80,000 miles in a three-month period using air transport between the land base stations. The route across the Pacific extended from San Francisco to Oahu (Hawaii), Johnston Island, Kwajalein, Guam, Tokyo, Tsingtao (China), Shanghai, Guam, and on to Manila and Bangkok.[130]

In 1954 and 1955, gravity surveys of the Pacific continental borderland off California northward to Vancouver Island were conducted by the University of California's Institute of Geophysics in cooperation with the U. S. Navy. The measurements were made with Vening-Meinesz pendulum apparatus on board U. S. Navy submarines during seven cruises.[131]

From the first cruise of the Dutch submarine *K II* until 1955, all reliable measurements of gravity at sea were made with the Vening-Meinesz pendulum apparatus in submarines.[132] At this time, the U. S. Navy Hydrographic Office (now U. S. Naval Oceanographic Office) conducted the first successful tests of a gravity meter aboard submarines. These tests were soon followed by tests on surface vessels, and, by 1957, a continuous record of gravity was successfully obtained from a surface ship.[133] Although moderate seas were required for the measurements, this new development made it possible to accumulate gravity data at sea much more rapidly than in the past. Further development of shipboard gravity meters led to tests in 1958 aboard several surface ships, including the research vessel *Horizon* of the University of California.[134] Following the tests, a gravity survey of the continental borderland off southern California was made and a full-scale survey along closely spaced tracks in the Gulf of California was completed in 1959 during the Scripps Institution of Oceanography's Vermillion Sea Expedition. Some 5000 miles of continuous data were obtained.[135]

The U. S. Navy also conducted a submarine gravity survey in 1958 in the vicinity of Clipperton Island. During 1960, the U. S. Navy made gravity observations on the nuclear submarine *Triton* while circumnavigating the world submerged. Continuous data were obtained along a track from the southern tip of South America across the South Pacific, through the Philippine and Celebes seas, and on into the Indian Ocean. In 1961, the *Rehoboth* of the Navy conducted a surface survey in conjunction with the University of California on which gravity, geomagnetic, bathymetric, and oceanographic data were obtained along several broadly spaced lines southwest of Hawaii. Additional surveys were conducted in the Solomon Islands area.[136]

During the 1961 comprehensive oceanographic program of the U. S. Coast and Geodetic Survey in the North Pacific, the *Pioneer* systematically gathered gravity data along closely spaced lines between meridians 155°W. and 160°W. from the Aleutian Trench south to latitude 43° N. Continuous magnetic profiles also were obtained along diagonal lines over the Aleutian Trench from Kodiak to Adak, and readings were taken at oceanographic stations along two meridians west of 160° W. Additional measurements were obtained by the *Surveyor* in 1962 over a route from Seattle westward to Okinawa via Hawaii, Wake, and Guam and later that year in the Chukchi Sea, across the Aleutian Trench, and across the Gulf of Alaska. Gravity was again observed by the *Pioneer* in the north Pacific. A regional survey on land was conducted during this period by the U. S. Geological Survey on the Alaska Peninsula and adjacent islands, to complement the ship observations.[137]

In the early 1960s, tests showed that airborne gravity measurements were possible and that the results were adequate for some geodetic and geophysical purposes. This advance opened the possibility of using aircraft for regional gravity surveys over oceanic areas. Use of the method at this stage of development, however, required numerous refinements, among which were accurate determination of aircraft position and motion over the sea.[138]

SEISMIC MEASUREMENTS

Seismology, the study of natural earthquakes, is the parent science of exploration seismology, a branch of geophysics that uses artificial sources of seismic energy to investigate the composition and geologic structure of the solid earth.[139] As early as 1933, oil geologists had obtained remarkable results with artificial seismic methods and research programs were being directed to their application in submarine geophysical investigations.[140] Advances by 1936 made seismic techniques available for structural studies of the submerged continental shelf.[141] Investigations along the United States Atlantic coast were underway in 1937 but were interrupted by World War II. Research during the war years resulted in improvements in both shallow-water and deep-water seismic surveys.[142] In 1946, after the end of the war, large quantities of surplus high explosives gave further impetus to seismic work at sea. Both reflection and refraction measurements from ships at sea have contributed immensely to scientific exploration of the Pacific Basin.[143]

The first extensive seismic program in the Pacific was that carried out aboard the *Albatross* in 1947–1948 during the Swedish Deep-Sea Expedition. This expedition provided sub-bottom reflection records along a route from Panama to Galapagos, latitude 18° N., Marquesas, Tahiti, Hawaii, Mindanao, and Java.[144]

After 1948, seismic-refraction surveys were made from San Diego to the Marshall Islands and south almost to the Tropic of Capricorn to provide information about the deep Pacific Basin, its atolls and islands, and the continental margin of North and Central America. These surveys included the Mid-Pacific Expedition (1950) and Capricorn Expedition (1952–1953) during which widely scattered refraction observations were made at forty-two stations in the central Pacific area, from latitude 22° S. to latitude 28° N. and from longitude 162° E. to longitude 112° W.[145] Special studies were made at Bikini and Eniwetok atolls,[146] and in the Tonga Trench area.[147] Also late in 1950, the British vessel *Challenger* entered the Pacific on a round-the-world cruise and spent more than a year there. As part of the vessel's oceanographic work, single-ship seismic refraction observations were made in deep-water areas, using a sono-radio buoy system.[148] Reflection measurements also were made and shallow-water investigations were conducted at the coral atolls of Funafuti and Nukufetau.[149]

In 1954, during the Acapulco Trench Expedition, seismic-refraction work was done by the Scripps Institution of Oceanography ships *Spencer F. Baird* and *Horizon* at seven locations in and near the Middle America Trench.[150] In November of the same year, a limited seismic-reflection survey was made in the equatorial Pacific by the *Baird*. This survey was conducted near longitude 125° W. and between latitude 3°30' N. and 13°30' N. to study aspects of marine sedimentation far from land, and in an area crossed by the Clipperton Fracture Zone.[151]

Ships of the Scripps Institution of Oceanography, on Expeditions Chinook and Mukluk, 1956–1957, made seismic-refraction and seismic-reflection studies in the Gulf of Alaska, the Bering Sea, and the northeastern Pacific Ocean. The seismic work included eighteen stations in abyssal areas of the northeastern Pacific, twenty near the coast of Alaska, [152] and five on the Hawaiian Ridge taken near the concluding portion of Expedition Chinook.[153] These surveys were followed by Scripps Expedition Downwind in 1957–1958, during which thirty-nine seismic-refraction stations were recorded in the central and southeast Pacific.[154]

In April 1962, during ocean-borne seismic profiling by the Scripps Institution of Oceanography along the northeast coast of Hawaii, seismic waves from explosions detonated at sea were recorded by seismographs of the Hawaiian Volcano Observatory network of the U. S. Geological Survey. Interpretation of these data provided new information about the oceanic crust and upper mantle beneath eastern Hawaii.[155]

Technological developments during the 1950s made continuous seismic-reflection profiling possible in shallow-water areas.[156] This type of profiling, which utilizes low-frequency, high-powered, electro-mechanical sound sources and improved graphic recording apparatus, was used in the late 1950s across the narrow continental shelves and upper basin slopes off southern California to measure the thickness of sediments and to record structural detail at shallow depth within the underlying bedrock.[157] The method also has been used during special survey work by the U. S. Geological Survey in the vicinity of Palau and Guam aboard the U. S. Coast and Geodetic Survey ship *Pioneer* in 1964.[158]

Much seismic exploration work has been done near land for mineral development and in the deeper Pacific areas to determine crustal thickness and depth of the Mohorovicic discontinuity. Much of the latter work was in conjunction with Project Mohole to select a deep-water drilling site. In 1963, a Pacific study was begun of deep-sea, ocean-bottom, seismic energy or earth noise characteristics and related geophysical conditions in the upper mantle. This effort was part of the Vela Uniform program[159] to detect and identify underground and underwater nuclear blasts. During the year 1963 more than 500 hours of deep-sea seismograms were obtained between the Aleutian Islands and New Zealand.[160]

HEAT-FLOW MEASUREMENTS

Measurement of terrestrial heat-flow by modern techniques began about 1939, but satisfactory methods of measuring heat-flow in the ocean floor were not developed until 1949.[161] The measurements, even on land, are not easily obtained and the data collected through 1964 show a very uneven geographical distribution. The only comprehensive summary of heat-flow measurements[162] is based on 780 heat-flow values, or measurements, and 678 heat-flow data—a datum representing one heat-flow value or the average of more than one value from nearby stations. The summary, after rejection of questionable data, includes 634 analyzed heat-flow data of which 561 or eighty-nine percent are for oceanic areas. Of these, 417 heat-flow data, or nearly seventy-five percent were obtained in the Pacific—largely by investigating groups at Scripps Institution of Oceanography and at Tokyo, which together accounted for seventy-five and five percent, respectively, of all analyzed data.

Most heat-flow measurements in the Pacific Basin have been obtained relatively recently. By 1956, only twenty-five measurements of heat flow had been made in the Pacific Ocean on four separate expeditions of the Scripps Institution of Oceanography as follows: Mid-Pacific Expedition, six; Scripps Capricorn Expedition, nine; and the Acapulco Trench and East Pacific Expedition, ten.[163] Since 1956, a large number of measurements have been made in the Pacific.[164] These include: (1) 243 measurements in the eastern and southeastern Pacific and thirty-six measurements in the northeast Pacific and Bering Sea by the Scripps Institution of Oceanography; (2) twelve measurements in the western Pacific off Japan on cruises by the Japanese vessel *Ryofu-Maru*; and (3) sixty-five additional measurements in the east Pacific Ocean by Lamont Geological Observatory during cruises 18 and 19 of the *Vema*.

In addition to heat-flow probes lowered from ships, several temperature measurements were made in a borehole on the Pacific Ocean floor about forty-five miles east of Isla de Guadalupe off Mexico during the preliminary drilling for Project Mohole in 1961. The measurements, which were obtained to depths of 500 feet down the hole, were compared with measurements by the probe technique made in the area after completion of the drilling.[165]

WEATHER OBSERVATIONS

Knowledge of the weather and climate of the vast Pacific region was gleaned very slowly in the early part of the twentieth century. The first observations and records were limited to those from widely separated land stations, research vessels on scientific cruises, and vessels of the steamship lines. The use of weather reports for forecasting was made possible by the development of the wireless and radio. In 1907, however, only one vessel operating in the Pacific Ocean was known to carry wireless equipment. Progress in building up the Pacific vessel weather-reporting service was severely limited during the next fourteen years. In 1919, the United States Weather Bureau was given authority by the government to appoint twelve vessels for this service in the Pacific. Observations were made at specified times of day and the information was then sent by radio to the Weather Bureau. In 1921, all Shipping Board vessels were instructed to cooperate in reporting weather observations to the fullest extent. By 1925, the aid of the Japanese was enlisted and reports were received from Japanese vessels north of latitude 45° N., and in the following year, from vessels south of latitude 45° N., thus providing additional coverage north of latitude 10° N. from the North American coast west to the 180th meridian. Prior to 1928, reports were made only from transoceanic ships. At this time, the Weather Bureau established a group of coastwise vessels as weather-reporting stations.

By 1929, a total of 240 vessels made Pacific weather observations and accounted for an average of about fifty vessel weather messages daily. The extensive development of this service made it possible to depict the pressure distribution over the Pacific Ocean and to initiate comprehensive studies of meteorological conditions in the Pacific.[166]

Ocean weather stations were first established in 1940 in the North Atlantic, during World War II. The Pacific program began in 1943 with two ships, both operated by the U. S. Navy. By the end of 1946, there were five stations in the Pacific. The Canadian operation of ocean weather station "P" was inaugurated in December 1950. In 1958, four permanent stations were operated in the North Pacific—"November" (latitude 30° N., longitude 140° W.) and "Victor" (latitude 31° N., longitude 164° E.) by the U. S. Coast Guard; "Papa" (latitude 31° N., longitude 145° W.) by Canada; and "Tango" (latitude 29° N., longitude 135° E.) by Japan—to record day-to-day weather sequences of sufficient length for determining climatic details. In recent years, ships manning these stations have been equipped to obtain oceanographic measurements.[167]

The accumulation of marine weather data made possible the publication of climatic atlases of the Pacific, including the U. S. Navy *Marine Climatic Atlas of the World*. Data for the atlases were obtained from ships of the U. S. Navy and Merchant Marine and those of other nations, notably British, German, Dutch, Canadian, and Japanese ships; from the North Pacific ocean stations manned by ships of the United States, Canada, and Japan; and from coastal and island stations operated by meteorological services of the United States, Chile, France, New Zealand, the United Kingdom, Australia, Venezuela, Japan, and the USSR.[168]

The Fourth Congress of the World Meteorological Organization at Geneva, Switzerland, April 1–27, 1963, adopted a new program for the exchange of marine climatological data and the preparation of climatic summaries. From the summaries of fixed and selected representative areas a *World Climatic Atlas* is planned.[169] Areas of responsibility in the Pacific are shown in Figure 42.

MODERN AIDS IN EXPLORATION

Mapping, Charting, and Aerial Photographic Surveys

Maps and charts have been important by-products of, and fundamental reference sources for, scientific exploring activity throughout the Pacific.[170] Because of their great number and variety, only passing reference can be made to them in this chapter. They are listed and described—according to types, scales, and areal coverage—in the published catalogs, lists, and guides of the mapping and charting offices of each country.[171] During this century many nations of the world, and particularly those bordering the Pacific Ocean, have carried out planned surveys of selected portions of the Pacific Basin, including the mapping of littoral and insular land areas. These extensive and continuous cartographic activities have been and will continue to be responsive to the rapidly accelerating commerce of the Pacific and to the development of its natural resources. Thus, a close relationship will continue between mapping programs and scientific exploration throughout the Pacific. The results of systematic programs of exploration and mapping during the past several decades are reflected in the excellent maps and charts of the whole Basin that have been published recently by the USSR[172] and the United States.[173]

Accurate large-scale mapping and charting of selected Pacific areas has been considerably expedited by the use of aerial photography. The practical utility of aerial photographic reconnaissance was recognized in World War I. During the later years of the war many advances were made in aerial photographic interpretation and measurements. These were followed by new applications in civil mapping programs. It was World War II, however, that provided the greatest stimulus for aerial photographic surveys. In the Pacific, large-scale use of photo-reconnaissance commenced with the United States offensive in 1942. As the range of photographic aircraft was increased, large areas of continental Asia and its offshore islands, including Japan, were mapped from aerial photographs.[174] By the end of the war, the need for better maps of the Pacific was so obvious that a Post Hostilities Mapping Program was developed to use the photographic aircraft and crews that were still overseas. This was followed by major efforts on the part of many agencies and countries to map the approximately nine million square miles of Pacific land. By 1963, map coverage was available for two to six million square miles at various scales of mapping. This compared with a total of 27,000 to 125,000 square miles twenty-two years earlier.[175]

Geodetic Control Surveys

It is interesting to note that as early as 1891, during investigations of the variation of latitude by the International Geodetic Association and U.S. Coast and Geodetic

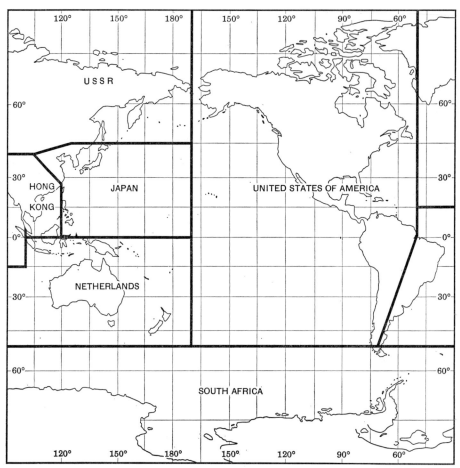

FIG. 42. Areas of responsibility for the collection and processing of marine climatic data in the Pacific, and the responsible members of the World Meteorological Organization. Adapted from H. C. Summer, 1963 [Note 176].

Survey, Waikiki in the Hawaiian Islands was selected as a special observation point because its longitude was about 180 degrees different from European stations.[176]

The importance of geodetic surveys grew rapidly after World War I with advances in geodetic techniques and the need to extend comprehensive mapping based on geodetic foundations. In the 1920s, geodetic surveys by the U. S. Coast and Geodetic Survey were extended through remote areas of Luzon in the Philippines. During World War II, an arc of triangulation was extended from the United States to Alaska and connections were made to isolated pieces of triangulation in Alaska, including work along the Aleutians. After the war, islands in the Bering Sea were connected by means of trilateration. Direct measurement of exceptionally long lines was accomplished by the electronic position indicator system. Since then, the need for even better geodetic control to satisfy military requirements has grown with the development of long-range ballistic missiles, especially those of intercontinental range.[177]

In 1951, the United States Army initiated a major survey program—the occulta-tion program—to accomplish geodetic connections between widely separated islands of the Pacific area and between these islands and continents bordering the Pacific. This program involves a technique whereby the elapsed time between the moon's occultation of a star at two widely separated points is recorded and mathematically reduced to distance to arrive at geographic positions. Operations under this program have been continuous within the Pacific area since the program's initiation. Due to lack of other systems in the past with potentials equal to this technique, occultation operations have been confined to exceptionally long lines.

During 1957, surveys by the ground and airborne Hiran (high precision shoran) trilateration technique were initiated in the Ryukyu Islands and extended northward to Japan and southward to northern Taiwan. Measurements that can be accomplished by this technique are usually limited to 500 miles because of the line-of-sight re-quirements. In 1959, surveys by this technique were initiated in the Marshall Islands where a trilateration network was established that connected the Marshall Islands to Wake Island.

During 1961, a Hiran traverse was initiated in the Hawaiian Islands and extended southward to Johnston Island. Azimuths were interjected into this traverse by the light-crossing method, this being the first project on which the method was used. In this method an airplane, flying at night and carrying a powerful light source, crosses the line between two distant points from which simultaneous observations are made to the light. As a result of the precise azimuths accomplished, the traverse was strengthened appreciably. Also during 1961, a gravity survey program was initiated in western Pacific areas to provide data for various geodetic studies.

Early in 1962, while the Hawaiian project was still underway, but scheduled for early completion, an additional Hiran project (the South Pacific project) was initiated in the Pacific area extending from Australia through eastern New Guinea north-eastward to the Marshall Islands. This project was later expanded to include an extension southward from the Marshall Islands into the Gilbert Islands. Other geodetic work in the Pacific area includes Secor (sequential correlation of range), an artificial earth satellite system. The Secor operations were initiated during the latter half of 1964 and extend from Japan southward to various islands.[178]

NAVIGATIONAL AIDS

Pacific exploration also has been advanced by the development of navigational aids, particularly those systems which have provided greater accuracy of position determination for oceanic surveys. The importance of long-range navigation (Loran) during World War II operations in the far-flung Pacific battle area was obvious. In the northern Pacific, the Aleutian Loran chain was operating in October 1943. In the same month, the Hawaiian chain commenced operation to provide coverage in the central and southwest Pacific. Other chains were established in the Phoenix and Marshall Islands in 1944 and across the Pacific by the war's end. Loran coverage was provided in the lower East Indies by 1944.

The advent of peace brought about a re-evaluation and realignment of Loran coverage in the Pacific to meet the needs of airlines, merchant ships, and military services. The Korean Conflict prompted the construction of additional chains of Loran stations to cover the Sea of Japan, the Formosa Strait, and southwards into the South China Sea. These stations, many of which were mobile units, were made permanent in 1954.

Research and development have produced further advancements in Loran systems and in 1961 Loran-C, a highly accurate navigational aid, became operational. Loran-C chains were established in the Aleutians to cover the north Pacific and at Midway and Johnston islands to provide coverage throughout the central Pacific. New construction will provide coverage in the Philippine Sea. Loran-A, sometimes called "Standard Loran," provides for Great Circle navigation across the North Pacific, passage through the central Pacific islands, and movement along the Asia coast. Loran-C, which is well suited for specialized oceanic survey requirements, covers the central Pacific, the northwestern Pacific, and the Arctic areas of the north Pacific Ocean.[179]

15

THE INTELLECTUAL ASSUMPTIONS AND CONSEQUENCES OF GEOGRAPHICAL EXPLORATION IN THE PACIFIC

WILCOMB E. WASHBURN*

Other chapters in this book have discussed the details of explorations into the Pacific by navigators of the world's great maritime nations. There is no need to summarize or recount those achievements. The intellectual assumptions and consequences of those explorations on the other hand, will be treated at length in this essay, both as they affected Europe's understanding of the Pacific, and Europe's understanding of herself.

HISTORICAL DEFINITION OF "THE PACIFIC"

Medieval cartography illustrates the mental conception that bound men to earth, their own earth. The sea is a bounds, a fringe, an encompassing barrier to man's home, the land. Not only in Europe was this so. In China, the "Middle Kingdom," and in Japan, the sea was a border to the land, and, although it provided watercourses for coastal trade, it circumscribed rather than impelled outward those societies which were inward looking.

The European Renaissance heralded the era of outward-looking societies: questing, curious, avaricious. The sea no longer bounds and binds; it provides a highway in every direction, broken only by the land. The Pacific Ocean, though the greatest ocean in the world, was the most remote from the source of this new fever. Before the Pacific could be reached by outsiders, the Atlantic had first to be conquered, Africa had to be rounded, and the Indian Ocean crossed. Both routes were difficult, yet the Pacific was reached from the east and from the west almost simultaneously.

It is necessary, of course, to define what we mean by the Pacific Ocean. Today there can be no doubt that we mean the physical reality of Pacific lands, waters, and peoples whose description and measurement, we can be confident, have now been accurately charted. But so long as the element of the unknown, the unexplored, and the uninvestigated remained, so long did imagination, ignorance, prejudice, and uncertainty influence the definition. Asians are sometimes surprised to recall that the "Indians" Columbus believed he had found in 1492, who populated what we now know to be the western shore of the Atlantic Ocean, where thought to occupy the western rim of the Pacific. The fate of the Indians of America makes such thoughts sobering as well as surprising. Navigators following Columbus at first embraced the same illusion that they had reached Asia, and though skepticism soon set in because of the disparity between Marco Polo's description of China and Japan and the reality of the new-found lands, Columbus, for one, until his dying day in 1506, believed that he had reached Asia.

---

*DR. WASHBURN is chairman of the department of American studies, the Smithsonian Institution, Washington.

Even after doubts that the new lands were part of Asia became common, the assumption that these lands were physically joined to Asia continued to be held by many cartographers and explorers. In 1542, the very year that Japan was entered by a European, the mapmaker Caspar Vopel drew North America and Asia as identical and wrote on the island of Haiti: "Zipangu *nunc* Hispaniola."[1] The actual arrival of Europeans in Japan cleared up the mystery that had previously bothered geographers, whether Japan (Zipangu) was one of the islands in the Caribbean or existed behind the newly discovered land masses. The supposed lack of space to accommodate both the new lands and a conventional positioning of China and Japan had forced scholars to make a choice.[2] A rough idea of the true width of the sea between the newly discovered lands and Asia, at least in the Southern Hemisphere, was first impressed upon Europeans by the epic voyage of Magellan and his men in 1519–1521. But it was not until the development of more efficient means of determining longitude that any scientific knowledge of the distances across the Pacific was achieved. One of Magellan's pilots, for example, misjudged, by 3000 miles, the width of the Pacific he had traversed.[3] It was not until the development of the accurate chronometer, and its efficient utilization by navigators like Cook in the eighteenth century, that the precise bounds of the Pacific became known.

MOTIVATION TO PACIFIC DISCOVERY

The approach to the Pacific from the east and from the west, although demonstrating different attitudes, reveals a single questing impulse. Approached from the east, by way of the Atlantic, the Pacific was discovered as part of the headlong rush to exploit the wealth of "The Indies"—the name was retained even after it was realized that the new lands did not represent the "real" Indies. Vasco Nuñez de Balboa's exploit, while not characterizing the spirit or technique of scientific discovery as we know them today, does reveal the early impulse that underlies them. In the course of his wealth-extracting activities in the Isthmus of Panama in 1513, Balboa went to attack the cacique Comogre of Comogra. In order to avoid a fight, the cacique treated with Balboa and presented him a tribute of gold and slaves. As the Spaniards proceeded to melt down the curiously wrought gold objects, they quarreled about the division of the loot. Suddenly Panciaco, eldest son of Comogre, struck the scales with his fist and scattered the gold in all directions. He pointed out the absurdity of valuing the gold not for the artistry with which it had been shaped, but for its simple unenhanced essence. If the Spaniards had such a curious fever for gold, he suggested, they should go beyond the mountains to a sea on the borders of which lived people who possessed vast quantities of gold. Balboa, thirsty for yellow metal, pressed through the jungle and on September 26, 1513, looked upon what he called the South Sea and the possession of which, with all the countries bordering on it, he modestly claimed for the King of Castile.[4]

The unhappy history of the destruction of the kingdom of Peru that followed is too well known to need repeating. But the dominant motive that led Europeans to the border of the Pacific from the east—the urge to find gold as portable wealth—should be emphasized. Here was no quest for knowledge, let alone respect for what was found. Here was no concern for the life that bordered the sea. Here was a passion, an emotion, as simple and as unadorned as its golden object.

Yet, when one compares the rash adventurism of Balboa, and of those who followed him, with the careful reconnoitering of Cook and his eighteenth-century followers, one sees that they express warring elements of a single psyche seeking to express itself both for good and evil as no civilization, perhaps, has ever so fully expressed itself before. In the eighteenth century, the productions of the Pacific craftsmen were neither ignored nor destroyed, nor were their social organizations ruthlessly over-turned. On the contrary, the cultural expressions of the peoples of the area were in-creasingly recorded by the pens of artists and scientists, and examples of "curiously wrought" objects of utility and art were brought home to grace the cabinets of in-quiring men.

It would be rash to distinguish the two approaches by the nationality of the dis-coverers, or by the time of their discoveries. Both the passion of the seeker-after-gold and the intelligence of the seeker-after-truth are combined in the inquisitive-acquisitive spirit of the European Renaisssance. Both contributed to the almost biological rapidity with which the Pacific was explored. Viewed in historical per-spective, the intrusion of Western nations into the Pacific Basin comprises but a few seconds on the watch of historic time. When it is remembered that the physical dis-tances were the greatest in the world and the technical capabilities of the explorers were by present standards primitive and crude, the speed and magnitude of the achievement is evident. Only a strong passion and developing technique could sustain such a movement.

The European approach to the Pacific from the west, once the southern tip of Africa had been rounded, followed the well-worn track of Moslem traders from East Africa across the Indian Ocean. Throughout the course of their penetration into the Pacific world, the Portuguese generally found that the Moslems had preceded them, usually by centuries. The role of the Moslem world in transmitting knowledge of the Asiatic world to Europe has never been fully assessed and may well have been more important than Europeans have realized. The transmission of classical knowledge to the West may not have been the only debt which Christianity owes to its traditional foe.[5]

The Portuguese, approaching the Pacific by way of Africa and the Indian Ocean, reached Malacca in 1509, and, in 1512—about the time Balboa looked out on the Pacific from the east—Abreu and Serrano sighted New Guinea from the west. The Portuguese reached Canton in 1514 and Japan in 1542. The power, wealth, virtue, skill, and craftsmanship of the great Oriental kingdoms would soon thereafter have their effect on Europe, as the long-sought-for porcelains, silks, spices, tea, and other material evidences of the fabulous world described by Marco Polo made their way by European bottoms to the peninsula of Europe.

Initially, however, the European penetration of the waters leading toward Asia was a physical achievement. The attitude that inspired and characterized the early voyages is best epitomized in Luiz de Cameõs' epic poem, Os Lusiadas (Lisbon, 1572), which is essentially a glorification of the Portuguese nation for accomplishing the hard physical task of reaching the East and conquering outposts throughout the area. One is reminded of the American pioneer's boastful pride in conquering the land and the Indians of the American West in the nineteenth century, though Ameri-ca never produced an epic to equal Camoes'.

But the East did not receive its lovers and plunderers passively. It shaped and changed them, in more ways than we are yet aware. Symbolic of the way in which the Orient affected its European discoverers was the practice, followed by Portuguese passengers sailing on the annual voyages from Lisbon to the East in the sixteenth century, of throwing overboard their spoons when they rounded the Cape of Good Hope. This action, to show that they would thereafter eat rice with their fingers, was a forceful expression of their intention to drop European standards of behavior and to adopt Oriental modes.[6] This willingness to adapt to the Oriental fashion was, unfortunately, often implemented at the level of the pleasure principle rather than at the highest intellectual levels. European attention was not seriously directed to Oriental religions and philosophy until the next century.

In the late sixteenth and early seventeenth centuries intellectual curiosity as well as trading acumen and religious zeal began to affect the European attitude toward the new world of the East. Jesuit missionaries, in the wake of Portuguese expansion, went to and reported upon the varied cultures with which they came into contact, and disseminated throughout Europe a wider knowledge of a wider world. Their letters and reports—in both manuscript and printed form—were absorbed by a voracious public which demanded to know more. Ignatius Loyola, who directed the Jesuit effort, reflects this new spirit in a letter of 1554 to Father Gaspar Barzaeus in Goa, in which he remarks that "some leading figures" in Rome desired information on the cosmography of the regions where the Jesuits are.

They want to know, for instance, how long are the days of summer and of winter; when summer begins; whether the shadows move towards the left or towards the right. Finally, if there are other things that may seem extraordinary, let them be noted, for instance, details about animals and plants that either are not known at all, or not of such a size, etc. And this news—sauce for the taste of a certain curiosity that is not evil and is wont to be found among men—may come in the same letters or in other letters separately.[7]

INTELLECTUAL IMPACT OF PACIFIC DISCOVERIES

The cultural requirements of the Pacific world forced those serving as intermediaries between East and West to an increased intellectualization of effort, not only to satisfy their countrymen in Europe but also to facilitate their purpose in the East. Men like the Jesuit Matteo Ricci, who arrived in China in 1583, found that they could establish a foothold in the kingdom of China by utilizing Western knowledge in fields such as astronomy, mathematics, and cartography, in which the West was ahead of the Chinese. Because of their intellectual contributions, Europeans like Ricci were welcomed, even though their purposes might be at variance with those of the Chinese. Their adoption of Chinese dress and their standing within the Chinese bureaucracy symbolize both Western accommodation to Chinese culture, and Chinese utilization of Western intellectuals.[8]

The precarious relationship of mutual respect between, and advantage to, both West and East could not long survive. Father Ricci and his Jesuits were soon challenged in China by the representatives of other Christian orders, who accused the Jesuits of carrying their accommodation to Chinese values to the point of betrayal of their Christian faith. It is perhaps significant that the Dominican friar who had the greatest role in making the so-called Chinese Rites controversy known within the Christian community was Domingo de Navarrete, and that he reached China by way of Mexico and the long trans-Pacific route from Acapulco to the Philippines. Navarrete's simple Dominican faith was not shaken by the complexities of nature or by the sophistication of the society he found on the western rim of the Pacific. He denounced Jesuit willingness to compromise with error and seemingly to accept Chinese doctrine on an equal plane with the simple truths expounded by the mendicant friars of his own Order. The resulting dissension, charges, and counter-charges helped to teach European intellectuals about the virtues of another system of morality, and to discredit Christianity itself at home. While Western Christianity was partially discrediting itself in the eyes of both Orientals and Europeans, the virtues of Chinese governmental organization were impressing themselves upon Europe. Even Navarrete, for all his refusal to compromise with Chinese religious ideas, filled his book with encomiums about the Chinese government, contrasting its ability to guarantee safety and prosperity, and to reward virtue and scholarship, with the inability of the Iberian countries to achieve similar standards.[9]

The most evident characteristics of Navarrete, his most recent editor points out, were "energy, zeal, bird-like alertness and interest in everything around him." His "love of nature and animals," while "never for their own sake, but only for them as symbols of divine providence," and his "curious scepticism" with regard to miracles mark him as a forerunner of the eighteenth-century scientific traveler.[10] Navarrete's commitment to his mission, however, prevented him from freely looking for truth outside the bounds of the truth he carried with him, and so his observations, while they may have led to the search for a new truth by others, did not trigger doubt or questioning in his own mind.

Even more pervasive and influential than Chinese ideas and ideals was the material culture of the Orient which was suddenly brought within the touch of European rulers. The hard-to-recall impact of Chinese porcelains on European culture is a chapter of significance to all students of western development. Visitors to Schönbrunn, the "imperial country house" in Vienna, will see evidence, in the Chinese rooms, of the awe and admiration with which the exquisite Chinese porcelains were displayed in Europe in the eighteenth century. The contrast between the simple earthenwares of Europe (and even the more refined wares of the Mediterranean and the Near East) and Oriental porcelain was one which affected the leaders of the West in their everyday life. It was not simply a question of taste; it was too obviously a case of superior artistry and superior technical skill on the part of the Orientals. Later, when Europeans succeeded in duplicating porcelain at Meissen and at Sèvres in the eighteenth century, a new flowering of European ceramic art began, a flowering which consciously and proudly imitated Oriental motifs, colors, and forms.

The new European relationship with the peoples of the Pacific as well as with the peoples of the Atlantic gave a great fillip to the formulation, by Western scholars, of what are now generally accepted principles of international law. The personal experiences of Grotius in dealing with suits arising from the capture of Portuguese prizes by Dutch ships in Asiatic waters, for example, encouraged a rethinking of the traditional basis of Western law and the law of nations. Though often formulating their treatises in classical terms with classical examples, the fathers of international law showed the influence of the physical and cultural worlds newly revealed in their time.[11]

Here again the contrast between the Pacific and the Atlantic, between the sixteenth and the seventeenth centuries, can be instructive. Francisco de Vitoria, generalizing from the Atlantic experience in the sixteenth century, succeeded in sustaining, in the new Atlantic environment, the traditional rights of Christianity, including the right to make war on a nation or people which refuses to allow the preaching of the Gospel. Grotius, in the seventeenth century, speaking from a wider knowledge of the relations of Europeans with Asiatics as well as with the natives of the Americas, reduced the parochial and dogmatic assumptions of European Christianity to less rigid and more accommodating principles. In each case, European legal assumptions reflected the realities of European power, although they were couched in terms of natural law and moral duty.[12]

The entrance of the Dutch, English, and other "interlopers" into the Pacific world formerly bound tightly to the Portuguese and Spanish interests introduced new concepts of thinking and acting, as well as a new power relationship in the area. The newcomers refused to accept the Pope's right to divide the world into Spanish and Portuguese spheres, and pursued their purposes without regard for Iberian pretensions or concerns. Most notable of these European "interlopers" were the Dutch, who ventured into the Pacific with a skill and competence that made them formidable rivals. The Dutch voyages were undertaken primarily for the trading interests of Dutch commercial organization rather than for glory and God.

The voyages of Abel Janszoon Tasman in 1642 and 1644 symbolize the nature of the seventeenth-century Dutch discoveries in the Pacific. Carefully organized by Governor-General Antonie Van Diemen, the representative of the Dutch East India Company in Batavia, and scientifically supported by the great surveyor and cartographer Frans Jacobszoon Visscher, the expeditions were essentially functions of a commercial company's need to know more precisely the nature of the territory within which it was expected to operate.[13] Just as the voyages were initiated for a commercial purpose, so they ceased for the same reason when it became evident that the southern Pacific had little to offer a trading company. They are not less significant scientific and secular achievements for that. The Dutch discoverers are deserving of the highest praise for the care with which they collected information and the comparative caution with which they treated the peoples they met, but their voyages fall between the wild assaults of the Spanish in the New World and the more detached quests of the official English and French expeditions of the eighteenth century.

Japan, like China, regarded its civilization as sufficient unto itself, and was rudely shocked when the inquiring, probing fingers of the West pulled back the curtain that screened it from outside examination. A partial window, it is true, was opened in the mid-sixteenth century, and, through Portuguese (and later Dutch) ships, trade and ideas flowed into and out of Japan in a carefully regulated fashion.[14] In the eighteenth century, however, Japan's open frontier on the north, in Hokkaido, where the fierce Ainu maintained their independence after centuries of retreat up the island of Honshu, was suddenly exposed to the Russians (Chapters 6 and 10). The Russians had completed their epic drive across Siberia and were now probing the offshore islands. In 1712 the Cossack Kosirewski traveled down the Kurils to Ostrov Kunashir, the last island before Yezo (Hokkaido) itself. In 1739 Martin Spanberg was ordered to "examine and describe in detail the Kuril Islands and then to proceed to Japan for the purpose of arousing their friendship with the Russians, so as to destroy their deep-rooted Asiatic seclusion."[15]

The Russian reconnaissance from the north created a fresh crisis in Japanese political and social affairs and stimulated her xenophobic temper and cartographic and political activity in her northern sector, as well.[16] By encouraging European exploration, the rumored riches of northern islands also aided in the process of penetrating the mystery surrounding the uncertain geography of the land north of Japan. Yezo was shown to be an island and not the continental land that some had imagined. Another area of the Pacific had been stripped of its legends and reduced to the hard facts of scientific cartography and national political rivalries.

THE SEARCH FOR PASSAGES TO THE ORIENT

The Pacific world which Europeans discovered contained within its borders the extremes of human and physical conditions: the most densely populated areas of the world—China and Japan—and the least populated; the most civilized areas and the least civilized; and a range of physical environment from arctic to tropical. Since the time of Marco Polo, the great goals of European expansion had been China, Japan, and the Spice Islands (Moluccas). The western rim of the Pacific continued to exert its pull throughout the succeeding centuries while the northern and eastern borders of the Pacific, particularly the sparsely populated reaches of the northwest coast of North America, continued to be the cursed barrier that blocked the hoped-for direct passage from Europe to Asia.

The searches for the Northwest and the Northeast Passages in the sixteenth century are of academic interest today because of their failure, but the energy, knowledge, wealth, and hopes—all centered on attaining the Pacific borders of China and Japan—that absorbed the unsuccessful explorers are a true part of the history of the Pacific. The Cathay Company of England left a record of its activities not in the courts of the Chinese emperors which it tried to reach, but in the frozen Arctic coast of Muscovy. Intrepid explorers like Sir Hugh Willoughby, Richard Chancellor, Stephen Burrough, and William Barents never reached their Oriental destinations. Similarly, the Northwest voyages of the Cabots, Giovanni da Ver-razano, the brothers Corte Real, Stephen Gomez, Martin Frobisher, Henry Hudson, and others had Pacific goals and intentions though they succeeded only in filling in the map of the frozen Canadian north. They failed even to exploit effectively the wealth of that region—notably fur—because their eyes were looking beyond to their Pacific goal. The commercial potentialities of the North were not realized until the eighteenth century, when a triangular trade evolved in manufactured goods of Europe, furs of the Northwest Coast, and porcelains and tea of China.

The annals of the seventeenth-century settlers of North America give ample evidence that the Europeans often looked over, or over-looked, the real land to which they had come, in anticipation of the Pacific land that remained an ideal in their minds. On January 8, 1621, Francis Billington, who had arrived on the *Mayflower* with the Plymouth Colony settlers, sighted from a treetop "a great sea, as he thought," which was soon found to be a lake. The lake, or large pond, from which the Town Brook of Plymouth rises, is still called "Billington Sea," and is a symbol of all the South Sea visions dreamed of by the early American settlers [17] (Plate 38, *facing page 285*).

Jean Nicollet, sent in the mid-1630s as an ambassador to a strange people beyond the Great Lakes, who might possibly be Oriental, provided himself with a ceremonial robe of Chinese damask embroidered with birds and flowers. When he approached the town of the people in question, who were Winnebago Indians living near the head of the Green Bay of Lake Michigan, he sent one of his Indian attendants to announce his coming, put on his robe of damask, and advanced to meet the waiting villagers with a pistol in each hand![18] The great explorer, Sieur de la Salle, penetrated the interior of North America but never reached the great sea that was his ultimate goal, while some of his less dedicated followers abandoned their efforts at discovery and returned to the place, a few miles west of Montreal, which is still named Lachine, in derision of La Salle's dream of a westward passage to China.[19]

The search for access to the Pacific led to a great increase in knowledge of the polar regions. Since all of the exploring nations were in the northern hemisphere, the Arctic was the first of the two polar areas to receive detailed geographic study. The reasons are apparent to anyone looking at a globe. The most direct route to the Orient from Europe is transpolar. With the land masses of North and South America in the more temperate climes continually interposing themselves between the European exploring nations and the sought-for Orient, increased attention was focused on the polar route. This activity, which began with the earliest post-Columbian explorations, continued until modern times, always frustrated by the eternal polar ice, an obstacle never practically overcome until the voyage of the atomic-powered submarine *Nautilus* in August, 1958, under the polar icecap. The premature vision of a transpolar route is incorporated in the maps of numerous cartographers who mixed fact, fancy, and hope in their delineation of the region (see Plates 39, 40, 41, and 42, *following this page*). The clearest projection of the hoped-for route to the Orient via the pole is shown on Philippe Buache's map of 1756 (Plate 41). [20]

The postulated Strait of Anian concept derived, in part at least, from the hope that no matter which way voyages of exploration proceeded — northwest or northeast — across the Arctic lands of North America or Asia, they would eventually find access to the warm waters and to the high civilizations of the Pacific. The existence of the Strait was not confirmed until the time of Bering and his successors, coming from the south. The frozen seas held back inquiry from the north, and blocked commercial utilization of the route even when known.[21]

Had Bering found no strait between Asia and America, or had it become apparent that there was a still higher connection between the land masses, would we now consider America a part of "Asia?" Would the concept of the "Western Hemisphere" lose its meaning? It is important to recall that the northern Canadian lands were considered by many, from the days of the Norsemen to the early sixteenth century, to be a promontory of Asia.[22]

Although the remarkable eighteenth-century exploits of Bering, in the Russian service, finally convinced most observers that Asia and America were separated, the width of separation was so narrow as to reduce the significance of the barrier. No

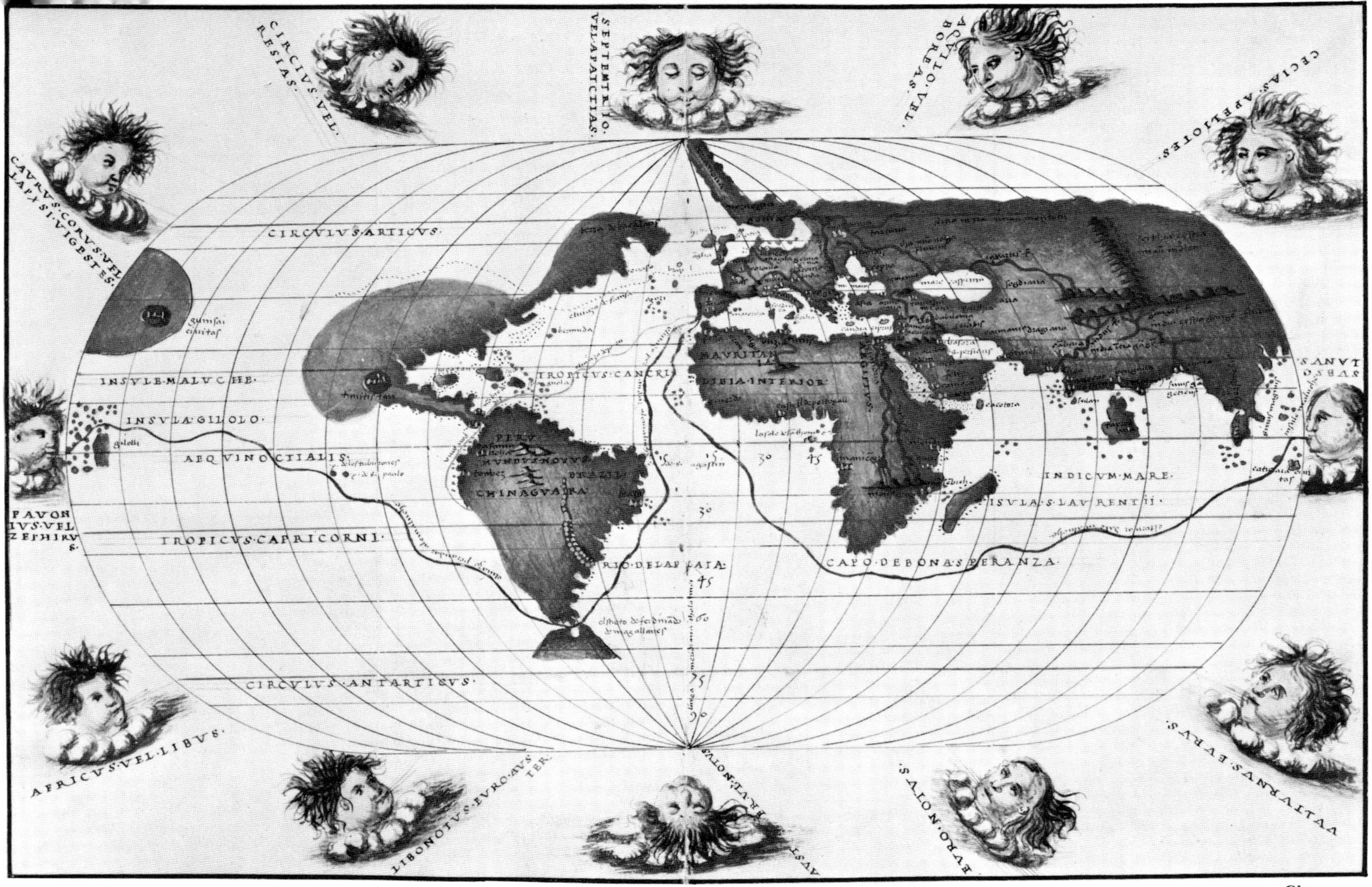

Chapter 15

Manuscript map of world by Baptista Agnese, mid-sixteenth century, showing known routes (solid line) between the Iberian peninsula and the Moluccas, and potential route (dotted line) between France and the Orient via the narrow land bridge of North America. (Courtesy of the Henry E. Huntington Library and Art Gallery, San Marino, Calif., HM25).

PLATE 39

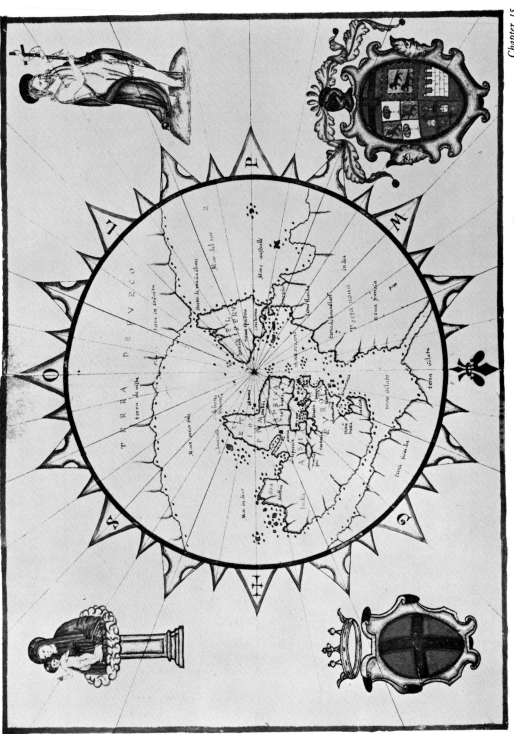

Manuscript map of the world enclosed within a large wind rose, one of six charts in the portolan atlas of Joan Oliva, 1594, showing hoped-for water passages through frozen northern sea. (Courtesy of the Newberry Library, Chicago.)

PLATE 40

Map showing route between Japan and Portugal via the "Icy or Great North Sea" of the Arctic. Originally appearing in Philippe Buache: "Géographie," *Memoirs of the Royal Academy of Sciences*, Paris, 1754, Pl. 1, page 20. The map is shown as it was reproduced, with English inscriptions, in David Henry: *An Historical Account of All the Voyages Round the World, Performed by English Navigators*, London, 1773–1774, Vol. 4. (Courtesy of the Yale University Library, New Haven.)

PLATE 41

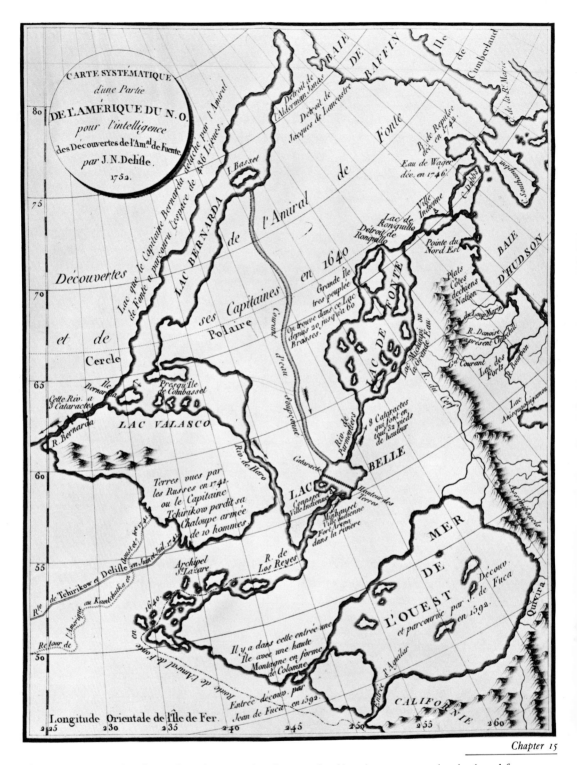

Optimistic cartography of the eighteenth century, based on actual and imaginary voyages, showing hoped-for passages to the Pacific via the elusive Northwest Passage. Engraving from Charles Pierre Claret de Fleurieu: *Voyage autour du monde, pendant les anneés 1790, 1791, et 1792, par Étienne Marchand*, Paris, 1798, Vol. 4. (Courtesy of the Newberry Library, Chicago.)

PLATE 42

better proof of the ability to overcome the barrier exists than the aboriginal population of America, and recent studies bid fair to establish even closer and more recent links between the Old World and the New World.[23] Yet, despite the genetic and physical relationship between the opposite sides of the Pacific Basin, a cultural distance separates them which is even greater and more difficult to overcome than the geographical distance.

While the hoped-for northern seas that would facilitate access to Asia from Europe proved increasingly to be land or unnavigable frozen seas, the opposite proved to be the case in the southern hemisphere. There, the rumored Terra Australis, which had been postulated by the Greeks and later thinkers to comprise a sort of counterweight to the northern hemisphere, was reduced by the end of Cook's voyages in the eighteenth century to a restricted polar land mass which would await the nineteenth and even the twentieth centuries to reveal itself completely. Its imagined mineral wealth proved a potent incentive to a determination of its actual bounds. Just as gold-roofed Japan had enticed the first European discoverers to risk crossing the unknown Ocean Sea to their west, so did a gold-rich Antipodes tempt Spanish intrusion to the south. The hopeful naming of the Solomon Islands is mute evidence of their persistent hope that the golden treasures of their Atlantic New World might be duplicated by diligent search of the new worlds of the Pacific.

RISE OF EUROPEAN SELF-DOUBT

European penetration throughout the reaches of the Pacific would not have been possible but for the development of scientific navigation and scientific cartography culminating in the invention of the chronometer, which Cook carried on his second voyage and which solved the problem of determining longitude. But it was the mental predisposition to seek out the new, both in its commercial, national, and religious aspects, that left the exploitation of the Pacific not to the more powerful, more wealthy, and more cultivated Oriental nations that already bordered on the sea, but to the few, tiny, ill-populated nation states of the European peninsula at the furthest remove from the Pacific.[24]

The Europeans went into the Pacific in search of a physical Antipodes. They found an intellectual and moral Antipodes. It is this aspect of exploration that overshadows—in cultural terms—the more prosaic filling in of the physical outline of the world's land and sea surfaces.

European intellectuals, reading the accounts of the explorers' contact with the denizens of the new worlds on both sides of the great ocean, often found superior virtue in both its sophisticated and primitive state. The virtues of the Chinese were celebrated by countless writers, as is discussed above. In a similar fashion, writers from Michel de Montaigne in the sixteenth century to Jean Jacques Rousseau in the eighteenth century found the American Indian superior to his conquerors in many and varying ways.[25] A similar admiration for the natural virtues of the Pacific islanders often affected European observers. The naked inhabitants of the south and central Pacific, as well as the natives of North and South America, provided evidence of the natural virtue of simple societies, in the same way that the great civilizations of China and Japan provided evidence of the civilized virtues of complex societies. Just as Chinese societal virtue became a byword to the dissatisfied intellectual of Europe, so did Tahitian mores provide an example to the European who saw nature's law rather than man's intellect as the proper governor of human behavior (Plate 43, *following page 332*).

Of course, the impression of distant virtue, whether revealed in the civilization of an urban society or in the breast of an individual in nature, was not universally accepted in Europe. There were those who denied; there were those who mocked; there were those who qualified. But Europeans of as varied character and of as varied centuries as Navarrete and Gauguin alike testify to the "other world" in mind and in heart that the explorers uncovered when they charted the vast reaches of the Pacific.

More importantly, the question of man's proper attitude to himself was suddenly raised by European contact with the peoples of the Pacific. Slowly, European man began to doubt the validity of the Christian measure which he so self-confidently used for comparison in the early stages of European expansion. By the time the great Pacific Basin was fully revealed to Europeans, the dogma of Christianity was being re-examined, whether by Jesuits accommodating themselves to the rites of China, or by ordinary seamen deciding that the Tahitian philosophy was more attractive than their own. Scientific and historically minded observers, both those on the ships of exploration, and those reading the reports of the voyages, speculated about the possible existence of a Golden Age in the Pacific as a matter of interest in itself, and as a corroboration of assumptions about a golden age in Europe's past. The enormous interest in, and dispute over, the "noble savage" received its principal support, though not its initial creation, from the peoples of the Pacific. It arose, moreover, as a corollary to the first scientific reconnaissance of the Pacific.

Captain James Cook's first voyage to the South Seas in 1768 is a landmark in the history of European scientific exploration. Promoted by the Royal Society and by the Admiralty, the voyage was commanded by an officer who was a good mathematician and outstanding hydrographer, and it carried a scientific party led by Joseph Banks which included two naturalists and two artists.[26] The detailed observations and records that they made of the landscapes, the peoples, and the plants of the South Seas laid the basis for an evolution in European thought that is a vital part of the European cultural heritage.

Learning is, in great measure, a demonstration of the comparative method. The observation of different plants, different peoples, different natural settings create, in any thinking mind, inevitable questions of why such differences exist. The Pacific Basin provided an unexcelled classroom and laboratory for the children of the Age of Enlightenment.

The several Cook voyages and their successors to the time of Darwin's famous voyage on the *Beagle* helped to lay the basis for the theory of biological evolution that has been so signal a contribution of Western thought. The steps leading to such a theoretical formulation required the patient collecting of observable differences and the discriminating analysis of the causes of those differences. Only the arduous physical exploration of large areas of the earth's surface and the intensive study of the evidence of life in the different parts of the globe could provide the necessary support for such a theory. It is a significant fact that the three scientists who did so much to establish the scientific basis of organic evolution—Charles Robert Darwin, Joseph Dalton Hooker, and Thomas Henry Huxley—spent the formative years of their lives as naturalists on scientific voyages in the Pacific region.[27]

The influence of the Pacific voyages on Western art was similarly dramatic. The stereotyped forms, poses, and theories of Western European neoclassic art were, at first, applied to the Pacific scene by the artists who journeyed forth with the early discoverers (Plate 44, *facing page 333*). But the new worlds of sense and experience which the Pacific provided shattered the concepts which had been constructed on the basis of Europe's past. The light in a tropical country is simply not the light of Italy. The deciduous and coniferous mantle of nature in European climes is irrelevant to most of the Pacific landscapes. And the Polynesian or Australian man simply does not fit the classical formulae of stance and expression developed in the European tradition. Hence, after an initial period in which artists attempted to apply Western theory to Pacific reality it soon appeared that Western theory was beginning to be shaped by the Pacific reality.

The wider world of sense data that gave the scientists aboard the exploring ships new ideas supplied similar thoughts to the artists. Having shattered the neoclassical artist's emotional commitment to the scene he was portraying in favor of a more detached, intellectual description of each separate object, the European artist in the Pacific was able to search for a new unifying concept in the same manner that the naturalist sought for order in the midst of the new world of empirical sense data. In the case of the artists, the urge to depict with precision both the individual specimen and the natural habitat with which it was so intimately connected led to the organization of the animals, people, rocks, and atmosphere in such a way as to depict *types* of conditions in particular geographical situations. The landscape painting resulting from this approach may therefore be called "typical landscape," and reflects both the impact of science upon art, in which the Pacific was a master teacher, and the discovery of the beauty of the world beyond Europe.[28] Nature, hitherto organized by the artist to serve an inherited philosophy, was reshaped in response to an emerging philosophy whose assumptions the artist could only dimly feel.

Architectural theory was similarly affected. Acute observers like William Hodges, the first professional landscape painter to visit India as well as the first to visit the South Seas, perceived that climatic conditions in tropical countries dictated types of architecture that violated Western canons of proper form, but which were not less beautiful or utilitarian.[29] A Greek temple was right in the clear light and on the imposing rocky pedestals of Attica but it did not seem to "work" in a tropical rainforest in southeast Asia. But if it was not right for southeast Asia, perhaps it was not right for northern Europe. In sum, the Pacific forced an intellectual reappraisal of European assumptions about their own cultures at home, even while their national presence, in the persons of traders and soldiers, was being extended in the Pacific.

It is a noteworthy fact that it was William Hodges, the artist on Cook's second

voyage, and the Forsters—Johann Reinhold and his son Georg—the naturalists on the
expedition, who inspired Alexander von Humboldt to prepare himself for a career
of scientific travel. As the great German scholar but it:

> If I may have recourse to my own experience, and what awakened in me the first beginnings
> of an inextinguishable longing to visit the tropics, I should name George Forster's descriptions
> of the islands of the Pacific—painting by Hodge [sic] in the house of Warren Hastings, in
> London, representing the banks of the Ganges—and a colossal dragon tree in an old tower in
> the Botanical Gardens of Berlin.[30]

The chain of circumstance leads on to the next great master scientist of the age,
Charles Robert Darwin, whose work was stimulated by Humboldt.[31]

Literature also changed under the impact of Pacific exploration, bringing to a
climax the imaginative revolution that commenced with the first transoceanic voyages. It is difficult for us today to realize how all-absorbing were the manifold reports
of the sixteenth-, seventeenth-, and eighteenth-century voyages. A French bibli-
ographer, overwhelmed by the tide in the eighteenth century, reported that this
massive flood, which displaced imaginative tales and romances from the reading
public's attention, was a "mine feconde" which was worked not only by ordinary
persons, but by naturalists and geographers, artists and antiquarians, political writers,
economists, and moral philosophers.[32]

Not only did the voyages stimulate the imaginations of writers, but the voyage
form itself was adopted and adapted to literary purposes. One observer points out
that four of the five great eighteenth-century English novelists, from Daniel Defoe
to Lawrence Sterne, wrote accounts of their own trips.[33] The sea had always been
woven into the heritage of English history and life, but it was not until the eighteenth
century that it succeeded in shaping the spirit of imagination to "produce a succession
of great works in prose and verse."[34] Though the Atlantic played its role, it was the
Pacific which stirred the English imagination most deeply.

The great literary artist and the great scientist have this in common: they perceive
more readily than most the existence and significance of distinctions between men
and between objects. A figure like Henry David Thoreau can find his universe around
Walden Pond and proudly say "I have traveled much in Concord," but as a result
Thoreau's universe is somehow narrow and brittle despite the force of a great mind
brought to bear upon it. By contrast, the opening up of the largest ocean and the
vastest countries forced those brought up within the confines of the narrower Atlantic
world to re-think the comparisons and relationships with which they were familiar
to encompass the new reality brought to light by the voyages to the far Pacific.

So difficult was it to grasp the reality of this new world that a whole genre—the
false voyage—was able to spring up to fill the interstices between the accounts of
real voyages and the imaginative accounts of writers like Jonathan Swift (*Gulliver's
Travels*) and Daniel Defoe (*Robinson Crusoe*).[35] A typical example of such a false
voyage, which was reproduced in numerous languages in many editions, and which
has been perceptively analyzed by a skilled editor, is *The Isle of Pines or, A late Discovery of a fourth Island near Terra Australis, Incognita by Henry Cornelius Van Sloetten.
Wherein is contained. A True Relation of certain English persons, who in Queen Elizabeths
time, making a Voyage to the East Indies were cast away, and wracked near to the Coast
of Terra Australis, Incognita, and all drowned, except one Man and four Women. And now*

OMAI a Native of UTAIETEA,
Brought into England in the Year 1774, by Tobias Furneaux Esq.r Commander of his Majesty's Sloop Adventure.

The arrival of Omai, a native of Tahiti, with Captain Tobias Furneaux on his return to England in 1774, created a minor sensation. Omai was feted, lionized, and idealized. Sir Joshua Reynolds painted his portrait. Writers made use of him, as the exemplar of the "noble savage," to satirize the morals and manners of English society. Copper engraving. (Courtesy of the Peabody Museum, Salem, Mass.)

PLATE 43

INHABITANTS AND MONUMENTS OF EASTER ISLAND.

Illustration from an account of the scientific voyage of the Comte de La Pérouse, 1785–1789, undertaken at the direction of Louis XVI, King of France. The engraving is based on a drawing by Duché de Vancy, one of the artists employed by La Pérouse. From *Voyage of La Pérouse Around the World,* edited by M. L. A. Milet-Mureau and translated from the French, London, 1798, Plate 11. (Courtesy of the Library of Congress, Washington.)

PLATE 44

lately Anno Dom. 1667. a Dutch Ship making a Voyage to the East Indies, driven by foul weather there, by chance have found their Posterity, (speaking good English) to amount (as they suppose) to ten or twelve thousand persons. The whole Relation (written and left by the Man himself a little before his death, and delivered to the Dutch by his Grandchild) Is here annexed with the Longitude and Latitude of the Island, the scituation and felicity thereof, with other matter observable. London, 1668.[36]

So fantastic did even the serious pursuit of the unknown seem to many writers that the scientific observer and collector often became figures of satire. Sir Nicolas Gimcrack is depicted, in Joseph Addison's *Tatler* essays (1710) as "the standard comic figure of a virtuoso," while both Swift's *Gulliver's Travels* (1728) and Alexander Pope's *New Dunciad* (1742) satirize scientific investigation.[37]

The Pacific was too remote, too varied, too fabulous to be quickly or fully comprehended by the European mind of the period. Yet the eventual emergence of romanticism (and, eventually, naturalism) in the fine arts, in the theatre, and in literature was influenced, in no small measure, by the experience of the Pacific expeditions. It is not impossible to conceive of Western society, had it not been for its Pacific experience, developing in the "classic" mode, shaping and polishing its own glorious tradition and excluding or distrusting external influences. After all, the great Oriental kindgoms had followed such a policy in terms of their own great traditions. A similar development might have taken place in Europe in the period following the Renaissance but for the fact that a physical questing in space as well as an intellectual questing in time and subject then marked European development.

The physical quest for the wealth of the Orient was in part achieved. But it was the education of the European mind in the course of pursuing that goal that gave the greatest returns. Europe found not only wealth and trade, but impressive alien traditions, incomprehensible in terms of Europe's own "classic" tradition. Instead of being confirmed in a European cultural view, Europe was thrown into a school of competing cultures, and the first progress toward a world view began to emerge.

The Atlantic civilizations of themselves could not, and did not, perform this function. The distinctions between Europe's own culture and that of the peoples living on the western rim of the Atlantic were not translated into doubts concerning the assumptions underlying European civilization. A few perceptive observers, like Montaigne, could incorporate the evidence of the empire of Montezuma and other Indian civilizations destroyed by the Spanish into a new European world view, but, on the whole, the impact of American Indian culture on European culture expressed itself in the superficial aspects of life: the smoking habit, the use of certain food plants, and the like. If anything, a re-enforcement of European pride and self-satisfaction occurred in the Atlantic Basin because of the ease with which a handful of armed Europeans could physically dominate, destroy, or exploit the environment and its human occupants. Successful achievement of the physical aims of European colonization, usually accompanied by the destruction of native cultures, did not encourage introspection and a re-evaluation of basic assumptions.

In the case of the Pacific, however, the peoples first encountered were not physically overwhelmed by the European "barbarians" (as the Chinese referred to them) who brought their sailing ships into Oriental waters. The Europeans paused when they entered the Pacific and took thought, and as a result a revolution occurred.

The Pacific did not provide an answer to the problems that faced Western man. Rather, it raised questions about himself that he had never asked before. Travelers went to the Pacific with varying assumptions and values, and returned with new questions which demanded new answers. Some found a golden age in which the laws of nature pointed to the proper rules of life. Some found a brutal land in which man had to improve upon nature to be human. Sometimes the same areas and the same peoples evoked two contrary sentiments. More often than not, however, residents of different areas, such as Tahiti and Australia, induced different reactions, and the time factor also affected the attitudes.[38] The eighteenth-century explorers, in achieving a scientific overview of the physical structure of the Pacific—its shorelines, sea depths, flora and fauna—raised fundamental biological, anthropological, and moral questions. The nineteenth century took giant strides toward solving the biological problems raised; the twentieth century bids fair to solve many of the anthropological questions. It is not inconceivable that the germs of scientific curiosity and common greed which impelled the first searching ships will find their conclusion in the solution of some of the moral problems that have ever been man's most insoluble mysteries.

NOTES

Chapter 1

THE PACIFIC BASIN: AN INTRODUCTION

1. Edwin H. Bryan, Jr.: "Check list of atolls," *Atoll Research Bull.*, no. 19, pp. 1–38, Wash., D. C., 1953, p. 1; and his "Discussion" in F. R. Fosberg (ed.): *Man's place in the island ecosystem*, Honolulu, 1963, 264 pp., p. 37.

2. Andrew Sharp: "Ancient voyagers in the Pacific," *Polyn. Soc. Mem.*, no. 32, pp. 1–191, Wellington, N. Z., 1956; and his *Ancient voyagers in the Pacific*, Middlesex, Engl., 1957, 240 pp.

3. Christopher Lloyd: *Pacific horizons, the exploration of the Pacific before Captain Cook*, London, 1946, 188 pp.; Andrew Sharp: *The discovery of the Pacific Islands*, Oxford, 1960, 259 pp.

4. William P. Morrell: *Britain in the Pacific Islands*, Oxford, 1960, 454 pp.

5. H. Morse Stephens and Herbert E. Bolton (eds.): *The Pacific Ocean in history; papers and addresses presented at the Panama-Pacific historical congress, held at San Francisco, Berkeley, and Palo Alto, California, July 19–23, 1915*, New York, 1917, 535 pp.

6. William L. Thomas, Jr.: "The variety of physical environments among Pacific Islands," in F. R. Fosberg (ed.): *op. cit.* [note 1], pp. 7–37.

7. Significant textual, cartographic, and graphic publications are listed in the extensive notes for each chapter (Editor).

8. S. Francisco Andrade: "El Océano Pacifico," *Boletin de la Soc. Geogr. de Colombia*, vol. 12, pp. 127–148, Bogota, 1954; Hans Plischke: "Der Stille Ozean, Entdeckung und Erschliesung . . . ," *Janus-Bücher: Berichte zur Weltgeschichte*, vol. 14, pp. 1–94, München, 1959; Felix Riesenberg: *The Pacific Ocean*, New York, 1940, 322 pp.; Gerhard Schott: *Geographie des Indischen und Stillen ozeans; in auftrage der Deutschen seewarte verfasst . . .* , Hamburg, 1935, 413 pp.; Harald U. Sverdrup, M. W. Johnson, and R. H. Fleming: *The oceans, their physics, chemistry and general biology*, New York, 1942, 1087 pp.; Harald U. Sverdrup: "The Pacific Ocean," *Science*, vol. 94, pp. 287–293, Lancaster, Pa., 1941.

9. Charles L. Barrett: *The Pacific, ocean of islands*, Melbourne, 1950 (?), 176 pp.; Charles M. Davis: *South Sea islands*, New York, 1957, 64 pp.

10. Kenneth B. Cumberland: *Southwest Pacific; a geography of Australia, New Zealand and their Pacific island neighborhoods*, London, 1956, 365 pp.; Edward D. Laborde (ed.): *Australia, New Zealand, and the Pacific islands*, London, 1952, 268 pp.; Kathleen W. Robinson: *Australia, New Zealand and the Southwest Pacific*, London, 1960, 340 pp.

11. Otis W. Freeman (ed.): *Geography of the Pacific*, New York, 1951, 573 pp. See especially the introductory chapter by the editor: "Geographic setting of the Pacific," pp. 1–13.

12. Beno Gutenberg and C. F. Richter: *Seismicity and the earth and associated phenomena*, Princeton, N. J., 1954, 310 pp.; Internat'l Volcanological Assoc.: *Catalogue of the active volcanoes of the world, including Solfatara fields*, Naples, Italy, 1951–63, including sixteen parts, thirteen of which deal with areas in the Pacific Basin as follows:

Part I. "Indonesia," M. Neumann van Padang, 1951, 271 pp.; Part II. "Philippine Islands and Cochin China," M. Neumann van Padang, 1953, 49 pp.; Part III. "Hawaiian Islands," Gordon MacDonald, 1955, 37 pp.; Part V. "Melanesia," N. H. Fisher, 1957, 105 pp.; Part VI. "Central America," F. Mooser, H. Meyer-Aldrich and A. R. McBerney, 1958, 146 pp.; Part VII. "Kurile Islands," G. S. Gorshkov, 1958, 99 pp.; Part VIII. "Kamchatka and continental areas of Asia," V. I. Vlodavetz and B. I. Piip, 1959, 110 pp.; Part IX. "United States of America," Howard A. Coombs and Arthur D. Howard, 1960, 68 pp.; Part X. "Antarctica," William H. Berninghausen and N. Neumann van Padang, 1960, 32 pp.; Part XI. "Japan, Taiwan, and Marianas," Hisashi Kuno, 1962, 332 pp.; Part XII. "Greece," G. C. Georgalas, 1962, 40 pp.; Part XIII. "Kermadec, Tonga, and Samoa," J. J. Richard, 1962, 38 pp.; Part XIV. "Archipelago de Colon, Isla San Felix, and Islas Juan Fernandez," A. F. Richards, 1963, 50 pp.; Part XV. "Chilean Continent," Lorenzo Casertano, 1963, 55 pp.; Part XVI. "Arabia and the Indian Ocean," M. Neumann van Padang, 1963, 64 pp.

13. C. A. Cotton: "The rim of the Pacific," *Geogr. Journ.*, vol. 124, pp. 223–231, London, 1958, p. 224.

14. F. A. Vening Meinesz: "The difference of the tectonic development on the east and the west side of the Pacific," *Koninkl. Nederl. Akad. van Wetens.*, *Proc.*, vol. 63, ser. B., pp. 26–31, Amsterdam, 1960.

15. J. H. F. Umbgrove: "Different types of island-arcs in the Pacific," *Geogr. Journ.*, vol. 106, pp. 198–209, London, 1945.

337

Chapter 1

16. Ernest C. Andrews: "The structure of the Pacific Basin," *Sixth Pac. Sci. Congr., Berkeley and Stanford, 1939, Proc.*, vol. 1, pp. 201–204, Berkeley, 1940; Robert L. Fisher and Roger Revelle: "The trenches of the Pacific," *Scientific Amer.*, vol. 193, Part 5, pp. 36–41, New York, 1955; Harry H. Hess: "Major structural features of the western North Pacific, an interpretation of H. O. 5485, Bathymetric Chart Korea to New Guinea," *Geol. Soc. Amer., Bull.*, vol. 59, pp. 417–445, New York, 1948; Charles B. Officer: "Southwest Pacific crustal structure," *Amer. Geophys. Union, Trans.*, vol. 36, pp. 449–459, Wash., D. C., 1955; Russell W. Raitt, Robert L. Fisher, and Ronald G. Mason: "Tonga Trench," *Geol. Soc. Amer., Spec. Papers*, vol. 62, pp. 237–254, New York, 1955.

17. H. W. Menard: "The East Pacific rise," *Science*, vol. 132, pp. 1737–1746, Wash., D. C., 1961.

18. C. A. Cotton: *op. cit.* [note 13].

19. Beno Gutenberg and C. F. Richter: *op. cit.* [note 12], p. 103.

20. Perry Byerly: "Pacific coast earthquakes," *Amer. Scientist*, vol. 41, pp. 572–595, New Haven, Conn., 1953.

21. Robert S. Dietz: "The Pacific floor," *Scientific Amer.*, vol. 186, part 4, pp. 19–23, New York, 1952; Robert L. Fisher and Roger Revelle: *op. cit.* [note 16], p. 38.

22. Frederick Betz, Jr., and Harry H. Hess: "The floor of the North Pacific Ocean," *Geogr. Rev.*, vol. 32, pp. 99–116, New York, 1942; Harry H. Hess: "Drowned ancient islands of the Pacific Basin," *Internat'l Hydrogr. Rev.*, vol. 24, pp. 81–91, Monaco, 1947, and also in *Amer. Journ. Sci.*, vol. 244, pp. 772–791, New Haven, Conn., 1946; Edwin L. Hamilton: "Sunken islands of the Mid-Pacific Mountains," *Geol. Soc. Amer., Mem.*, vol. 64, pp. 1–97, New York.

23. Edwin L. Hamilton: *ibid.*

24. Kenneth O. Emery, J. I. Tracey, and H. S. Ladd: "Geology of Bikini and nearby atolls; Part 1. geology," *U. S. Geol. Surv., Prof. Paper*, no. 260A, pp. 1–265, Wash., D. C., 1954.

25. Richard F. Flint: *Glacial and Pleistocene geology*, New York, 1957, 553 pp.

26. F. P. Shepard and H. E. Suess: "Rate of post-glacial rise of sea-level," *Science*, vol. 123, pp. 1082–1083, Lancaster, Pa., 1956; Herold J. Wiens: *Pacific island bastions of the United States*, Princeton, N. J., 1962, 127 pp.

27. Herbert E. Gregory: "Types of Pacific islands," *Third Pan-Pac. Sci. Conf. Tokyo, 1926, Proc.*, vol. 2, pp. 1663–1673, Tokyo, 1928.

28. Brian Essai: *Papua and New Guinea: A contemporary survey*, Melbourne, 1961, 255 pp.

29. R. A. Derrick: *The Fiji Islands; a geographical handbook*, Suva, 1957, 334 pp.

30. Jean P. M. LeBorgne: *Géographie de la Nouvelle-Calédonie et des Isles loyauté*, Nouméa, New Caledonia, 1957, 307 pp.

31. D. W. McKenzie: *Man, map and landscape in New Zealand*, Wellington, N. Z., 1958, 3 vols.

32. Risaburo Tayama: ". . . Coral reefs in the South Seas . . . ," *Japan, Hydrogr. Off., Bull.*, vol. 11, pp. 1–292, Tokyo, 1952.

33. Edwin H. Bryan, Jr.: "Check list . . ." [note 1].

34. F. R. Fosberg: "Quantitative description of the coral atoll ecosystem," *Atoll Research Bull.*, no. 81, pp. 1–11, Wash., D. C., 1961; and his "Vegetation of central Pacific atolls, a brief summary," *Atoll Research Bull.*, no. 23, pp. 1–23, Wash., D. C., 1953.

35. J. I. Tracey, Jr., and P. E. Cloud, Jr., and K. O. Emery: "Conspicuous features of organic reefs," *Atoll Research Bull.*, no. 46, pp. 1–3, Wash., D. C., 1955.

36. Herold J. Wiens: *Atoll environment and ecology*, New Haven, Conn., 1962, 532 pp., pp. 32–35.

37. Earl L. Stone, Jr.: "Summary of information on atoll soils," *Atoll Research Bull.*, no. 22, pp. 1–4, Wash., D. C., 1953.

38. Blumenstock, David I.: "Distribution and characteristics of tropical climates," *Ninth Pac. Sci. Congr. Bangkok, 1957, Proc.*, vol. 20, pp. 3–24, Bangkok, 1958.

39. Jen-hu Chang: "Comparative climatology of the tropical western margins of the Northern Oceans," *Assoc. Amer. Geogr., Annals*, vol. 52, pp. 221–227, Lawrence, Kans., 1962.

40. David I. Blumenstock (ed.): "A report on typhoon effects upon Jaluit Atoll [Marshall Islands]," *Atoll Research Bull.*, no. 75, pp. 1–105, 1961, Wash., D. C.; K. P. Kidd and C. K. Reed: "Typhoons of the Southwest Pacific, 1945," *Amer. Meteorol. Soc., Bull.*, vol. 27, pp. 288–305, New York, 1946.

41. U. S. Weather Bureau: *U. S. Navy marine climatic atlas of the world.* Vol. 2, *North Pacific Ocean;* Vol. 5, *South Pacific Ocean*, Wash., D. C., 1956.

42. A. M. Muromçev: *Scheme of general circulation of the Pacific Ocean waters (T323R)*, Ottawa, 1959, 6 pp.

43. John A. Knauss: "The Cromwell Current," *Scientific Amer.*, vol. 204, part 4, pp. 105–116, New York, 1961; M. Tsuchiya: "An oceanographic description of the equatorial current system of the Western Pacific," *Oceanog. Mag.*, vol. 13, pp. 1–30, Tokyo, 1961.

44. Gerhard Schott: "The distribution of rain over the Pacific Ocean," *Fifth Pac. Sci. Congr., Victoria and Vancouver, 1933, Proc.*, vol. 3, pp. 1987–1990, Toronto, 1934; Gerhard Schott: *Geographie des Indischen und Stillen Ozeans*, Hamburg, 1935, 413 pp.; Takeshi Sekiguchi: "The rainfall distribution in the Pacific region," *Seventh Pac. Sci. Congr., Auckland and Christchurch, 1949, Proc.*, vol. 3, pp. 101–102, Wellington, 1952; C. J. Seelye: "Rainfall and its variability over the central and southwestern Pacific," *N. Z. Journ. Sci. and Techn.*, sect. B, vol. 32, part 2, pp. 11–24, Wellington, 1952.

45. Jen-hu Chang: *op. cit.* [note 39].

46. Gerhard Schott: "Die aufteilung der drei ozeane in natürliche regionen," *Peterm. Geogr. Mitt.*, vol. 82, pp. 165–170, 218–222, Gotha, 1936.

47. Glenn T. Trewartha: *The earth's problem climates*, Madison, Wisc., 1961, 334 pp., pp. 13–33, 86–88, 174–179.

48. J. Gentilli: "Climatology of the Central Pacific," *Seventh Pac. Sci. Congr., Auckland and Christchurch, 1949, Proc.*, vol. 3, pp. 92–100, Wellington, 1952.

49. B. J. Garnier: *The climate of New Zealand; a geographic survey*, London, 1958, 191 pp.

50. Bernard W. Smith: *European vision and the South Pacific, 1768–1850: a study in the history of art and ideas*, Oxford, 1960, 287 pp.

51. Stephen Haden-Guest (ed.): "A world geography of forest resources," *Amer. Geogr. Soc., Spec. Pub.*, no. 33, pp. 1–736, New York, 1956. See "Oceania," pp. 611–630.

52. K. H. Marshall: "Plants and vegetation of New Caledonia," *Wellington Bot. Soc., Bull.*, vol. 27, pp. 19–21, Wellington, 1954.

53. Felix M. Keesing: "Field guide to Oceania," *Nat'l Res. Council, Field Guide Series*, no. 1, pp. 1–51, Wash., D. C., 1959.

54. Jacques Barrau: "Plant introduction in the tropical Pacific; its role in economic development," *Pacific Viewpoint*, vol. 1, pp. 1–10, 1960; Andrew H. Clark: *The invasion of New Zealand by people, plants and animals; the South Island*, New Brunswick, N. J., 1949, 465 pp.; W. R. B. Oliver: "Changes in the flora and fauna of New Zealand," *Forest and Bird . . .*, vol. 113, pp. 9–13, Wellington, 1954.

55. W. B. Johnston: "Human geography of the Pacific: a review," *N. Z. Geographer*, vol. 13, pp. 67–82, Auckland, 1957; W. B. Johnston: "The Cook Islands; land use in an island group of the south-west Pacific," *Journ. of Tropical Geography*, vol. 13, pp. 38–57, 1959; D. W. McKenzie: *op. cit.* [note 31].

56. A. Grenfell Price: *The Western invasions of the Pacific and its continents; a study of moving frontiers and changing landscapes, 1513–1958*, Oxford, 1963, 263 pp.

Chapter 2
THE ART AND SCIENCE OF NAVIGATION IN RELATION TO GEOGRAPHICAL EXPLORATION BEFORE 1900

1. George Chapman (tr. and ed.): *The Odysseys of Homer*, London, 1897, 2 vols., vol. 1, pp. 197–222.

2. John H. Rose: *Man and the sea; stages in maritime and human progress*, New York, 1936, 288 pp., pp. 20–21.

3. George Rawlinson (ed.): *The History of Herodotus . . .*, London, 1858–1860, 4 vols., vol. 3, pp. 28–29.

4. American Bible Society: *The Holy Bible . . .*, New York, 1956, 1 Kings 9, verses 27–28.

5. Horace L. Jones (tr.): *The geography of Strabo . . .*, London, 1917–23, 8 vols., vol. 2, pp. 157–159.

6. Louis R. Nougier, J. Beaujeu, and M. Mollat: *Histoire Universelle des Explorations*, Paris, 1955, vol. 1, p. 201.

7. Edward H. Bunbury: *A history of ancient geography among the Greeks and Romans from the earliest ages till the fall of the Roman Empire*, London, 1883, 2 vols., vol. 1, pp. 122–123.

8. *Ibid.*, vol. 2, pp. 4–5.

9. *Ibid.*, vol. 1, pp. 318–335.

10. Horace L. Jones: *op. cit.* [note 5], vol. 1, pp. 48–51.

11. Eva G. R. Taylor: *The haven-finding art; a history of navigation from Odysseus to Captain Cook*, London, 1956, 295 pp., p. 49.

12. Horace L. Jones: *op. cit.* [note 5], vol. 1, pp. 232-235, 398-399.

13. *Ibid.*, vol. 1, pp. 236-237.

14. Edward H. Bunbury: *op. cit.* [note 7], vol. 1, p. 600.

15. Eva G. R. Taylor: *op. cit.* [note 11], pp. 43-46.

16. Louis R. Nougier and others: *op. cit.* [note 6], vol. 1, p. 202.

17. Walter W. Hyde: *Ancient Greek mariners*, New York, 1947, 360 pp., p. 15.

18. The former is available in modern translation as *Der Periplus des erythräischen Meeres von einem Unbekannten* (Leipzig, 1883, 188 pp.); Strabo's *Geographia*, completed before 20 A.D., was first printed in an edition published in Venice in 1496 (166 leaves).

19. Horace L. Jones: *op. cit.* [note 5], vol. 1, pp. 22-25.

20. *Ibid.*, vol. 1, pp. 504-505.

21. *Ibid.*, vol. 1, pp. 361-367.

22. George A. L. Sarton: *Introduction to the history of science*, Carnegie Inst. Publ. no. 376, Wash., D.C., 1927-28, 3 vols., vol. 1, p. 273.

23. Thomas L. Heath: *The Copernicus of antiquity (Aristarchus of Samos)*, London, 1920, 59 pp. However, such a theory might be inferred from Anaxagoras' obscure philosophical systems. Charles J. Singer: *A short history of science to the nineteenth century*, Oxford, 1941, 399 pp.

24. American Bible Society: *op. cit.* [note 4], Acts 27, verse 28. Among the many references to ships and sailing in this well-known chapter the allusion to soundings in this verse is of particular interest.

25. Horace L. Jones: *op. cit.* [note 5), vol. 8, pp. 22-29.

26. Thomas K. Derry and Trevor I. Williams: *A short history of technology from earliest times to A.D. 1900*, Oxford, 1960, 782 pp., pp. 196-197.

27. Eva G. R. Taylor: *op. cit.* [note 11], pp. 6-20 and illustration opp. p. 37.

28. George F. Hourani: *Arab seafaring in the Indian Ocean in ancient and early medieval times*, Princeton, N. J., 1951, 131 pp., p. 61.

29. Lionel Casson: *The ancient mariners; seafarers and sea fighters of the Mediterranean in ancient times*, New York, 1959, 286 pp., p. 10.

30. George Rawlinson: *op. cit.* [note 3], vol. 3, pp. 30-31.

31. Edward H. Bunbury: *op. cit.* [note 7], vol. 1, pp. 534-541.

32. *Ibid.*, vol. 2, p. 351.

33. J. W. McCrindle (trans. and ed.): "The Christian topography of Cosmas an Egyptian monk," *Hakly. Soc. Works, Series 1*, vol. 98, pp. 1-398, London, 1897, p. 365.

34. George F. Hourani: *op. cit.* [note 28], p. 63.

35. Joseph Needham: *Science and civilization in China*, Cambridge, Eng., 1954, 4 vols., vol. 3, p. 565.

36. G. S. Laird Clowes: "Ships of early explorers," *Geogr. Journ.*, vol. 69, pp. 216-235, London, 1927, p. 222.

37. Alexander von Humboldt was among those who held the opinion that the compass was transmitted westward from China by the Arabs (E. C. Otté, tr.): *Cosmos: a sketch of a physical description of the universe*, New York, 1878, pp. 628-629). Other scholars do not subscribe to this view (Eva G. R. Taylor: *op. cit.* [note 11], p. 96). Joseph Needham: *op. cit.* [note 35], vol. 4, pp. 330-331, postulates: ". . . overland westward transmission, . . ." while others, including Lynn White: *Medieval technology and social change*, Oxford, 1962, 194 pp., p. 132, affirm that the Arab sailors obtained the compass from the Latin West.

38. George F. Hourani: *op. cit.* [note 28], p. 109.

39. George H. T. Kimble: *Geography in the middle ages*, London, 1938, 272 pp., p. 47.

40. George F. Hourani: *op. cit.* [note 28], pp. 100-104.

41. Richard L. Bowen: "Arab dhows of eastern Arabia," *Amer. Nept.*, vol. 9, pp. 87-132, Salem, Mass., 1949, p. 93; also by the same author "Egypt's earliest sailing ships," *Antiquity*, . . . , vol. 24, pp. 117-131, Newbury, Eng., 1960, p. 125.

42. George A. L. Sarton: *op. cit.* [note 22], vol. 1, p. 17.

43. Eva G. R. Taylor: *op. cit.* [note 11], pp. 76-77.

44. Charles R. Beazley: *The dawn of modern geography. A history of exploration and geographical science* . . . , London, 1897-1906, 3 vols., vol. 2, pp. 17-22.

45. Louis R. Nougier and others: *op. cit.* [note 6], vol. 1, pp. 283-301.

46. J. W. McCrindle: *op. cit.* [note 33], pp. 30-31.

47. John K. Wright: ". . . The geographical lore of the time of the Crusades; a study in the history of medieval science and tradition in western Europe," *Amer. Geogr. Soc., Res. Series*, no. 15, pp. 1-563, New York, 1925, p. 54. Dover ed. (Dover Pubs., Inc.), 1965, p. 54.

48. John Healey (tr.): *Aurelius Augustinus: The city of God (De civitate Dei)* ..., London, 1947, 2 vols., vol. 2, pp. 114–115.

49. John K. Wright: *op. cit.* [note 47], pp. 49 and 75.

50. *Ibid.*, pp. 11–12.

51. Charles R. Beazley: *op. cit.* [note 44], vol. 3, pp. 508–509, and Eva G. R. Taylor: *op. cit.* [note 11], pp. 95–96.

52. George H. T. Kimble: *op. cit.* [note 39], pp. 91–92.

53. Eva G. R. Taylor: *op. cit.* [note 11], p. 101.

54. Lynn Thorndike (ed. and tr.): *The sphere of Sacrobosco and its commentators*, Chicago, 1949, 496 pp., p. 1.

55. John K. Wright: *op. cit.* [note 47], pp. 72–82.

56. *Ibid.*, p. 79.

57. John K. Wright: "Notes on the knowledge of latitudes and longitudes in the Middle Ages," *Isis*, vol. 5, pp. 75–98, Cambridge, Mass., 1923, p. 89.

58. John K. Wright: *op. cit.* [note 47], pp. 97–99.

59. Silvanus P. Thompson: "The rose of the winds: the origin and development of the compass-card," *Brit. Acad. London, Proc.*, 1913–1914, pp. 179–209, London, 1919 (?). Plates I-VI.

60. Lynn Thorndike: *The history of medieval Europe*, New York, 1917, 682 pp., p. 345–346.

61. Eva G. R. Taylor: *op. cit.* [note 11], pp. 104–121.

62. John Frampton (tr.): *The most noble and famous travels of Marco Polo, together with the travels of Nicolò de' Conti*, London, 1929, 381 pp., p. lvi.

63. Charles R. Beazley and E. Prestage (trs.): "G. Eannes de Azurara: The chronicle of the discovery and conquest of Guinea," *Hakly. Soc. Works, Series 1*, vols. 95 and 100, London, 1896–1899, vol. 95, p. 17.

64. George H. T. Kimble: "Portuguese policy and its influence on fifteenth century cartography," *Geogr. Rev.*, vol. 23, pp. 653–659, New York, 1933, p. 656. This is identified by some authorities as Marino Sanudo's *Mappamundi*, ca. 1320.

65. Charles R. Beazley and E. Prestage: *op. cit.* [note 63], vol. 95, pp. 33–35.

66. Boies Penrose: *Travel and discovery in the Renaissance, 1420–1620*, Cambridge, Mass., 1952, 369 pp., pp. 269–273.

67. Gerald R. Crone (tr. and ed.): "The voyages of Cadamosto and other documents on western Africa in the second half of the fifteenth century," *Hakly. Soc. Works, Series 2*, vol. 80, pp. 1–159, London, 1937, p. 2.

68. Charles R. Beazley and E. Prestage: *op. cit.* [note 63], vol. 100, pp. cxliv–cl.

69. John F. Meigs: *The story of the seaman; being an account of the ways and appliances of seafarers of ships from the earliest time until now*, Philadelphia, 1924, 2 vols. vol. 2, p. 532.

70. Ahmad ibn Mājid al-Saʾdī: *Três roteiros desconhecidos [por T. A. Chumovsky] de Ahmad ibn Mājid al-Saʾdī O piloto árabe de Vasco da Gama*, Lisboa, 1959, 195 pp. (?), p. 18. For an illustration of the kamal and many of the instruments referred to in this chapter see Eva G. R. Taylor and M. W. Richey: *The geometrical seaman; a book of early nautical instruments*, London, 1962, pp. 47–48.

71. E. G. Ravenstein (tr.): "Roteiro da viagem. A journal of the first voyage of Vasco da Gama, 1497–1499," *Hakly. Soc. Works, Series 1*, vol. 99, pp. 1–256, London, 1898, pp. 198–199.

72. John F. Meigs: *op. cit.* [note 69], vol. 2, pp. 535–537.

73. E. G. Ravenstein: *op. cit.* [note 71], pp. 167–169.

74. Benjamin Keen (tr. and annot.): *The life of Admiral Christopher Columbus by his son, Ferdinand*, New Brunswick, N.J., 1959, 316 pp., pp. 14–15.

75. Samuel E. Morison: *Admiral of the ocean sea, a life of Christopher Columbus*, Boston, 1942, 680 pp., p. 104.

76. Clements R. Markham (tr.): "Colombo C.: Journal ... (during his first voyage, 1492–93) and documents relating to the voyages of John Cabot and Gaspar Corte Real," *Hakly. Soc. Works, Series 1*, vol. 86, pp. 1–259, London, 1893, p. 23.

77. Boies Penrose: *op. cit.* [note 66], p. 265.

78. Clements R. Markham: *op. cit.* [note 76], p. 200 and footnote. For a new interpretation of this subject see David B. Quinn: "The argument for the English discovery of America between 1480 and 1494," *Geogr. Journ.*, vol. 127, part 3, pp. 277–285, London, 1961.

79. John N. L. Baker: ... *A history of geographical discovery and exploration*, London, 1931, 543 pp., pp. 85–103.

80. James Burney: *A chronological history of the discoveries in the South sea or Pacific ocean ...*, London, 1803–1817, 5 vols., vol. 1, pp. 40–43.

81. Charles R. Beazley and E. Prestage: *op. cit.* [note 63], vol. 95, pp. xcvii–xcviii.

82. Edward L. Stevenson: "The geographical activities of the Casa de la Contratación," *Assoc. Amer. Geogr., Annals*, vol. 17, pp. 39–59, Nashville, 1927.

83. John N. L. Baker: *op. cit.* [note 79], pp. 112–130.

84. Thomas L. Heath: *op. cit.* [note 23], p. 1.

85. John L. E. Dreyer: *Tycho Brahe, a picture of scientific life and work in the sixteenth century*, Edinburgh, 1890, 405 pp., pp. 2–9.

86. Johannes Mueller (Regiomontanus): *Der deutsche kalendar des Johannes Regiomontan, Nürnberg, um 1474* . . . , Leipzig, 1937, 20 pp.

87. Alexander Pogo: "Gemma Frisius, his method of determining differences of longitude by transporting timepieces (1530), and his treatise on triangulation (1533) . . . ," *Isis*, vol. 22 (64), 469–506, Bruges, 1935, pp. 469–485.

88. Clements R. Markham: *op. cit.* [note 76], pp. xxxviii-xl.

89. Duane H. Du B. Roller: *The De magnete of William Gilbert*, Amsterdam, 1959, 196 pp., p. 47.

90. Sylvanus P. Thompson: "William Gilbert and terrestrial magnetism," *Geogr. Journ.*, vol. 21, pp. 611–618, London, 1903.

91. David W. Waters: *The art of navigation in England in Elizabethan and early Stuart times*, New Haven, Conn., 1958, 696 pp., pp. 95–105.

92. Lawrence C. Wroth: *The way of a ship; an essay on the literature of navigation science*, Portland, Me., 1937, 91 pp., pp. 54–55.

93. Eva G. R. Taylor: *The mathematical practitioners of Tudor and Stuart England*, Cambridge, Eng., 1954, 442 pp., pp. 327–328.

94. Boies Penrose: *op. cit.* [note 66], pp. 269–273.

95. Eva G. R. Taylor: *op. cit.* [note 11], p. 205.

96. Albert H. Markham (ed.): "The voyages and works of John Davis the navigator," *Hakly. Soc. Works, Series 1*, vol. 59, pp. 1–392, London, 1880, pp. lv-lvi.

97. J. B. Hewson: *A history of the practice of navigation*, Glasgow, 1951, 270 pp., pp. 114–117 and illustration on p. 115.

98. Lawrence C. Wroth: *op. cit.* [note 92], pp. 61–64.

99. E. C. Otté and B. H. Paul: *op. cit.* [note 37], vol. 2, p. 631.

100. Eva G. R. Taylor: *op. cit.* [note 11], illustration opp. p. 196.

101. William L. Clowes and others: *The royal navy, a history from the earliest times to the present* . . . , Boston, 1897–1903, 7 vols., vol. 1, p. 604.

102. G. M. Asher (tr. and ed.): "Henry Hudson, the navigator. The original documents in which his career is recorded, collected, partly translated, and annotated . . . ," *Hakly. Soc. Works, Series 1*, vol. 27, pp. 1–292, London, 1860, pp. 23–44.

103. John J. Fahie: *Galileo, his life and work*, London, 1903, 451 pp., pp. 74–97.

104. John J. Fahie: *Memorials of Galileo Galilei, 1564–1642*, London, 1929, 172 pp., p. 135 and illustration opp. p. 124.

105. Christiaan Huygens: *Œuvres complètes publiées par la Société hollandaise des sciences*, La Haye, 1888–1950, 22 vols., vol. 22, p. 580.

106. Eva G. R. Taylor: "The geographical ideas of Robert Hooke," *Geogr. Journ.*, vol. 89, pp. 525–538, London, 1937.

107. Edward W. Maunder: *The Royal observatory, Greenwich. A glance at its history and work*, London, 1900, 320 pp., p. 40.

108. Some scholars have proposed that this phenomenon should be known as declination and that the term variation be reserved for secular variation. However, the word variation is used in this study for "the angle between magnetic north and true north" for two reasons: 1) this is earlier usage and 2) it is still the preferred term among navigators. *Van Nostrand's Scientific Encyclopedia* . . . , Princeton, N. J., 1958, 1839 pp., p. 387, states the case thus: "Most surveyors, some geologists and a few other scientists use the term 'declination' instead of 'variation' for this angle [defined above]. The standard practice in the American air services, and in the U. S. Navy and Merchant Marine is to use the term variation." See also the entry under "Variation of the Compass" in Nathaniel Bowditch: ". . . American practical navigator, an epitome of navigation and nautical astronomy, originally by Nathaniel Bowditch, LL.D.," *U.S.H.O. Publ.*, no. 9, pp. 1–391, Wash., D. C., 1962 (reprint of 1958 edition).

109. Duane H. Du B. Roller: *op. cit.* [note 89] p. 159. Gilbert also believed that the earth's magnetic poles coincide with the poles of the earth (poles of rotation, i.e., geographical or astronomical poles).

110. Arthur R. Hinks: Review of "S. Chapman: 'Edmond Halley as physical geographer and the story of charts' in Occasional Notes, Royal Astronomical Society, No. 9, 15 pp., 1951," *Geogr. Journ.*, vol. 98, pp. 293–296, London, 1941.

111. John Smith (Captain): "A sea grammar," *Travels*, vol. 2, pp. 223–229, 1907. Among other things Smith warns the seaman against having iron nails in the compass box.

112. Joseph C. Shipman: "William Dampier, seaman-scientist," *Univ. of Kansas Publ. in Library Sci. Series no. 15*, pp. 1–63, Lawrence, Kans., 1962.

113. John Masefield (ed.): *Dampier's voyages; consisting of a new voyage round the world, a supplement to the Voyage round the world* . . . , New York, 1906, 2 vols., vol. 1, pp. 4–5.

114. Lawrence C. Wroth: *op. cit.* [note 92], p. 78.

115. "Zounds, man! We could as soon find out the longitude!" This is Marlow's reaction to rambling directions given him by Tony Lumkin in Oliver Goldsmith: *She stoops to conquer, and The good-natured man. With an introduction by Henry Morley*, London, 1905, 191 pp. Jonathan Swift also makes several allusions to longitude in his writings.

116. David Brewster: . . . *The life of Sir Isaac Newton*, New York, 1831, 323 pp., p. 231.

117. Norman J. W. Thrower: "The discovery of the longitude: observations on carrying timekeepers for determining longitude at sea, 1530–1770," *Navigation* . . . , vol. 5, pp. 375–381, Los Angeles, 1957–1958.

118. Rupert T. Gould: *The marine chronometer; its history and development*, London, 1923, 287 pp.

119. Raleigh A. Skelton: "Captain James Cook as a hydrographer," *Mar. Mirr.*, vol. 40, pp. 91–119, London, 1954, pp. 109–113.

120. Grenville D. Zerfass: "Two mirrors: the story of the invention of the sextant," *Navigation* . . . , vol. 3, pp. 131–138, Los Angeles, 1952.

121. John Hadley: "A spirit level to be fixed to a quadrant for taking a meridional altitude at sea, when the horizon is not visible," *Roy. Soc., Philos. Trans., London*, vol. 38 (430), pp. 167–172, London, 1735.

122. J. B. Hewson: *op. cit.* [note 97], p. 84.

123. Nathaniel Bowditch: *op. cit.* [note 108], p. 6.

124. Thomas K. Derry and Trevor I. Williams: *op. cit.* [note 26], pp. 365–370.

125. Alfred B. Lubbock: *The China clippers*, Glasgow, 1922, 388 pp., pp. 1–3.

126. G. S. Laird Clowes: *op. cit.* [note 36], pp. 226–229, and illustrations on p. 227 and opp. p. 229.

127. Charles L. Lewis: *Matthew Fontaine Maury, the pathfinder of the seas*, Annapolis, Md., 1927, 264 pp., p. 44.

128. Jaquelin A. Caskie: *Life and letters of Matthew Fontaine Maury*, Richmond, Va., 1928, 191 pp., pp. 28–44.

129. Thomas K. Derry and Trevor I. Williams: *op. cit.* [note 26], p. 376.

130. Grenville D. Zerfass: "What's our speed? The evolution of ship logs," *Navigation* . . . , vol. 3, pp. 232–239, Los Angeles, 1953. A discussion of speed and distance measurement at sea, from a piece of wood tossed overboard (the ancient ship log which gave its name to all such devices) to the electrical submerged-rotator logs of today.

131. Constantine J. Phipps, 2nd Baron Mulgrave: *A voyage towards the North Pole undertaken by His Majesty's command, 1773*, London, 1774, 253 pp. This account of the expedition by its leader Captain C. J. Phipps, later Lord Mulgrave, is a model of journal writing and scientific reporting. Historians have been eager to point out that Horatio Nelson served as a midshipman on this voyage.

132. William Thomson, 1st Baron Kelvin: . . . *Popular lectures and addresses*, London and New York, 1891–1894, 3 vols., vol. 3, pp. 337–369.

133. *Ibid.*, pp. 295–322.

134. Nathaniel Bowditch: *op. cit.* [note 108], p. 32.

135. Thomas K. Derry and Trevor I. Williams: *op. cit.* [note 26], pp. 621–622.

136. Nathaniel Bowditch: *op. cit.* [note 108], p. 47.

137. Frank B. Goodrich: *The history of the sea, a graphic description of maritime adventures, achievements, explorations, discoveries and inventions* . . . , Philadelphia, 1873 (?), 784 pp., pp. 630–650.

Chapter 3

MAP COMPILATION, PRODUCTION, AND RESEARCH IN RELATION TO GEOGRAPHICAL EXPLORATION

[Editor's note] The following fundamental works by R. A. Skelton should be listed at the outset: (a) "Charts and views drawn by Cook and his officers and reproduced from the original manuscript," in *The journals of Captain Cook on his voyage of discovery*, Portfolio, Cambridge, Engl., 1955, 58 views and 8 pp. text; (b) *Decorative printed maps of the 15th to 18th centuries; a revised edition of old decorative maps and charts*, by Arthur L. Humphreys, London and New York, 1952, 80 pp. and 81 maps; (c) "Early maps and the printer," *Printing Review, 1951–52*, pp. 26–29, London, 1953; (d) Skelton, R. A. (ed.): *History of cartography by Leo Bagrow*. Rev. and enl. by R. A. Skelton, London, 1964, 312 pp.; (e) "Explorers' maps. I. The northeast passage," *Geogr. Mag.*, vol. 26 (3), pp. 119–131, London, 1953; (f) "Explorers' maps. II. The northwest passage, Frobisher to Parry," *Geogr. Mag.*, vol. 26 (4), pp. 192–205, London, 1953; (g) "Explorers' maps. III. Cathay or a new world? The discovery of America from Columbus to Magellan," *Geogr. Mag.*, vol. 26, pp. 519–533, London, 1954; (h) "Explorers' maps. IV. The Portuguese seaway to the Indies," *Geogr. Mag.*, vol. 26 (11), pp. 610–623, London, 1954; (i) "Explorers' maps. V. European rivalry for the Spice Islands," *Geogr. Mag.*, vol. 26 (12), pp. 627–638, London, 1954; (j) "Explorers' maps. VI. Marco Polo and his successors," *Geogr. Mag.*, vol. 27 (6), pp. 267–280, London, 1954; (k) "Explorers' maps. VII. The Far East in the 16th and 17th centuries," *Geogr. Mag.*, vol. 27 (7), pp. 339–351, London, 1954; (l) "Explorers' maps. VIII. The Spanish in the Pacific," *Geogr. Mag.*, vol. 27 (11), pp. 543–556, London, 1955; (m) "Explorers' maps. X. James Cook and the mapping of the Pacific," *Geogr. Mag.*, vol. 28, pp. 95–106, London, 1955; (n) "Explorers' maps. XI. The new world in the 16th century," *Geogr. Mag.*, vol. 28, pp. 439–450, London, 1956; (o) "Explorers' maps. XII. North America from sea to sea, 1600–1800," *Geogr. Mag.*, vol. 28, pp. 489–501, London, 1956; (p) *Explorers' maps; chapters in the cartographic record of geographical discovery*," London, 1958, 337 pp.

1. Samuel E. Morison: *Portuguese voyages to America in the fifteenth century*, Cambridge, Mass., 1940, 151 pp., ch. I; and Wilcomb E. Washburn: "The meaning of 'discovery' in the fifteenth and sixteenth centuries," *Amer. Hist. Rev.*, vol. 48, pp. 1–21, Richmond, Va., 1962.

2. Armand Rainaud: *Le continent austral; hypothèses et découvertes*, Paris, 1893, 490 pp., part 1; and Lawrence C. Wroth: "The early cartography of the Pacific," *Bibl. Soc. Amer.*, *Papers*, vol. 38 (2), pp. 87–268, New York, 1944, pp. 91–104.

3. Lawrence C. Wroth: *ibid.*, p. 93.

4. Pierre d'Ailly: *Imago mundi*, Louvain, ca. 1483, 172 leaves, ch. XIX. See also Pierre d'Ailly: ... *Imago mundi, de Pierre d'Ailly* ..., Paris, 1930–1931, in 3 vols.; and Pierre d'Ailly: *Imago mundi*, translated from the Latin by Edwin T. Keever, from "the Latin photostat of a printed copy in the British Museum," Wilmington, N. C., 1948, 92 pp.

5. Cf. Michael C. Andrews: "The study and classification of medieval mappae mundi," *Archaeologia*, vol. 75, pp. 61–76, London, 1926; Richard Uhden: "Zur Herkunft und Systematik der mittelalterlichen Weltkarten," *Geogr. Zeit.*, vol. 37, pp. 321–340, Leipzig, 1931; and Marcel Destombes (ed.): *Monumenta cartographica vetustioris aevi, A.D. 1200–1500, vol. 1, Mappemondes*, 322 pp., Amsterdam, 1964, in French.

6. Roberto Almagià: "I mappamondi di Enrico Martello e alcuni concetti geografici di Cristoforo Colombo," *La Bibliofilia*, vol. 42, pp. 27–44, 1940.

7. Armando Cortesão: ... *Cartografia portuguesa antiga*, Lisboa, 1960, 195 pp., pp. 166–169.

8. José Pulido Rubio: *El piloto mayor de la Casa de la Contratación de Sevilla; pilotos mayores, catedráticos de cosmografía y cosmógrafos*, Sevilla, 1950, 983 pp., pt. I.

9. Lawrence C. Wroth: *op. cit.*, [note 2], pp. 126–127.

10. Cited by Charles R. Boxer: "South China in the sixteenth century, being the narratives of Galeote Pereira, Fr. Gaspar de Cruz, O. P. [and] Fr. Martín de Rada, O.E.S.A. (1550–1575)," *Hakluyt. Soc., Works*, Series 2, vol. 106, pp. 1–388, London, 1953, p. lxx.

11. Alexander Dalrymple: *An account of the discoveries made in the South Pacific Ocean, previous to 1764. Part I* ... London, printed in 1767, and published in 1769, 103 pp.

12. Armand Rainaud: *op. cit.* [note 2], pt. II.

13. Armando Cortesão and Avelino Teixeira da Mota: *Portugaliae monumenta cartographica*, vol. 3, pp. 71–72 and plate 363, Lisboa, 1960.

14. Resolutions of the States-General, dated 15 April 1592, cited in Frederik C. Wieder (ed.): *Monumenta cartographica* . . ., The Hague, 1925–1933, 5 vols.

15. George C. Henderson: *The discoverers of the Fiji islands: Tasman, Cook, Bligh, Wilson, Bellingshausen*, London, 1933, 324 pp., ch. IV; and Johannes Keuning: "Hessel Gerritsz," *Imago Mundi*, vol. 6, pp. 49–66, Stockholm, 1949.

16. Jan E. Heeres: *Het aandeel der Nederlanders in de ontdekking van Australië 1606–1765* (*the part borne by the Dutch in the discovery of Australia*), Leiden and London, 1899, 256 pp., p. 52.

17. William Wales: *Astronomical observations made in the voyages . . . for making discoveries in the Southern Hemisphere . . .*, London, 1788, 146 pp., p. 108. [See also his *The original astronomical observations made in the course of a voyage towards the South Pole, . . . in the years 1772–1775*, London, 1788, 385 pp. (Editor)].

18. Cited by K. St. B. Collins in his "Admiral Sir Francis Beaufort," *Navigation . . .* vol. 11, pp. 266–281, London, 1958, p. 266.

19. Lloyd A. Brown: *The story of maps*, Boston, 1951, 397 pp., p. 282.

Chapter 4

GEOGRAPHICAL KNOWLEDGE OF THE PACIFIC PEOPLES

1. Francis T. Palgrave (comp.): *A golden treasury of English verse*, New York, 1935, 460 pp. For the quotation from Keats see CCX, p. 199. [Editor]

2. Peter H. Buck: *Vikings of the sunrise*, New York, 1938, 335 pp.

3. Andrew Sharp: *Ancient voyagers in the Pacific*, Harmondsworth, Middlesex, Eng., 1957, 240 pp.; Andrew Sharp: *Ancient voyagers in Polynesia*, Berkeley, Calif., 1963, 159 pp.

4. W. E. L. H. Crowther: "Method of migration of the extinct Tasmanian race," *Polyn. Soc., Journ.*, vol. 46, pp. 225–231, New Plymouth, N. Z., 1937; D. S. Davidson: "Transport and receptacles in aboriginal Australia," *Polyn. Soc., Journ.*, vol. 46, pp. 175–205, New Plymouth, N. Z., 1937, pp. 176–177.

5. Frederick D. McCarthy: " 'Trade' in aboriginal Australia, and 'trade' relationships with Torres Strait, New Guinea and Malaya," *Oceania . . .*, vol. 9, pp. 405–438; vol. 10, pp. 80–104, 171–195, Sydney, 1939.

6. *Ibid.*, vol. 10, pp. 98–99.

7. Ronald M. Berndt and Catherine H. Berndt: *Arnhem Land, its history and its people*, Melbourne, 1954, 243 pp., esp. pp. 3–75; Arthur Capell: "Mythology in Northern Kimberley, North-West Australia," *Oceania . . .*, vol. 9, pp. 382–404, Sydney, 1939, esp. pp. 403–404; Frederick D. McCarthy: *op. cit.* [note 5]; Frederick D. McCarthy: "The Oceanic and Indonesian affiliations of Australian aboriginal culture," *Polyn. Soc. Journ.*, vol. 62, pp. 243–261, Wellington, 1953; Frederick D. McCarthy: "Report on Australia and Melanesia," *Asian Persp.*, vol. 5, pp. 141–155, Hong Kong, 1962; J. G. Nelson: "Pre-European trade between Australia, Indonesia, and the Asiatic mainland," *Canadian Geographer*, vol. 5(4), pp. 18–22, Ottawa, 1961.

8. Ronald M. Berndt and Catherine H. Berndt: *ibid.*, p. 60.

9. Frederick D. McCarthy: *op. cit.* [note 5], pp. 180–183; Alfred C. Haddon and James Hornell: "Canoes of Oceania . . .," *Bernice P. Bishop Mus., Spec. Papers*, vols. 27–29, Honolulu, 1937–1938, vol. 28, pp. 179–200; Alfred C. Haddon and others: *Reports of the Cambridge Anthropological Expedition to Torres Straits*, Cambridge, Eng., 1912–1935, 6 vols., vol. 1, pp. 295–297.

10. William Churchill: "Sissano; movements of migration within and through Melanesia," *Carnegie Inst. of Wash., Publ.*, no. 244, pp. 1–181, Wash., D. C., 1916, p. 10; Gerrit Jan Held: *The Papuas of Waropen*, The Hague, 1957, 384 pp., p. 4–5 and 15; Alfred C. Haddon and James Hornell: *ibid.*, pp. 40, 116, 152–153, 302 and 320; Alphonse Reisenfeld: *The megalithic culture of Melanesia*, Leiden, 1950, 736 pp., pp. 513 and 519–520.

11. Stephen W. Reed: "The making of modern New Guinea, with special reference to culture contact in the mandated territory," *Amer. Philos. Soc., Mem.*, vol. 18, pp. 1–326, Philadelphia, 1943, p. 45.

12. Alphonse Reisenfeld: *op. cit.* [note 10], p. 345.

13. William Churchill: "The Polynesian wanderings; tracks of the migration deduced from an examination of the proto-Samoan content of Efaté and other languages of Melanesia," *Carnegie Inst. Wash., Publ.*, no. 134, pp. 1–516, Wash., D. C., 1911, p. 490.

14. Bronislaw Malinowski: *Argonauts of the western Pacific: an account of native enterprise and adventure in the archipelagoes of Melanesian New Guinea*, London, 1922, 527 pp., pp. 219–228.

15. C. E. Fox: "Prefixes and their function in Oceanic languages (ma, nga)," *Polyn. Soc., Journ.*, vol. 57, pp. 227–255, New Plymouth, N. Z., 1948, p. 253.

16. F. L. S. Bell: "Travel and communication in Tanga," *Oceania* . . . , vol. 21, pp. 81–106, Sydney, 1950, p. 83, n. 5.

17. A. C. Haddon and James Hornell: *op. cit.* [note 9], vol. 28, p. 42.

18. Robert H. Codrington: *The Melanesians: studies in their anthropology and folklore*, Oxford, 1891, 410 pp., p. 11.

19. T. H. Harrisson: "Living with the people of Malekula," *Geogr. Journ.*, vol. 88, pp. 97–127, London, 1936, p. 100.

20. Alphonse Reisenfeld: *op. cit.* [note 10], p. 543; Alfred C. Haddon and James Hornell: *op. cit.* [note 9], vol. 28, p. 3.

21. Robert C. Suggs: *The island civilizations of Polynesia*, New York, 1960, 256 pp.; pp. 68–72; Robert C. Suggs: *Archaeology of Nuku Hiva*, 1961, pp. 11–12 and 175–176; Jack Golson: "Report on New Zealand, Western Polynesia, New Caledonia, and Fiji," *Asian Persp.*, vol. 5 (2), pp. 166–180, Hong Kong, 1961, p. 176.

22. Cited in Martha Beckwith: "Polynesian story composition," *Polyn. Soc., Journ.*, vol. 53, pp. 177–203, Wellington, N. Z., 1944, pp. 200–201.

23. For examples of the traditional location of Hawaiki in Asia see: Abraham Fornander: *An account of the Polynesian race; its origin and migrations and the ancient history of the Hawaiian people to the times of Kamehameha I*, London, 1878–1885, 3 vols., vol. 1, pp. 5–25; Elsdon Best: "The origin of the Maori. The hidden homeland of the Maori, and its probable location," *Polyn. Soc., Journ.*, vol. 32, pp. 10–20, New Plymouth, N. Z., 1923; S. Percy Smith: *Hawaiki: The original home of the Maori* . . . , Christchurch, N. Z., 1921, 223 pp., p. 7; Edward Tregear: *The Maori race*, Wanganui, N. Z., 1904, 592 pp., pp. 552–560.

For Savaii as Hawaiki see Horatio Hale: "Migrations in the Pacific Ocean," *Amer. Journ. Sci. and Arts*, series 2, vol. 1 (3), pp. 317–332, New Haven, Conn., 1846, pp. 321–323; Robert C. Suggs: *op. cit.* [note 21], pp. 86–101; Andrew Sharp: *Ancient voyagers in Polynesia, op. cit.* [note 3], pp. 75–86.

For Raiatea as Hawaiki see Peter H. Buck: *op. cit.* [note 2], pp. 67–100.

For Hakai Straits as Hawaiki see Thor Heyerdahl: *American Indians in the Pacific; the theory behind the Kon-Tiki expedition*, London, 1952, 821 pp., pp. 169–178.

24. S. Percy Smith: "Hawaiki: the whence of the Maori: being an introduction to Rarotonga history," *Polyn. Soc., Journ.*, vol. 7, pp. 1–48, Wellington, N. Z., 1898, pp. 14–15.

25. S. Percy Smith: "The fatherland of the Polynesians. Aryan and Polynesian points of contact," *Polyn. Soc. Journ.*, vol. 28, pp. 18–30, Wellington, N. Z., 1919, p. 24; S. Percy Smith: *op. cit.* [note 23], p. 7; Elsdon Best: *op. cit.* [note 23], pp. 12–14.

26. Thor Heyerdahl: *op. cit.* [note 23], p. 753.

27. Peter H. Buck: *op. cit.* [note 2], p. 115.

28. S. Percy Smith: *op. cit.* [note 24], pp. 10–11.

29. S. Percy Smith: "Notes on the geographical knowledge of the Polynesians," *Austral. Assoc. Adv. Sci., Rept.*, vol. 7, pp. 801–816, Sydney, 1898, p. 816.

30. Andrew Sharp: *Ancient voyagers in the Pacific, op. cit.* [note 3], pp. 33, 40.

31. *Ibid.*, p. 30.

32. Douglas L. Oliver: *The Pacific Islands*, Garden City, New York, 1961, 456 pp., pp. 69–70.

33. Andrew P. Vayda: "Polynesian cultural distributions in new perspective," *Amer. Anthrop.*, vol. 61, pp. 817–828, Menasha, Wis., 1959, p. 817.

34. Edwin N. Ferdon, Jr.: "Polynesian origins. Theories of migration from Asia or America obscure the probability that the culture had many sources," *Science*, vol. 141, pp. 499–505, Lancaster, Pa., 1963, p. 501.

35. Ward H. Goodenough: "Oceania and the problem of controls in the study of cultural and human evolution," *Polyn. Soc., Journ.*, vol. 66, pp. 146–155, Wellington, N. Z., 1957, pp. 146–149; Ward H. Goodenough: "Migrations implied by relationships of New Britain dialects to Central Pacific languages," *Polyn. Soc., Journ.*, vol. 70, pp. 112–126, Wellington, N. Z., 1961, p. 113.

36. Brett Hilder: "Primitive navigation in the Pacific-III," *Polyn. Soc., Journ.*, vol. 71 (4), (Supplement), pp. 81–97, Wellington, N. Z., 1962.

37. Keith Sinclair: *A history of New Zealand*, Harmondsworth, Middlesex, Eng., 1959, 320 pp., pp. 17–18. See also edition for 1961.

38. Kenneth B. Cumberland: "Moas and men: New Zealand about A. D. 1250," *Geogr. Rev.*, vol. 52, pp. 151–173, New York, 1962, pp. 158–160.

39. Kenneth P. Emory: "The origin of the Hawaiians," *Polyn. Soc., Journ.*, vol. 68, pp. 29–35, Wellington, N. Z., 1959, p. 30; and personal communication.

40. Alexander Spoehr: "Marianas prehistory: archaeological survey and excavations on Saipan, Tinian, and Rota," *Chicago Natural History Mus., Fieldiana, Anthrop. Papers.*, vol. 48, pp. 1–187, Chicago, 1957, p. 176; and personal communication.

41. Robert C. Suggs: *Archaeology . . . , op. cit.* [note 21], pp. 73–85.

42. Roger Duff: "Pacific adzes and migrations (a reply to Andrew Sharp)," *Polyn. Soc., Journ.*, vol. 69, pp. 276–282, Wellington, 1960.

43. G. H. Heyen: "Primitive navigation in the Pacific," *Polyn. Soc., Journ.*, vol. 71, (mem. no. 34) pp. 64–79, Wellington, N. Z., 1963. See also in Jack Golson (ed.): "Polynesian navigation," *Polyn. Soc., Mem.*, no. 34, pp. 64–79, Wellington, N. Z., 1963.

44. J. P. Frankel: "Polynesian navigation," *Navigation . . .*, vol. 9, pp. 35–47, Los Angeles, 1962; J. P. Frankel: "Polynesian migration voyages: accidental or purposeful?," *Amer. Anthrop.*, vol. 65, pp. 1125–1127, Menasha, Wis., 1963.

45. G. S. Parsonson: "The settlement of Oceania: An examination of the accidental voyage theory," *Polyn. Soc., Journ.*, vol. 71 (mem. no. 34), pp. 11–63, Wellington, N. Z., 1963.

46. G. M. Dening: "The geographical knowledge of the Polynesians and the nature of inter-island contact," *Polyn. Soc., Journ.*, vol. 71 (mem. no. 34), pp. 102–131, Wellington, N. Z., 1963.

47. Peter H. Buck: *op. cit.* [note 2], p. 148.

48. Leslie G. Kelly: "Cook Island origin of the Maori," *Polyn. Soc., Journ.*, vol. 64, pp. 181–196, Wellington, N. Z., 1955, pp. 181–182.

49. Robert C. Suggs: *op. cit.* [note 21], pp. 11 and 181.

50. G. S. Parsonson: *op. cit.* [note 45], p. 58.

51. G. H. Heyen: *op. cit.* [note 43], p. 66.

52. *Ibid.*, p. 76.

53. William T. Pritchard: *Polynesian reminiscences; or, life in the South Pacific islands*, London, 1866, 428 pp., p. 406.

54. James Cook: *A voyage towards the South Pole, and round the world. Performed in His Majesty's ships the Resolution and Adventure, in the years, 1772, 1773, 1774, and 1775. Written by James Cook, commander of the Resolution . . .*, London, 1777, 2 vols., vol. 1, p. 216.

55. G. S. Parsonson: *op. cit.* [note 45], p. 35; G. M. Dening: *op. cit.* [note 46], p. 131; James Morrison: *The journal of James Morrison, boatswain's mate of the Bounty . . .*, London, 1935, 242 pp., pp. 204–205.

56. George W. Anderson: *A new, authentic, and complete collection of voyages round the world*, London, 1784, 3 vols., vol. 2, p. 157.

57. Bolton G. Corney (ed. and tr.): "The quest and occupation of Tahiti by emissaries of Spain during the years 1772–1776. Told in dispatches and other contemporary documents," *Hakly. Soc., Works*, series 2, vols. 32, 36, 43, London, 1913–1919, vol. 36, p. 284.

58. Arthur Grimble: "Gilbertese astronomy and astronomical observances," *Polyn. Soc., Journ.*, vol. 40, pp. 197–224, Wellington, N. Z., 1931, pp. 197–200.

59. M. W. Makemson: *The morning star rises, an account of Polynesian astronomy*, New Haven, Conn., 1941, 301 pp.

60. Hugh Rodman: "The sacred calabash," *Polyn. Soc., Journ.*, vol. 37, pp. 75–85, New Plymouth, N. Z., 1928, see note by Stokes, pp. 85–87; Chester B. Duryea, Jr.: "Au Sujet de la Calebasse sacrée des Îles Hawaii," *Soc. Océaniennes, Bull.*, vol. 7(8), pp. 259–263, Papeete, Tahiti, 1947, see note in same volume by Peter H. Buck, pp. 290–291; Alfred C. Haddon and James Hornell: *op. cit.* [note 9], vol. 27, 1937, p. 26.

61. Ernest and Pearl Beaglehole: "Ethnology of Pukapuka," *Bernice P. Bishop Mus., Bull.*, no. 150, pp. 1–419, Honolulu, 1938, p. 353; G. M. Dening: *op. cit.* [note 46], p. 119.

62. Harold Gatty: *Nature is your guide; how to find your way on land and sea by observing nature*, New York, 1958, 287 pp.

63. J. P. Frankel: *op. cit.* [note 44].

64. Brett Hilder: "Review of J. P. Frankel's 'Polynesian navigation,' " *Navigation . . .*, vol. 10, pp. 188–191, Wash., D. C., 1963.

65. Brett Hilder: *op. cit.* [note 36].

66. G. S. Parsonson: *op. cit.* [note 45], p. 26. See also Harold Gatty: *op. cit.* [note 62], pp. 33–37; G. M. Dening: *op. cit.* [note 46], pp. 114–115; Taylor White: "On the use of birds in navigation," *Polyn. Soc., Journ.*, vol. 16, pp. 92–93, Wellington, N. Z., 1907; Alfred C. Haddon and James Hornell: *op. cit.* [note 9], vol. 27, p. 146; James Hornell: "The role of birds in early navigation," *Antiquity; . . .*, vol. 79, pp. 142–149, Gloucester, Eng., 1946.

67. Andrew Sharp: *Ancient voyagers in the Pacific, op. cit.* [note 3], p. 50; Andrew Sharp: *Ancient*

voyagers in Polynesia, op. cit. [note 3], pp. 41–42; Andrew Sharp: "Polynesian navigation to distant islands," *Polyn. Soc., Journ.*, vol. 70, pp. 219–226, Wellington, N. Z., 1961, p. 224.

68. Brett Hilder: *op. cit.* [note 36], pp. 81–83.

69. G. M. Dening: *op. cit.* [note 46], p. 118.

70. James Wilson: *A missionary voyage to the Southern Pacific Ocean, performed in the years 1796, 1797, 1798, in the ship Duff*, London, 1799, 420 pp., p. lxxxvi.

71. Andrew Sharp: *Ancient voyagers in the Pacific, op. cit.* [note 3], p. 47.

72. John Williams: *A narrative of missionary enterprises in the South Sea Islands*, London, 1837, 589 pp., pp. 98, 104 note, 504–505, 511.

73. William Ellis: *Narrative of a tour through Hawaii, or Owhyhee* . . . , London, 1826, 442 pp., pp. 371–374.

74. Robert C. Suggs: "Historical traditions and archaeology in Polynesia," *Amer. Anthrop.*, vol. 62 (5), pp. 764–773, Menasha, Wis., 1960, p. 771.

75. G. H. Heyen: *op. cit.* [note 43], p. 76.

76. Andrew Sharp: *op. cit.* [note 3], p. 136.

77. W. J. L. Wharton (ed.): *Captain Cook's journal during his first voyage round the world, 1768–1771*, 1893, pp. 121–122.

78. Bolton G. Corney (ed. and tr.): *op. cit.* [note 57], p. 272.

79. Elmer D. Merrill: "The botany of Cook's voyages and its unexpected significance in relation to anthropology, biogeography, and history," *Chronica Botanica*, vol. 14 (5–6), pp. 164–384, Waltham, Mass., 1954, pp. 219–220.

80. Robert C. Suggs: *op. cit.* [note 21], pp. 113 and 173.

81. Andrew P. Vayda: *op. cit.* [note 33].

82. Roger Duff: "Neolithic adzes and eastern Polynesia," in J. D. Freeman and W. R. Geddes (eds.): *Anthropology in the South Seas; essays presented to H. D. Skinner*, pp. 121–147, New Plymouth, N. Z., 1959, p. 144.

83. Andrew Sharp: "Pacific adzes and migrations," *Polyn. Soc., Journ.*, vol. 69, pp. 39–42, Wellington, N. Z., 1960, p. 40.

84. Roger Duff: *op. cit.* [note 82], pp. 276 and 281.

85. Edwin N. Ferdon, Jr.: *op. cit.* [note 34], p. 499.

86. William Ellis: *op. cit.* [note 73], p. 327.

87. John Williams: *op. cit.* [note 72], pp. 365 and 504–505.

88. William T. Pritchard: *op. cit.* [note 53], pp. 402–403.

89. For example see Roland B. Dixon: "The long voyages of the Polynesians," *Amer. Philos. Soc., Proc.*, vol. 74(3), pp. 167–175, Philadelphia, Pa., 1934; and his "The long voyages of the Polynesians," *Polyn. Soc., Journ.*, vol. 44 (1), p. 59, Wellington, N. Z., 1935; and especially Jack Golson (ed.): " 'Polynesian navigation.' A symposium on Andrew Sharp's theory of accidental voyages . . . ," *Polyn. Soc. Mem.*, no. 34, pp. 1–153, Wellington, N. Z., 1963, p. 5; and G. M. Dening: *op. cit.* [note 46], see "Table II. A table of accidental and deliberate voyages in the South Pacific," pp. 137–153.

90. Personal communication from R. Gerard Ward, University College, London. Gerard Ward and John Webb of the University of Minnesota calculated the hypothetical movements of drifting voyagers, basing the direction of movement on wind and current conditions plotted for 5° squares in the tropical Pacific. The predominant movement was westward with occasional easterly voyages.

91. See for example Thomas Gladwin: "Canoe travel in the Truk area: Technology and its psychological correlates," *Amer. Anthrop.*, vol. 60, pp. 893–899, Menasha, Wis., 1958, p. 898; Friedrich Ratzel: *The history of mankind*, New York, 1896–1898, 3 vols., vol. 1, p. 119.

92. William T. Pritchard: *op. cit.* [note 53], p. 406.

93. Johann R. Forster: *Observations made during a voyage round the world, on physical geography, natural history, and ethic philosophy* . . . , London, 1778, 649 pp., p. 509.

94. Andrew Sharp: *Ancient voyagers in Polynesia, op. cit.* [note 3], pp. 39–40.

95. Otto von Kotzebue: *A voyage of discovery, into the South sea and Beering's straits, for the purpose of exploring a north-east passage, undertaken in the years 1815–1818 at the expense of His Highness* . . . , London, 1821, 3 vols., vol. 2, pp. 240–242, vol. 3, p. 111.

96. For reference to Father Paul Clain, June 10, 1697, see in James Burney: *A chronological history of the discoveries in the South sea or Pacific ocean* . . . , London, 1803–1817, 5 vols., vol. 5, p. 9.

97. Otto von Kotzebue: *op. cit.* [note 95], vol. 3, p. 139.

98. Otto Sittig: "Compulsory migrations in the Pacific Ocean," *Smiths. Inst. Ann. Rept.* for 1895, pp. 519–535, Wash., D. C., 1895, p. 524.

99. Joseph E. Weckler, Jr.: ". . . Polynesians, explorers of the Pacific," *Smiths. Inst. War Background Studies*, no. 6, pp. 1–77, Wash., D. C., 1943, pp. 69–70.

100. G. M. Dening: *op. cit.* [note 46], pp. 129–130.

101. Frederick W. Beechey: *Narrative of a voyage to the Pacific and Beering's strait, . . .* , London, 1831, 2 vols., vol. 1, p. 185.

102. John C. Beaglehole (ed.): "The journals of Captain James Cook on his voyages of discovery," *Hakly. Soc., Works, Extra Series*, no. 34, vol. 1, "The voyage of the Endeavour, 1768–1771," Cambridge, Eng., 1955, 284 + 684 pp., and no. 35, vol. 2, "The voyage of the Resolution and Adventure, 1772–1775," Cambridge, Eng., 1961, 170 + 1021 pp., vol. 1, pp. 156–157.

103. Friedrich Ratzel: *op. cit.* [note 91], p. 64.

104. David Porter: *Journal of a cruise made to the Pacific Ocean, by Captain David Porter, in the United States frigate Essex, in the years 1812, 1813, and 1814*, New York, 1822, 2 vols., vol. 2, p. 52.

105. John Williams: *op. cit.* [note 72], p. 58.

106. Raymond W. Firth: "History and traditions of Tikopia," *Polyn. Soc., Mem.*, no. 32, pp. 1–224, Wellington, N. Z., 1961, p. 151.

107. G. M. Dening: *op. cit.* [note 46], p. 128, note 214.

108. Ward H. Goodenough: "Oceania . . . ," *op. cit.* [note 35], pp. 148–149; Alan H. Smith "Micronesia," *Asian Persp.*, vol. 2 (1), pp. 68–85, Tucson, Ariz., 1958, pp. 70–71.

109. Alexander Spoehr: *op. cit.* [note 40], p. 176.

110. Alexander Spoehr: "Time perspective in Micronesia and Polynesia," *Southwestern Journ. of Anthrop.*, vol. 8, pp. 457–465, Albuquerque, N. M., 1952, p. 463.

111. Douglas Osborne: "Archaeology in Micronesia. Background, Palau studies and suggestions for the future," *Asian Persp.*, vol. 5 (2), pp. 156–163, Hong Kong, 1961, pp. 157–158.

112. Ward H. Goodenough: "Native astronomy in Micronesia: a rudimentary science," *Sci. Mon.*, vol. 73, pp. 105–110, Wash., D. C., 1951, pp. 106–107; Ward H. Goodenough: *Native astronomy in the Central Carolines*, Philadelphia, Pa., 1953, 46 pp.

113. William Davenport: "Marshall Islands navigational charts," *Imago Mundi*, vol. 15, pp. 19–26, Leiden, Netherlands, 1960, p. 19.

114. Otto Finsch: *Ethnologische erfahrungen und belegstrücke aus der Südsee*, n.p., (?) 1893; an English translation in typescript has been deposited in the Sinclair Library, University of Hawaii, Honolulu, p. 81; U. H. H[all]: "A Marshall Island chart," *Univ. of Penn. Mus. Journ.*, vol. 10, pp. 35–42, Philadelphia, Penn., 1919, pp. 41–42.

115. Ward H. Goodenough: *op. cit.* [note 112], p. 108.

116. William Dampier: *A new voyage round the world . . .* , London, 1703–1709, 3 vols., vol. 1, p. 300; Alfred C. Haddon and James Hornell: *op. cit.* [note 9], vol. 27, p. 439.

117. Jacques É. V. Arago: *Narrative of a voyage round the world, in the Uranie and Physicienne corvettes, commanded by Captain Freycinet, during the years 1817, 1818, 1819, and 1820; on a scientific expedition undertaken by order of the French government . . .* , London, 1823, 2 vols., vol. 1, p. 16.

118. Arthur F. Grimble: "Canoes in the Gilbert Islands," *Roy. Anthrop. Inst. Journ.*, vol. 54, pp. 101–139, London, 1924, p. 133.

119. Roland W. Force: "Leadership and cultural change in Palau," *Chicago Natural Historical Mus., Fieldiana, Anthrop. Papers*, vol. 50, pp. 1–221, Chicago, 1960, p. 22.

120. H. D. Skinner: "Some aspects of the history of Polynesian material culture," *Polyn. Soc., Journ.*, vol. 60, pp. 40–45, Wellington, N. Z., 1951, p. 45.

121. Marcian Pellett and Alexander Spoehr: "Marianas archaeology: report on an expedition in Tinian," *Polyn. Soc., Journ.*, vol. 70, pp. 321–325, Wellington, N. Z., 1961.

122. Douglas Osborne: "The Palau Islands: stepping stones into the Pacific," *Archaeology*, vol. 2, pp. 162–171, New York, 1958, pp. 168–171; Allan H. Smith: "Micronesia," *Asian Persp.*, vol. 3 (1), pp. 53–55, Hong Kong, 1959, p. 54.

123. Inez de Beauclair: "Some ancient beads of Yap and Palau," *Polyn. Soc., Journ.*, vol. 72 (1), pp. 1–10, Wellington, N. Z., 1963, pp. 3–4.

124. Personal communication from Leonard Mason, Department of Anthropology, University of Hawaii, Honolulu.

125. James Burney: *op. cit.* [note 96], pp. 9–10.

126. Otto von Kotzebue: *op. cit.*, [note 95], vol. 3, pp. 92 and 139.

127. Ernst G. Sarfert: "Zur kenntnis der schiffahrtskunde der Karolinen," *Deutsche Gesell. für Anthropologie, Ethnologie und Urgeschichte, Korrespondenz-blatt*, vol. 42, pp. 131–136, Leipzig, 1911, p. 134.

128. P. Hambruch: "Die schiffahrt auf den Karolinen und Marshallinseln," *Meereskunde Sammlung Volkstümlicher Vorträge zum verständnis der Nationalen Bedeutung von Meer und Seewesen*, vol. 66, p. 25, Berlin, 1912.

129. Laura Thompson: "The native culture of the Marianas islands," *Bernice P. Bishop Mus., Bull.*, no. 185, pp. 1–48, Honolulu, 1945, p. 41.

130. Frederick W. Christian: *The Caroline Islands; travel in the sea of little lands*, London, 1899, 412 pp., pp. 318–320; John H. Brandt: "Nan Matol: ancient Venice of Micronesia [Ponape]," *Archaeology*, vol. 15 (2), pp. 99–107, New York, 1962, pp. 106.

131. William A. Lessa: "Ulithi and the outer native world," *Amer. Anthrop.*, vol. 52, pp. 27–52, New York, 1950, pp. 42, 48–49; William A. Lessa: "Myth and blackmail in the Western Carolines," *Polyn. Soc., Journ.*, vol. 65, pp. 65–74, Wellington, N. Z., 1956, pp. 66–71; Edwin G. Burrows and Melford E. Spi.o: *An atoll culture; ethnography of Ifaluk in the central Carolines*, New Haven, Conn., 1957, 355 pp., pp. 7–10.

132. Alfred C. Haddon and James Hornell: *op. cit.* [note 9], vol. 27, p. 439.

133. Ward H. Goodenough: *op. cit.* [note 112], p. 105.

134. Thomas Gladwin and Seymour B. Sarason: *Truk: Man in paradise*, New York, 1953, 655 pp., p. 39; Thomas Gladwin: *op. cit.* [note 91], pp. 893–894.

135. Jacques É. V. Arago: *op. cit.* [note 117], p. 13.

136. Andrew Sharp: *Ancient voyagers in the Pacific, op. cit.* [note 3], pp. 79–81.

137. Otto von Kotzebue: *op. cit.* [note 95], vol. 2, pp. 233 and 240–241, vol. 3, pp. 83 and 111; Laura Thompson: *op. cit.* [note 129], pp. 25 and 41; Robert R. Solenberger: "Contrasting patterns of Carolinian population distribution in the Marianas," in Anthony F. C. Wallace (ed.): *Men and Cultures*, 1956, pp. 513–518; Frederick W. Christian: *op. cit.* [see footnote 130], p. 20.

138. George Anson: *A voyage round the world, . . ., sent upon an expedition to the South-Seas . . .*, London, 1749, 417 pp., pp. 339–343; Alfred C. Haddon and James Hornell: *op. cit.*, [note 9], vol. 27, pp. 417 and 440; Douglas Osborne: *op. cit.* [note 111], p. 162.

139. Captain Winkler: "On sea charts formerly used in the Marshall Islands, with notices on the navigation of these islanders in general"; *Smiths. Inst. Ann. Rept., 1899*, pp. 487–508, Wash., D. C., 1901, p. 502.

140. For distances covered by Marshallese voyagers see Friedrich Ratzel: *op. cit.* [note 91], pp. 167 and 170; Alfred C. Haddon and James Hornell: *op. cit.* [note 9], vol. 27, p. 374; Henry Lyons: "The sailing charts of the Marshall Islanders," *Geogr. Journ.*, vol. 72, pp. 325–328, London, 1928, p. 325; U. H. H[all]: *op. cit.* [note 114], pp. 35–42; "Editorial Note 292," *Polyn. Soc., Journ.*, vol. 28 (4), p. 234, Wellington, N. Z., 1919.

141. Brett Hilder: *op. cit.* [note 36], p. 88.

142. Andrew Sharp: *Ancient voyagers in Polynesia, op. cit.* [note 3], pp. 82, 192–193.

143. Charles Wilkes: *Narrative of the United States exploring expedition. During the years 1838, 1839, 1840, 1841, 1842*, Philadelphia, Penn., 1845, 5 vols., vol. 5, p. 82.

144. Charles M. Woodford: "The Gilbert Islands," *Geogr. Journ.*, vol. 6, pp. 325–350, London, 1895, p. 342; G. H. Heyen: *op. cit.* [note 43], p. 69.

145. H. C. Maude and H. E. Maude: "The social organization of Banaba or Ocean Island, Central Pacific," *Polyn. Soc., Journ.*, vol. 41, pp. 262–301, New Plymouth, N. Z., 1932, p. 284.

146. Raymond W. Firth: *op. cit.* [note 106], p. 158; Raymond W. Firth: *We, the Tikopia . . .*, London, 1936, pp. 82–83; Alfred C. Haddon and James Hornell: *op. cit.* [note 9], vol. 28, p. 78; G. S. Parsonson: *op. cit.* [note 45], pp. 48–49.

147. Charles Wilkes: *op. cit.* [note 143], pp. 81–82; Charles M. Woodford: *op. cit.* [note 144], p. 342; Charles M. Woodford: "On some little-known Polynesian settlements in the neighbourhood of the Solomon Islands," *Geogr. Journ.*, vol. 48, pp. 26–54, London, 1916, p. 28.

148. Arthur F. Grimble: *op. cit.* [note 118], p. 209; Arthur F. Grimble: "From birth to death in the Gilbert Islands," *Roy. Anthrop. Inst., Journ.*, vol. 51, pp. 25–54, London, 1921, pp. 49–54; Arthur F. Grimble: "The migrations of a pandanus people, as traced from a preliminary study of food, food-traditions, and food-rituals in the Gilbert Islands," *Polyn. Soc., Mem.*, no. 12, pp. 1–112, Wellington, N. Z., 1933–1934, pp. 10 and 57–59.

149. H. E. Maude: "The evolution of the Gilbertese boti," *Polyn. Soc., Journ., Suppl.*, vol. 72 (1), pp. 1–68, Wellington, N. Z., 1963, pp. 5–7.

150. Robert C. Suggs: *op. cit.* [note 21], p. 99.

151. Alfred C. Haddon and James Hornell: *op. cit.* [note 9], vol. 27, p. 319; G. S. Parsonson: *op. cit.* [note 45], pp. 37–39.

152. Walter Lawry: *A second missionary visit to the Friendly and Feejee Islands, in the year 1850*, London, 1851, 270 pp.

153. Charles Wilkes: *op. cit.* [note 143], vol. 3, p. 347.

154. Alfred C. Haddon and James Hornell: *op. cit.* [note 9], vol. 27, p. 334, and vol. 28, p. 67.

155. Thomas Williams and James Calvert: *Fiji and the Fijians*, New York, 1858, 551 pp., p. 85.

156. William Mariner: *An account of the natives of the Tonga Islands in the South Pacific Ocean . . .*, London, 1817, 2 vols., p. 417.

157. Peter Dillon: *Narrative and successful result of a voyage in the South seas performed by order of the government of British India, to ascertain the fate of La Perouse's expedition*, London, 1829, 2 vols., vol. 2, pp. 78–79.

158. Arthur M. Hocart: "Lau Islands, Fiji," *Bernice P. Bishop Mus., Bull.*, no. 62, pp. 1–241, Honolulu, 1929, p. 230.

159. George Turner: *Nineteen years in Polynesia: Missionary life, travels and researches in the islands of the Pacific*, London, 1861, 548 pp., p. 270.

160. Peter H. Buck: *op. cit.* [note 2], pp. 294–297; Peter H. Buck: "Samoan material culture," *Bernice P. Bishop Mus., Bull.*, no. 75, pp. 1–724, Honolulu, 1930, p. 417.

161. Jack Golson: "Report on New Zealand, Western Polynesia, New Caledonia, and Fiji," *Asian Persp.*, vol. 5, pp. 166–180, Hong Kong, 1961, pp. 175–176.

162. See Derrick in Gilbert D. Kennedy: *op. cit.* [note 146], p. 42; Raymond W. Firth: *op. cit.* [note 106], pp. 86, 93, 109–120; Arthur G. Grimble: "The migrations . . . ," *op. cit.* [note 148], pp. 67–70.

163. Ernest and Pearl Beaglehole: *op. cit.* [note 61], p. 417; J. J. K. Hutchin: "Traditions and some words of the language of Danger or Pukapuka Island," *Polyn. Soc., Journ.*, vol. 13, pp. 173–174, Wellington, N. Z., 1904, p. 173; G. M. Dening: *op. cit.* [note 46], pp. 119–122; William Burrows: "Some notes and legends of a South Sea Island. Fakaofo of the Tokelau or Union Group," *Polyn. Soc., Journ.*, vol. 32, pp. 143–173, New Plymouth, N. Z., 1923, pp. 145–149.

164. Edwin M. Loeb: "History and traditions of Niue," *Bernice P. Biship Mus., Bull.*, no. 32, pp. 1–226, Honolulu, 1926, pp. 12, 23–24, 29.

165. Edward W. Gifford: "Tongan society," *Bernice P. Bishop Mus., Bull.*, no. 61, pp. 1–366, Honolulu, 1929, pp. 12–15; William W. Gill: *Myths and songs from the South Pacific*, London, 1876, 328 pp., pp. 167, 287, 288.

166. John C. Elliott, former Governor of American Samoa, in a personal communication (January 9, 1962) maintains that there are strong traditions in Manua, and particularly in Tau, of deliberate voyages to and from Tau and Tahiti.

167. Horatio Hale: *op. cit.* [note 23].

168. J. L. A. de Quatrefages de Bréau: *Les Polynésiens et leurs migrations*, Paris, 1866, 199 pp., pp. 109–110 and 136–139.

169. Friedrich Ratzel: *op. cit.* [note 91], p. 165.

170. James Cook and James King: *A voyage to the Pacific Ocean . . . 1776, 1777, 1778, 1779 and 1780 . . .*, London, 1784, 3 vols., vol. 1, p. 371.

171. James Wilson: *op. cit.* [note 70], p. liv.

172. William Diapea: *Cannibal Jack; the true autobiography of a white man in the South Seas . . .*, London, 1928, 241 pp., pp. 109 and 111–112.

173. Basil H. Thomson: *The diversions of a prime minister*, Edinburgh and London, 1894, 407 pp., p. 307.

174. William Mariner: *op. cit.* [note 156], vol. 1, p. 346.

175. Peter Dillon: *op. cit.* [note 157], vol. 2, p. 112; Raymond W. Firth: *op. cit.* [note 106], pp. 93 and 109–114; Raymond W. Firth: "Anuta and Tikopia: Symbiotic elements in social organization," *Polyn. Soc., Journ.*, vol 63 (2), pp. 87–131, Wellington, N. Z., 1954, p. 123; Charles M. Woodford: "Some account of Sikaiana or Stewart's Island in the British Solomon Islands protectorate," *Man*, vol. 6, pp. 164–169, London, 1906, pp. 167–168; Charles M. Woodford: *op. cit.* [note 147], p. 28; G. S. Parsonson: *op. cit.* [note 45], p. 48.

176. Jean Guiart: "Les origines de la population d'Ouvea (Loyalty) et la place des migrations en cause sur le plan général oceanien," *Soc. d'Études Ocean . . . , Bull.*, vol. 7 (4), pp. 149–159, Papeete, 1950, pp. 150 and 156; K. J. Hollyman: "Polynesian influence in New Caledonia: the linguistic aspect," *Polyn. Soc., Journ.*, vol. 68 (4), pp. 356–389, Wellington, N. Z., 1959, pp. 362–364.

177. G. S. Parsonson: *op. cit.* [note 45], pp. 49–50.

178. Henry B. Guppy: *The Solomon Islands and their natives*, London, 1887, 384 pp., pp. 100, 251 and 277.

179. C. M. Woodford: *op. cit.* [note 147], p. 40.

180. G. S. Parsonson: personal communication.

181. Ernest E. V. Collocot: "Tales and poems of Tonga," *Bernice P. Bishop Mus., Bull.*, no. 46, pp. 1–169, Honolulu, 1928, p. 12; Edward W. Gifford (comp.): "Tongan myths and tales," *Bernice P. Bishop Mus., Bull.*, no. 8, pp. 1–207, Honolulu, 1924, pp. 153 and 163; William Mariner: *op. cit.* [note 156], pp. 330, 207 and 338–339.

182. Andrew Sharp: "Polynesian navigation: Some comments," *Polyn. Soc., Journ.*, vol. 72 (4),

Chapter 4

pp. 384–386, Wellington, N. Z., 1963, p. 385; Clements R. Markham (trans. and ed.): "The voyages of Pedro Fernandez de Quiros, 1595 to 1606," *Hakly. Soc. Works*, series 2, vols. 14–15, London, 1904, vol. 15, pp. 360–366 and 529.

183. Peter Dillon: *op. cit.* [note 157], vol. 1, p. 294.

184. C. M. Woodford: *A naturalist among the head-hunters. Being an account of three visits to the Solomon islands in the years 1886, 1887, and 1888*, London, 1890, 249 pp., p. 241.

185. Raymond W. Firth: *op. cit.* [note 106], pp. 61–62 and 120.

186. Kenneth P. Emory: "Changing hidden worlds of Polynesia," mimeographed address presented before the Social Science Association in Honolulu, December 3, 1962; Kenneth P. Emory: "East Polynesian relationships: settlement pattern and time involved as indicated by vocabulary agreements," *Polyn. Soc., Journ.*, vol. 72 (2), pp. 78–100, Wellington, N. Z., 1963.

187. Robert C. Suggs: *The Island Civilizations . . .*, *op. cit.* [note 21], p. 180.

188. Andrew Sharp: *Ancient voyagers in Polynesia*, *op. cit.* [note 3], pp. 133–134.

189. G. M. Dening: *op. cit.* [note 46], p. 103 and 105.

190. Teuira Henry: "Ancient Tahiti," *Bernice P. Bishop Mus., Bull.*, no. 48, pp. 1–651, Honolulu, 1928, pp. 399–402.

191. S. Percy Smith: "5. Notes on the geographical knowledge of the Polynesians," *Austral. Assoc. Adv. Sci., 1891, Rept., Christchurch, N. Z.*, vol. 3, pp. 280–310, Sydney, 1891; see also for 1898, vol. 7, pp. 801–816.

192. Andrew Sharp: *Ancient voyagers in Polynesia*, *op. cit.* [note 3], pp. 83–85.

193. Horatio Hale: *op. cit.* [note 23], pp. 323–324; Horatio Hale: *United States exploring expedition, 1838–1842 . . . Ethnography and Philology*, Philadelphia, 1846, 666 pp., p. 123.

194. S. Percy Smith: *op. cit.* [note 24], p. 162.

195. Andrew Sharp: *Ancient voyagers in Polynesia*, *op. cit.* [note 3], p. 81.

196. John C. Beaglehole: *op. cit.* [note 102], vol. 1, p. 131.

197. Johann R. Forster: *op. cit.* [note 93], p. 524.

198. John C. Beaglehole: *op. cit.* [note 102], vol. 1, p. 157.

199. For differing assessments of the value of Tupaia's claims and the range of his personal knowledge, see Andrew Sharp: *Ancient Voyagers in Polynesia*, *op. cit.* [note 3], pp. 39–40; John C. Beaglehole: *op. cit.* [note 102], vol. 1, p. 157; G. S. Parsonson: *op. cit.* [note 45], pp. 45–48; G. M. Dening: *op. cit.* [note 46], pp. 127–128; Jack Golson (ed.): "Polynesian navigation. Part II. A symposium on Andrew Sharp's theory of accidental voyages," *Polyn. Soc., Journ., Supplement*, vol. 71 (4), pp. 81–153, Wellington, N. Z., 1962, Table 1, pp. 132–136; Bolton G. Corney (ed. and trans.): *op. cit.* [note 57], vol. 2, p. xxii; and J. Peter White: "Tupaia's voyages: A note on the MSS," *Polyn. Soc., Journ.*, vol. 70 (3), pp. 471–473, Wellington, N. Z., 1961.

200. W. J. L. Wharton (ed.): *op. cit.* [note 77], pp. 87 and 229; John C. Beaglehole (ed.): *op. cit.* [note 102], vol. 1, p. 117.

201. Lewis A. de Bougainville: *A voyage round the world. Performed by order of His most Christian Majesty, in the years 1766, 1767, 1768, and 1769 . . .*, translated by John R. Forster, London, 1772, 476 pp., p. 281; Louis A. de Bougainville: *Voyage autour du Monde par la frégate du Roi La Boudeuse, et la flûte L'Étoile, en 1766, 1767, 1768, & 1769*, Paris, 1771, 417 pp.; p. 236.

202. G. M. Dening: *op. cit.* [note 46], p. 106.

203. G. S. Parsonson: *op. cit.* [note 45], p. 47, note 211, and personal communication.

204. See, for instance, Peter H. Buck: "Arts and crafts of the Cook Islands," *Bernice P. Bishop Mus., Bull.*, no. 179, pp. 1–533, Honolulu, 1944, pp. 11–13, 176, 363 and 411–412; William H. Gill: *From darkness to light in Polynesia . . .*, London, 1894, 383 pp., pp. 34, 235, and 263; William H. Gill: *Historical sketches of savage life in Polynesia . . .*, London, 1880, 232 pp., pp. 14–22; John Williams; *op. cit.* [note 72], p. 511; H. E. Maude and Marjorie T. Crocombe: "Rarotongan sandalwood. The visit of Goodenough to Rarotonga in 1814," *Polyn. Soc., Journ.*, vol. 71 (1), pp. 32–56, Wellington, N. Z., 1962, p. 52.

205. Roger Duff: "Archaeological expedition to Rarotonga," *Canterbury Mus., Ann. Rept.*, pp. 27–29, Christchurch, N. Z., 1963.

206. Andrew Sharp: *Ancient voyagers in the Pacific*, *op. cit.* [note 3], p. 189.

207. G. M. Dening: *op. cit.* [note 46], p. 107.

208. John Williams: *op. cit.* [note 72], p. 511.

209. William W. Gill: *Historical sketches . . .*, *op. cit.* [note 204], p. 189.

210. Peter H. Buck: "Mangaian society," *Bernice P. Bishop Mus., Bull.*, no. 122, pp. 1–207, Honolulu, 1934, pp. 37–43.

211. Bolton G. Corney (ed. and trans.): *op. cit.* [note 57], vol. 1, p. 306.

212. Peter H. Buck: "Ethnology of Manihiki and Rakahanga," *Bernice P. Bishop Mus., Bull.*, no. 99, pp. 1–238, Honolulu, 1932, pp. 14–20.

213. John C. Beaglehole: *op. cit.* [note 102], vol. 1, pp. 157, 291, and 292; G. M. Dening: *op. cit.* [note 46], p. 106.

214. Robert T. Aitken: "Ethnology of Tubuai," *Bernice P. Bishop Mus., Bull.*, no. 70, pp. 1–169, Honolulu, 1930, pp. 6, 25, 32–33, and 53–54.

215. John Hawkesworth (comp.): *An account of the voyages undertaken by the order of His present Majesty for making discoveries in the Southern hemisphere . . .*, London, 1778, 3 vols., vol. 3, p. 279; John C. Beaglehole: *op. cit.* [note 102], vol. 1, p. 157.

216. John C. Beaglehole (ed.): *op. cit.* [note 102], vol. 1, p. 245; George W. Anderson: *op. cit.* [note 56], pp. 51–54.

217. See especially S. Percy Smith: *op. cit.* [note 191], 1891, pp. 280–310, and 1898, pp. 801–816.

218. For a summary see Peter H. Buck: *The coming of the Maori*, Wellington, N. Z., 1950, 551 pp., pp. 5–38.

219. Personal communications from David Simmons, Otago Museum, Dunedin and from Bruce Biggs, University of Auckland, N. Z.

220. See for example Jack Golson: "Archaeology, tradition and myth in New Zealand pre-history," *Polyn. Soc., Journ.*, vol. 69 (4), pp. 397–399, Wellington, N. Z., 1960.

221. G. M. Dening: *op. cit.* [note 46], p. 118.

222. W. E. Gudgeon: "An ancient name of New Zealand," *Polyn. Soc., Journ.*, vol. 18 (2), p. 98, Wellington, N. Z., 1909, p. 98, note p. 202; J. T. Large: "Ruatapu—a celebrated Maori ancestor—and his Cook Island descendants," *Polyn. Soc., Journ.*, vol. 15 (4), pp. 213–219, Wellington, N. Z., 1906; Leslie G. Kelly: *op. cit.* [note 48], pp. 187, 194.

223. H. D. Skinner: "[482] Greenstone in the Cook Group," *Polyn. Soc., Journ.*, vol. 42 (3), pp. 225–226, New Plymouth, N. Z., 1933, note 482.

224. George Graham: "Ngutu-Au (an ancient people who visited New Zealand)," *Polyn. Soc., Journ.*, vol. 14 (3), pp. 159–160, Wellington, N. Z., 1905.

225. Raymond W. Firth: *Primitive economics of the New Zealand Maori*, London, 1929, 505 pp., pp. 427–442.

226. Peter H. Buck: *op. cit.* [note 218], pp. 41, 46, and 54; George Graham: "Tainui," *Polyn. Soc., Journ.*, vol. 60 (2), pp. 80–92, Wellington, N. Z., 1951, p. 90.

227. Alexander Shand: "The Moriori people of the Chatham Islands: Their traditions and history," *Polyn. Soc., Journ.*, vol 7 (2), pp. 73–88, Wellington, N. Z., 1898, p. 84; G. M. Dening: *op. cit.* [note 46], pp. 108–109; Horatio Hale: *op. cit.* [note 23].

228. Frederick D. McCarthy: "The oceanic . . . ," *op. cit.* [note 7], p. 256; H. D. Skinner: "A greenstone adze or axe from northern Tasmania," *Polyn. Soc., Journ.*, vol. 45 (1), pp. 39–42, New Plymouth, N. Z., 1936; W. W. Thorpe: "Evidence of Polynesian culture in Australia and Norfolk Island," *Polyn. Soc., Journ.*, vol. 38 (2), pp. 122–126, New Plymouth, N. Z., 1929.

229. W. W. Thorpe: *ibid*; Frederick D. McCarthy: "Norfolk Island: Additional evidence of a former native occupation," *Polyn. Soc., Journ.*, vol. 43 (4), pp. 267–270, Wellington, N. Z., 1934.

230. William Ellis: *Polynesian researches*, London, 1853, 3 vols., vol. 3, p. 305.

231. Bengt E. Danielson: *Work and life on Raroia; an acculturation study from the Tuamotu group, French Oceania*, London, 1956, 244 pp., p. 69.

232. For different viewpoints on the origin and nature of Marquesan settlements see especially Robert C. Suggs: *op. cit.* [note 21], pp. 163, 179, 183; Robert C. Suggs: *The hidden worlds of Polynesia; the chronicle of an archaeological expedition to Nuku Hiva in the Marquesas Islands*, New York, 1962, 247 pp., pp. 230–232; Robert C. Suggs: "The derivation of Marquesan culture," *Roy. Anthrop. Inst. . . . , Journ.*, vol. 91, pp. 1–10, London, 1961; Andrew Sharp: "Interpreting eastern Polynesian prehistory," *Polyn. Soc., Journ.*, vol. 70 (3), pp. 349–351, Wellington, N. Z., 1961; Andrew Sharp: "Fact and fancy in the Marquesas group," *Polyn. Soc., Journ.*, vol. 71 (1), pp. 122–124, Wellington, N. Z., 1962; Andrew Sharp: *Ancient voyagers in Polynesia, op. cit.* [note 3], pp. 133–134.

233. Edward S. C. Handy: "The native culture in the Marquesas," *Bernice P. Bishop Mus., Bull.* 9, pp. 1–358, Honolulu, 1923; Edward S. C. Handy: "Marquesan legends," *Bernice P. Bishop Mus., Bull.* 69, pp. 1–138, Honolulu, 1930, pp. 91–92, 118–121, 128, 131, 137.

234. Clements Markham: *op. cit.* [note 182], vol. 1, p. 152.

235. David Porter: *op. cit.* [note 104], pp. 51, 134.

236. G. M. Dening: *op. cit.* [note 46], p. 109.

237. Wilhelm G. Solheim, II: "Eastern Asia and Oceania," *Asian Persp.*, vol. 6 (1–2), pp. 1–7, Hong Kong, 1962, pp. 3–4; Kenneth P. Emory: *op. cit.* [note 186], p. 1; Kenneth P. Emory: "East Polynesian . . . ," *op. cit.* [note 186], pp. 95–100.

238. William Ellis: *op. cit.* [note 73], pp. 69–70 and 297.

239. For Hawaiian traditions of voyaging see (among others): Abraham Fornander: *op. cit.*

[note 23]; Abraham Fornander: "Fornander collection of Hawaiian antiquities and folk-lore . . . gathered from original sources . . . ," *Bernice P. Bishop Mus., Mem.*, vols. 4–6, Honolulu, 1916–1917; David Malo: "Hawaiian antiquities, translated from the Hawaiian by Nathaniel B. Emerson, 1898," *Bernice P. Bishop Mus., Spec. Publ.*, no. 2, pp. 1–278, Honolulu, 1951, pp. 5–8; Martha W. Beckwith (ed.): "Kepelino's traditions of Hawaii," *Bernice P. Bishop Mus., Bull.*, no. 95, pp. 1–206, Honolulu, 1932, p. 189; Nathaniel B. Emerson: "The long voyages of ancient Hawaiians," *Hawaiian Hist. Soc. Papers.*, no. 5, pp. 1–34, Honolulu, 1893, pp. 5, 13; Kenneth P. Emory: *op. cit.* [note 39], pp. 29–31.

240. J. F. G. Stokes: "Spaniards and the sweet potato in Hawaii and Hawaiian-American contacts," *Amer. Anthrop.*, vol. 34 (4), pp. 594–600, Menasha, Wis., 1932.

241. James Hornell: "Was there pre-Columbian contact between the peoples of Oceania and South America?" *Polyn. Soc., Journ.*, vol. 54 (4), pp. 167–191, Wellington, N. Z., 1945, p. 169; review of paper by J. F. G. Stokes: "Japanese cultural influences in Hawaii," in *Polyn. Soc., Journ.*, vol. 44 (1), pp. 62–63, Wellington, N. Z., 1935; J. G. Nelson: "Drift voyages between eastern Asia and the Americas," *Canadian Geographer*, vol. 6 (2), pp. 54–59, Ottawa, 1962; Henry H. Howarth: "Buddhism in the Pacific," *Roy. Anthrop. Inst. . . . , Journ.*, vol. 51, pp. 279–287, London, 1921, pp. 282–284; Otto Sittig: *op. cit.* [note 98], pp. 529–531.

242. Kenneth P. Emory: "Archaeology of Nihoa and Necker Islands," *Bernice P. Bishop Mus., Bull.*, no. 53, pp. 1–124, Honolulu, 1928, pp. 3, 8, 9 and 120.

243. For contrasting viewpoints on Mangarevan contacts see Honoré Laval: . . . *Mangareva; l'histoire ancienne d'un peuple polynesien. Mémoires ethnographiques conservés aux archives de la Congrégation des sacrés-coeurs de Picpus* . . . , Braine-le-Comte, Belge, 1938, 378 pp., p. 362; S. Percy Smith: "Notes on the Mangareva or Gambier group of islands, Eastern Polynesia," *Polyn. Soc., Journ.*, vol. 27 (3), pp. 115–131, New Plymouth, N. Z., 1918, pp. 126–128; William Ellis: *op. cit.* [note 230], vol. 1, p. 50; G. M. Dening: *op. cit.* [note 46], p. 108; Kenneth P. Emory: "Archaeology of Mangareva and neighboring atolls," *Bernice P. Bishop Mus., Bull.*, no. 163, pp. 1–76, Honolulu, 1939, pp. 41–42 and 53–74.

244. Johann R. Forster: *A voyage round the world; in His Britannic Majesty's sloop Resolution, commanded by James Cook, during the years 1772, 3, 4 and 5*, London, 1777, 2 vols., vol. 1, p. 601.

245. Thor Heyerdahl and Edwin N. Ferdon (eds.): "Archaeology of Easter Island," *Norwegian Archaeological Expedition to Easter Island and the East Pacific in 1955–1956, Rept.*, vol. 1, pp. 1–559, Chicago, 1961, pp. 13–16, 41.

246. For an English language summary of Barthel's work see Robert C. Suggs: "Polynesia," *Asian Persp.*, vol. 2 (1), pp. 61–62, Tucson, Ariz., 1959; Robert C. Suggs: *The island civilizations . . . , op. cit.* [note 21], pp. 186–188; Howard La Fay: "Easter Island and its mysterious monuments," *Nat'l Geogr. Mag.*, vol. 121 (1), pp. 90–117, Wash., D.C., 1962, p. 111.

247. Emilio Estrada and Betty J. Meggers: "A complex of traits of probable transpacific origin on the coast of Ecuador," *Amer. Anthrop.*, vol. 63 (5), pp. 913–939, Menasha, Wis., 1961; Emilio Estrada and Betty J. Meggers: "Possible transpacific contact on the coast of Ecuador," *Science*, vol. 135 (3501), pp. 371–372, Lancaster, Pa., 1962; Wilhelm G. Solheim, II: "Eastern Asia and Oceania," *Asian Persp.*, vol. 5 (1), pp. 5–15, Hong Kong, 1961, p. 12.

248. James Hornell: *The island civilizations . . . , op. cit.* [note 241], p. 180; Thor Heyerdahl: *op. cit.* [note 23], p. 572.

249. Robert C. Suggs: *op. cit.* [note 21], pp. 207–208; Edward S. C. Handy: *op. cit.* [note 233], p. 131.

250. Robert Heine-Geldern: "Heyerdahl's hypothesis of Polynesian origins: A criticism," *Geogr. Journ.*, vol. 116, pp. 183–192, London, 1950.

251. Clements R. Markham: *op. cit.* [note 182], vol 1, pp. 227–228.

252. Otto von Kotzebue: *op. cit.* [note 95], vol. 2, pp. 84–132.

253. Lewis A. de Bougainville: *op. cit.* [note 201], pp. 268–269 and 275.

254. Bolton G. Corney (ed. and tr.): *op. cit.* [note 57], vol. 2, pp. 284, 304.

Chapter 5

GEOGRAPHICAL EXPLORATION BY THE CHINESE

1. Hirosi Nakamura: "Old Chinese world maps preserved by the Koreans," *Imago Mundi*, vol. 4, pp. 3–22, Stockholm, 1947.

2. Gustaaf Schlegel: "Problèmes géographiques, les peuples etrangers chez les historiens chinois," *T'oung-Pao* . . . , vol. 3, pp. 101–168, vol. 4, pp. 323–360, and vol. 5, pp. 179–233, Leiden, 1892–1894.

3. Te-Khun Cheng: "A supplementary note on the Shan Hai Ching," *Yenching Journ. of Chinese Studies*, no. 7, pp. 1376–1380, Peking, 1930.

4. E. J. Eilet: "Travels of the Emperor Mu," *China Rev.*, vol. 17, pp. 17–247, Hong Kong, 1888.

5. Kuan-chou Ho: "The Shan Hai Ching: the date of its author and its scientific value," *Yenching Journ. of Chinese Studies*, no. 7, pp. 1347–1375, Peking, 1930; Te-khun Cheng (trans.): "The travels of Emperor Mu," *Roy. Asiatic Soc., No. China Br., Journ.*, vol. 64, pp. 124–142, and vol. 65, pp. 128–149, Shanghai, 1933 and 1934; Léopold de Saussure: "The calendar of the Muh Tien Tzu Chuan," *New China Rev.*, vol. 2, p. 513, Shanghai, 1920; and Léopold de Saussure: "Le voyage de Mou Wang et l'hypothèse d'Ed. Chavannes," *T'oung Pao* . . . , Series 2, vol. 20, 19–31, Leiden, 1921.

6. Chieh-kang Ku and Shu-yeh T'ung: "Anti-Han Chinese concept of the world" *Yu-Kung* (The Chinese Historical Geography. Semi-Monthly Magazine) vol. 5, nos. 3 and 4, pp. 97–120, Peking, 1936; Ch'ang-ch'ün Ho: "post-Han Chinese knowledge of the world," *Yu-Kung* (The Chinese Historical Geography. Semi-Monthly Magazine) vol. 5, nos. 3 and 4, pp. 121–136, Peking, 1936.

7. Hu Shih: "Religion and philosophy in Chinese history," in Hêng-chê Zen (ed.): *Symposium on Chinese culture* . . . , Shanghai, 1931, 373 pp., p. 31.

8. C. W. Wang: "Chung chao tung lu Kao (On the communication routes between China and Japan)," *Yu-kang* (The Chinese Historical Geography. Semi-Monthly Magazine) vol. 3, pp. 11–23, Peking, 1935.

9. Tingsen S. Wei: "Yayoi culture—the first Chinese culture in Japan," *Chinese Culture*, vol. 1 (3), pp. 124–143, Taipei, 1958.

10. Tingsen S. Wei: *Hsu Fu yu jih Peng* (Hsu Fu and Japan), Hong Kong, 1953, p. 9.

11. Tingsen S. Wei: *Jih pên shên wu K'ai Kuo Hsin K'ao* (Jimbu Kaikoku Shinko: A new study on the founding of the Japanese monarchy by Emperor Jimbu), Hong Kong, 1950, pp. 123–126.

12. Tingsen S. Wei: *op. cit.* [note 9] p. 143.

13. Tingsen S. Wei: *op. cit.* [note 10] pp. 37–64.

14. Yao Nan and Hsu Yu: *Ku Tai Nan Hai Shih Ti Tsung K'ao* (Research on the history and geography of ancient southern sea archipelago), Chungking, 1943, 88 pp.

15. Cheng-chun Fung: *Kun Lun chih Nan Hai Hu Tai Hang Hsin K'ao*, (Research on the history and geography of ancient southern sea archipelago), Chungking, 1943; and Cheng-chun Fung: *Chung-kuo Nan Yang chao Tung shih* (The history of communication in the South Sea of China), Hong Kong, 1963.

16. Ch'ang-ch'üan Ho: *Ku Tai Hsi Yao Chao Tung Yu Fa-Hsien Yin T'u Hsün li* (Ancient communication in western land and Fa Hsien's travel in India), Hankow, 1965.

17. Joseph Needham and Ling Wang: *Science and civilization in China*, Cambridge, England, 1954–1962, 4 vols. See vol. 3, *Mathematics and the sciences of the heavens and the earth* . . . , Cambridge, 1959, p. 511.

18. Paul Pelliot: "Les grandes voyages maritimes chinois au début du XVe siècle," *T'oung Pao* . . . , Series 2, vol. 30, pp. 237–452, and vol. 31, p. 274, Leiden, 1933 and 1935.

19. W. F. Mayers: "Chinese explorations of the Indian Ocean during the fifteenth century," *China Review*, vol. 3, pp. 219 and 331, and vol. 4, p. 61, Hong Kong, 1875.

20. Jan J. L. Duyvendak: *China's discovery of Africa* . . . , London, 1949, 35 pp., p. 35.

21. Jen-chih Hou: "Tsai So Wei Hsin Hang Ru Ti Fa Shien Yu I Ch'ien Chung-Kuo Yü Tung Fei Chih Chian Ti Shang Chao Tung (The sea route between China and eastern Africa before the discovery of the new navigating route)," *K'o Hsüeh T'ung Pao*, no. 11, p. 984, Peking, 1964.

22. Chu Chieh: *Cheng Ho, San Lien*, Peking, 1956, 124 pp., p. 23.

23. Hsu Yü-hu: *Cheng Ho P'ing Ch'uan* (A biography of Cheng Ho), Taipei, 1958, 200 pp. p. 6.

24. Han Wu: "Shi lu Shih chi Ch'ien Chüng-Kuo Nan Yang yü (China and South Sea Islands before the 16th century)," *The Tsing Hua Journal*, vol. 11, No. 1, pp. 137–186, Peking, 1936, and

Yu-hu Hsu: "Cheng Ho Hsi Hsi yang chi Yuan Yin Hsin tan (The new exploration for Cheng Ho's expedition)," *Continental Mag.*, vol. 16 (1), pp. 19–23, Taipei, 1958.

25. C. Whiting Bishop: "Chinese voyages to the Indian Ocean in the early fifteenth century," *Geogr. Rev.*, vol. 24, pp. 672–674, New York, 1934.

26. Cheng-chun Fung: *Ying Yai Sheng Lan Chiao Chu* (Note on the triumphant vision of the starring raft), Shanghai, 1935, 72 pp. Jan J. L. Duyvendak: "Sailing directions of Chinese voyages," *T'oung Pao*, vol. 34, pp. 230–237, Leide, 1938; and Jan J. L. Duyvendak: "Ma Huan re-examined," *Verhandelingen der Koninklijke Akad. van Wetenschappen te Amsterdam, Afdeeling Letterkunde*, vol. 32, (3), pp. 1–74, Amsterdam, 1933.

27. Joseph Needham and Ling Wang: *op. cit.* [note 17], p. 143.

28. Chü-Hsien Wei: *Chung-Kuo Jên Fa Hsien Ao-Chou* (Chinese discovery of Australia), Hong Kong, 1960, 182 pp.

29. C. T. Kwan: "Cheng Ho Hsia Hsi Yang Ti Ch'uan (The ship Cheng Ho sailed)," *Eastern Miscellany*, vol. 43, pp. 5–10, Shanghai, 1947; and C. P. Pao: "Cheng Ho Hang Hai Chih Chie Tui (A study of Cheng Ho's fleet)," *Continental Mag.*, vol. 18 (1), pp. 5–10, 1959.

30. W. Z. Mulder: "The 'Wu-Pei-Chih' charts," *T'oung Pao . . . , Series 2*, vol. 37, pp. 1–14, Leiden, 1943–1944.

31. Wen-tao Fan: "Cheng Ho Hang Hai T'u Kao (A study of Cheng Ho's navigating charts)," *Nan Yang Journ.*, Chungking, 1943.

32. J. V. Mills: "Chinese coastal maps," *Imago Mundi*, vol. 11, pp. 151–168, Leiden, 1954.

33. Li Ch'ien Chang: *Tung Hsi Yang K'ao Chung Chih Chên lu* (The compass directions in the study of the east and west oceans), Singapore, 1947, 35 pp.

34. Paul Pelliot: *op. cit.* [note 18], p. 268.

35. Hsien Ta: *Cheng Ho Hang Hait'u* (Cheng Ho's navigating map), Shanghai, 1961, 66 pp., p. 16.

Chapter 6
GEOGRAPHICAL EXPLORATION BY THE JAPANESE

The following brief list of references will be helpful to a study of the subject of this chapter [Editor]:

A. BIBLIOGRAPHIES: Richard K. Beardsley: "Bibliographic materials in the Japanese language on Far Eastern archaeology and ethnology," *Univ. Mich., Center for Japanese Studies. Bibliographical Series*, no. 3, pp. 1–74, Ann Arbor, Mich., 1950; Henri Cordier: *Bibliographie des ouvrages relatifs à l'ile Formose*, Paris, 1893, 50 pp.; Henri Cordier: *Bibliotheca japonica; dictionnaire bibliographique des ouvrages relatifs à l'Empire japonais rangés par ordre chronologique jusqu' à 1870, . . . ,* Paris, 1912, 762 pp.; Émile Gaspardone: "Les bibliographies japonaises," *Bull. de la Maison Franco-Japonaise*, 1933, pp. 29–115, Paris, 1933; John W. Hall: "Japanese history; a guide to Japanese reference and research materials," *Univ. of Mich. Center for Japanese Studies, Bibliographical Series*, no. 4, pp. 1–165, Ann Arbor, 1954; Ivar Hallberg: *L' Extrême Orient dans la littérature et la cartographie de l' Occident des XIIIe, XIVe, et XVe siècles; étude sur l' histoire de la géographie*, Göteborg, Sweden, 1907, 573 pp.; Julius H. Klaproth: *Catalogue des livres imprimés, des manuscrits et des ouvrages chinois, tartares, japonais, etc., composant . . . ,* Paris, 1839, 2 vols. in 1; Oskar Nachod: *Bibliography of the Japanese empire, 1906–1926 . . . ,* London, 1928, 2 vols.; Oskar Nachod: *Bibliographie von Japan, 1906–1926 . . . ,* Leipzig, 1928, 2 vols.; Léon Pagès: *Bibliographie japonaise ou Catalogue des ouvrages relatifs au Japon qui ont été publiés le XVe siècle jusqu' à nos jours, . . . ,* Paris, 1859, 67 pp.; James A. Robertson: *Bibliography of early Spanish-Japanese relations*, Yokohama, 1915, 170 pp.; Philipp F. von Siebold: *Catalogus librorum et manuscriptorum japonicorum a Ph. Fr. de Siebold collectorum*, Lingduni-Batavorum, 1845, 51 pp.; Philipp F. von Siebold: *Catalogue de la bibliothèque, apportée au Japon . . . pour servir à l'étude sciences physiques, geographiques, . . . ,* Tokyo, 1936, 106 pp.; Ssu-yu Teng and others: *Japanese studies on Japan & the Far East; a short bibliographical introduction*, Hong Kong, 1961, 485 pp.; Japanese and English; Friedrich von Wenckstern: *A bibliography of the Japanese empire; being a classified list of all books, essays and maps in European languages relating to Dai Nihon . . . 1859–1906*, Leiden, 1895–1897, 2 vols.

B. HISTORICAL GEOGRAPHY AND HISTORY: Faustin de Autremont: "Les premiers rapports de l'Europe et du Japon," *Le Revue Hebdomadaire*, vol. 34, pp. 597–620, Paris, 1895; William G. Aston:

"Russian descents in Saghalien and Itorup in the years 1806 & 1807," *Asiatic Soc. of Japan, Trans.*, vol. 1, pp. 78–86, Yokohama, 1882; Shintaro Ayuzawa: "Karafuto, Chishima no shiteki kosatsu (An historical investigation of Sakhalin and the Kurile Islands)," *Nihon Rekishi*, vol. 42, pp. 2–5, Tokyo, 1951; Shintaro Ayuzawa: *Sakoku jidai Nihon-jin no kaigai chishiki (Japanese knowledge of overseas regions during the period of national seclusion)*, Tokyo, 1953, 498 pp.; Carl W. Bishop: "The historical geography of early Japan," *Geogr. Rev.*, vol. 13 (1), pp. 40–63, New York, 1923; Charles W. Brooks: *Japanese wrecks, stranded and picked up adrift in the North Pacific Ocean, ethnologically considered, as furnishing evidence of a constant infusion of Japanese blood among the coast tribes of northwestern Indians*, San Francisco, 1876, 23 pp.; Hubert Cieslik: *Hoppo Tankenki (Accounts of the exploration of the northern regions)*, Tokyo, 1962, 122 pp. with the original text of the reports of Ezo by G. de Angelis and Diogo Carvalho; Armando Cortesão, "The first account of the Far East in the sixteenth century—the name 'Japan' in 1513," *Intrent'l Geogr. Congr., Netherlands 1938, Compte Rendus*, vol. 2, pp. 145–152, Leiden, 1938; Sebastiano Crino: "La prima carta geografica inedita del Giappone portata in Italia nel 1585 e rinvenuta in una filza di documenti reguardanti el commercio dei . . .," *Revista Marittima*, vol. 10, pp. 257–284, Rome, 1931; Erik W. Dahlgren: "A contribution to the history of the discovery of Japan," *Japan Soc., Trans. and Proc.*, vol. 11, pp. 239–260, London, 1914; James M. Dixon: "Early Mexican and Californian relations with Japan," *So. Calif., Hist. Soc., Publ.*, vol. 8 (3), pp. 217–227, Los Angeles, 1912; Hirondo Hirabayashi: "The discovery of Japan from the north," *Japan Quart.*, vol. 4, pp. 318–328, Tokyo, 1957; Rokuro Kuwata: "Jodai tozai kotsu shiwa (An historical survey of the maritime intercourse between East and West in ancient times)," *Kaitoku*, vol. 23, pp. 1–12, Tokyo, 1952; Katsumi Mori: "O-sen raiko izen no kaigai kotsu to gijutsuteki seiyaku (Japanese sea traffic before the coming of European ships and its technical limitation)," Nihon Rekishi, vol. 28, pp. 13–19, Tokyo, 1950; N. G. Munro: "Primitive culture in Japan," *Asiatic Soc. Japan, Trans.*, vol. 34, pp. 1–198, Tokyo, 1906; James Murdock and Isoh Yamagata: *A history of Japan . . .*, London, 1903–1926, 3 vols.; James Murdock and Isoh Yamagata: *A history of Japan during the century of early foreign intercourse (1542–1651)*, Kobe, 1903, 743 pp.; Oskar Nachod: *Ein unentdecktes goldland. Ein beitrag zur geschichte der entdeckungen im nordlichen Grossen ocean*, Tokyo, 1900, 140 pp.; Zelia Nuttal: ". . . The earliest historical relations between Mexico and Japan, from original documents in Spain and Japan," *Univ. of Calif., Publ. Archaeology and Ethnology*, vol. 4 (1), pp. 1–47, Berkeley, 1906; Zelia Nuttal: "Las primeras relaciones entre Mexico y el Japon," *Sociedad Geografica Estadisdica Mexicana, Boleten.*, vol. 2, pp. 300–318 and 358–389, Mexico City, 1907; N. Peri: "Essai sur les relations du Japon et de l' Indochine aux XVIe et XVIIe siècle," *École Française d'Extrême-Orient, Bull.*, vol. 23, pp. 1–104, Hanoi, 1923; Robert K. Reischauer: *Early Japanese history (ca. 40 B.C.—1167 A.D.)*, Princeton, N. J., 1937, 2 vols.; L. de Rosny: "L' Isle Yezo et ces inhabitants d' après les géographes japonaises et les relations des voyageurs européens," *Revue Orientale et Americaine*, vol. 1, pp. 380–390, Paris, 1859; and André Wedemeyer: *Japanische Frühgeschichte. Untersuchungen zur Chronologie und Territorial verfassung von Altjapan bis zum 5. Jahrhundert nach Christ*, Leipzig, 1930, 346 pp.

C. HISTORICAL CARTOGRAPHY: Takejiro Akioka: *Nippon chizu-shi* (A history of Japanese cartography), Tokyo, 1955, 217 pp.; Takejiro Akioka: Momoyama jidai no yon sekaizu byobu ni tsuite. "(The four world maps of the Momoyama era)," *Jimbun Chiri*, vol. 7, pp. 1–2, Kyoto, 1956; Takejiro Akioka: "A history of cartography of Japan," *Japan Science Review: Literature, Philosophy and History*, vol. 8, pp. 7–9, Tokyo, 1957; Takejiro Akioka and Nobuo Muroga: "A short history of ancient cartography in Japan," *Internt'l Geogr. Union, Regional Conf. in Japan, 1957, Proc.*, pp. 57–60, Tokyo, 1957; Shintaro Ayuzawa: *Sakoku jidai no sekai chirigaku (World geography during the period of national isolation)*, Tokyo, 1943, 363 pp.; Shintaro Ayuzawa: *Nihon bunka-shi-jo ni okeru Rimato no sekai-zu* (The position of Matteo Ricci's world map in Japanese cultural history), Tokyo, 1944, 185 pp.; Shintaro Ayuzawa: "The types of world maps made in Japan's age of national isolation," *Imago Mundi*, vol. 10, pp. 123–128, Leiden, 1953; Shintaro Ayuzawa: "Mateo Ritchi no sekaizu ni kansuru shiteki kenkyu—Kinsei Nippon ni okeru sekai chiri chishiki no shuryu . . .," *Yokohama Municipal University, Journ.*, vol. 18, pp. 1–239, Yokohama, 1953; George H. Beans: "A list of Japanese maps of the Tokugawa era," *Tall Tree Library*, Publ. no. 23, pp. 1–51, Jenkintown, Pa., 1951; George H. Beans: "A list of Japanese maps of the Tokugawa era," *Tall Tree Library*, Publ. no. 24, pp. 1–40, Jenkintown, Pa., 1955; G. Collingridge: "The early cartography of Japan," *Geogr. Journ.*, vol. 3, pp. 403–409, London, 1894; Erik W. Dahlgren: ". . . Les débuts de la cartographie du Japon," *Archives d'Études Orientales . . .*, vol. 4, pp. 1–65, Upsala, 1911; Henri Froidevaux: "L' évolution de la cartographie du Japon," *La Géographie*, vol. 22, pp. 409–416, Paris, 1910; Birger Gezelius: *Japan i västerländsk framställning till omkring år 1700; ett geografiskt-kartografiskt försök*, Linkoping, Sweden, 1910, 185 pp.; Edward Heawood: "A seventeenth-century Japanese map of the world," *Geogr. Journ.*, vol. 52, pp. 303–308, London, 1918; Tetsuro Ikeda:

"World maps in Japan before 1853," *Internt'l Geogr. Congr., Netherlands, 1938, Compte Rendus,* vol. 2 (D), pp. 355–361, Amsterdam, 1938; Mikinosuke Ishida: "A brief note on the two old European maps of Japan recently discovered," *Monumenta Nipponica,* vol. 1, pp. 259–265, Tokyo, 1938; Georg Kerst: "Die älteste japanische Karte von Ostasien," *Peterm. Geogr. Mitt.,* vol. 97, pp. 33–34, Gotha, 1953; George Kish: "The cartography of Japan during the middle Tokugawa era: A study in cross-cultural influences," *Assoc. Amer. Geogr., Annals,* vol. 37, pp. 101–119. Lancaster, Pa., 1947; George Kish: "Some aspects of the missionary cartography of Japan during the sixteenth century," *Imago Mundi,* vol. 6, pp. 39–47, Stockholm, 1949; George Kish: "A map of the world on an old Imari plate," *Far Eastern Ceramic Bull.,* vol. 6, pp. 29–32, Cambridge, Mass., 1954; Kay Kitagawa: "The map of Hokkaido of G. de Angelis, c. 1621," *Imago Mundi,* vol. 7, pp. 110–114, 1950; Julius H. Klaproth: *Observations sur la carte l' Asie publiée en 1822, par Aaron Arrowsmith,* Paris, 1826, 27 pp.; E. B. Knobel: "Ino Chukei and the first survey of Japan," *Geogr. Journ.,* vol. 42, pp. 246–250, London, 1913; Chohei Kudo: "A summary of my studies of Girolamo de Angelis' Yezo map," *Imago Mundi,* vol. 10, pp. 81–86, Leiden, 1953; M. Kurita: *Nihon kohan chizu shusei* (Sammlung alter Drucke von Japanischen Karten), Osaka, 1932, 142 pp.; Melvin P. McGovern: "A list of Nagasaki maps printed during the Tokugawa era," *Imago Mundi,* vol. 15, pp. 105–110, 1960; Yoshio Mikami: *Study of land surveying in Japan,* Tokyo, 1947, 218 pp.; Nobuo Muroga and Kazutaka Unno: "Nippon ni okeru Bukkyōkei Sekaizu ni tsuite (The Buddhist world maps in Japan)," *Chirigakushi-Kenkyu,* vol. 1, pp. 67–141, Tokyo, 1957; Nobuo Muroga and Kazutaka Unno: "The Buddhist world maps in Japan," *Japan Science Rev.: Humanistic Studies,* vol. 10, pp. 10–13, Tokyo, 1959; Nobuo Muroga and Kazutako Unno: "The Buddhist world map in Japan and its contact with European maps," *Imago Mundi,* vol. 16, pp. 48–69, Amsterdam, 1962; Oskar Nachod: "Zur Kartographie Japans," *Zeitsch. Gesell. Erdk. zu Berlin, 1910,* pp. 196–204, Berlin, 1910; Hirosi Nakamura: "Les cartes du Japon qui servaient de modèle aux cartographes européens au début des relations de l' Occident avec le Japon," *Monumenta Nipponica,* vol. 2 (1), pp. 100–123, Tokyo, 1939; Hirosi Nakamura: Sengoku jidai no Nihon zu "(The maps of Japan of the period of the civil wars, XVth to XVIth centuries)," *Yokohama Univ., Journ.,* Series A—II, vol. 58, pp. 1–100, Yokohama, 1957; Martin Ramming: "The evolution of cartography in Japan," *Imago Mundi,* vol. 2, pp. 17–21, London, 1937; Boleslaw Szcześniak: "The Antoine Gaubil maps of the Ryukyu Islands and southern Japan," *Imago Mundi,* vol. 12, pp. 141–149, Leiden, 1955; Philipp F. von Siebold: *Geschichte der Entdeckungen im Seegebiete von Japan, nebst Erklaerung des Atlas von Land- und Seekarten vom japanischen Reiche,* Leiden, 1852, 204 pp.; K. Takagi: *Nihon chizu-sokuryo shoshi* (Short history of Japanese maps and surveying), Tokyo, 1931, 170 pp.; K. Takagi: "Old astronomical survey used for mapping in Japan," *Geodetic Soc. Japan, Journ.,* vol. 43 (2), pp. 59–61, Tokyo, 1957; Pál Teleki: "Japans Rolle in der geschichte der Entdeckung Amerikas," *Foldrajzi Kozlemenyek* (Geographische Mitteilungen der Ungarischen Geographischen Gesellschaft), vol. 34 (1), pp. 1–10, Budapest, 1906; Pál Teleki: "Les preuves cartographiques des premières notions des Européens sur les îles du Japon avant et après sa découverte," *Ninth Internt'l Geogr. Congr., Geneva, 1908, Compte Rendu,* vol. 3 (149), pp. 420–424, Geneva, 1908; Pál Teleki: ... *Atlas zur geschichte der kartographie der japanischen inseln* ..., Budapest, 1909, 184 pp. and 54 maps; and Wilcomb E. Washburn: "Japan on early European maps," *Pacific Hist. Rev.,* vol. 21 (3), pp. 221–236, Berkeley, Calif., 1952.

1. For information about these Japanese pirates and the Red Seal ships see: Charles R. Boxer: *The Christian century in Japan, 1549–1650,* Berkeley, Calif., 1951, 535 pp. For references to early voyages see: August Pfizmaier: "Zwei reisen nach dem westen Japans in den jahren 1369 and 1389 n. Chr.," *Kon. Acad. der Wissenschaften, Vienna. Philosophisch-Historische Classe. Denkschriften,* vol. 32, pp. 93–188, Vienna, 1882; August Pfizmaier: "Die älteren reisen nach den osten Japans," *Kon. Akad. der Wissenschaften, Vienna, Philosophisch-Historische Classe. Denkschriften,* vol. 31, pp. 115–210, Vienna, 1881; and Martin G. T. Ramming (comp.): *Katalog der Austellung alter japanischer Karten und Plaene,* Berlin, 1934, 48 pp.

2. Sources of information on Date Masamune's ambassadorial efforts in Rome may be found in: Tokyo Daigaku Shiryo Henzansho (comp.): *Dai Nippon Shiryo* (Japanese historical materials), pt. 12, vol. 12, Tokyo, 1909.

3. Ezo generally is identified with the Ainu, aborigines of Hokkaido and Karafuto (Sakhalin Island), though some scholars hold a different view. In any case, the word "Ezo" is a somewhat indefinable designation of the aboriginal inhabitants of Japan's northern frontier in early historical times. It also refers to the land where the Ainu lived, which has included Hokkaido (Ezo proper), Sakhalin Island (Karafuto or Kita-Ezo), the Kuril Islands (Chishima-retto) and at times even Kamchatka. For discussions of this subject see Hiroshi Tanaami: "Kodai Emishi to Ainu (The ancient Emishi and the Ainu)," in Kodaishi Kenkyukai (ed.): *Ezo,* pp. 1–56, Tokyo, 1956. For

additional information see Hokkaido-cho: *Shinsen Hokkaido shi* (The history of Hokkaido, newly compiled), Sapporo, Hokkaido, 1936–1937, 7 vols.; Shin'ichiro Takakura: "The Ainu of northern Japan; a study in conquest and acculteration (Ainu seisaku shi), translated and annotated by John A. Harrison," *Amer. Philos. Soc., Trans., n.s.,* vol. 50 (4), pp. 1–88, Phila., Penn., 1960; and Shin'-ichiro Takakura: *Hokkaido shoshi* (A short history of Hokkaido) Tokyo, 1956, 272 pp.

4. Nobuo Muroga: "Abe-no-Hirafu Hokusei Ko (The expedition to the north by Abe-no-Hirafu)," *Shirin,* vol. 39 (5), pp. 353–369, Kyoto, 1956. For studies of the Edo period see Makoto Abe: "Edo-makki ni okeru Karafuto Tanken (the exploration of Karafuto in the late Edo period)," *Nippon Rekishi Chiri Gakkai,* vol. 63, p. 3, Tokyo, 1934; and Makoto Abe: "Edo jidai no Chirigaku (Geographical studies in the Edo period)," *Shinko Dai-Nippon shi,* vol. 5, Tokyo, 1942.

5. A concise history of the discovery of Ezo as given by a Westerner may be found in John A. Harrison: *Japan's northern frontier; a preliminary study in colonization and expansion, with special reference to the relations of Japan and Russia,* Gainesville, Fla., 1953, 202 pp., especially Appendix I, pp. 145–164; and John A. Harrison: "Notes on the discovery of Yezo," *Assoc. Amer. Geogr., Annals,* vol. 40, pp. 254–266, Lancaster, Pa., 1950.

6. The most valuable works on Japanese maps of Ezo are: Shinchiro Takakura and Teikichi Shibata: "Waga Kuni ni okeru Karafuto Chizu Sakuseishi (A history of Japanese maps of Karafuto)," "Waga Kuni ni okeru Chishima Chizu Sakusei-shi (A history of Japanese maps of the Kuril Islands)," and "Waga Kuni ni okeru Hokkaido-honto Chizu no Hensen (The transition of Japanese maps of Hokkaido)," all in *Hoppo Bunka Kenkyu Hokoku,* vols. 2–4 and 7 (1936, 1940, 1942 and 1952). See also Koreto Ashida: "Old maps of Hokkaido," in Bunmei Kyokai (ed.): *Dai Nippon,* Tokyo, 1936; and Koreto Ashida: "Karafuto no Chizugaku-shi-jo ni okeru aru Kosatsu (A study of the historical cartography of Karafuto)," *Shien,* vol. 4 (6), Hiroshima, 1930.

7. A few fragmentary records of this expedition are collected in Hokkaido: Kyodo-shiryo Kenkyukai (comp.): *Kaifu-maru Kiji* (Documents concerning Kaifu-maru), Sapporo, 1959. See also Motoharu Fujita: *Nisshi Kotsu no Kenkyu* (Studies of the intercourse between Japan and China), Tokyo, 1938, pp. 345–359.

8. A number of works on the history of Russo-Japanese relations have been published. See especially Frank A. Golder: *Russian expansion on the Pacific, 1641–1850; an account of the earliest and later expeditions made by the Russians along the Pacific coast of Asia and North America; including some related expeditions to the Arctic regions,* Cleveland, 1914, 368 pp., which is a classic. The latest and the most comprehensive work is George A. Lensen: *The Russian push toward Japan; Russo-Japanese relations, 1697–1875,* Princeton, N. J., 1959, 553 pp., with an extensive bibliography. Standard works in Japanese include Yasukazu Suematsu: *Kinsei ni okeru Hoppomondai no Shinten* (The development of the northern region problem in modern times), Tokyo, 1928; Kiyoshi Tahobashi: *Kindai Nippon Gaikoku Kankei-shi* (A history of the foreign relations of modern Japan), Tokyo, 1930. See also Fukusai Hayashi: *Tsuko Ichiran* (Collection of documents concerning Japan's communication with foreign countries, compiled in 1853), Tokyo, 1913, vols. 7 and 8.

9. Julius H. Klaproth translated Hayashi's work into French as *San Kokf tsou ran to sets, ou Aperçu général des trois royaumes,* Paris, 1832.

10. In Jean B. B. d'Anville's *Nouvel atlas de la Chine, de la Tartarie chinoise et du Thibet; contenant les cartes générales & particulières de ces pays, ainsi que la carte du royaume de Corée,* La Haye, 1737, an atlas of 12 pp. text and 42 maps, two islands of Sakhalin (Karafuto) are represented in one map, one of which is "Saghalien Anga Hata" drawn on the authority of the Jesuits' survey of China and the other is "Terra d'Esso" drawn on the basis of Maerten Gerritszoon Vries' map. But in the *Carte d'Asie* published in 1752 by the same author "Terra d'Esso" was drawn as a peninsula to the south of the Amur River estuary. The composition of this map is very similar to that of Hayashi's map of Ezo. D'Anville's *Carte d'Asie* was adopted by Covens and Mortier in their atlas, which was introduced into Japan and partly translated by Katsuragawa Hoshu, the physician to the Shogun and the celebrated scholar and expert in western learning. Since it appears that Katsuragawa is the author of the preface to Hayashi's work we may safely say that Hayashi was directly affected by Covens. For examples of Ezo shown on D'Anville's map see Pál Teleki: *Atlas zur Geschichte der Kartographie der japanischen inseln,* Budapest, 1909, pp. 159–161.

11. Hironaga Matsumae, the chief retainer of the Matsumae clan, wrote the *Matsumae-shi* (Description of Matsumae) in 1781.

12. John W. Hall: "Tanuma Okitsugu, 1719–1788, forerunner of modern Japan," *Harvard-Yenching Institute, Mono. Series,* vol. 14, pp. 1–208, Cambridge, Mass., 1955.

13. Maps made by Mogami were known in Europe through the reproductions by Philipp F. von Siebold in his *Nippon. Archiv zur Beschreibung von Japan und dessen Neben-und Schutzländern: Jezo mit den Südlichen Kurillen, Krafto, Koorai, und den Liukiu-Inseln,* Leyden, 1832–1854, 16 parts,

see part 7. For a biography of Mogami see Shinsaku Minagawa: *Mogami Tokunai*, Tokyo, 1943. For a study of Honda Toshiaki see Donald Keene: *The Japanese discovery of Europe: Honda Toshiaki and other discoverers, 1720–1798*, London, 1952, 246 pp.

14. For studies of repatriated castaways, such as Daikokuya Kodayu and others, see George A. Lensen: *op. cit.* [note 8]; Martin G. T. Ramming: *Reisen schiffbrüchiger Japaner im XVIII Jahrhundert*, Berlin, 1931, 90 pp.; Takayoshi Kamei (comp.): *Hokusa Bunryaku* (A brief account of the travels in the north, original written by Katsuragawa Hoshu in 1794), Tokyo, 1937; and Takayoshi Kamei: *Daikokuya Kodayu*, Tokyo, 1964.

15. Ryokichi Otani: *Tadataka Ino, the Japanese land-surveyor*, Tokyo, 1932, 358 pp., pp. 81–86. This map was later incorporated into the *Dai Nippon Enkai Yochi Zenzu* (Map of the whole coast of Japan) which Ino completed by years of laborious surveying.

16. Details of the exploration by Takahashi and Nakamura are given in *Kyumeiko-ki* written in 1807 by Habuto Masayasu, the Shogunate magistrate at Matsumae, and later incorporated in the *Shinsen Hokkaido-shi* (A history of Hokkaido, newly compiled), Sapporo, Hokkaido, 1936, see vol. 5.

17. The Russian envoy again repatriated four Japanese castaways on his visit to Japan in 1804. See Martin G. T. Ramming: *op. cit.* [note 14] pp. 50–59, and his *Russland-Berichte schiffbrüchiger Japaner aus den jahren 1793 und 1805 und ihre Bedeutung fur die Abschliessungspolitik der Tokugawa*, Berlin, 1930, 86 pp.; and Kisaku Otomo (comp.): *Kankai Ibun* (Strange tales of voyages round the world;) originally written by Otsuki Gentaku in 1807, Tokyo, 1944.

18. The late Professor Leo Bagrow expressed opposition to the view that Mamiya was the discoverer of the strait. See his "A few remarks on the map of the Amur to Tarter Strait and Sakhalin," *Imago Mundi*, vol. 12, pp. 127–136, 1955. For a biography of Mamiya see Tomio Hora: *Mamiya Rinzo*, Tokyo, 1960, 342 pp. For a brief history of Karafuto and Hokkaido including references to Mamiya's role in their exploration see Tomio Hora: *Karafuto-shi Kenkyu* (A study in the history of Karafuto), Tokyo, 1956, 253 pp.; and John A. Harrison: "Kita Yezo Zusetsu, or a description of the island of northern Yezo by Mamiya Rinso," *Amer. Philos. Soc., Proc.*, vol. 99 (2), pp. 95–117, Phila., Pa., 1955.

19. Philipp F. von Siebold: *op. cit.* [note 13] pt. 1, pp. 129–131 and pt. 7, pp. 167–196; Philipp F. von Siebold: *Atlas von Land-und Seekarten vom Japanischen Reiche*, Leiden, 1841, vol. 7, plate 25. See also related reference to Siebold under HISTORICAL CARTOGRAPHY (above).

20. George A. Lensen: *op. cit.* [note 8]; George A. Lensen: *Russia's Japan expedition of 1852 to 1855*, Gainesville, Fla., 1955, 208 pp.; John A. Harrison: *op. cit.* [note 5] p. 39; and Yoshi S. Kuno: *Japanese expansion on the Asiatic continent; a study in the history of Japan with special reference to her international relations with China, Korea and Russia*, Berkeley, Calif., 1937–1940, 2 vols.

21. Matsuura published many other books and maps of Ezo, contributing largely to the improvement and diffusion of knowledge of the northern regions. See also Frederick Starr: "The old geographer—Matsuura Takeshiro," *Asiatic Soc. Japan, Trans.*, vol. 44 (1), pp. 1–19, Tokyo, 1916; and Takezo Yoshida: *Hyoden Matsuura Takeshiro*, Tokyo, 1963.

22. Nobuo Muroga: "Ezo-chi, sono Chirigukushi-teki Imi (The land of Ezo, its significance in the history of geography)," in Kyoto Teikoku Daigaku Shigaku-ka (ed.): *Kigen 2600 Nen Kinen Ronbunshu*, pp. 979–1001, Kyoto, 1941.

23. Kobayashi Toyoaki accompanied Mogami Tokunai to Sakhalin in 1792 as a botanist and wrote the *Ezo-chi Somoku-zu* (An herbal of Ezo) based on the materials he collected. In 1799 an investigation of the flora of Ezo was conducted by Shibue Chohaku, physician to the Shogun, and others. Important publications that resulted from this investigation included *Toyu Kisho* (A journal from East Ezo), and *Hokuyu Somoku-cho* (A notebook of plants of the north), and forty volumes of specimens of plants and herbs. Frequent mention of the mode of living of the Ainu may be found in the books and reports of explorers and resident officials. The most important works on this subject include *Ezo-to Kikan* (Wonders of Ezo) by Hata Aokimaru (the pen name of the shogunate official Murakami Shimanojo), and *Ezo Seikei Zusetsu* (Illustrated description of the life of Ezo) by Hata Teiren (Murakami Teisuke, son of Shimanojo). A study of the Ainu language was made by the shogunate's interpreter, Uehara Kumajiro, who in 1792 published *Ezo Hogen Moshiogusa* (Vocabulary of the Ezo language) which was translated by Siebold and served as a valuable source for August Pfizmaier's: "Vocabularium der Aino-sprache," *Kon. Akad. der Wissenschaften Vienna. Philosophisch-Historische Classe. Denkschriften*, vol. 5 (1), pp. 137–230, Vienna, 1854.

24. The Nansei Islands comprise two principal units: the Satsunan and the Ryukyu. The former is part of Kagoshima Prefecture and the latter constitutes Okinawa Prefecture, now under United States provisional government. The first mention of the Nansei Islands is found in Nihon Shoki

(Chronicle of Japan, written in 720 A.D.) which states that some native inhabitants of Yaku Island came to Japanese Imperial Court in 616 A.D.

25. For full details of the Shimazu expedition in 1609 see Kagoshima-ken (ed.): *Kagoshima-ken-shi* (The history of Kagoshima Prefecture), vol. 2, pp. 621–638, Tokyo, 1940.

26. Ishinosuke Yamakata: *Ogasawara-to-shi* (Description of the Ogasawara Islands), Tokyo, 1906, pp. 72–78.

27. Shimaya was the author of a book on navigation similar to the *Genna Kokai-ki* which was compiled from Western sources. For example see Itaru Imai: "Shimaya Kenryu no Kokai-jutsu (Art of navigation of Shimaya Kenryu)," *Rangaku Shiryo Kenkyukai Hokoku*, no. 104, pp. 1–10, 1962.

28. Details of Shimaya's expedition are recorded in Tokei Matsuura: *Nagasaki Gaikoku Shuran* (Collection of documents concerning foreign affairs), Mss., 1810. See also Ishinosuke Yamakata: *op. cit.* [note 26] pp. 72–89. The results of this expedition by Shimaya were introduced to the Western world by such orientalists as Engelbert Kaempfer: *The history of Japan, giving an account of the ancient and present state and government of the empire,* . . . , London, 1727, 2 vols.; Jean P. Abel-Rémusat: *Nouveaux mélanges asiatiques; ou, Recueil de morceaux de critiques et de mémoires, relatifs aux religions, aux sciences* . . . , Paris, 1829, 2 vols.; Julius H. Klaproth: *Mémoires relatifs à l'Asie, contenant des recherches historiques, géographiques et philologiques sur les peuples de l'Orient,* Paris, 1824–1828, 3 vols., vol. 2, pp. 190–199; and Matthew C. Perry: *Narrative of the expedition of an American squadron to the China seas and Japan, performed in the years 1852, 1853 and 1854* . . . , Wash., D. C., 1856, 3 vols., vol. 1, pp. 197–199.

29. Takejiro Akioka: "Ogasawara Shoto Hakkenshi no Kihon Shiryo, Chizu ni tsuite (Fundamental materials and maps regarding the discovery of the Bonin Islands), *Kaijishi Kenkyu*, no. 1, pp. 6–26, 1963 and no. 2, pp. 45–57, 1965; and Toichiro Kimura: "Mujinto no Chizu (Maps of the Bonin Islands)," *Jinbun Chiri*, vol. 17 (4), pp. 432–438, Tokyo, 1965.

30. Makoto Abe: "Mujinto Chosa Tanken Shi (A history of exploration of the Bonin Islands)," *Rekishi Kyoiku*, vol. 17 (12), pp. 1065–1072, 1933.

31. Choun Takano: *Takano Choei Den* (A life of Takano Choei), Tokyo, 1943, pp. 364–377; and Shosuke Sato: *Yogakushi Kenkyu Josetsu* (Introduction to the history of Western learning), Tokyo, 1964, pp. 234–246.

32. Lionel B. Cholmondeley: *The history of the Bonin islands from the year 1827 to the year 1876, and of Nathaniel Savory one of the original settlers; to which is added a short supplement dealing with the islands after their occupation by the Japanese,* London, 1915, 178 pp., pp. 9–22; Basil Hall: *Account of a voyage of discovery to the west coast of Corea, and the great Loo-Choo island; with an appendix, containing charts, and various hydrographical and scientific notices,* London, 1818, 222 pp.; Basil Hall: *Narrative of a voyage to Java, China, and the great Loo-Choo Island* . . . , London, 1857, 81 pp.; Basil Hall: *Voyage to Loo-Choo, and other places in the eastern seas, in the year 1816* . . . , Edinburgh, 1826, 322 pp.; and Matthew C. Perry: *op. cit.* [note 28] vol. 1, p. 200.

33. For full details of the expedition of 1861 see I. Yamakata: *op. cit.* [note 26] pp. 116–159; K. Tahobashi: "Nasanieru Savoi to Ogasawara-jima (Nathaniel Savoy and the Ogasawara Islands)," *Rekishi Chiri*, vol. 39 (1, 2, 5, 6), pp. 26–37, 119–137, 361–378 and 444–455, 1921; and vol. 40 (2 and 4), pp. 84–95 and 255–267, 1922; Kenji Kiyono: "Nihon saisho no Ogasawara-jima Kaitaku Nisshi, Abe Rekisai cho Nansho koki (The oldest journal of the development of the Bonin Islands by Abe Rekisai)," in Yoshitaro Hirano and Kenji Kiyono: *Taiheiyo no Minzoku-Seijigaku,* pp. 359–397, Tokyo, 1942.

34. Nippon Kagakushi Gakkai (ed.): *Nippon Kagaku Gijutsu Taikei* (A general history of science and technique in Japan), vol. 14, pp. 126–128, Tokyo, 1965.

35. Shinichiro Takakura: *Chishima Gaishi* (Outline history of the Kuril Islands) Tokyo, 1960, pp. 131–136. See also Nobu Shirase: *Chishima Tanken Roku* (A record of the exploration of the Kuril Islands), Tokyo, 1897. Lieutenant Shirase was a member of Gunji's party. In 1910 he led an expedition to the Antarctic continent.

36. Nippon Kagakushi Gakkai: *op. cit.* [note 34] p. 202. See also Suirobu (ed.): *Suirobu Hachi-junen no Rekishi* (History of eighty years of the Hydrographic Division), Tokyo, 1952.

37. Michitaka Uda: *Sekai Kaiyo Tankenshi* (History of exploration of the oceans of the world), Tokyo, 1955, pp. 190–195.

38. Nippon Kagakushi Gakkai: *op. cit.* [note 34] p. 204; and *ibid.*, pp. 197–201.

Chapter 7

GEOGRAPHICAL EXPLORATION BY THE SPANIARDS

1. To my knowledge there is no comprehensive list of or guide to the collections of travels and reports pertinent to the Pacific Ocean or to the period of great explorations. I have found the following most useful. Edward G. Cox (comp.): ". . . A reference guide to the literature of travel, including voyages, geographical descriptions, adventures, shipwrecks, and expeditions," *Univ. Wash., Publ. Lang. and Lit.*, vols. 9 and 10, Seattle, Wash., 1935–1938; and Edward Lynam (ed.): "Richard Hakluyt & his successors; a volume issued to commemorate the centenary of the Hakluyt Society," *Hakly Soc., Works, Series 2*, vol. 93, pp. 1–192, London, 1946. See also the discussion and listings in Donald D. Brand: *Coastal study of southwest Mexico*, Austin, Tex., 1957–1958, 2 vols., vol. 1, Appendix, pp. 49–65.

2. These and other writers will be cited fully in the appropriate places.

3. James Burney: *A chronological history of the discoveries in the South Sea or Pacific Ocean . . .*, London, 1803–1817, 5 vols.; William T. Brigham: "An index to the islands of the Pacific Ocean: . . .," *Bernice P. Bishop Mus., Mem.*, vol. 1 (2), pp. 5–172, Honolulu, 1900; and Lawrence C. Wroth: "The early cartography of the Pacific," *Bibl. Soc. Amer., Papers*, vol. 38 (2), pp. 87–268, New York, 1944.

4. Carl E. Meinicke: *Die Inseln des Stillen Oceans; eine geographische Monographie*, Leipzig, 1875–1876, 2 vols. (2nd ed. 1888), and his earlier articles cited in the text; Andrew Sharp: *The discovery of the Pacific Islands*, Oxford, 1960, 259 pp. Also, the United States Navy Hydrographic (and since July 1962 the Naval Oceanographic) Office, *Sailing directions*, have been useful, such as numbers 78, 79, 80, 84, 123 A-B, 164, 165 A-B, 166, 169, 173–176, which cover the Pacific of interest to us, excepting the Pacific coasts of the United States.

5. There are many scattered references to a few unpublished manuscripts. Among the most substantial listings are V. Vicente Vela and Julio F. Guillén y Tato: *Índice de la colección de documentos de Fernández de Navarrete que posee el Museo Naval*, Madrid, 1946, 362 pp.; and Pascual de Gayangos y Arce: *Catalogue of the manuscripts in the Spanish language in the British museum*, London, 1875–1893, 4 vols. See also Donald D. Brand: *op. cit.* [note 1], pp. 72–78, 83–87, and 107–122. Further leads are provided in Martín Fernández de Navarrete: *Biblioteca marítima española*, Madrid, 1851, 2 vols.; and João A. de Mascanenhas Judice, Visconde de Lagôa: *Grandes e humildes na epopeia portuguesa do Oriente (séculos XV, XVI e XVII)*, Lisboa 1942–1947, 3 vols. (incomplete).

6. The Spanish Crown gave numerous detailed instructions concerning the duties and objectives of exploring expeditions, as in various sections of the *Recopilación de leyes de los reynos de las Indias . . .* Madrid, 1681— and other editions. Many useful data are collected in José de Veitia Linaje: *. . . Norte de la contratación de las Indias Occidentales*, Sevilla, 1672, 2 vols. in 1, and other editions; Manuel de la Puente y Olea: *Estudios Españoles. Los trabajos geográficos de la Casa de Contratación*, Sevilla, 1900, 451 pp.; Clarence H. Haring: *Trade and navigation between Spain and the Indies in the time of the Hapsburgs*, Cambridge, Mass., 1918, 371 pp. and his *. . . El comercio y la navegación entre España y las Indias en época de los Hapsburgos . . .*, Mexico, 1939, 460 pp.; and José Pulido Rubio: *El piloto mayor de la Casa de la Contratación de Sevilla; pilotos mayores, catedráticos de cosmografía y cosmógrafos*, Sevilla, 1950, 983 pp. (his 1923 first edition of 299 pp. has some material not included in this enlarged and revised edition).

7. The only terms applied to the ships of the Magellanic fleet were *nao* and *navío*, which meant only that they were decked sailing ships. Concerning the *Victoria* see Gervasio de Antíñano y de Galdácano: *La arquitectura naval española (en madera), bosquejo de sus condiciones y rasgos de su evolución*, Madrid, 1920, 427 pp., who, on p. 97, points out that the much-copied representation of the *Victoria* is a composite anachronism.

8. Useful background data on ships and nautical terminology can be gleaned from Diego García de Palacio: *Instrucion nauthica, para el buen uso, y regimiento de las naos, su traca, y gouierno conforme a la altura de Mexico*, Mexico, 1587, 156 pp. (a facsimile reprint was published in Madrid in 1944, 156 pp.); Cesáreo Fernández Duro: *Disquisiciones náuticas . . .*, Madrid, 1876–1881, 6 vols., especially libro V. *a la mar madera*, which also includes the famous *Itinerario de Navegacion* of about 1575 by Jhoan de Escalante de Mendoza on pp. 412–515; Enrico Alberto d'Albertis: "La costruzioni navali e l' arte della navigazione al tempo di Cristoforo Colombo," *Raccolta di Documenti e Studi Pubblicati dalla R. Commissione Colombiana pel Quarto Centenario dalla Scoperta dell' America*, pt. 4, vol. 1, pp. 1–240, Roma, 1893; Cesáreo Fernández Duro: *Armada española desde la unión de los reinos de Castilla y de Aragón*, Madrid, 1895–1903, 9 vols.; Gervasio de Artíñano y de Galdácano; *op. cit.* [note 7]; and José María Martínez-Hidalgo y Terán (ed.): *Enciclopedia general del mar*, Madrid, 1957–1958, 6 vols.

9. The manuals used by the navigators are not listed in the equipment of the expeditions. It is only from an occasional last will or testament or from an inventory of the effects of a dead man (or occasionally from the inventory of items seized or confiscated) that we obtain a few titles. Apparently the tables most used were those in some edition of Abraham ben Samuel Zacuto: *Almanach perpetuum celestium motuum (Radix 1473) Tabulae astronomicae, Edition 1496 Leiria*, Munich, 1915, 335 pp. and earlier editions. During the sixteenth, seventeenth, and eighteenth centuries the Spanish navigators used principally various editions of Martín Fernández de Enciso: *Suma de geographia . . .*, Sevilla, 1519, 75 pp., Francisco Faleiro (Falero): *Tratado del esphera y del arte del marear . . . Edition 1535 Sevilla*, Munich, 1915, 102 pp.; Pedro Nunes (Núñez): *Tratado da sphera com a Theorica do sol-da lua*, Lisboa, 1537, 180 pp.; Pedro de Medina: *Arte de navegar en que se contienen todas las reglas . . .*, Valladolid, 1545; Martín Cortés: *Breve compendio de la sphera y de la arte de navegar . . .*, Sevilla, 1551, 100 sheets (approx.); Rodrigo Zamorano: *Compendio de la arte de navegar*, Sevilla, 1581; Diego García de Palacio: *ibid.*, [note 8]; Pedro Porter y Casanate: *Reparos a errores de la navegación*, Zaragoza, 1634; Francisco de Seixas y Lovera: *Theatro naval hydrographico, de los fluxos y refluxos y de las corrientes de los mares, . . .*, Madrid, 1688, 104 pp.; Ioseph González Cabrera Bueno: *Navegación especulativa y práctica, con la explicación de algunos instrumentos . . .*, Manila, 1734, 394 pp.; Jorge Juan y Santacilia: *Compendio de navegación para el uso de los cavalleros guardias-marinas*, Cádiz, 1757, 1944 pp.; Jorge Juan y Santacilia: *Examen marítimo theórico práctico, . . .*, Madrid, 1771, 2 vols.; and Antonio de Ulloa: *Conversaciones de Ulloa con sus tres hijos en servicio de la marina . . .*, Madrid, 1795, 263 pp.

10. Among the more useful works, in approximate chronological order, are Josef de Espinosa y Tello (ed.): *Memorias sobre las observaciones astronómicas, hechas por los navegantes Españoles en distintos lugares del globo . . .*, Madrid, 1809, 2 vols.; Alexander de Humboldt: *Examen critique de l'histoire de la géographie du nouveau continent, et des progrès de l'astronomie nautique aux 15ᵐᵉ et 16ᵐᵉ siècles*, Paris, 1814-1834, 5 vols., and definitive edition 1836-1839; Martín F. de Navarrete: *Disertación sobre la historia de la náutica, y de las ciencias matemáticas que han contribuido á sus progresos entre los Españoles . . .*, Madrid, 1846, 421 pp.; Casáreo Fernández Duro: *op. cit.* [note 8], especially libro IV, "Los Ojos en el Cielo," 1879; Timoteo Bertelli: "La declinazione magnetica e la sua variazione nello spazio scoperte da Cristoforo Colombo," *Raccolta di Documenti e Studi Pubblicati dalla R. Commissione Colombiana pel Quarto Centenario dalla Scoperta dell' America*, part 4, vol. 2, pp. 9-99, Roma, 1892; Manuel de la Puente y Olea: *op. cit.* [note 6]; Joaquim Bensaúde: *Histoire de la science nautique Portugaise à l'époque des grandes découvertes . . .*, Lisbonne, 1924, vol. 1, pp. 1-35 which are followed by a facsimile reprint of the *Regimento do estrolabio e do quadrante. Tractado da spera do mundo* of ca. 1509; Louis A. de Morais e Sousa: *A sciência náutica dos pilotos portugueses nos séculos XV e XVI*, Lisboa, 1924, 2 pts. in 4 vols.; Segundo de Ispizúa: *. . . Historia de la geografía y de la cosmografía en las edades antigua y media con relación a los grandes descubrimientos marítimos realizados en los siglos XV y XVI por españoles y portugueses*, Madrid, 1922-1926, 2 vols.; Abel Fontoura da Costa: *A marinharia dos descobrimentos*, Lisboa, 1933 (34?), 511 pp., second edition 1939, 532 pp.; António Barbosa: *Novos subsídios para a história da ciência náutica portuguesa da época dos descobrimentos*, Porto, 1948, 332 pp. (enlarged revision of a 1937 edition); Salvador García Franco: *Historia del arte y ciencia de navegar; desenvolvimiento histórico declos cuatro términos' de la navegación*, Madrid, 1947, 2 vols.; Carlos V. Gago Coutinho: *A náutica dos descobrimentos, os descobrimentos maritimos vistos por um navegador . . .*, Lisboa, 1951-1952, 2 vols.

11. Outstanding early Iberian writings include Pedro Núñez 1537, Francisco Faleiro 1535, and Martín Cortés 1551, who postulated a magnetic pole [note 9]; Alonso de Santa Cruz: *Libro de las longitudines y manera que hasta agora se ha tenido en el arte de navegar . . .*, Sevilla, 1921, 151 pp. (finished in the 1560's but not published until 1921 in Sevilla by Antonio Blázquez y Delgado Aguilera); and Pedro de Medina: *Regimiento de navegación*, Sevilla, 1563. Useful historical discussions will be found in such modern writers as Espinosa 1809, Humboldt 1836-1839, Navarrete 1846, Bertelli 1892, Puente y Olea 1900, and García Franco 1947 [note 10]; and in Armando Cortesão: *. . . Cartografia e cartógrafos portugueses dos séculos XV e XVI*, Lisboa, 1935, 2 vols.

12. Carlos Viegas Gago Coutino: *op. cit.* [note 10], vol. 1, pp. 109-124, makes a very strong case against the determination of latitude at sea by other than noon solar observation.

13. On the general subject of longitude see such publications as Alonso de Santa Cruz: *op. cit.* [note 11]; Manuel de la Puente y Olea: *op. cit.* [note 6], pp. 349-363; and Salvador García Franco: *op. cit.* [note 10], pp. 269-390.

14. In this connection it is interesting to compare the longitudes given by Pigafetta in James A. Robertson: *Magellan's voyage around the world, by Antonio Pigafetta . . .*, Cleveland, 1906, 2 vols.; and Albo in Martín F. de Navarrete: *Colección de los viajes y descubrimientos que hicieron por mar los Españoles desde fines del siglo XV . . .*, Madrid, 1825-1837, 5 vols., see in vol. 5, which was published in 1837. Pigafetta (pp. 108 and 109) gives the longitude of the east side of Leyte Gulf in the Philip-

pines at 161° from the line of demarcation. Albo (p. 220) gives the longitude of the same locality as 189° from the *línea meridiana*. Later on Albo (p. 222) gives the longitude of Brunei in Borneo as 205° 5' from the *línea de la demarcación*. All of these values are erroneous, but they will serve to illustrate the nature of discrepancies, disagreements, and lack of precisely stated lines of reference. Nevertheless, if we subtract the real difference in longitude between the eastern Philippine location and Albo's longitude for Brunei (some 11 degrees) from Albo's Brunei longitude, we obtain a reading of some 190° west of the Line of Demarcation for the Philippine location which might indicate that Albo's 189° from an undefined *línea meridiana* was Albo's way to maintain intellectual honesty and yet not upset Spanish claims to this region. However, probably all of this was accidental, since Albo's longitude for Brunei was too far east by some 17 degrees.

15. Cesáreo Fernández Duro: *op. cit.* [note 10], *Disquisiciones* . . . , pp. 275–285; Konrad Kretschmer: *Die entdeckung Amerika's in ihrer bedeutung für die geschichte des weltbildes*, Berlin, 1892, 471 pp. and atlas; Nils A. E. Nordenskiöld: . . . *Periplus; an essay on the early history of charts and sailing directions;* . . . , Stockholm, 1897, 208 pp. and 60 pl. of maps; Manuel de la Puente y Olea: *op. cit.* [note 6], pp. 253–322; Erik W. Dahlgren: ". . . Were the Hawaiian Islands visited by the Spaniards before their discovery by Captain Cook in 1778?," *Kungl. Svenska Vet. Handl.*, vol. 57 (4), pp. 1–220, Stockholm, 1916; Edward Heawood: "The world map before and after Magellan's voyage," *Geogr. Journ.*, vol. 57, pp. 431–446, London, 1921; Frederik C. Wieder (ed.): *Monumenta cartographica* . . . , The Hague, 1925–1933, 5 vols.; Armando Cortesão: *op. cit.* [note 11]; Henry R. Wagner: *The cartography of the northwest coast of America to the year 1800*, Berkeley, 1937, 2 vols.; Julio F. Guillén y Tato: *Cartografía marítima española en torno a varios de los problemas de su estudio* . . . , Madrid, 1943, 67 pp. (not consulted); Lawrence C. Wroth: *op. cit.* [note 3]; Salvador García Franco: *op. cit.* [note 10], pp. 11–86; José Pulido Rubio: *op. cit.* [note 6], pp. 255–453; Berwick (Duque de Alba): *Mapas Españoles de América, siglos XV-XVII*, Madrid, 1951; Raleigh A. Skelton: *Explorers' maps; chapters in the cartographic record of geographical discovery*, London, 1958, 377 pp.; Armando Cortes~o and Avelino Teixeira da Mota: *Portugaliae monumenta carthographica*, Lisboa, 1960–1962, 6 vols.

16. The literature on Magellan and the Magellanic expedition is enormous, and it is exceeded in number of pieces and in bulk only by the literature pertaining to Columbus and his several voyages. However, most of the articles, monographs, and books are popular, repetitive, and unscholarly, and make little contribution to the subject. In this note are cited representative items, including some popular works and all that I consider useful excepting some of the publications which are primarily useful for basic documentation, which are cited in a later note. Diego Barros Arana: *Vida i viajes de Hernando de Magallanes*, Santiago de Chile, 1864, 148 pp. (reprinted in Buenos Aires in 1945); Francis H. H. Guillemard: *The life of Ferdinand Magellan, and the first circumnavigation of the globe, 1480–1521*, London, 1890, 353 pp. (reprints some documents, mainly from Navarrete *op. cit.* [note 14]); Vicente Llorens Asensio: *La primera vuelta al mundo. Relación documentada del viaje de Hernando de Magallanes y Juan Sebastián del Cano, 1519–1522*, Sevilla, 1903, 179 pp. (lists pertinent documents in the Archivo General de Indias and reproduces some documents, pp. 89–179); Oscar Koelliker: *Die erste umsegelung der erde durch Fernando de Magallanes und Juan Sebastian del Cano, 1519–1522*, München and Leipzig, 1908, 297 pp.; Jean Denucé: "Magellan; la question des Moluques et la première circumnavigation du globe," *Acad. Roy. Belgique, Mem.*, Series 2, vol. 4 (3), pp. 1–433, Bruxelles, 1908–1911; Pablo Pastells and Constantino Bayle: . . . *El descubrimiento del Estrecho de Magallanes en conmemoración del IV centenario*, Madrid, 1920, 2 vols. (vol. 1 contains material on the Moluccan voyages and provides a few hitherto unpublished documents and a listing of pertinent documents); José Toribio Medina: *El descubrimiento del Océano pacífico; Vasco Núñez de Balboa, Hernando de Magallanes y sus compañeros*, Santiago de Chile, 1913–1920, 3 vols. (vol. 3, Fernando de Magallanes, includes a very useful biography, bibliography, and reprinting of documents and extracts from early historians, as well as a few "new" documents); George E. Nunn: "Magellan's route in the Pacific," *Geogr. Rev.*, vol. 24 (4), pp. 615–633, New York, 1934 (a stimulating discussion, with good listing of basic sources); Stefan Zweig: *Magellan, pioneer of the Pacific*, London, 1938, 311 pp. (original German edition . . . *Magellan, der mann und seine tat*, Wien, 1938, 370 pp.) is romantic and personalized; Visconde de Lagôa: . . . *Fernão de Magalhãis* . . . , Lisboa, 1938, 2 vols. (the most scholarly study of Magellan to date; vol. 1 contains the life of Magellan and vol. 2 is a detailed study of the voyage based on all known sources); Enrique Ruiz-Guiñazú: *Proas de España en el mar magallánico*, Buenos Aires, 1945, 170 pp. (a partisan pro-Elcano text primarily concerned with Argentine waters and with Spanish discovery of the Falkland Islands but useful for the map reproductions); Amando Melón y Ruiz de Gordejuela: "Los primeros tiempos de la colonización. Cuba y las Antillas. Magallanes y la primera vuelta al mundo," *Historia de América* . . . , vol. 6, pp. 1–748, Barcelona, 1952 (typical of the pro-Elcano nationalistic school of writers); Charles McK. Parr: *So*

noble a captain; the life and times of Ferdinand Magellan, New York, 1953, 423 pp. (romantic and pro-Magellan, with a list of Magellanic transcriptions from the Archivo General de Indias, Sevilla).

17. Probably three-masted two-decked ships, square rigged (*velas redondas*) on the foremast and mainmast, and triangular-rigged (*vela latina*) on the mizenmast. As implied in note 7, there is no contemporary description or representation of the *Victoria* or of any of the other sailing ships. The ships depicted on various charts, such as the one by Ribero in 1529, are generalized inventions of the cartographer.

18. It is impossible to convert these tonnages accurately into modern tonnages [note 8]. The best summary discussion of this matter that I have seen so far is in Visconde de Lagôa: *op. cit.* [note 16], vol. 1, pp. 251–257, although there remains much room for doubt and controversy.

19. The basic documents concerning the ships, equipment, supplies, and crews are in the Archivo General de Indias, Sevilla, especially among the *Papeles de Maluco*. These were first published by Martín F. de Navarrete: *op. cit.* [note 14], also Madrid, 1858–1880, 5 vols., and Buenos Aires, 1945–1946. Two more volumes of this series by Navarrete are still in manuscript in the Museo Naval, Madrid. The material pertinent to Magellan's ships and crews are in vol. 4, pp. 3–26, and documents 17 and 18, pp. 162–188. These documents and further documents from the Archivo General de Indias, have been published by José T. Medina: *Colección de documentos inéditos para la historia de Chile, desde el viaje de Magallanes hasta la batalla de Maipo, 1518–1818*, Santiago de Chile, 1888–1902, 30 vols., vol. 1, especially pp. 113–147. A number of these documents or abstracts have been published elsewhere, as in Francis H. H. Guillemard: *op. cit.* [note 16]. The best discussion we have seen of the officers and crews is in Visconde de Lagôa: *op. cit.* [note 16], vol. 1, pp. 265–315.

20. As has been pointed out by many others, chronologic gaps in accounts by Iberian and other navigators from Roman Catholic countries frequently can be filled in quite accurately or conflicting dates given in various accounts can be rectified by consulting the religious calendar.

21. The account by Antonio Pigafetta, an Italian supernumerary on the *Trinidad*, and later on the *Victoria*, is the best known of all the Magellanic accounts, and it gives the greatest amount of general information. Unfortunately, however, it is poor on details of navigation. Of the four early manuscripts extant (composed about 1525), that in Italian in the Ambrosian Library in Milan is generally considered to be the best. This was published in somewhat garbled form by Amoretti in Milan in 1800, which edition unfortunately was used for the English translation in Henry E. J. S. (Lord) Stanley (of Alderley): "The first voyage round the world by Magellan. Translated from the accounts of Pigafetta, and other contemporary writers," *Hakly. Soc., Works*, vol. 52, pp. 1–257, London, 1874, pp. 33–163; and by Medina: *op. cit.* [note 19], vol. 2, pp. 417–524, in Spanish translation from the 1801 French edition of Amoretti. Andrea da Mosto (ed.): "Il primo viaggio intorno al globo di Antonio Pigafetta, e le sue Regole sull' arte del navigare . . . ," *Raccolta di Documenti e Studi . . . R. Commissione Colombiana pel Quarto Centenario dalla Scoperta dell' America*, part 5, vol. 3, pp. 49–112, Roma, 1894, provides a fairly accurate but modernized version of the Ambrosian account. The edition I consider the best, and from which I quote (vol. 33, p. 69) is the English translation accompanied page for page by the original Italian of the Ambrosian manuscript, by James A. Robertson: "Magellan's voyage around the world by Antonio Pigafetta," in Emma H. Blair and James A. Robertson (eds.): *The Philippine Islands, 1493–1898; explorations by early navigators, descriptions of islands and their peoples . . . , tr. from the originals*, Cleveland, 1903–1909, 55 vols., see vols. 33 and 34, and James A. Robertson (tr. and ed.): *Magellan's voyage around the world, by Antonio Pigafetta; the original text of the Ambrosian Ms., with English translation, notes, bibliography and index*, Cleveland, 1906, 3 vols. The text of the French Ms. 5650 in the Bibliothèque Nationale, Paris, is provided by Jean Denucé: *Pigafetta. Relation du premier voyage autour du monde par Magellan. 1519–1522. Édition du texte francaise d'après les manuscrits de Paris et de Cheltenham*, Anvers, 1913, 290 pp. Denucé also has utilized the other two manuscripts in French and the Ambrosian manuscript. The Italian Camillo Manfroni published a version of the Ambrosian account in 1928. The most recent treatment is the interesting version by the Visconde de Lagôa: *op. cit.* [note 16], vol. 2, pp. 7–215, which combines the Ambrosian text and the French Ms. 5650, with notes from all other known accounts of the Magellanic expedition. The Pigafetta account was first published in French translation in an abbreviated form in Paris about 1525-1535, and next in Italian in 1536 and in 1550, in English in 1555, and in Latin in 1555. Altogether there have been published some 30 editions of Pigafetta in at least seven languages.

22. Pigafetta in Emma H. Blair and James A. Robertson (eds.): *ibid.*, vol. 33, pp. 75–77; and Jo~o de Barros: *Tercera década da Asia de Joam de Barros: Dos feytos que os Portugueses fizeram no descobrimento & conquista dos mares & terras do Oriente*, Lisboa, 1563, 266 pp., libro 5, cap. 9. Barros, Portuguese royal chronicler, is a primary source concerning Magellan. He had at his disposal the charts, sailing directions, and logs which the Portuguese governor of the Moluccas, Antonio de

Brito, took from the captured *Trinidad* in 1522, as well as the letters (probably 1513–1515, and perhaps later) from Magellan to his friend Francisco Serr˜o (Serrano in Spanish) who lived in the Moluccas in 1512–1521, which letters Brito found in the effects of Serrão and also sent to Portugal. The captured papers undoubtedly included the account or log by Magellan as well as the effects of the royal pilot and cosmographer Andrés de San Martín, as the *Trinidad* continued to be the flagship of the expedition even after the death of Magellan. Brito enumerates some of these items in his 1523 letter to the Portuguese king. This was copied by J. B. Muñoz from the original in Torre do Tombo archives; published by Martin F. de Navarrete: *op. cit.* [note 14], vol. 4, pp. 305–311, and reprinted by José T. Medina: *op. cit.* [note 19], vol. 1, pp. 323–330, and by others). Fernão Lopes de Castanheda: *Historia do descobrimento & conquista da India pelos Portugueses*, Coimbra, 1551–1561, 8 vols. and later editions, liv. 6, cap. 41, mentions that Brito found on the *Trinidad* books belonging to San Martín, two planispheres made by Pedro Reinel for Magellan, and various papers of the pilots. No one has used these materials since Jo˜o de Barros (excepting possibly Antonio de Herrera), and they have been missing since the Lisboa earthquake of 1755 or earlier. The first complete edition of Jo˜o de Barros: *Decada primeira [terceira] da Asia de Joao de Barros, dos feitos que os portugueses fezerão no descobrimento & conquista dos mares & terras do Oriente*, was Lisboa, 1628, 3 vols.; the most-used edition is that of Lisboa, 1777–1778, 13 pts. in 24 vols.; and the most recent edition, Lisboa, 1945–1948, is in 4 vols. In connection with the San Martín papers, it should be pointed out here that the previously unknown . . . *Descripción de los reinos, . . . Libro que trata del descubrimiento y principio del estrecho que se llama de Magallanes, por Ginés de Mafra, . . .*, published in Madrid, 1920 in *Tres Relaciones* (219 pp.) by Antonio Blásquez y Delgado Aguilera from a manuscript found in the Biblioteca Nacional in Madrid, could not be based on more than Mafra's memory of what he might have read in a Tratado begun by San Martín. Mafra was a captive of the Portuguese for some time, and he was separated from the San Martín papers after their seizure by Brito in 1522 or, as Mafra claimed (Martin F. de Navarrete: *op. cit.* [note 14], vol. 4, p. 387), in 1526 in Lisboa.

23. The Pigafetta manuscripts contain 23 crude charts, which have been reproduced by such as Andrea da Mosto: *ibid.*; James A. Robertson (tr. and ed.): *ibid.*; Jean Denucé: *ibid.*; and Visconde de Lagôa: *op. cit.* [note 16]. On the first sketch map is shown South America south of about latitude 32° S., the Estreto Patagonico, and a land mass south of the strait which runs off the south side (top) of the map. After the Pigafetta sketch, there is much confusion concerning the earliest maps (manuscript and published) that show the Strait of Magellan. The reader is referred to the text and reproductions in Nils A. E. Nordenskiöld: *op. cit.* [note 15]; Edward Heawood: *op. cit.* [note 15]; Lawrence C. Wroth: *op. cit.* [note 3]; Enrique Ruiz-Guiñazú: *op. cit.* [note 16]; Berwick (Duque de Alba): *op. cit.* [note 15]; and to Vittore Bellio: "Notizia delle più antiche carte geografiche che si trovano in Italia riguardanti l'America," *Raccolta di Documenti e Studi . . . R. Commissione Colombiana pel Quarto Centenario dalla Scoperta dell' America*, part 4, vol. 2, pp. 101–221, Roma, 1892; and Julio F. Guillén y Tato: *Monumenta chartográfica indiana, Parte 1, Regiones del Plata y Magallánica*, Madrid, 1942.

24. Besides the Pigafetta account there are four accounts by participants in the voyage across the Pacific which merit consideration: Francisco Albo: *Diario ó derrotero*, Ms. in Archivo General de Indias, first published by Martín F. de Navarrete: *op. cit.* [note 14], vol. 4, pp. 209–247, and reprinted many times since. Albo, who began as boatswain on the *Trinidad* and reached Spain as pilot of the *Victoria*, provides (pp. 216–220) the most detailed navigational data existing for the Pacific voyage. Lord Stanley of Alderley: *op. cit.* [note 21], pp. 211–236, gives an English translation from a manuscript copy in the British Museum. The "narratione di un Portoghese compagno di Odoardo Barbosa (the anonymous Portuguese, perhaps Vasco Gomes Gallego the younger), published by Giovanni B. Ramusio in his *Primo volume, & seconda editione delle navigationi et viaggi . . .*, Venetia, 1554, f. 480, and reprinted many times including José T. Medina: *op. cit.* [note 19], vol. 2, pp. 395–398. The "Roteiro da viagem de Fernam de Magalh˜es," first published in *Acad. Real Sci. Lisboa. Coll . . . Hist. e Geogr. das Nações Ultramarinas*, vol. 4, (2), pp. 145–176, Lisboa, 1826, and reprinted several times as in José T. Medina: *ibid.*, vol. 2, pp. 398–417. Three Mss., all in Portuguese (in Lisbon, Paris, and Madrid), are known of this undated *roteiro* by a Genoese Pilot (probably León Pancaldo, who started as an able-bodied seaman *marinero* and became pilot of the *Trinidad*). The fourth account is the Libro by Ginés de Mafra (who also started as a *marinero* on the *Trinidad* and then rose to near-pilot rank), which was published by Antonio Blázquez y Delgado Aguilera: *op. cit.* [note 22] and which we know only as cited by Visconde de Lagôa: *op. cit.* [note 16], vol. 2, in comparing discrepancies or additions of various accounts to that of Pigafetta. The mss. is in the Biblioteca Nacional in Madrid.

Two other first-hand accounts exist. *A Viágem de Fernão Magalhães por uma Testemunha Presencial* (Martym Dayamôte—Martín López de Ayamonte—an ordinary seaman on the *Victoria* who deserted on Timor and was captured by the Portuguese), published by Antonio Baião in *Arquivo Histórico de Portugal*, Lisboa, vol. 1, pts. 5 and 6, pp. 276–281, 1933, from a Ms. in the Torre do Tombo archives. It is of no use in connection with the Pacific voyage. Not seen by me is an anonymous relation (Ms. in the University of Leiden Library) published by de Jong as *Um Roteiro inédito da circumnavegação de Fernão de Magalhães*, Coimbra, 1937.

There are in addition five or six writers who used first-hand information. Maximilianus Transylvanus (as under-secretary to Emperor Charles V, and whose father-in-law's brother was Cristóbal de Haro) interviewed Elcano and the others who returned on the *Victoria*, and on October 23, 1522, wrote a letter in Latin from Valladolid to (his father?) Matthieu Lang, Cardinal Archbishop of Salzburg. This letter, printed in Cologne in January of 1523, was the first published account of the circumnavigation of the globe. It has been reprinted in many editions and translations. I have used the version published by Martín F. de Navarrete: *op. cit.* (note 14], vol. 4, pp. 249–284. Antonio de Brito, Portuguese governor of the Moluccas, 1522–1525, in 1522 seized the *Trinidad* and May 6, 1523 wrote a letter to the Portuguese king João III which includes information about the Magellanic expedition evidently based on the records captured and interrogation of the prisoners. This letter was first published by Martín F. de Navarrete: *op. cit.* [note 14], vol. 4, pp. 305–311, from a copy made by Muñoz of the fragmentary letter in the Torre do Tombo archives [note 22]. A somewhat different version has been published in Academia das Sciencias de Lisboa: *Alguns documentos do Archivo nacional da Torre do Tombo, acerca das navegações e conquistas portuguezas . . .*, Lisboa, 1892, 551 pp., pp. 464–470. Peter Martyr (Pietro Martire D'Anghiera), who interviewed the survivors who reached Sevilla in 1522, published an account of the circumnavigation in his *De orbe nouo Decadas*, Alcalá, 1530, década 5, lib. 7, which has been reprinted many times in various languages. I have used the Buenos Aires, 1944, edition of the *Décadas del Nuevo Mundo*, as mentioned in note 22, made use of much first-hand material in his *Décadas da Asia*, Lisboa, 1563, década 3, lib. 5, caps. 8, 9, and 10. A useful account is that given by Antonio de Herrera y Tordesillas: *Historia general de los hechos de los Castellanos en las islas y tierra firme del mar océano . . .*, Madrid, 1601–1615, 8 vols. in 4, década 2, lib. 9, caps. 10–15, década 3, lib. 1, caps. 3–4, and 9–12, década 3, lib. 4, caps. 1–2, and elsewhere, published in 1601. I have used the 12 vol. Madrid, 1934–1953 edition, based on the Barcia edition of 1726–1730. Herrera was the official *cronista-mayor de Indias*, beginning in 1596, and had unequaled access to sources including many now lost. Other sixteenth and early seventeenth century authors, such as López de Gómara, 1553, Oviedo y Valdés 1557, and Argensola 1609, are to be considered secondary and less reliable sources.

25. Albo, Anonymous Portuguese, Barros, Brito, Genoese Pilot, Herrera, Mafra, Peter Martyr, Pigafetta, M. Transylvanus. Latitudes, when given, vary from 19° S. to 10°5′ S. for the Isla Primera or San Pablo, and from 14° S. to about 7° S. for Tiburones Island. Distances between these two Islas Desventuradas were estimated to be 50 leagues, 200 leagues, (the modal figure), nine degrees, and 800 miles.

26. Andrew Sharp: *op. cit.* [note 4], pp. 5–6, provides a reasonable discussion. Carl E. Meinicke: *op. cit.* [note 4], has been followed by most writers until the appearance of Sharp's book in 1960. Meinicke tends to be dogmatic and curt in his identifications, but his two volumes also contain much geographic and ethnographic information.

27. Although both Albo (p. 219) and Pigafetta (p. 99) refer to the triangular or lateen sails on the boats used by the islanders, apparently the thieving qualities of the natives made the greater impression in giving a name to the islands. The various modern authors who have assumed that the names Jubagana and Acacan, given only by Maximilianus Transylvanus (in Martín F. de Navarrete: *op. cit.* [note 14], vol. 4, pp. 267–268), applied to islands in the Ladrones apparently did not realize that Transylvanus omitted the Ladrones completely in his account. A comparison of Maximilianus Transylvanus with Albo (p. 220) and Pigafetta (pp. 103–113) shows clearly that Transylvanus was referring to the islands at the northeastern entrance to Leyte Gulf and the Surigao Strait.

28. The account by Pigafetta (pp. 103–113 and map) provides the most details and place names. Albo (p. 220), the Genoese Pilot (p. 404) and Transylvanus (pp. 267–268) also are useful although somewhat unclear and confusing. From data in the four accounts we can identify Samar (Zamal), Suluan (Zuluan), Homonhón (Humunu, Aguada, Buenas Señales, Gada, Acacan), Manicari (Abarien), southeast Leyte (Hiunanghan, Yunagan, Jubagana), Hibuson (Ibusson), and southern Leyte with Panaon Island (Ceilon, Selán, Cenalo, Seilani). For identifications in this part of the Philippines and for all of the archipelago we have used U. S. Hydrographic Office: *Sailing directions for the Philippine Islands*, nos. I, II, and III, Washington 1955 and 1956, and the pertinent charts; Philippine Office, Census Office: *Census of Philippine Islands taken under the direction of the Philippine Legislature in the year 1918*, Manila, 1920–1921, 4 vols. in 6, see vol. 1, *Geography, history and climatology;* U. S. Bureau of Insular Affairs: *A pronouncing gazetteer and geographical dictionary of the*

Chapter 7

Philippine Islands, United States of America, with maps, charts, and instructions, Wash., D. C., 1902, 933 pp.; and Carlos Quirino: *Philippine Cartography, 1320–1899*, Manila, 1959, 140 pp. The actual identifications, however, are my own.

29. The accounts concerning the voyage of the *Trinidad* are few and several are not well known. The items with substantive information are: João de Barros: *op. cit.* [note 22], década 3, liv. 5, cap. 10; Brito in Martín F. de Navarrete: *op. cit.* [note 14], vol. 4, pp. 305–311; the Genoese Pilot in José T. Medina *op. cit.* [note 19], vol. 2, pp. 414–417; Antonio de Herrera y Tordesillas: *op. cit.* [note 24], década 3, lib. 1, cap. 11, and década 3, lib. 4, cap. 2; Declaraciones of Gómez de Espinosa, Mafra and Pancaldo, in Valladolid in 1527, in Martín F. de Navarrete: *op. cit.* [note 14], vol. 4, pp. 378–388; Probanza de la Posesión del Maluco, in Valladolid in 1527, in José T. Medina: *op. cit.* [note 19], vol. 2, pp. 153–180; and Gómez de Espinosa, Carta al Rey dated January 12, 1525 from Cochin in India, in Vicente Llorens Asensio: *op. cit.* [note 16], pp. 162–166, and reprinted in José T. Medina: *op. cit.* [note 16], pp. 106–108.

30. Andrew Sharp: *op. cit.* [note 4], pp. 8–11, provides a reasonable identification for these and some of the other islands encountered on this voyage.

31. "Relación escrita ... por Andrés de Urdaneta," in Martín F. de Navarrete: *op. cit.* [note 14], vol. 5, pp. 401–439 (the specific citation is on p. 404). Urdaneta, protege of Elcano, provides the best account of events in the Moluccas where he lived in 1526–1535. The best account for navigational details, including an excellent description of the Strait of Magellan, is that by the pilot Martín de Uriarte which is incorporated (pp. 242–291) in the "Derrotero del viaje y navegación de la Armada de Loaisa" written in Tidore in 1528 by the last commander of the expedition Hernando de la Torre. This was first published by Martín F. de Navarrete: *op. cit.* [note 14], vol. 5, pp. 241–313. Both documents are in the Archivo General de Indias, Sevilla. Useful running accounts are in Gonzalo F. de Oviedo y Valdés: *Historia general y natural de las Indias, islas y tierra—firma del mar océano, ...*, Valladolid, 1557, but see lib. 20, caps. 5–36, in vols. 4 and 5 of the 14 vols. of the Asunción edition of 1944–1945; and Antonio de Herrera y Tordisillas: *op. cit.* [note 24] and the Madrid 1934 edition in 17+ vols. in which see década 3, lib. 7, caps. 5 and 7, década 3, lib. 9, caps. 4–6, 9 and 11, década 4, lib. 1, caps. 2–5, etc.

32. The basic source is Gonzalo F. Oviedo y Valdés: *op. cit.* [note 31], lib. 20, cap. 12. Oviedo met Padre Juan de Areizaga (chaplain on the *Santiago*) in Madrid in 1535, and was able to make use of the complete report prepared by Areizaga which is now lost. Herrera and others either copy, paraphrase, or summarize Oviedo.

33. Andrew Sharp: *op. cit.* [note 4], pp. 11–13. See also Samuel E. Morison: "Historical notes on the Gilbert and Marshall islands," *Amer. Nept.*, vol. 4, pp. 87–118, Salem, Mass., 1944, for suggestions concerning this and other Spanish discoveries.

34. There are three basic sources for the Saavedra voyages. What is apparently the diary kept by Saavedra himself until his death in October of 1529 was in a book brought back by the notary Francisco Granada. A *relación del viaje* was abstracted, and Martín F. de Navarrete: *op. cit.* [note 14], vol. 5, pp. 465–475, reproduced the imperfect copy in the Escorial library. Vicente de Nápoles, one of the few survivors, made two depositions in Madrid in 1534 concerning the expedition. These have been published in Martín F. de Navarrete: *op. cit.* [note 14], vol. 5, pp. 476–486 (from a Ms. in the Archivo General de Indias, Sevilla); and in the *Colección de documentos inéditos ... de Indias*, Madrid, 1866, vol. 5, pp. 68–96 (from the Muñoz transcriptions). The two Nápoles accounts are useful in filling in some of the gaps in the Saavedra account, but over-all the Saavedra account is the most precise and accurate. Ione S. Wright: "Voyages of Alvaro de Saavedra Cerón, 1527–1529," *Univ. Miami Hispanic-American Studies*, no. 11, pp. 1–127, Coral Gables, Fla., 1951, gives a general survey and some documents, but the route identifications are not reliable. See Andrew Sharp: *op. cit.* [note 4], pp. 16–23, for well-reasoned identifications of the islands discovered.

35. The Spanish names of the Micronesian island groups encountered in the voyage of 1529 are given by Antonio Galvão in his ... *Tratado dos descobrimentos*, Lisboa, 1563. We have used the fine third Portuguese edition edited by Visconde de Lagôa: ... *Tratado dos descobrimentos ...*, Porto, 1944, 506 pp. The material on Saavedra is on pp. 224–230 (1563 transcription) and on pp. 423–429. Galvão was Portuguese governor of the Moluccas in 1536–1540, and possibly had seen in India or Portugal the various papers taken from the *Florida* in 1529.

36. The source most commonly used is Antonio Galvão: *ibid.*, pp. 251–253, and pp. 444–445 in the 1944 edition. Diogo do Couto, Portuguese chronicler who completed the *Décadas da Asia* of João de Barros in Década 5, liv. 6, cap. 5, Lisboa, 1612, [note 22] has the ship wandering to latitude 29° S., up to 25° N., and then back to and along the equator. Unfortunately, I have not seen an unpublished account by one of the few survivors (Miguel Noble) which may be Ms. no. 2,222 in the Martín F. de Navarrete Collection of the Museo Naval in Madrid.

37. Andrew Sharp: *op. cit.* [note 4], pp. 24–26; H. E. Maude: "Spanish discoveries in the Central

Pacific," *Polyn. Soc., Journ.*, vol. 68, pp. 285–326, Wellington, 1959; Samuel E. Morison: *op. cit.;* Carl E. Meinicke: *op. cit.* [note 4]; et al.

38. Andrew Sharp: *op. cit.*, pp. 26–32, sums up the evidence for most of the islands discovered by the Villalobos expedition in Micronesia and Melanesia.

39. Magellan had named the archipelago San Lázaro. For years the Spaniards also used the name Islas del Poniente, since they sailed west to reach them. In time, the *Felipinas* became *Filipinas* and the name spread to cover all of Spanish Indonesia.

40. In addition to Andrew Sharp: *op. cit.* [note 4], there are useful discussions of the Villalobos expedition in Erik W. Dahlgren: *op. cit.* [note 15], pp. 28–33, and in Henry R. Wagner: *Spanish voyages to the northwest coast of America in the sixteenth century*, San Francisco, 1929, 571 pp., pp. 99–101. The basic sources are the *Relación* written for the Emperor Charles V by García de Escalante Alvarado in Lisbon, August 1, 1548, in *Colección de documentos inéditos . . . de Indias: op. cit.* [note 34], vol. 5, pp. 117–209; Fray Gerónimo de Santisteban 'Relación diaria," written for the Viceroy Mendoza in Cochin, India, January 22, 1547, *Colección de documentos inéditos . . . de Indias: op. cit.* [note 34], vol. 14, pp. 151–165; *Relazione* by Juan Gaytan (Gaetano) published by Giovanni B. Ramusio *op. cit.* [note 24], vol. 1, fol. 375v°, 1st ed., 1550, and later editions; and Antonio Galvão: *op. cit.*, pp. 274–278 and pp. 464–468 in the 1944 edition.

41. Probably named for the nickname of the *San Juan de Letran.* See García de Escalante Alvarado: *ibid.*, p. 122. A *relación* by De la Torre, used by the Legazpi navigators, apparently has been lost.

42. The basic accounts are brief and somewhat contradictory. For example, Escalante Alvarado, who was not on this expedition [note 40], (pp. 159–160) mentions an island group named Hombres Blancos because of the light-skinned natives; but Santiesteban, a participant [note 40] (p. 162) notes one light-skinned man in a group of dark-skinned natives; and Juan Pablo de Carreón (Carrión), who also was along, states that they saw only *negros* (in a letter of advice concerning the proposed Legazpi expedition of 1564, in *Colección de documentos inéditos . . . de ultramar*, Madrid, 1885–1932, 25 vols., vol. 2, p. 206).

43. José Toribio Medina: *op. cit.* [note 16], vols. 1 and 2 bring together the pertinent (published and unpublished) material.

44. Berwick (Duque de Alba): *op. cit.* [note 15], on plate VIII reproduces a map by Alonso de Santa Cruz in the Archivo Histórico Nacional, Madrid, dated about 1536 which shows Malpelo.

45. Berlanga's Carta al Emperador, dated April 26, 1535 from Villanueva de Puerto Viejo (Ecuador), is in the Archivo General de Indias, and was first published in the *Colección de documentos inéditos, relativos al descubrimiento, conquista y organización de las antiguas posesiones españoles de América y Oceanía, sacados, de los archivos del reino, y muy especialmente del de Indias*, Madrid, 1864–1884, 42 vols., vol. 41, pp. 538–544. The islands visited probably were Barrington (=Santa Fe) and Charles (=Floreana = Santa María). Some useful accounts, in the rather large literature on the Galápagos are: Carlos M. Larrea: "Descubrimiento del Archipélago de Galápagos por navegantes españoles,' *Informaciones Científicas Nacionales, Boletín*, no. 72, pp. 241–266, Quito, 1955; C. William Beebe: *Galapagos, world's end*, New York and London, 1924, 443 pp., pp. 332–416; Marcos Jiménez de la Espada: "Las islas de los Galápagos y otras más á poniente," *Sociedad Geográfica de Madrid, Boletín*, vol. 31, pp. 351–402, Madrid, 1891. A good example of typical slighting of Spanish sources and exploration is the otherwise excellent Joseph R. Slevin: "The Galapagos Islands; a history of their exploration," *Calif. Acad. Sci., Occas. Papers*, no. 25, pp. 1–150, San Francisco, 1959.

46. The account of Rivadeneira is given by Pedro Cieza de León, "Guerra de Quito," first published completely in *Nueva Biblioteca de Autores Españoles . . . Historiadores de Indias, . . .*, vol. 2, pp. 241–246, Madrid, 1909. The large island with the active volcano probably was Albemarle (=Isabela). Although commented on by Alonso de Santa Cruz in his Islario of the 1540's, apparently the first published depiction of the Galápagos Islands is on a map of 1570 by Abraham Ortelius: *Theatrum Orbis Terrarum*, Antwerpiae, 1570, 53 double maps. For a detailed description of this work see Jan Denucé: *Oudnederlandsche kaartmakers in betrekking met Plantijn*, Antwerp, 1912–1923, 2 vols., see vol. 2, pp. 92–94.

47. The ". . . Islario general de todas las islas del mundo" written about 1541–1545 by Alonso de Santa Cruz, was published in the *Boletín de la Real Sociedad Geográfica*, vol. 60, pp. 7–88, 231–264, 383–392, and 491–516, and vol. 61, pp. 69–128, 271–288, 437–480, and 505–728, Madrid, 1918 and 1919, accompanied by 120 maps. Lamina 3 shows the islands, and p. 725 has the textual discussion. Gonzalo F. Oviedo y Valdés: *op. cit.* [note 31], lib. 39, cap. 1, in his description of the Pacific coast of South America written about 1546, mentions the expedition and having seen a sketch map of the southern portion of the coast which he did not use because he did not know who made the map. There is some useful background material in *Colección de diarios y relaciones para la historia de los viajes y descubrimientos*, Madrid, 1943, vol. 1, pp. 13–26.

48. No actual account has been preserved from the Ulloa expedition, but Francisco Vidal Gor-

Chapter 7

maz (ed.) reconstructed the voyage from scattered data in "Documentos relativos a la historia náutica de Chile," *Anuario Hidrográfico de la Marina de Chile*, vol. 6, pp. 435–452, Santiago de Chile, 1880. It is apparent that the magnetic needle still had a declination to the west in the southeast Pacific in 1554. Francisco Vidal Gormaz also in vol. 5 of the *Anuario* ..., pp. 390–395 and 402–442, 1879, provides excellent notes to logs and accounts of the Strait of Magellan by Albo, Urdaneta, and Uriarte. In vol. 5, pp. 482–520 of the *Anuario* ... is reprinted the Cortés account of 1557–1558 (first published by Claudio Gay in 1852 from a document in the Archivo General de Indias, Sevilla); and in vol. 6, pp. 453–525 is reprinted the Ladrillero account of 1557–1559 (first published by Miguel Luis Amunátegui in 1879 from a document in the Archivo General de Indias, Sevilla). Although Chapter 7 does not consider the Sarmiento voyage of 1579–1580 from Perú to the Strait, it should be mentioned here that excellent notes to this voyage are in the *Anuario* ..., vol. 7, pp. 413–542, Santiago de Chile, 1881. The first map we know that incorporated the results of these voyages is that of 1562 by Bartolomé Olives (in the Vatican Library; reproduced by Enrique Ruiz-Guiñazú: *op. cit.* [note 16], p. 99), which in the legend states that Olives made use of the information about the Chilean coast brought to Europe in 1562 by Don García (the Chilean governor).

49. The most comprehensive treatment of Juan Fernández to date is that by José T. Medina: *El piloto Juan Fernández, descubridor de las islas que llevan su nombre y Juan Jufré, armador de la expedición que hizo en busca de otras en el mar del Sur;* ..., Santiago de Chile, 1918, 261 pp. There is no doubt concerning the discovery of San Félix and San Ambrosio in 1574, as cited by Pedro Sarmiento de Gamboa (who knew Juan Fernández) in his writings published as *Viajes al estrecho de Magallanes*, Madrid, 1768, p. 49. However, Sarmiento and Fernández evidently identified these islands with the Islas Desventuradas of Magellan. The only source for the supposed voyage to the coast of the "Tierra firme Austral" is a *Memorial* by Dr. Juan Luis Arias (written about 1621), which has been reprinted by José T. Medina: *ibid.*, pp. 228–255, as well as widely elsewhere, as for example in Clements Markham (trans. and ed.): "The voyages of Pedro Fernandez de Quiros, 1595 to 1606," *Hakly. Soc., Works, Series 2*, vols. 14–15, London, 1904; "Memorial to Philip III, king of Spain by Juan Luis Arias" is in vol. 15, pp. 517–536.

50. The pertinent documents will be found in José T. Medina: *op. cit.* [note 16], vol. 2, including a *cédula* of 1524 (pp. 93–94), which contains the first mention of coconut palms found growing in the Americas, and various documents (pp. 272–317, 367–381, and 445–484).

51. The basic document is a letter of March 6, 1524 from Gil González Dávila to the King of Spain (which is in the Archivo General de Indias, Sevilla), first published by Manuel M. de Peralta: *Costa-Rica, Nicaragua y Panamá en el siglo XVI, su historia y sus límites según los documentos del Archivo de Indias de Sevilla, del de Simancas, etc.,* ..., Madrid, 1883, 832 pp., pp. 3–26. Gonzalo F. Oviedo y Valdés: *op. cit.* [note 31], repeatedly and at length criticized the claims of Espinosa and Castañeda and of González de Avila and Niño in lib. 29, caps. 13 and 21, and lib. 39, cap. 2. It is evident that both the leagues traveled and the latitude attained do not jibe with any of the contemporary maps whose makers evidently had access to the *derrotero* of Andrés Niño (now lost) for the place names between the Gulf of Nicoya and the "Sierras de Gil González Dávila" placed near what would be the eastern beginnings of the Gulf of Tehuantepec. See the Spanish map of 1527 attributed (among others) to Fernando Colón and the Ribero map of 1529, published by Johann G. Kohl: *Die beiden ältesten general-karten von Amerika. Ausgeführt in den jahren 1527 und 1529 auf befehl kaiser Karl's V* ..., Weimar, 1860, 185 pp. Francisco López de Gómara: *La istoria de las Indias. Y conquista de Mexico*, Çaragoça, 1552, gives a casual corroboration of the claims as far as Guatemala by mentioning ships reported along the Guatemala coast by Indians talking with Spanish explorers in Guatemala in 1523 (see vol. 1, p. 349 of the 1954 Barcelona edition).

52. For a brief study of some of these early ports see Donald D. Brand: "The development of Pacific coast ports during the Spanish colonial period in Mexico," in *Estudios Antropológicos Publicados en Homenaje al Doctor Manuel Gamio;* pp. 577–591, Mexico, 1956. Also see Woodrow W. Borah: "Early colonial trade and navigation between Mexico and Peru," *Ibero-Americana*, no. 38, pp. 1–170, Berkeley, 1954.

53. Cartographically, Grijalva has been credited only with the discovery of *Santo Tomàs* (Isla Socorro, or, as it has recently been renamed Isla de Juárez). However, the basic document surviving (Relación y derrotero de una armada ... por Hernando de Grijalva y el Piloto Martín de Acosta, in the Archivo General de Indias, Sevilla, published in *Colección de documentos inéditos de Indias:* [note 45], vol. 14, pp. 128–142) clearly describes the discovery of the Isla de los Inocentes on December 28, 1533, nine days after the discovery of Santo Tomás. The description and location (pp. 135–136) indicate that Isla San Benedicto of today is the only possible identification.

54. See Donald D. Brand: *op. cit.* [note 1], Appendix pp. 3–6, 125–132, for a brief discussion of the 1527–1534 period.

55. The pertinent documents for the voyages of Ulloa and Bolaños, and the later voyages of

Cabrillo, Cermeño, and Viscaíno have been utilized expertly by Henry R. Wagner: *op. cit.* [note 40]; and to this substantial work Wagner has added his magnificent study of the cartographic record [note 15]. I am merely summarizing some of Wagner's work and conclusions.

56. In addition to the above-mentioned works by Wagner, we should cite the last published work by the Portuguese historian, the Visconde de Lagôa: *Joãn Rodrigues Cabrilho*, Lisboa, 1958. See also Henry R. Wagner: "Juan Rodríguez Cabrillo, discoverer of the coast of California," *Calif. Hist. Soc., Spec., Publ.*, no. 17, pp. 1–94, San Francisco, 1941.

57. Nearly all of the pertinent documents are in the Archivo General de Indias, Sevilla, and have been used and cited by Wagner. The charts made during the survey by the self-styled cosmographer Jerónimo Martín de Palacios were copied or redrawn by the cosmographer of New Spain Enrico Martínez and have been published in Alvaro del Portillo y Díez de Sollano: "Descubrimientos y exploraciones en las costas de California," *Publicaciones de la Escuela de Estudios Hispano-Americanos de Sevilla, Ser. 2: Monografías*, no. 7, pp. 1–540, Madrid, 1947. See also Francisco Carrasco y Guisasola (ed.): *Documentos referentes al reconocimiento de las costas de las Californias desde el cabo de San Lucas al de Mendocino . . . en el Archivo de Indias*, Madrid, 1882, 107 pp. An example of the continued use of the Vizcaíno (actually Ascensión-Bolaños) *derrotero* is to be found in Joseph González Cabrera Bueno: *op. cit.* [note 9].

58. Most of the pertinent documents are in the Archivo General de Indias, Sevilla, of which selections have been published in two volumes "De las Islas Filipinas," *Colección de Documentos Inéditos Relativos al Descubrimiento . . . de Ultramar*, vols. 2 and 3, Madrid, 1886–1887. Unfortunately, the editors saw fit to omit some of the *derreteros* with navigational data. Nevertheless, much useful information will be found in vol. 2, pp. 119–138, 205–210, 217–351 (especially 218–252), 373–427 (chiefly 375–395), and 427–456; and vol. 3, pp. 1–76 (mainly 1–29 and 65–73), 91–225 (179–188 for the *San Gerónimo*), 226–243, and 371–475 (the voyage of the *San Gerónimo* is pp. 380–454). Brief but competent outlines of the voyages of the fleet and of the *San Lucas, San Pedro*, and *San Gerónimo* are given in Erik W. Dahlgren: *op. cit.* [note 15], pp. 33–39, and Henry R. Wagner: *op. cit.* [note 40], pp. 101–120; and modern scholarship with reference to identifications of the islands discovered or rediscovered is expressed in Andrew Sharp: *op. cit.* [note 4], pp. 32–39. Sharp identifies Los Barbudos as Mejit in the eastern Marshalls; Los Placeres as Ailuk, Pájaros as Jemo, Las Hermanas as Wotho (perhaps discovered by Villalobos), and the low islands as Ujelang (discovered by Saavedra)—all in the Marshalls.

59. We are not here concerned with the reasons which led Arellano and Martín to make only a perfunctory search for the remainder of the Legazpi fleet in the Philippines before attempting the solo voyage back across the Pacific. The fact remains that the *San Lucas* accomplished the return voyage successfully and was the first to do so. The contemporary literature indicates strongly that by 1564 the Spanish pilots in the Pacific area had concluded that a return voyage could be made by (1) leaving from a more northern latitude than the Moluccas or Mindanao, and (2) departing during a favorable season, *i.e.*, late spring or summer. Probably Urdaneta had no more to do with selecting a favorable route and season than Juan Pablo de Carrión (who had been with Villalobos, and who was to have been *almirante* in the Legazpi fleet until a dispute arose between him and Urdaneta). In any case, the evidence from the previous unsuccessful attempts was available to all the pilots including Lope Martín. He should be given credit for the successful act even though his motivation may have been unethical.

60. General background is provided by William L. Schurz: *. . . The Manila galleon . . .* , New York, 1939, 453 pp. An excellent bibliography accompanies what is primarily a commercial statistical study by Pierre Chaunu: *Les Philippines et le Pacifique des Ibériques (xvie, xviie, xviiie siècles); introduction méthodologique et indices d'activité*, Paris, 1960, 301 pp. Erik W. Dahlgren: *op. cit.* [note 15], pp. 40–138, provides the most information on individual voyages that has been published to date. James Burney: *op. cit.* [note 3] is useful despite the poor quality of the maps and sources available to him at the time of writing. Scattered through the great compilation by Emma H. Blair and James A. Robertson (eds.): *op. cit.* [note 21], are many data concerning the Manila and Acapulco ships. Henry R. Wagner: *op. cit.* [note 40], pp. 125–153 has a useful summary concerning the much-publicized voyages of Gali and of Unamuno. With the exception of the voyages of Gali in 1582–1584, first published by Jan H. van Linschoten: *Itinerario, voyage ofte schipvaert van Jan Huygen van Linschoten naer Oost ofte Portugaels Indien . . .* , t' Amstelredam 1595–1596, 3 vols. in 1; see Johan C. M. Warnsinck (ed.): "Jan Huygen van Linschoten. Itinerario, van voyage ofte schipvaert van Jan Huygen van Linschoten naer Oost ofte Portugaels Indiën, 1579–1592," *Linschoten-Vereeniging, Werken*, vol. 43, 's Gravenhage, 1939, especially "Reys-Gheschrift vande navigatien der Portugaloyers" on pp. 274–369; and of Unamuno in 1587 (see Henry R. Wagner: *op. cit.* [note 40], pp. 481–504; and Santiago Montero Díaz: "El viaje de Pedro de Unamunu por el Pacífico y Costa de Méjico," *Revista de Archivos, Bibliotecas y Museos*,

vol. 51, pp. 416–440, Madrid, 1930), the logs of "Manila galleons" prior to 1699 have been lost or destroyed. Furthermore, there are no sixteenth or seventeenth century charts of the north Pacific in the Archivo General de Indias, Sevilla. Erik W. Dahlgren and others have made use of a manuscript copy in the British Museum (Additional Manuscripts 19,293) of an abstract Pedro de Antioquia made about 1742 of 30 logs that covered the period 1699 to 1740. The observations and comments by Hernando de los Ríos Coronel (commander of the *Espíritu Santo*, 1605) are available in a manuscript, copies of which are in the Biblioteca Nacional in Madrid, and in the British Museum. María Lourdes Díaz-Trechuelo: "Dos nuevos derroteros del Galeón de Manila (1730–1773)," *Anuario de Estudios Americanos*, Sevilla, vol. 13, pp. 1–83, Sevilla, 1956, gives a summary of the log of the *Buen Fin* 1773 accompanied by reproductions of original charts made by the second pilot José Vázquez. José de Espinosa y Tello (ed.): *op. cit.* [note 10], provides many useful but scattered bits of information.

61. Erik W. Dahlgren: *op. cit.* [note 15], pp. 49–51, and references cited by him.

62. One of the pilots with Vizcaíno, Lorenzo Vázquez, surveyed the coast from Uraga to Nagasaki, but it is not clear whether the eastern or western route was surveyed. The basic *relación* has been published in *Colección de documentos inéditos de Indias . . .* , vol. 8, pp. 101–199, Madrid, 1867, especially pp. 163–184. See also, among several publications on the subject, Zelia Nuttall: ". . . The earliest historical relations between Mexico and Japan, from original documents preserved in Spain and Japan," *Univ. of Calif., Publ. Amer. Arch. and Ethnol.*, vol. 4 (1), pp. 1–47, Berkeley, 1906; Naojiro Murakami: "Japan's early attempts to establish commerical relations with Mexico," in Henry M. Stephens and Herbert E. Bolton (eds.): *The Pacific Ocean in History*, pp. 467–480, New York, 1917; Cristóbal Ariza Torres: *Datos históricos sobre don Rodrigo de Vivero y el general Sebastián Vizacaíno encontrados en el Archivo de Indias*, Madrid, 1926, 146 pp.

63. Erik W. Dahlgren: *op. cit.* [note 15], pp. 96–97, has cited the sources and summarized the evidence. See also Charles Le Gobien: *Histoire des isles Marianes nouvellement converties à la religion chrestienne . . .* , Paris, 1700, 433 pp., p. 377.

64. The islands in the Japanese Nanpō Shotō long have been a cartographer's headache and apparently anathema for the historian. See U. S. Hydrographic Office: "Sailing Directions for Nanpo Shoto," *H. O. Publ.*, no. 1232, pp. 1–33, Wash., D. C. 1945. Suggested references are Carl E. Meinicke: *op. cit.* [note 4], vol. 2; and Hyman Kublin: "The discovery of the Bonin islands: A reexamination," *Assoc. Amer. Geogr. Annals*, vol. 43, pp. 27–46, Wash., D. C., 1953.

65. María Lourdes Díaz-Trechuelo: *op. cit.* [note 60], pp. 53–72; Andrew Sharp: *op. cit.* [note 4], pp. 127–128.

66. Andrew Sharp: *op. cit.* [note 4], pp. 147–151. The Comte de Lapérouse apparently acquired a somewhat incorrect copy of a narrative of the Maurelle voyage while in the Philippines in 1787, and this narrative was in the Lapérouse papers published by Louis M.A.D. de Milet de Mureau: *Voyage de La Pérouse autour du Monde*, Paris, 1797–1798, 4 vols. and an atlas. We have used the Londres, 1799 edition, vol. 1, pp. 201–248. There are actually two *diarios* of this voyage (one by Maurelle in the Archivo General de Indias, Sevilla, and another more extensive account by the pilot Vázquez in the Museo Naval in Madrid). A version written for the use of Malaspina is in José de Espinosa y Tello (ed.): *op. cit.* [note 10], vol. 2, Memoria 3a. Ricardo Beltrán y Rózpide: *La Polinesia; descubrimiento . . .* , Madrid, 1884, 297 pp., pp. 104–112 gives an abstract from the Museo Naval *diario* and reproduces a Ms. chart. See also the brief article by Francisco de las Barras de Aragón: "Un gran marino español del siglo XVIII; don Francisco Antonio Maurelle," *Las Ciencias*, año 16 (1), Madrid, 1951, based on the Archivo General de Indias, Sevilla, copy of the Maurelle *diario*.

67. H. E. Maude: *op. cit.* [note 37], pp. 299–305, has marshalled the evidence in a most convincing fashion. The identification of Jesús with Nukufetau, favored by many writers, is not reasonable.

68. There are eight accounts of this expedition extant which cover all or part of the period 1567–1569. Six of these have been translated and edited by William A.T.-A. Amherst (Lord Amherst of Hackney) and Basil Thomson: "The discovery of the Solomon islands by Alvaro de Mendaña in 1568," *Hakly. Soc., Works*, series 2, vols. 7–8, London, 1901. The other two items, by Pedro Sarmiento de Gambóa and of minor importance, are in the Archivo General de Indias, Sevilla. See also Clements R. Markham (trans. and ed.): "Narratives of the voyages of Pedro Sarmiento de Gambóa to the straits of Magellan, with notes and an introduction," *Hakly. Soc., Works*, vol. 91, pp. 1–401, London, 1895; and Pedro Sarmiento de Gambóa: *Viaje al estrecho de Magallanes por el capitán Pedro Sarmiento de Gambóa en los años de 1579. y 1580. y noticia de la expedición que despues hizo para poblarle*, Madrid, 1768, 402+ pp. Of primary importance are: the log or narrative of the chief pilot Hernán Gallego (known in three copies—one belonging to Lord Amherst, one in the Biblioteca Nacional in Madrid, and one in the British Museum); an incomplete

narrative by Mendaña in the Archivo General de Indias, Sevilla, published in *Colección de documentos inéditos de Indias*, vol. 5, pp. 221–285, Madrid, 1866; and the narrative by the purser and official chronicler Gómez Hernández Catoira, rich in ethnographic data, which is British Museum Additional Manuscript 9, 944. Although the Solomon Islands were placed on a manuscript map by López de Velasco (Descripción de las Yndias del Poniente, *ca.* 1575–1580) which was published in Antonio de Herrera y Tordesillas in 1601; and also appear on a world map by Abraham Ortelius in his *Théâtre de l'univers, contenant les cartes de tout le monde. Avec une brieve déclaration d'icelles . . .* , Anvers, 1587, 243 pp. incl. 112 colored maps; their actual location and identity were lost until Philippe Buache published his *Considérations géographiques et physiques sur les nouvelles découvertes au nord-est de l'Asie et au nord-ouest de l'Amerique avec les Memoires relatifs*, Paris, 1781, 11 maps (published in Fleurieu in 1790) and at least theoretically solved the problem and Antone R. J. de B. d'Entrecasteaux: *Voyage de Dentrecasteaux envoyé à la recherche de La Pérouse . . . , 1791, 1792, 1793, . . .* , Paris, 1807–1808, 2 vols. and an atlas, in 1793 identified the group on the spot with "discoveries" made by English and French explorers in the 1760's. An outstanding job of identifying the individual islands was made by Henry B. Guppy: *The Solomon Islands and their natives*, London, 1887, 384 pp. who published an abstract of the journal by Hernán Gallego on pp. 192–245. Guppy's identifications were better than those by Carl E. Meinicke [note 4]. The suggestions of these men were studied by Charles M. Woodford who took the narratives of the Mendaña expedition with him to the Solomons to make identifications most of which were incorporated in the William A.T.-A. Amherst and Basil Thomson publication cited above. See Charles M. Woodford: "Exploration of the Solomon Islands," *Roy. Geogr. Soc., Proc.*, vol. 10, pp. 351–376, London, 1888. The most recent summation of identifications is in Andrew Sharp: *op. cit.* [note 4], pp. 42–48.

69. Andrew Sharp: *op. cit.* [note 4], pp. 50–55, summarizes identifications of islands discovered by this expedition. H. E. Maude: *op. cit.* [note 37], pp. 305–310, gives a well-reasoned discussion of the identifications of San Bernardo and La Solitaria.

70. Quirós himself in two accounts is practically the only source for the 1595–1596 expedition. Antonio de Morga published Quirós' report to him in his *Sucesos de las Islas Filipinas . . .* , Mexico, 1609, 172 pp. This has been reprinted in numerous editions. We have used the Emma H. Blair and James A. Robertson edition: *op. cit.* [note 21], vols. 15 and 16, especially vol. 15, pp. 102–116 which makes use of the notes in José Rizal (ed.): *Sucesos de las islas Filipinas por el doctor Antonio de Morga, . . . 1609, . . . neuvamente sacada á luz y anotada por José Rizal*, Paris, 1890, 374 pp., and those in the 1868 edition by Henry E. J. S. Stanley (trans. and ed.). This report and the fuller report by Quirós (copies of which are in the Biblioteca del Palacio Real and in the Museo Naval, Madrid) have been translated and edited by Clements R. Markham: "The voyages of Pedro Fernández de Quirós, 1595 to 1606," *Hakly. Soc., Works, Series 2*, vols. 14 and 15, London, 1904. Some additional information is provided by Cristóbal Suárez de Figueroa: *Hechos de Don García Hurtado de Mendoza, quarto marqués de Cañete . . .* , Madrid, 1613, 324 pp., and later editions (see pp. 150–182 of the 1864 Santiago de Chile edition). Most of the basic documents concerning the voyages of Quirós were first published by Justo Zaragoza (ed.): *. . . Historia del descubrimiento de las regiones austriales hecho por el general Pedro Fernández de Quirós*, Madrid, 1876–1882, 3 vols.

71. H. E. Maude: *op. cit.* [note 37], pp. 310–326, has summarized the evidence concerning these islands, as well as one encountered later in the Gilberts. Andrew Sharp: *op. cit.* [note 4], pp. 56–66, discusses all of the discoveries of this expedition. The various sources are not in agreement as to names given the islands or the dates of discovery.

72. The basic documents are the narrative or history which Quirós dictated to his friend, the poet Luis Belmonte y Bermúdez, part of which was utilized by Juan de Torquemada: *Los veynte y un libros Rituales y Monarchía Yndiána con el origen y guerras de los Yndios Occidentales, de sus poblaciones descubrimientos . . .* , Sevilla, 1615, 3 vols., lib. 5, caps. 64–69; the log or *diario* of the *piloto mayor* Gaspar González de Leza (manuscript in the Biblioteca Nacional, Madrid); Torres' letter to the king of July 12, 1607 from Manila (of which several copies exist, including one in the Biblioteca Nacional, and the one translated by Alexander Dalrymple which was published by James Burney: *op. cit.* [note 3], vol. 2, pp. 467–478); and a large number of *memoriales* by Quirós and others (most of which are in the Archivo General de Indias, Sevilla, and some of which have been published in *Colección de documentos de Indias: op. cit.* [note 45], vol. 5, pp. 497–518). Justo Zaragosa (ed.): *op. cit.* [note 70], first published most of the pertinent material, in the original language. Vol. 1 contains the long narrative dictated by Quirós to Belmonte (who was on the last voyage), which covers the three Peruvian voyages. The log by Leza is in vol. 2, along with eight of the *memoriales* of which the longest and most informative (manuscript in Biblioteca del Palacio Real) is on pp. 280–388. This last *memorial* includes an abstract of a letter of 1607 from Torres to Quirós. The more important of these documents have been translated and edited by Clements R. Markham: *op. cit.* [note 70]. Henry N. Stevens and George F. Barwick (trans. and ed.): "New light

373

on the discovery of Australia as revealed by the journal of Captain Don Diego de Prado y Tovar," *Hakly. Soc., Works, Series 2*, vol. 64, pp. 1–261, London, 1930, reproduce bilingually a long-lost *relación* by Prado which Stevens' company had purchased at a Sotheby auction of manuscripts collected by Sir Thomas Phillipps. Stevens' treatment of Prado, however, is rather naive as he did not seem to realize that Prado was only the nominal commander and the real judgement and decision required in navigating a ship almost always rested with the pilot who in this case had been the *almirante* of the fleet.

73. Pedro Sarmiento de Gamboa: *op. cit.* [note 49]; and Pablo Pastells and Constantino Bayle: *op. cit.* [note 16], vol. 2.

74. Bartolomé García de Nodal y Gonzalo de Nodal: *Relación del viaje que por orden de Su Mag⁴ y acuerdo del Real consejo de Indias . . . al descubrimiento del estrecho nuebo de S. Vicente y reconosimiento del de Magallanes*, Madrid, 1621.

75. William Betagh: *A voyage round the world. Being an account of a remarkable enterprize, begun in the year 1719, chiefly to cruise on the Spaniards in the great South ocean . . .*, London, 1728, 342 pp., pp. 276–278.

76. The marine experiences and navigational and hydrographic data of Juan and Ulloa are scattered through their voluminous publications, of which three works are the most important. Jorge Juan y Santacilia and Antonio de Ulloa: *Relación histórica del viaje a la América Meridional . . . para medir algunos grados de meridiano terrestre . . .*, Madrid, 1748, 4 vols. in 2; a fifth volume of which is entitled *Observaciones astronómicas, y phísicas; . . . de las quales se deduce la figura, y magnitud de la tierra, y se aplica a la navegación*, Madrid, 1748, 396 pp. By the same authors, a pirated version of a report (written in 1749) which was published as . . . *Noticias secretas de América (siglo XVIII)* in London in 1826, and in *Biblioteca Ayacucho*, vols. 31 and 32, Madrid, 1918. Antonio de Ulloa was the author of *Conversaciones de Ulloa con sus tres hijos en servicio de la marina . . .*, Madrid, 1795.

77. The basic documents concerning the second European visit to Easter Island were located by Bolton G. Corney in the Archivo General de Indias, Sevilla, and in the Museo Naval, and were translated and edited by him as "The voyage of Captain Don Felipe González in the ship of the line San Lorenzo . . . to Easter island in 1770–1771 . . . ," *Hakly. Soc., Works, Series 2*, vol. 13, pp. 1–176, London, 1908. The chief sources are the log of González and especially the journals of two of the navigating officers which contain notes on the natives.

78. Although no significant discoveries were made by these three voyages, there did result from them a considerable body of important ethnographic information. The chief sources are narratives and logs by Boenechea and Conacorsi for the first voyage; by Gayangos and especially Andía for the second voyage; and by Lángara for the third voyage. These items and many others—most of them previously unpublished—have been translated and edited by Bolton G. Corney: "The quest and occupation of Tahiti by emissaries of Spain during the years 1772–1776. Told in dispatches and other contemporary documents . . . ," *Hakly. Soc., Works, Series 2*, vols. 32, 36, and 43, London, 1913–1919. Most of the items published are derived from manuscripts in the Archivo General de Indias, Sevilla, and the Museo Naval. However, the *diario* of the interpreter, Máximo Rodríquez, covering approximately a year spent in Tahiti, is based on the only copy known, which was discovered in the library of the Royal Geographical Society in London.

79. Copies of most of the narratives of the commanding officers and logs of the navigating officers are in the Archivo General de Indias, Sevilla, the Archivo General de la Nación, México, and the Museo Naval, Madrid. V. Vincente Vela and Julio F. Guillén y Tato: *op. cit.* [note 5] list those in the Museo Naval. The most useful discussion of these voyages and the pertinent sources will be found in Henry R. Wagner: *op. cit.* [note 15], especially vol. 1, pp. 158–238, and Henry R. Wagner: *Spanish explorations in the Strait of Juan de Fuca*, Santa Ana, Calif. 1933, 323 pp. A concise summary is provided by C. H. Little: "Spanish explorations in British Columbia," *Canadian Geogr. Journ.*, vol. 61 (4), pp. 138–150, Ottawa, 1960. The classic work is José Espinosa y Tello: *Relación del viaje hecho por las goletas Sutil y Mexicana en el año de 1792, para reconocer el estrecho de Fuca; con una introducción en que se da noticia de lax expediciones executadas anteriormente por los españoles en busca del paso del noroeste de la América . . .*, Madrid, 1802, 185 pp. and an atlas of 17 plates. The introduction to this work, by Martín Fernández de Navarrete, is a summary of the history of exploration along the Pacific coast of New Spain. Many data are to be found in José Espinosa y Tello: *op. cit.* [note 10], which reprints (Memoria Segunda, in vol. 1) *Observaciones practicadas en las costas del continente de América, etc.*, which was first published in 1805 as an appendix to the above-cited work (1802) by José Espinosa y Tello. The probably fictitious voyages of Lorenzo Ferrar Maldonado, 1588, Juan de Fuca, 1592, and Bartolomé de Fonte, 1640, have been treated by Martín F. de Navarrete and his son Eustaquio Fernández de Navarrete in their "Examen histórico-crítico de los viajes y descubrimientos apócrifos del Capitán Lorenzo Ferrar Maldonado, de Juan de Fuca y del Almirante Bartolomé de Fonte," *Colección de Documentos Inéditos para la*

Historia de España, vol. 15, pp. 5–363, Madrid, 1849. A more recent treatment is by Henry R Wagner: "Apocryphal voyages to the northwest coast of America," *Amer. Antiq. Soc., Proc., new series*, vol. 41 (1), pp. 179–234, Worcester, 1931. The best known single voyage, that of 1775, is represented by the *diario* of Francisco Antonio Maurelle, first published in English translation by Daines Barrington in London, in 1781, and reprinted with notes by Thomas C. Russell (ed.): *Voyage of the Sonora in the second Bucareli expedition to explore the Northwest coast, survey the port of San Francisco . . . the journal kept in 1775 on the Sonora, by Don Francisco Antonio Maurelle . . .* , San Francisco, 1920, 120 pp. This can be compared with the "Navegación hecha por Don Juan Francisco de la Bodega y Quadra," in *Colección de diarios . . . : op. cit.* [note 47], vol. 2, pp. 97–133. A number of other accounts also have been published.

80. Letters from several of the Jesuit fathers have been published in various editions of the *Lettres édifiantes et curieuses écrites des missions étrangères . . .* , Paris, 1703–1776, 34 vols. A new edition was published in Paris, 1780–1783, 26 vols. Letters by Clain, Le Gobien, Cantova, and others will be found in volumes issued in 1705, 1715, 1728, 1770, etc. *Diarios* of several of the pilots are in the Archivo General de Indias, Sevilla. See Erik W. Dahlgren: *op. cit.* [note 15], pp. 188–190. Quite useful also are Charles Le Gobien: *op. cit.* [note 63]; Pedro Murillo Velarde: *Geographia histórica, donde se describen los reynos . . .* , Madrid, 1752, 10 vols., especially vols. 8 and 9; and Pedro Murillo Velarde: *Historia de la Provincia de Philipinas de la Compañía de Jesús*, Manila, 1749, 419 pp.

81. Useful works for identification in this wideflung group of islands are Andrew Sharp: *op. cit.* [note 4], previous citations and pp. 90–91, 94–95, 183, and 189; Carl E. Meinicke: *op. cit.* [note 4], vol. 2; Frederick W. Christian: *The Caroline Islands; travel in the sea of the little lands*, London, 1899, 412 pp.; Luis de Ibáñez y García: *Historia de las islas Marianas con su derrotero, y de las Carolinas y Palaos, desde el descubrimiento por Magallanes en el año 1521, . . .* , Granada, 1886, 207 pp.; E. Pastor y Santos: *Territorios de soberanía española en Oceanía*, Madrid, 1950, 151 pp.; sections by A. Eilers, G. Thilenius, H. Nevermann, and A. Krämer in Georg Thilenius (ed.): *Ergebnisse der Südsee—Expedition, 1908–1910* of the Hamburgische Wissenschaftliche Stiftung, Hamburg, 1914–, especially II. Ethnographie B. (= Mikronesien), vol. 3, pt. 1, 1917, vol. 8, 1934, vol. 9, pts. 1 and 2, 1935 and 1936, vol. 11, pt. 1, 1938; José de Espinosa y Tello (ed.): *op. cit.* [note 10], vol. 2, Memoria 3a; and Adam J. von Krusenstern: *Atlas de l'océan Pacifique*, St. Petersbourg, 1827 (1826–1838), 42 maps, with the accompanying *Recueil de mémoires hydrographiques, pour servir d'analyse et d'explication à l'Atlas del'océan Pacifique par le commodore de Krusenstern*, St. Petersbourg, 1824–1827, 3 vols., (in Russian and French), see especially Part 2, North Pacific, 1827, and in 1834/35 supplementary volume, and corrected edition of the atlas in 1838.

82. The chief sources to date on Malaspina are Pedro de Novo y Colson (ed.): *Viaje político-científico alrededor del mundo por las corbetas Descubierta y Atrevida . . .* , Madrid, 1885, 681 pp.; and José de Espinosa y Tello (ed.): [note 10]. Most of the papers of this expedition are in the Museo Naval, Madrid.

83. Part of this little-known voyage has been reported by a French officer, Marquis de Poterat, who accompanied the squadron until 1800, and published the *Journal d' un voyage au Cap de Horn, au Chile, au Pérou, au Iles Philippines, et à la côte de la Nouvelle-Espagne . . .* , Paris, 1815, 192 pp.

84. Augustín J. Barreiro: *. . . Historia de la Comisión científica del Pacífico (1862 a 1865) . . .* , Madrid, 1926, 525 pp.

85. Eduardo Iriondo: *. . . Impresiones del viaje de circunnavegación de la fragata blindada "Numancia,"* reprint ed., Madrid, 1941. The official report appeared in the *Anuario de la Dirección de Hidrografía*, Año VI, Madrid, 1868, 119 pp.

Chapter 8

GEOGRAPHICAL EXPLORATION BY THE PORTUGUESE

1. Henry Yule (trans. and ed.): "Cathay and the way thither; being a collection of medieval notices of China . . . New edition rev. throughout in the light of recent discoveries, by Henri Cordier," *Hakly. Soc., Works*, Series 2, vols. 38, 33, 37, and 41, London, 1913–1916, especially in vol. 1, Preliminary essay. See also Friedrich Hirth and W. W. Rockhill (trans. and eds.): *Chau Ju-Kau: His work on the Chinese and Arab trade in the twelfth and thirteenth centuries, entitled Chu-fan-chi*, St. Petersburg, 1911, 288 pp.; John V. G. Mills: "Notes on early Chinese voyages," *Roy. Asiatic Soc., Journ.*, pp. 3–25. London, 1951; T'ién tsê Chang: *. . . Sino-Portuguese trade from*

Chapter 8

1514 to 1644; a synthesis of Portuguese and Chinese sources, Leyden, 1934, 157 pp.; and Charles R.
Boxer (ed.): "South China in the sixteenth century, being the narratives of Galeote Pereira, Fr.
Gaspar da Cruz [and] Fr. Martin de Rada, 1550–1575," *Hakly. Soc., Works, Series 2*, vol. 106,
pp. 1–388, London, 1953, especially the Introduction and works cited on pp. xviii–xix.

2. Armando Cortesão (trans. and ed.): "The Suma oriental of Tomé Pires, an account of the
East, from the Red sea to Japan . . . and the book of Francisco Rodrigues . . . ," *Hakly. Soc., Works,
Series 2*, vols. 89–90, London, 1944, pp. lxxvii–lxxxiv and map opp. p. lxxx of vol. 89. See also
discussion of the resultant charts by Francisco Rodrigues in Armando Cortesão: . . . *Cartografia e
cartógrafos portugueses dos séculas XV e XVI*, Lisboa, 1935, 2 vols., vol. 2, pp. 122–130; and the
chapter by Armando Cortesão in Antonio Baião and others (eds.): *História da expansão portuguesa
no mundo*, vol. 2, pp. 129–150, Lisboa, 1939, especially pp. 140–143. No journal or log of the
voyage is known to exist. Consequently, details must be obtained from the sixteenth century
chroniclers. See Hernani A. Cidade and Manuel Múrias (eds.): . . . *Asia, de João de Barros. Dos feitos
que os portugueses fizeram no descobrimento e conquista dos mares e terras do Oriente* . . . , Lisboa, 1945–
1948, 4 vols., see Década III, liv. 5, cap. 6; Antonio Galvão: . . . *Tratado dos descobrimentos. 3.
ed. Minuciosamente anotada e comentada pelo visconde de Lagôa* . . . , Pôrto, 1944, 504 pp., pp. 168–174
and 366–377; Fernão Lopes de Castanheda: *História do descobrimento & conquista da India pelos
Portugueses* . . . , Coimbra, 1552–1561, 8 vols., livro 3, caps. 75 and 86; and Gaspar Corrêa (who
wrote about the middle of the sixteenth century): *Lendas da India*, . . . , Lisboa, 1858–1864, 4
vols., livro 2, caps., 30 and 31.

3. Antonio Galvão: *ibid.*, pp. 172 and 373.

4. These voyages are reported only in João de Barros in 1563, for which see Hernani A. Cidade
and Manuel Múrias (eds.): *op. cit.* [note 2], Década 3, livro 3, cap. 3, livro 4, caps. 3 and 7, and livro
5, cap. 3.

5. Armando Cortesão: *op. cit.* [note 2] in *História* . . . , vol. 2, pp. 156–159; and the section and
bibliography (pro-discovery) in Jaime Cortesão: *Os descobrimentos Portugueses*, Lisboa, 1962, 2 vols.,
vol. 2, pp. 223–238. Includes excellent reproductions of maps.

6. J. O. Nelson: "Pre-European trade between Australia, Indonesia, and the Asiatic mainland," *Canadian Geogr.*, vol. 5, pp. 18–22, Ottawa, 1961.

7. Armando Cortesão: *op. cit.* [note 2], *Historio* . . . , pp. 159–162 give the best summary of this
discovery. See also Andrew Sharp: *The discovery of the Pacific Islands*, Oxford, 1960, 259 pp.,
pp. 13–15. The basic sources are Fernão Lopes de Castanheda: *op. cit.* [note 2], livro 6, cap. 127;
João de Barros in Hernani A. Cidade and Manuel Múrias (eds.): *op. cit.* [note 2], Década 3, livro
10, cap. 5; and Antonio Galvão: *op. cit.* [note 2], pp. 219 and 420.

8. Antonio Galvão: *ibid.*, pp. 256–257, 274–275, 449–450 and 465 is our sole authority for
the Castro discovery. If there were a discovery, we would say it was that by Rocha and Sequeira.
See also Andrew Sharp: *ibid.*, pp. 15–16.

9. Antonio Galvão: *op. cit.* [note 2], p. 280.

10. There are apparently no first-hand accounts or logs extant of the early Portuguese voyages
in the China seas. The pertinent information is scattered through the chronicles of such as João
de Barros, Fernão Lopes de Castanheda, Gaspar Corrêa, and Antonio Galvão cited in note 2, and
in some official letters. Armando Cortesão: *op. cit.* [note 2], *História* . . . , pp. 162–167; Armando
Cortesão (trans. and ed.): *op. cit.* [note 2], "The Suma oriental . . . ," pp. 120 and 283; and T'ien tsê
Chang: *op. cit.* [note 1], pp. 35–38, have summarized the extant data concerning Alvares and
other of the early Portuguese traders who went to China in junks. See also Jose M. Braga: *The
western pioneers and their discovery of Macao*, Macau, 1949, 248 pp., and his *Les pionniers de l'Occident
et la decouverte de Macao*, Saigon, 1950, 59 pp.

11. Most of the information concerning Tomé Pires and this voyage has been brought together
by Armando Cortesão (trans. and ed.): *op. cit.* [note 2], "The Suma oriental . . . ," especially pp.
xxx–xxxvii. See also Charles R. Boxer: *op. cit.* [note 1], pp. xx–xxiv, and pp. 313–326; and T'ien
tsê Chang: *op. cit.* [note 1].

12. Among the chief sources on the three-man involuntary voyage to Japan are: Antonio Galvão:
op. cit. [note 2], pp. 273 and 463–464; Fernão Mendes Pinto: *Peregrinaçam de Fernam Mendez
Pinto* . . . , Lisboa, 1614, 303 pp., chaps. 132–137; Diogo do Couto: *Década da Asia*, . . . , Década
5, Lisboa, 1602, livro 8, cap. 12. The pro-Mendes Pinto school includes Armando Cortesão: *op.
cit.* [note 2], "História . . . ," pp. 168–172, and Armando Cortesão (trans. and ed.): *op. cit.* [note
2], "The Suma oriental . . . ," vol. 89, pp. xlix–lxi; and Jord~o A. de Freitas: "Fern~o Mendes
Pinto," *História da Literatura Portuguesa Ilustrada*, vol. 3, pp. 53–64, Lisboa, 1932. Among the
many writers who do not see a parallel between the lack of veracity imputed to Fernão Mendes
Pinto, and the similar attitude once held toward Marco Polo, are Charles R. Boxer (ed.): *op. cit.*

[note 1], p. xxi; Georges Le Gentil: *Les Portugais en Extrême Orient. Fernão Mendes Pinto, un precurseur de l' exotisme au XVI e siècle*, Paris, 1947, 344 pp.; Georg Schurhammer: "Fernão Mendes Pinto und seine 'Peregrinaçam,'" *Asia Mayor*, vol. 3, pp. 1–107, Leipzig, 1927; see also Charles R. Boxer: *Fidalgos in the Far East, 1550–1770; fact and fancy in the history of Macao*, The Hague, 1948, 297 pp.; Maurice Collis: *The grand perigrination, being the life and adventures of Fernão Mendes Pinto*, London, 1949, 313 pp.; introduction by Jacinto I. de Brito Rebelo to the 1908 Lisboa edition of the Peregrinação; and the introduction by Jordão A. de Freitas to the 1930 Lisboa edition of the Peregrinação. More general works with useful background on the early European period of contacts with Japan include James Murdoch and Isoh Yamagata: *A history of Japan . . .*, London, 1925–1926, 3 vols.; see vol. 2. "During the century of early foreign intercourse (1542–1651)"; and George Sansom: *A history of Japan*, Stanford, Calif., 1958–1963, 3 vols., vol. 2.

13. The rutter by Rodrigues is in Armando Cortesão (trans. and ed.): *op. cit.* [note 2], vol. 90, pp. 301–302. *The Livro de Marinharia* was published by Jacinto I. de Brito Rebelo, Lisboa, 1903. The rutters collected by Jan Huygen van Linschoten have been published in various editions of the *Itinerario* which was first issued in Amsterdam, 1595–1596. The various cartographers referred to above have been discussed by Armando Cortesão: *op. cit.* [note 2], . . . *Cartografia* . . . . See also Jules E.-T. Hamy: *Études historiques et géographiques*, Paris, 1896, 480 pp., especially pp. 145–177 on the Reinel.

Chapter 9

GEOGRAPHICAL EXPLORATION BY THE DUTCH

1. The classic bibliography for Dutch voyages is Pieter A. Tiele: *Mémoire bibliographique sur les journaux des navigateurs néerlandais réimprimés dans les collections de deBry et de Hulsius, et dans les collections hollandaises du XVII siècle, et sur les anciennes éditions hollandaises des journaux de navigateurs*, Amsterdam, 1867, 372 pp.

2. For an annotated index of vols. I–L of the *Linschoten-Vereeniging* see: D. Sepp and others (comps.): *Tresoor der zee-en landreizen; beredeneerd register op de werken der Linschoten-Vereeniging*, 's Gravenhage, 1939–1957, 2 vols.

3. An extract of van Noort's journal was published in 1601, a few months after his return. In 1602 appeared several editions in Dutch, one in French, one in Latin, and three in German. The first English (abridged) version was published in Samuel Purchas: *Purchas his pilgrimes . . .*, London, 1625, 4 vols. The modern authoritative edition is Jan W. IJzerman (ed.): "De reis om de wereld door Olivier van Noort, 1598–1601, met inleiding en aanteekeningen . . .," *Linschoten-Vereeniging, Werken*, vols. 27–28, 's Gravenhage, 1926. Additional information on the fate of the ship *Hendrick Frederick* may be found in Engel Sluiter: *Bijdragen voor vaderlandsche geschiedenis en oudheidkunde*, series 7, vol. 8, parts 1–2, pp. 34–48, 's Gravenhage, 1937.

4. Frederik C. Wieder (ed.): "De Reis van Mahu en de Cordes door de Straat van Magalh˜es naar Zuid-Amerika en Japan 1598–1600," *Linschoten-Vereeniging, Werken*, vols. 21, 22, and 24, 's Gravenhage, 1923–1925. A chronological bibliography is listed in vol. 24, pp. 153–160.

5. The experiences of the crew of this ship are told in "Wijdtloopigh Verhael," etc., Amsterdam (1600), also in Theodor De Bry: *Grand Voyages*, vol. 9 (2), Frankfurt, 1601 and numerous later editions, among them Frederik C. Wieder: *ibid.*, vol. 21, pp. 135–245.

6. Jan Outghersz: *Nieuwe Volmaeckte Beschryvinghe der vervaerlijcker Strate Magelhani . . .*, Amsterdam, [1600 (?)].

7. Frederik C. Wieder: *op. cit.* [note 4], vol. 22, gives in great detail the historical cartography of the Strait of Magellan, with bibliography, maps, and comparative tables of place names.

8. The account of his voyage appeared first under the title *Oost ende West-Indische Spiegel der Nieuwe Navigaties (also: der 2. leste Navigatien) . . .*, Leyden, 1619. For a modern English translation see John A. J. de Villiers (trans. and ed.): "The East and West Indian mirror, being an account of Joris Speilbergen's voyage round the world (1614–1617) and the Australian navigation of Jacob Le Maire," *Hakly. Soc., Works*, series 2, vol. 18, pp. 1–272, London, 1906. The modern Dutch edition is J. C. M. Warnsinck (ed.): "De reis om de wereld van Joris van Spilbergen 1614–1617," *Linschoten-Vereeniging, Werken*, vol. 47, parts 1–2, 's Gravenhage, 1943.

9. J. C. M. Warnsinck (ed.): *ibid.*, part 1, p. 96.

10. The two basic sources are: (1) Willem C. Schouten van Hoorn: *Journal ofte Beschrijvinghe*

van de wonderlicke reyse, . . . inde jaren 1615, 1616 en 1617 (published by Willem Jansz. [Blaeu]), Amsterdam, 1618, 92 pp.; and (2) Jacob Le Maire: *Spieghel der australische navigatie, door den-wijt vermaerden ende cloeckmoedighen zee-heldt . . .*, Amsterdam, 1622, 85 pp. The journal of Jacob Le Maire was seized by the East India Company and later released to Jacob's father, Isaac, since Jacob had died on the voyage home. Isaac edited the journal and prefaced it with his own study of all voyages to the Strait of Magellan. In the meantime, Schouten's journal had been published by Blaeu, doubtless in collusion with the East India Company. This account deprecated the role of the Le Maires in the adventure and made Schouten the real hero of the story. There are numerous editions of these journals. The modern Dutch edition is: W. A. Engelbrecht and P. J. van Herwerden (eds.): "De ontdekkingsreis van Jacob Le Maire en Willem Cornelisz Schouten in de jaren 1615–1617. Journalen, documenten en andere bescheiden," *Linschoten-Vereeniging, Werken*, vol. 49 (in two vols.), 's Gravenhage, 1945.

11. W. A. Engelbrecht and P. J. van Herwerden (eds.): *ibid.*, vol. 1, pp. 109–132, and vol. 2, pp. 33 and 126–148.

12. W. A. Engelbrecht and P. J. van Herwerden (eds.): *ibid.*, vol. 1, pp. 37–39. Cape Horn is actually at 55° 59′ south latitude. The error, much larger than usual in the logs of those days, has never been adequately explained: W. A. Engelbrecht and P. J. van Herwerden (eds.): *ibid.*, vol. 2, pp. 100–103.

13. Jacob Le Maire had with him a Dutch translation of one of the memoranda of Quirós, in which the latter petitioned his king for permission to conduct further explorations. For details see W. A. Engelbrecht and P. J. van Herwerden (eds.): *ibid.*, vol. 2, pp. 60–64.

14. The identifications are from W. A. Engelbrecht and P. J. van Herwerden (eds.): *ibid.*, vol. 2, pp. 189–190. See also Andrew Sharp: *The discovery of the Pacific islands*, Oxford, 1960, 259 pp., p. 74.

15. On first thought it is puzzling to read in these and other reports that the inhabitants of islands, supposedly never before visited by Europeans, were so keen on obtaining iron. O. von Kotzebue's observations in the Marshall Islands (1817) may provide the answer. The islanders told him that their iron tools had arrived on logs and driftwood; later, wandering on the beach at Wotje, he found "such a piece of wood, with nails in it, on the shore." The use of the terms *oubas, oubi*, (or *ubi*) and *patattes* in Dutch journals may refer to sweet potatoes (in Indonesia called *ubi jawa, katela*, or *batata*; not to be confused with *ubi kayu* or *katela puhun*, which is cassava). However, the sailors were no botanists, and may have obtained yams. In Indonesia the sweet yam (*Dioscorea alata*) is called *ubi kelapa*.

16. N. MacLeod: *De Oost-Indische compagnie als Zeemogendheid in Azië*, Rijswijk (Z. H.), 1927, 2 vols., vol. 1, pp. 313–315. Also Andrew Sharp: *op. cit.* (note 14), pp. 79–80.

17. The classic study, favoring the thesis of Portuguese priority, is that of Richard H. Major: "Early voyages to Terra Australis, now called Australia . . . ," *Hakly. Soc., Works*, vol. 25, pp. 1–200, London, 1859. For a recent review of the argument (and its rejection) see Andrew Sharp: *The discovery of Australia*, Oxford, 1963, 338 pp., pp. 1–16.

18. Jan E. Heeres: *Het aandeel der Nederlanders in de ontdekking van Australië, 1606–1765*, Leiden, 1899, 256 pp. Includes English text on the opposite pages under the title: *The part borne by the Dutch in the discovery of Australia*, Leiden, London, 1899. This volume contains a collection of relevant documents and a number of map reproductions. Quotations from Heeres in the text of this chapter are from this publication.

19. This chart was found in Vienna by Frederik C. Wieder and has been reproduced in his *Monumenta cartographica: reproductions of unique and rare maps, plans and views in the actual size of the originals; accompanied by cartographical monographs*, The Hague, 1925–1933, 5 vols., see vol. 5, plate 125. Andrew Sharp: *op. cit.* [note 17] has a partial reproduction op. p. 16. For a general description of the voyage see Jan E. Heeres: *ibid.*, pp. v–vi and 5–6. A contemporary report appeared in Samuel Purchas: *op. cit.* [note 3], vol. 1, book 3, p. 385.

20. Hessel Gerritsz' map of 1622 carries a notation with reference to a Spanish vessel that may have passed south of New Guinea.

21. See the chart by upper steersman Arend Martensz de Leeuw on board the Pera, reproduced in full size in Frederik Muller: *Remarkable maps of the XVth, XVIth and XVIIth centuries, reproduced in their original size*, Amsterdam, 1894–1899, 6 vols. in 4 parts, vol. 2, plate 5; in reduced form in Jan E. Heeres: *op. cit.* [note 18], p. 46.

22. The full journal of Carstensz has been published in Jan E. Heeres: *op. cit.* [note 18], pp. 21–44; ref. on p. 34.

23. For documentary evidence of the discoveries on the west coast see Jan E. Heeres: *op. cit.* [note 18].

24. Villem de Vlamingh, on the *Geelvinck*, found this memento in 1697, and replaced it by a new one, recording Hartog's and his own visit. The original of Hartog is now in the Rijksmuseum in Amsterdam.

25. Hessel Gerritsz' map of 1618, but with revisions for later years, gives an excellent picture of what was known in the late 1620's. Reproduction in Jan E. Heeres: *op. cit.* [note 18], map 5 at end of volume.

26. For the instruction of 1636 see Jan E. Heeres: *op. cit.* [note 18], pp. 64–67, and for the instruction of 1642, see note 29, below.

27. There are extant three variant, and not necessarily direct, transcripts of Tasman's journal (actually journal-extract) of his first voyage. One is in the State Archives in The Hague, another, the so-called Huydecoper copy, is in the Mitchell Library in Sydney, Australia, and the third is in the British Museum, London. The first, which carries Tasman's signature, has been published in facsimile, with all charts, profiles and illustrations, by Jan E. Heeres: *Abel Tasman's journal of his discovery of Van Diemen's land and New Zealand in 1642, with documents relating to his exploration of Australia in 1644* . . . , Amsterdam, 1898, 195 pp., together with an English translation, biography of Tasman, and other pertinent information. A more up-to-date work in Dutch is R. Posthumus Meyjes (ed.): "De reizen van Abel Janszoon Tasman en Franchoys Jacobszoon Visscher, . . . in 1642/3 en 1644," *Linschoten-Vereeniging, Werken*, vol. 17, pp. i–xcvii and 1–229, 's Gravenhage, 1919. Especially to be noted is the discussion of source materials (pp. lxii–lxxiv and 261–272) in which the author differs with Heeres in the evaluation of the various transcripts and their maps.

28. Franchoys J. Visscher: "Memorandum concerning the Discovery of Southland" in R. Posthumus Meyjes (ed.): *ibid.*, Supplement H, pp. 160–163.

29. "Instruction for the skipper-commander Abel J. Tasman . . . Batavia 13 August 1642," in R. Posthumus Meyjes (ed.): *ibid.*, Supplement E, pp. 144–154.

30. R. Posthumus Meyjes (ed.): *ibid.*, "Cargo list," Supplement G, pp. 157–159.

31. For a detailed identification of Tasman's log see Andrew Sharp: *op. cit.* [note 17], pp. 81–85.

32. From Tasman's journal, R. Posthumus Meyjes (ed.): *op. cit.* [note 27], pp. 43–44. The Huydecoper copy has these remarks under 21 December, and in somewhat different wording, the main difference being "believe" instead of "trust."

33. R. Posthumus Meyjes (ed.): *ibid.*, pp. 42–43.

34. R. Posthumus Meyjes (ed.): *ibid.*, pp. xlvii–xlviii and xcii–xcv. Both Huydecoper and the Archives transcript have a copy of this chart, the former being of better quality. For full reproduction see Frederik C. Wieder (ed.): *Monumenta cartographica* . . . , The Hague, 1925–1933, 5 vols. Vol. IV, plates 94–96. For a line drawing showing gap in coast line, see Jan E. Heeres (ed.): *op. cit.* [note 27], p. 112.

35. Letter from Governor-General and Council to Directors dated 22 December 1643, R. Posthumus Meyjes, (ed.): *ibid.*, Supplement K, pp. 166–168.

36. No journal of the second voyage has survived. The instructions and some other pertinent documents have been published in R. Posthumus Meyjes (ed.): *ibid.*, Supplements K–N, pp. 166–184. The route (as well as that of the first voyage) is shown on a composite map, dated 1644. A poor line tracing of this map accompanied Jacob Swart's edition of Tasman's Journal (of his first voyage) in 1860. The map later came into the possession of a member of the Bonaparte family, and now is in the Mitchell Library, Sydney. According to a statement on the map it was put together from various sources, including data from Tasman. A reproduction (in English translation) of the old tracing appeared in Jan E. Heeres' *Tasman's Journal* [note 27]. For a detail see Andrew Sharp: *op. cit.* [note 17], opp. p. 88. For further discussion of Swart's copy of this map see R. Posthumus Meyjes (ed.): *op. cit.* [note 27], pp. lxxvi–lxxx, and Jan E. Heeres: *op. cit.* [note 27], section xl.

37. The composite map of 1644 [note 36] shows a solid coast line curving from (the present) New Guinea eastwards and then back westwards to the tip of the Cape York peninsula. This observation could not have been made from Tasman's course as shown on the map.

38. The name Carpentaria—after Pieter de Carpentier, Governor-General 1623–1627—does not appear on any maps or other documents relating to Tasman's voyages. Apparently van Diemen did the christening. See R. Posthumus Meyjes (ed.): *op. cit.* [note 27], p. lxxxvi, note 4.

39. For a detailed tracking of Tasman's route along the Australian coast see Andrew Sharp: *op. cit.* [note 17], pp. 89–90.

40. Letter from Governor-General and Council to Directors dated 23 December 1644, in R. Posthumus Meyjes (ed.): *op. cit.* [note 27], Supplement N, pp. 182–184.

41. R. Posthumus Meyjes (ed.): *ibid.*, pp. xcii–xcvii.

42. Willem J. Blaeu shows these new names on his map of 1648. See in his *Le théâtre du monde;*

ou, Nouvel atlas contenant les chartes et descriptions de tous les pays de la terre . . . , Amsterdam, 1646–1650. 6 vols. in 4 vols.

43. Roggeveen's original journal is lost; a copy was found only in 1836. The early books about the voyage by "T. D. H." (1728) and K. F. Behrens are unreliable. Roggeveen's journal (copy) was first published in 1838. There is an annotated edition by F. E. Mulert (ed.): "De reis van Mr. Jacob Roggeveen ter ontdekking van het Zuidland (1721–1722), verzameling van stukken . . . ," *Linschoten-Vereeniging, Werken*, vol. 4, pp. 1–331, 's Gravenhage, 1911. There is also a fragment of a copy of the journal of Captain Bouman, first published in 1911, and utilized by Mulert. For a complete bibliography see Mulert, pp. 315–319. This edition also contains a chapter by W. van Bemmelen in which he uses Roggeveen's observations on magnetic declination to construct an isogonic map of the southern Pacific for 1722.

44. For documents regarding Arend Roggeveen's project see F. E. Mulert (ed.): *ibid.*, pp. 3–20.

45. William Dampier: *A new voyage round the world* . . . , London, 1697, p. 352. A companion of Davis had placed the "small, low sandy island" at 27° 20′ s. lat. for which see Lionel Wafer: *A new voyage and description of the isthmus of America* . . . , London, 1699, 224 pp., pp. 213–214. See also Andrew Sharp: *op. cit.* [note 14], pp. 88–90.

46. Roggeveen states "ubas roots." Captain Bouman does not mention them, but tells of "jannes" (yams) and "backovens" (bananas). See note 15.

47. F. E. Mulert (ed.): *op. cit.* [note 43], pp. 121–122.

48. In the planning stage of the expedition, Jan Roggeveen (brother of Jacob) had given sound advice on the prevention of scurvy. Among others, he made the suggestion that water cress should be grown aboard—an excellent but not very feasible proposal in view of the paucity of water on shipboard in those times. For Jan Roggeveen's memorandum see F. E. Mulert (ed.): *ibid.*, pp. 26–37 (on foods, pp. 32–33, 36 and 37).

49. Jan W. IJzerman (ed.): "Dirck Gerritsz Pomp, alias Dirck Gerritsz. China, de eerste Nederlander die China en Japan bezocht, 1544–1604 . . . ," *Linschoten-Vereeniging, Werken*, vol. 9, pp. 1–195, 's Gravenhage, 1915.

50. The third volume (vol. 24) of Frederik C. Wieder (ed.): *op. cit.* [note 4] is devoted to "The first Dutch ship in Japan."

51. Frederik C. Wieder (ed.): *ibid.*, vol. 24, p. 73.

52. Bishop Restarick's article appeared in the *Honolulu Advertiser* of December 24, 1922, and was reprinted, together with supplementary data from his correspondence with Wieder in Frederik C. Wieder (ed.): vol. 24, pp. 147–149. Quotations are taken from the latter source.

53. The voyage is fully dealt with in Jan Verseput (ed.): "De reis van Mathijs Hendriksz. Quast en Abel Jansz. Tasman ter ontdekking van de goud- en zilvereilanden, 1639," *Linschoten-Vereeniging, Werken*, vol. 56, pp. 1–130, 's Gravenhage, 1954. The journal of the voyage is in the State Archives in The Hague. For an evaluation of the voyage see Jan E. Heeres: *op. cit.* [note 27], pp. 15–37.

54. Jan Verseput (ed.): *ibid.*, pp. 22–23, with the reproductions of profile sketches. See also Hyman Kublin: "The discovery of the Bonin Islands: a re-examination," *Assoc. Amer. Geogr., Annals*, vol. 43 (1), pp. 27–46, Wash., D. C., 1953.

55. Pieter A. Leupe (ed.): *Reize van Maarten Gerritsz Vries in 1643 naar het noorden en oosten van Japan, volgens het journaal gehouden door C. J. Coen, op het schip Castricum* . . . , 's Gravenhage, 1858, 440 pp. A summary may be found in N. MacLeod: *op. cit.* [note 16], vol. 2, pp. 332–333.

56. B. Hoetink (ed.): "Verhaal van het vergaan van het jacht de Sperwer en van het wedervaren der schipbreukelingen op het eiland Quelpaert en het vasteland van Korea (1653–1666) . . . door Hendrik Hamel," *Linschoten-Vereeniging, Werken*, vol. 18, pp. 1–165, 's Gravenhage, 1920. This work contains a bibliography of earlier editions. At least three versions were published in the Netherlands in 1668. Two French translations and at least one German translation appeared in the next four years.

57. On the name "Quelpaert" see B. Hoetink (ed.): *ibid.*, pp. xli–l.

Chapter 10
GEOGRAPHICAL EXPLORATION BY THE RUSSIANS

1. The authors have tried to confirm the information used in compiling this chapter by reference to the original and primary sources, to publications by travelers and explorers, to cartographic materials, and to other documents. Inasmuch as the chapter is brief, the authors have used summarized surveys containing corresponding detailed documents. All dates, unless otherwise indicated, are given in the new style.

2. For summaries of geographical exploration during the seventeenth century see Dmitrii M. Lebedev: *Geografia v Rossii XVII veka—dopetrovskoy epokhi* (Geography in Russia of the seventeenth century—Period before Peter I), Moskva-Leningrad, 1949, 233 p..; and a collection of documents by N. S. Orlova (comp.): *Otkrytiya russkikh zemleprokhodtsev i polyarnykh morekhodov XVII veka na severo-vostoke Azii. Sb. dokumentov* (Discoveries of Russian land explorers and polar seamen of the seventeenth century in northeastern Asia. Volume of collected documents), Moskva, 1951.

3. N. N. Stepanov: "Pervaya russkaya ekspeditsiya na Okhotskom poberezh'ye (First Russian expedition on the Okhotsk coast)," *Izvestiya Vsesoyuz. Geogr. o-va*, vol. 90 (5), Moskva, 1958, pp. 438–452.

4. I. I. Ogryzko: "Otkrytiye Kuril'skikh ostrovov (A discovery of Kuril Islands)," *Uchenyye Zapiski Leningrad Gos. un-ta no. 157, Seriya Fakul'teta Narodov Severa*, Leningrad, 1953, pp. 169–172.

5. The first information about this trip appeared in the press in 1742, with more details in 1758. There were later communications, as for example, see Lev S. Berg: *Otkrytiye Kamchatki i ekspeditsii Beringa, 1725–1742* (The discovery of Kamchatka and Bering's expeditions, 1725–1742), Moskva and Leningrad, 1946, third ed., p. 27.

6. [Andre F. B.] D[eslandes?]: *Histoire généalogique des Tatars traduite du manuscrit tartare, etc.*, Leyde, 1726, pp. 108–109.

7. G. Maydel': *Puteshestviye po Severo-vostochnoy chasti Yakutskoy oblasti v 1868–1870 godakh* (Travel across the northeastern part of the Yakutsk region in 1868–1870), St. Petersburg, 1894, vol. 1.

8. Dmitrii M. Lededev: *Geografiya v Rossii petrovskogo vremeni* (Geography in Russia of the Peter I period), Moskva and Leningrad, 1950, pp. 37–49.

9. *Ibid.*, pp. 50–51, 62, and 63.

10. A. Titov: *Sibir' v XVII veke* (Siberia in the seventeenth century), Moskva, 1890.

11. A. V. Yefimov (ed.): *Atlas geograficheskikh otkrytiy v Sibiri i v Severo-Zapadnoy Amerike, XVII i XVIII vv* (Atlas of geographical discoveries in Siberia and in northwestern America, seventeenth and eighteenth centuries), Moskva and Leningrad, 1964, map 28.

12. V. I. Grekov: "O chertezhe vsey Sibiri do kitayskogo tsarstva i do Nikaskogo (On a chertezh' of entire Siberia up to the Chinese kingdom and the Nikask)," *Akad. Nauk SSSR, Izv., Seriya Geogr.*, no. 2, pp. 80–88, Moskva, 1959.

13. A. V. Yefimov (ed.): *op. cit.* (note 11), map 32.

14. A. V. Yefimov (ed.): *op. cit.* [note 11], map 34.

15. A. V. Yefimov (ed.): *op. cit.* [note 11], map 42.

16. A. V. Yefimov (ed.): *op. cit.* [note 11], maps 48, 49, and 50.

17. Some interesting cartographic representations of the first quarter of the eighteenth century, by the level of their production, could be dated as the end of the seventeenth century. Such are, for instance, the "Draft of Ivan Lvov," in which there are for the first time the rough outlines of Bering Strait as shown on map 55 in A. V. Yefimov: *op. cit.* [note 11]; and the draft by I. Kozirevsky associated with his trip in 1713 to the Kuril Islands and rather correctly indicating by inscriptions the position of twenty-one islands and of "Matsmai" (Hokkaido) as noted in I. I. Ogryzko *op. cit.* [note 4], pp. 202–203.

18. A. V. Yefimov (ed.): *op. cit.* [note 11], maps 33, 58 and 74.

19. O. A. Yevteyev: *Pervyye russkiye geodezisty na Tikhom okeane* (The first Russian geodesists on the Pacific Ocean), Moskva, 1950; and A. V. Yefimov (ed.): *op. cit.* [note 11], map 61.

20. For a biographical sketch of Vitus Jonassen Bering see: Cornelia Goodhue: *Journey into the fog: the story of Vitus Bering and the Bering Sea*, Garden City, N. Y., 1944, 179 pp.; Peter Lauridsen: *. . . Vitus Bering: the discoverer of Bering Strait . . .*, Chicago, 1889, 232 pp.; Vasilii M. Pasetskii: *Vitus Bering*, Moskva, 1958, 45 pp.; Josef Petersen: *Vitus Bering, der Seefahrer. Aus dem Dänischen übers*, Hamburg, 1947, 251 pp., Valdemar Rørdam: *. . . Dansk liv*, København, 1938, 159 pp.; and

Erling Stensgård: *Den danske søfarer og opdagelsesrejsende Vitus Bering, 1681–1741, i den danske litteratur og presse, en bibliografi*, Horsens, Denmark, 1941, 19 pp. [Edit.].

21. A. Pokrovskiy (comp.): *Ekspeditsiya Beringa, Sb. dokumentov* (Bering's expedition; a volume of collected documents), Moskva, 1941, p. 66.

22. A. V. Yefimov (ed.): *op. cit.* [note 11], map 63.

23. V. I. Grekov: *Ocherki iz istorii russkikh geograficheskikh issledovaniy v 1725–1765 gg.* (Sketches from the history of Russian geographical researches during the years 1725–1765), Moskva, 1960, pp. 38–39.

24. Jean B. Du Halde: *Description géographique, historique, chronologique, politique, et physique de l'empire de la Chine et de la Tartarie chinoise . . .* , Paris, 1735, 4 vols.

25. Jean B. B. d'Anville: *Nouvel atlas de la Chine, de la Tartarie chinoise et du Thibet; contenant les cartes générales & particulieres de ces pays . . .* , La Haye, 1737, 12 pp. text, 42 maps.

26. A. V. Yefimov (ed.): *op. cit.* [note 11], maps 71, 107, and 111; and V. I. Grekov: *op. cit.* [note 23], p. 270.

27. V. I. Grekov: *ibid.*, pp. 49–53.

28. Philippe Buache: *Considérations géographiques et physiques sur les nouvelles découvertes au nord de la Grande Mer appelee vulgairement la Mer du Sud, avec des cartes qui y sont relatives . . .* , Paris, 1752–1753, map II.

29. V. I. Grekov: *op. cit.* [note 23], pp. 102 and 104.

30. A. V. Yefimov (ed.): *op. cit.* [note 11], maps 104 and 105.

31. Frank A. Golder: ". . . Bering's voyage; an account of the efforts of the Russians to determine the relation of Asia and America," *Amer. Geogr. Soc., Res. Series*, nos 1–2, New York, 1922–1925, vol. 2, p. 72; Pál Teleki (comp.): *Atlas zur Geschichte der Kartographie der Japanischen Inseln . . .* , Leipzig, 1909, 184 pp. and maps.

32. Philippe Buache: *op. cit.* [note 28], maps I, IV, and X.

33. Vitus Bering died in December 1741 on Ostrov Beringa.

34. A. V. Yefimov (ed.): *op. cit.* [note 11], maps 97, 100, and 101.

35. Gerhard Müller: *Opisaniye morskikh puteshestviy po Ledovitomu i po Vostochnomu moryu s rossiyskoy storony uchinennykh. Sochineniya i perevody k pol'ze i uveseleniyu sluzhashchiye* (Description of sea travels in the Arctic Ocean and the Eastern Sea organized on the Russian port. Writings and translations serving to the use and amusement). St. Petersburg, 1758, vols. 7 and 8.

36. A. V. Yefimov (ed.): *op. cit.* [note 11], map 111.

37. V. I. Grekov: *op. cit.* [note 23], p. 167.

38. Lev S. Berg: *op. cit.* [note 5], p. 94. L. H. Stejneger: *Georg Wilhelm Steller, the pioneer of Alaskan natural history*. Cambridge, Mass., 1936.

39. S. P. Krasheninnikov: *Opisaniye zemli Kamchatki*, Moskva and Leningrad, 1949.

40. An extensive reference list dealing with these voyages is given in V. I. Grekov: *op. cit.* [note 23].

41. *Ibid.*, p. 189.

42. Lev S. Berg: *op. cit.* [note 5], p. 15.

43. Aleksandr I. Andreyev (ed.): *Russkiye otkrytiya v Tikhom okeane i Severnoy Amerike v XVIII i XIX vekakh* (Russian discoveries in the Pacific Ocean and in North America during the eighteenth and nineteenth centuries), Moskva—Leningrad, 1944, pp. 28–37; and Aleksandr I. Andreyev (ed.): *Russkiye otkrytiya v Tikhom okeane i Severnoy Amerike v XVIII veke* (Russian discoveries in the Pacific Ocean and in North America during the eighteenth century), Moskva, 1948, pp. 113–120.

44. A. V. Yefimov (ed.): *op. cit.* [note 11], maps 149 and 153.

45. V. I. Grekov: *op. cit.* [note 23] p. 173; and A. V. Yefimov (ed.): *op. cit.* [note 11], map 140.

46. A review of all of these voyages is given in Dmitrii M. Lebedev: *Ocherki po istorii geografii v Rossii XVIII veka—1725–1800 gg.* (Sketches of the history of geography in Russia during the eighteenth century—1725–1800), Moskva, 1957.

47. A. P. Sokolov: "Ekspeditsiya k Aleutskim ostrovam Krenitsyna i Levasheva 1764–1769 gg. (Expedition to the Aleutian Islands by Krenitzin and Levashov in 1764–1769)," *Zapiski Gidrografich Departamenta*, part 10, pp. 70–103, St. Petersburg, 1852.

48. William Coxe: *Account of the Russian discoveries between Asia and America . . .* , London, 1780, 454 pp.

49. A. V. Yefimov (ed.): *op. cit.* [note 11], maps 151 and 152.

50. Ivan F. Kruzenshtern: *Sobraniye sochineniy, sluzhashchikh razborom i iz" yasneniyem Atlasa Yuzhnogo morya* (Collected works serving to review and explain the atlas of the Southern Sea), St. Petersburg, 1823–1826, part 2, XXIV, p. 5.

51. G. A. Sarychev: *Puteshestviye flota kapitana Sarycheva po severo—vostochnoy chasti Sibiri,*

Ledovitomu moryu i Vostochnomv Okeanu . . . s 1785 po.1793 gg. (Travel of navy Captain Sarychev in the northeastern part of Siberia, the Arctic Ocean, and the Eastern Ocean . . . during the period from 1785 to 1793), St. Petersburg, 1802, 2 vols.

52. G. A. Sarychev: *Atlas severnoy chasti Vostochnogo okeana* (Atlas of the northern part of the Eastern Ocean), St. Petersburg, 1826.

53. Ivan F. Kruzenshtern: *op. cit.* [note 50], part 2, xxiii, pp. 3–5.

54. Alexander G. Findlay: *A directory for the navigation of the North Pacific Ocean; with descriptions of its coasts, islands, etc., from Panama, to Behring Strait, and Japan; its winds, currents and passages*, London, 1886, p. 669.

55. We call such expeditions "cruises" when the ships round only Cape Horn or Cape of Good Hope (the smaller part of the cruise being in the Far East).

56. N. N. Zubov: *Otechestvennyye moreplavateli-issledovateli morey i okeanov* (Russian seamen-researchers of seas and oceans), Moskva, 1954, pp. 146–147.

57. Lev. S. Berg: "Otkrytiya russkikh v Tikhom okeane (Russian discoveries in the Pacific Ocean)," v kn *Tikhiy okean. Russkiye nauchnyye issledovaniya*, Leningrad, 1926, p. 23; N. A. Ivashintsov: *Russkige krugosvetnyye puteshestviga s 1803 po 1849 gg.* (Russian around-the-world travels from 1803–1849), St. Petersburg, 1872, pp. 89–92.

58. A representative example of voyages that resulted in big scientific achievements may be found in a list of the main instruments available on the Kruzenshtern-Lisiansky expedition of 1803–1806: a telescope for taking observations on the shore, compasses, sextants, "passage instruments" (including Trowton's instrument), quadrants, barometers, electric motors, hydrometers, thermometers (including Six's minimum-maximum thermometer), artificial magnets, and chronometers.

59. Frank Debenham (ed.): "The voyage of Captain Bellingshausen to the Antarctic seas, 1819–1821," *Hakly. Soc. Works, Series 2*, vols. 91–92, London, 1945, p. 39.

60. In a number of cases it is impossible to determine the names of the people who discovered these islands. As established much later, sometimes during the twentieth century, some of them had been seen or visited by earlier travelers, but no record of them was made in literature or on maps used by navigators of that period. Accordingly, the Russian seamen mentioned below determined the position of the islands and carefully described and plotted them on maps, actually rediscovered them, and through the medium of publication made this knowledge available to the body of science for the first time.

61. These ethnographic, historical, and economic data are not reviewed here.

62. Space does not permit us to describe the routes of individual expeditions. For this information the reader is referred to the maps pertaining to this chapter, especially to Fig. 29.

63. Ivan F. Kruzenshtern: *Puteshestviye vokrug sveta v 1803, 1804, 1805, i 1806 godakh* (Voyage around the world in 1803, 1804, 1805, and 1806), St. Petersburg, 1809–1812, 3 vols.

64. *Ibid.*, vol. 1, pp. 273, 277–278. For instance, Hokkaido and Ostrov Kunashir were shown as one island on the maps of the South Sea by Aaron Arrowsmith in 1821 and on John Purdy's world map of 1822. See also Ivan F. Kruzenshtern: *op. cit.* [note 50], part 2, p. 4.

65. Ivan F. Kruzenshtern: *Atlas k puteshestviyu vokrug sveta kapitana Kruzenshtern* (Atlas to the trip around the world by Captain Kruzenshtern), St. Petersburg, 1813; and Ivan F. Kruzenshtern: *Atlas zur Reise um die Welt Spb. 1814*, St. Petersburg, 1827 (1838?).

66. Alexander G. Findlay: *op. cit.* [note 54], p. iv.

67. Ivan F. Kruzenshtern: *op. cit.* [note 63], vol. 2, pp. 182–216.

68. I. Gorner: "Stepen' temperatury morskoy vody v raznykh glubinach (Sea temperatures at different depths)," in Ivan F. Kruzenshtern: *op. cit.* [note 63], vol. 3, pp. 263–264.

69. Yu. M. Shokal'skiy: *Okeanografiya*, Petrograd, 1917, republished in 1959, Introduction, p. 33.

70. I. Gorner: *op. cit.* [note 68], p. 277.

71. D. F. Rudovits: "Pervoye russkoye krugosvetnoye plavaniye 1803–1806 gg. (First Russian trip around the world in 1803–1806)," *Trudy Gos. Okeanograf, Inst.*, no. 27 (36), Leningrad, 1954, pp. 5–7.

72. I. Gorner: "Udel'naya tyazhest' morskoy vody (Specific weight of sea water)," in Ivan F. Kruzenshtern: *op. cit.* [note 63], vol. 3, pp. 333–341.

73. Ivan F. Kruzenshtern: *op. cit.* [note 63], vol. 3, pp. 149–183.

74. Ivan F. Kruzenshtern: *ibid.*, vol. 1, p. 229 and vol. 3, p. 165.

75. I. Gorner: "O kolebaniyakh barometra mezhdu tropikami (On barometric fluctuations between the tropics)," v kn Ivan F. Kruzenshtern: *op. cit.* [note 63], vol. 3, pp. 228–259.

76. Ivan F. Kruzenshtern: *Atlas Yuzhnogo morya* (Atlas of the Southern Sea), St. Petersburg, 1824–1826, 2 vols.

77. Ivan F. Kruzenshtern: *op. cit.* [note 50]; and Ivan F. Kruzenshtern: *Dopolneniye k izdannym*

v 1826 i 1827 godakh ob" yasneniyam osnovaniy, posluzhivshikh dlya sostavleniya Atlasa Yuzhnogo morya (Addition to the explanations published in 1826 and 1827 of the material that served as a basis for the compilation of the Atlas of the Southern Sea), St. Petersburg, 1836.

78. Alexander G. Findlay: *op. cit.* [note 51], p. iv.

79. Yuri F. Lisyanskiy: *Puteshestviye vokrug sveta v 1803, 1804, 1805 i 1806 Rodakh na dorable "Neve"* (Trip around the world in 1803, 1804, 1805, and 1806 in the ship "Neva"), St. Petersburg, 1812, 2 vols.

80. Yuri F. Lisyanskiy: *ibid.*, vol. 2, pp. 113, 114, 136 and 137.

81. Yuri F. Lisyanskiy: *Sobraniye kart i risunkov, prinadlezhazhchikh k puteshestviyu Yuriya Lisyanskogo na korable "Neve"* (Collection of maps and drawings pertaining to the voyage of Yuri Lisyanski on the ship "Neva"), St. Petersburg, 1812.

82. V. M. Golovnin: *Sokrashehennyye zapiski Golovnina o plavanii yego na shlyupe "Diane" deya opisi Kuril' shikh ostrovov, v 1811 g.* (Abbreviated notes of Golovnin on his cruise in the sloop "Diana" to describe the Kuril Islands), St. Petersburg, 1819.

83. Alexander G. Findlay: *op. cit.* [note 54], pp. 736–737.

84. V. M. Golvnin: *Puteshestiviye vokrug sveta, sovershennoye na voyennom shlyupe "Kamchatke" v 1817, 1818 i 1819 godakh* (Round-the-world voyage made on a navy sloop "Kamchatka" in 1817, 1818, and 1819), St. Petersburg, 1822, 2 vols.

85. Otto Ye. Kotzebue: *Puteshestviye v Yuzhnyy okean i v Beringov proliv dlya otyskaniya severovostochnogo morskogo prokhoda, predprinyatoye v 1815, 1816, 1817 i 1818 godakh na korable "Ryurike"* (Trip to the Southern Ocean and to Bering Strait to find the northeastern sea passage undertaken in 1815, 1816, 1817, and 1818 in the ship "Riurik"), St. Petersburg, 1821–1823; and *Atlas k puteshestviyu leytenanta Kotzebu na korable "Ryurike"* (Atlas to the voyages of Lieutenant Kotzebue in the ship "Rurik"), St. Petersburg, 1821–1823.

86. Otto Ye. Kotzebue: *Puteshestviye vokrug sveta, sovershennoye na voyennom shlyupe "Predpriyatiye" v 1823, 1824, 1825 i 1826 godakh* (Voyage round-the-world made in a sloop of the navy "Predpriatie" in 1823, 1824, 1825, and 1826), St. Petersburg, 1828.

87. Ivan F. Kruzenshtern: *op. cit.* [note 50], vol. 2, XXXVI, pp. 3, 4, 7.

88. One of many examples that researches by Kotzebue (as by many other explorers) were accompanied by discoveries of details which verified and corrected previous data, is a description of a group of Rumiantzev Islands (Otdia or Wotje Atoll) where he found sixty-five small coral islets. See Otto Ye. Kotzebue: *op. cit.* [note 85], vol. 2, pp. 148–149.

89. Otto Ye. Kotzebue: *op. cit.* [note 86], pp. 58–59, and others.

90. For example, the data on the Riurik chain (Arutua) which James Cook had discovered by passing it at a distance in 1774, whereas Kotzebue passed not more than a mile distant and found that it consisted of a great number of islands. He established their approximate boundaries astronomically. Ivan F. Kruzenshtern: *op. cit.* [note 50], vol. 1, xix, pp. 15–17.

91. Detailed information on these discoveries and researches can be found in Otto Ye. Kotzebue: *op. cit.* [note 85], vol. 1, ch. VII, and vol. 2, chs. XI-XIII; and Otto Ye. Kotzebue: *op. cit.* [note 86]. Maps of the islands have been published by him in his Atlas, *op. cit.* [note 85]. It should be noted that owing to his unusual caution Kotzebue does not consider himself the discoverer of the Aratika group as he notes on page 52 in his work, *op. cit.* [note 86]. Andrew Sharp in his *The Discovery of the Pacific Islands*, Oxford, 1960, 259 pp., pp. 206–207 attributes these discoveries to Kotzebue. Kotzebue also added much information on Arutua ranges in Tuamotu Archipelago, which appears to certify him as the virtual discoverer of this chain.

92. Otto Ye. Kotzebue: *op. cit.* [note 85], vol. 1, pp. 117–119.

93. Otto Ye. Kotzebue: *op. cit.* [note 85], vol. 3, p. 381.

94. Referring to vol. 3 of Kotzebue's monograph, Charles R. Darwin in his *The structure and distribution of coral reefs*, London, 1874, p. 116, attributes these views to Chamisso. However, in vol. 3 the corresponding article is in a section written "by other authors" and probably belongs to Eschscholtz, for which see Emil H. DuBois-Reymond: *Adelbert von Chamisso als Naturforscher . . .*, Leipzig, 1889, 63 pp.

95. Otto Ye. Kotzebue: *op. cit.* [note 85], vol. 1, p. 89 and vol. 3, pp. 423–426.

96. Otto Ye. Kotzebue: *op. cit.* [note 85], vol. 3, pp. 423–424.

97. M. A. Rykachev: "Ekspeditsiya *Challenger'a* i noveyshiye issledovaniya okeanov v fizicheskom otnoshenii voobshche (The Challenger expedition and the latest researches from the point of view of physics in general)," *Morskoy Sbornik*, vol. 182 (1), Neofits. otdel, 1881, p. 12.

98. S. O. Makarov: "Vityaz" i Tikhiy okean ("Vitiaz" and the Pacific Ocean), St. Petersburg, 1894, 2 vols. p. 247.

99. Otto Krümmel: *Handbuch der Ozeanographie*, Stuttgart, 1907, vol. 1, p. 371.

100. Emil Lenz: "Physikalische Beobachtungen, angestellt auf einer Reise un die Welt unter dem Commando des Capitains von Kotzebue in den Jahren 1823–1826," *Acad. des Sciences, Mémoires*, vol. 1, pp. 221–344, St. Petersburg, 1831, p. 281.

101. Emil Lenz: "Bemerkungen über die Temperatur des Weltmeeres in verschiedenen Tiefen," *Acad. des Sciences, Classe Physico-Mathematique*, Bull. no. 5 (5), pp. 65–74, St. Petersburg, 1847.

102. Joseph Prestwich: "Tables of temperatures of the sea at various depths below the surface, taken between 1749 and 1868; collated and reduced, with notes and sections," *Roy. Soc., Proc.*, vol. 22, pp. 462–468, London, 1874; and Joseph Prestwich: "Tables of temperatures of the sea at various depths below the surface, taken between 1749 and 1868; collated and reduced with notes and sections," *Philosophical Trans.* vol. 165, pp. 587–674, London, 1876.

103. Fedor P. Lütke: *Puteshestviye vokrug sveta, sovershennoye na voyennom shlyupe "Seniavine" v 1826, 1827, 1828 i 1829 godakh. Otdeleniye istoricheskoye* (Travel around the world made on a navy sloop "Seniavin" in 1826, 1827, 1828, and 1829. Historical division), St. Petersburg, 1834–1836, 3 vols.; and Fedor P. Lütke: *Puteshestviye vokrug sveta, sovershennoye na voyennom shlyupe "Senyavine" v 1826, 1827, 1828, and 1829 godakh. Otdeleniye morekhodnoye* (Travel around the world made on a navy sloop "Seniavin" in 1826, 1827, 1828, and 1829. Navigation division), St. Petersburg, 1835.

104. Fedor P. Lütke: *ibid., . . . Otdeleniye istoricheskoye*, vol. 1, p. 8.

105. Alexander G. Findlay: *op. cit.* [note 54], p. 970; and Charles R. Darwin: *op. cit.* [note 25], p. 212.

106. Fedor P. Lütke: *op. cit.* [note 103] . . . *Odteleniye morekhodnoye*, pp. 193–356.

107. Alexander G. Findlay: *op. cit.* [note 54], pp. iv and 707.

108. Fedor P. Lütke: *Atlas k puteshestviyu vokrug sveta* (Atlas of a voyage around the world), St. Petersburg, 1835, 6 pp. text and 34 double-page maps.

109. Fedor P. Lütke: *op. cit.* [note 103], . . . *Odteleniye morekhodnoye*, pp. 180–186.

110. Fedor P. Lütke: *op. cit.* [note 103], . . . *Odteleniye morekhodnoye*.

111. Faddey F. Bellinsgausen: *Dvukhkratnyye izyskaniya v Yuzhnom Ledovitom okeane i plavaniya vokrug sveta v prodolzheniye 1819, 1820 i 1821 godov, sovershennyye na shlyupalch "Vostoke" i "Mirnom"* (Two research voyages in the Antarctic Ocean and a round-the-world cruise during 1819, 1820, and 1821 on the sloops "Vostok" and "Mirny"), St. Petersburg, 1831, 2 vols.

112. The first description of this cruise was published in Russia in 1831. The latest Soviet ed. (1960) preserves the text of the first with quite insignificant changes (orthography, certain terms, etc.). The 1960 ed. includes an introductory article and comments by the editor E. E. Schwede. We give references to the 1831 edition. For a recent English translation see Frank Debenham (ed.): "The voyage of Captain Bellingshausen to the Antarctic Seas, 1819–1821," *Hakly. Soc., Works, Second Series*, vols. 91–92, London, 1945 [Edit.].

113. Faddey F. Bellinsgausen: *op. cit.* [note 111], vol. 1, p. 17.

114. Faddey F. Bellinsgausen: *op. cit.* [note 111], vol. 1, ch. 4, and vol. 2, ch. 5.

115. Faddey F. Bellinsgausen: *Atlas k puteshestviyu kapitana Bellinsgauzena* (Atlas of the voyage of Captain Bellinsgausen), St. Petersburg, 1831, maps 34–53. An example of the occasional impossibility of definitely establishing the names of the original discoverers is evidenced by Ivan F. Kruzenshtern in his *Dopolneniye . . . , op. cit.* [note 77], vol. 2, p. 33, where he considers the discovery of Groupe Raevski by Bellinsgausen as doubtful, whereas Andrew Sharp: *op. cit.* [note 91], pp. 196–197, gives the discovery to Bellinsgausen.

116. The survey of the South Shetland Islands set a new standard for polar charts, and the field work from which the chart was produced was never surpassed until steam replaced sail. See Frank Debenham: *op. cit.* [note 112], p. xvi. For the discovery of the Antarctic Continent see Faddey F. Bellinsgausen: *op. cit.* [note 111], pp. 171–172.

117. Faddey F. Bellinsgausen: *op. cit.* [note 111], pp. 177–178.

118. Faddey F. Bellinsgausen: *op. cit.* [note 111], pp. 188–192.

119. Faddey F. Bellinsgausen: "Doneseniye kapitana 2 ranga Bellinsgausena iz porta Zhaksona o svoyem plavanii (Report of Captain of the Second Rank Bellinsgausen from Port Jackson on his trip)," *Zapiski Izdavayemyye Gos. Admiralteyskim Departamentom*, vol. 5, St. Petersburg, 1823.

120. V. L. Lebedev: "Geograficheskiye nablyudeniya v Antarktike . . . (Geographical Observations in the Antarctic . . .)," V kn: *Antarktika. Doklady Komissii, 1960 g*, Moskva, 1961. Corresponding parts of the photocopies are given.

121. V. L. Lebedev: *ibid.*; and V. L. Lebedev: "Resheniye spornykh voprosov antarkticheskoy istorii na novoy osnove (Solution of disputable problems of the Antarctic history on a new basis)," V kn: *Antarktika. Doklady komissii, 1962 g*, Moskva, 1963.

122. Faddey F. Bellinsgausen: *op. cit.* [note 111], vol. 2, pp. 238–242.

123. Yu. M. Shokal'skiy: *op. cit.* [note 69], Introduction, p. 34.

124. Here the word *matyoroy* is close to the modern concept of the word "continental."

125. Faddey F. Bellinsgausen: *op. cit.* [note 111], vol. 2, p. 249.

126. Faddey F. Bellinsgausen: *op. cit.* [note 111], vol. 2, p. 255.

127. Yu. M. Shokal'skiy: "Stoletiye so vremeni otpravleniya Russkoy antarkticheskoy ekspeditsii pod komandoyu F. Bellinsgausena i M. Lazareva 4 iyulya 1819 g. iz Kronshtadta (Hundred years since the departure of the Russian Antarctic expedition under the command of F. Bellinsgausen and M. Lazarev on July 4, 1819 from Kronshtadt)," *Izvestiya Russkogo Geogr. o-va*, vol. 60 (2), Moskva, 1928, pp. 195–197.

128. I. M. Simonov: "Izvestiya o puteshestvii kapitana Bellinsgauzena v 1819–1821 gg. po Tikhomu okeanu, po yuzhnym polyarnym moryam (Information on a voyage by Captain Bellingshausen in the Pacific Ocean and southern polar seas in 1818–1821)," *Severnyy Arkhiv, Razdel IV*, no. 19, 1824.

129. Faddey F. Bellinsgausen: *op. cit.* [note 111], vol. 2, part 5.

130. Faddey F. Bellinsgausen: *op. cit.* [note 115].

131. A. P. Lazarev: *Zapiski o plavanii voyennogo shlyupa "Blagonamerennogo" v Beringov proliv i vokrug sveta* (Notes on the cruise of the navy sloop "Blagonamerenny" into Bering Strait and around the world), Moskva, 1950, p. 76.

132. G. I. Nevel'skoy: *Podvigi russkikh morskikh ofitserov na kraynem vostoke Rossii 1849–1855* (Exploits of Russian naval officers in the extreme east of Russia in 1849–1855), St. Petersburg, 1878.

133. N. A. Ivashintsov: *op. cit.* [note 57], pp. 89–92.

134. S. O. Makarov: *op. cit.* [note 98], vol. 1, pp. 233–234.

135. N. A. Ivashintsov: *op. cit.* [note 57], pp. 96–97.

136. *Ibid.*, p. 111.

137. *Ibid.*, pp. 109–111, 118–123.

138. *Ibid.*, pp. 123–127.

139. The main source for studying the above-mentioned researches during the nineteenth century is Belov, Planson, and Klykov (comps.): *Kratkiy istoricheskiy ocherk gidrografii russkikh morey* (Brief historical review of the hydrography of Russian seas), St. Petersburg, 1899, see part 2., Eastern Ocean. With the exception of specially indicated instances, we have also used the following papers: Ivan F. Kruzenshtern: papers cited above; M. D. Teben'kov: *Atlas severozapadnykh beregov Ameriki ot Beringova proliva do mysa Korrientes i ostrovov Aleutskikh . . .* (Atlas of the northwestern coasts of America from Bering Strait up to Cape Corrientes and of the Aleutian Islands . . .), St. Petersburg, 1852 and his *Gidrograficheskiye zamechaniya k Atlasu severozapadnykh beregov Ameriki . . .* (Hydrographic remarks to the Atlas of the northwestern coasts of America . . .), St. Petersburg, 1852; P. A. Tikhmenev: *Istoricheskoye obozreniye obrazovaniya Rossiysko-Amerikankoy Kompanii* (Historical survey of the Russian-American Company), St. Petersburg, 1861, part 1; and A. M. Bukhteyev: "Ocherk posledovatel'nogo khoda i sovremennogo sostoyaniya opisi russkikh morey (Review of the consecutive progress and present state of the descriptions of Russian seas)," *Zapiski po Gidrografii*, no. 30, St. Petersburg, 1909.

140. See part 10 (1) in *Zapiski Gidrograficheskogo Departamenta* (Memoirs of the Hydrographic Department), St. Petersburg, 1852, pp. 156–162.

141. A. P. Sokolov: "Opis' Udskogo berega i Shantarskikh ostrovov poruchika Kozmina v 1829–1831 gg. (Description of the Uda coast and Shantar Islands by Lieutenant Kozmin in 1829–1831)," *Zapiski Gidrograficheskogo Departamenta*, part 4, St. Petersburg, 1846, pp. 1–78.

142. M. D. Teben'kov: *op. cit.* [note 139].

143. M. D. Teben'kov: *op. cit.* [note 139].

144. John N. L. Baker: *. . . A history of geographical discovery and exploration*, London, 1937, 552 pp., p. 398.

145. K. S. Staritskiy: *Gidrograficheskaya komandirovka v Vostochnyy okean v 1865–1871 godakh kapitan-leyt. Staritskogo* (Hydrographic researches in the Eastern Ocean during 1865–1871 by Lieutenant-Captain Staritzky), St. Petersburg, 1873.

146. *Ibid.*, p. 58.

147. M. L. Onatsevich: *Sobraniye nablyudeniy, proizvedennykh vo vremya gidrograficheskoy komandirovki v Vostochnyy okean 1874–1877 g.* (Collection of observations made during a hydrographic survey in the Eastern Ocean in 1874–1877), St. Petersburg, 1878.

148. L. I. Shrenk: *Ocherki fizecheskoy geografii Severo-Yaponskogo morya* (Sketches of the physical geography of the seas north of Japan), St. Petersburg, 1869.

149. L. I. Shrenk: *O techeniyakh Okhotskogo. Yaponskogo i smezhnykh s nimi morey* (On the currents in the Sea of Okhotsk, Sea of Japan and adjacent seas), St. Petersburg, 1874.

150. S. O. Makarov: *op. cit.* [note 98], p. 226.

151. Their summary is given in Belov, Planson, and Klykov (comps.): *op. cit.* [note 139], pp. 43–96. It is also possible to form an idea of the number of descriptions by the fact that a map attached to the book shows the routes of at least one hundred ships that were engaged in the compilation of these descriptions.

152. N. N. Zubov: *op. cit.* [note 56], pp. 300–306.

153. S. O. Makarov: *op. cit.* [note 98].

154. *Ibid.*, vol. 1, pp. 8, 9, 14, 15.

155. *Ibid.*, vol. 1, pp. 42–44.

156. Otto Krümmel: "Ueber einige neuere Beobachtungen an Aräometern," *Hydrographie und Maritimen Meteorologie, Annalen*, vol. 22, pp. 415–427, Berlin, 1894.

157. Yu. M. Shokal'skiy: "S. O. Makarov i yego raboty po okeanografii (S. O. Makarov and his work in oceanography)," *Izvestiya Russkogo Geogr. o-va*, vol. 61 (2), Moskva, 1929, p. 264.

158. S. O. Makarov: *op. cit.* [note 98], vol. 2, pp. 213, 214, 416.

159. On this point see Yu. M. Shokal'skiy: *op. cit.* [note 157]; and A. D. Dobrovol'skiy: *Admiral S. O. Makarov—puteshestvennik; geograf* (Admiral S. O. Makarov—traveler and geographer), Moskva, 1948; A. M. Muromtsev: *Osnovnyye cherty gidrologii tikhogo okeana* (Main features of the hydrology of the Pacific Ocean), Leningrad, 1958.

160. S. O. Makarov: *op. cit.* [note 98], vol. 1, p. 155.

161. *Ibid.*, pp. 256 and 265.

162. Otto Krümmel: "S. O. Makaroff Witias und Stille Ozean," *Petermanns Mitteilungen*, vol. 40, Geographischer Literaturbericht no. 720, Gotha, 1894, p. 190.

Chapter 11

GEOGRAPHICAL EXPLORATION BY THE FRENCH

1. Pierre Benoît: . . . *Océanie Française*, Paris, 1933, 152 pp.; George V. Blue: "French interests in Pacific America in the eighteenth century," *Pacific Hist. Rev.*, vol. 4, pp. 246–266, 1935; W. W. Bolton: "Discovery and discoverers of French Oceania," *Pacific Islands Monthly*, vol. 9 (7), pp. 32–33, Sydney, 1939; W. W. Bolton: "Liste des îles des Etablissements français de l'Océanie Dates de leur découverte et noms des navigateurs," *Soc. des Études Océan., Bull.*, vol. 6, pp. 272–275, Paris, 1940; L. et F. Chabonis: *Petite histoire naturelle des Établissements français de l'Océanie . . .*, Saint-Amand-Montrond, 1954, 2 vols.; Harold M. Cooper: *French exploration in South Australia, with especial reference to Encounter Bay, Kangaroo Island, the two gulfs, and Murat Bay, 1802–1803*, Adelaide, Austr., 1952, 200 pp.; Erik W. Dahlgren: *De franska sjöfärderna till Söderhavet i början af adertonde seklet; en studie i historisk geografi*, Stockholm, 1900, 430 pp.; Erik W. Dahlgren: *Les relations commerciales et maritimes entre la France et les côtes de l'océan Pacifique (commencement du XVIIIe siècle)*, Paris, 1909, 1 vol.; Erik W. Dahlgren: "Voyages français à destination de la mer du Sud avant Bougainville (1695–1749)," *Nouvelles Archives Missions Scientifiques*, vol. 14, pp. 423–568, Paris, 1907; Paul Fournier: . . . *Voyages et découvertes scientifiques des missionnaires naturalistes français à travers le monde pendant cinq siècles XVe à XXe*, Paris, 1932, 258 pp.; R. Hervé: "Australia in French geographical documents of the Renaissance," *Roy. Austr. Hist. Soc., Journ. and Proc.*, vol. 41 (1), pp. 23–38, Sydney, 1955; Charles A. Julien (ed.): *Les techniciens de la colonisation (XIXe–XXe siècles)*, Paris, 1947 (?), 321 pp.; Charles A. Julien: *Les voyages de découverte et les premiers établissements (XVe–XVe siècles)*, Paris, 1948, 533 pp.; Charles A. Julien, J. Bruhat and V. Genet: *Histoire de l'Expansion et de la Colonisation françaises*, Paris, 1948– , 6 vols.; Charles A. Julien: *Histoire de l'Océanie*, Paris, 1942, 127 pp.; Bjarne Kroepelien: *Livres sur les établissements français de l'Océanie et sur les mers adjacentes, . . .*, Oslo, 1934, 21 pp., Charles G. M. B. de La Roncière: *Histoire de la marine française . . .*, Paris, 1899–1932, 6 vols.; Ernest Scott: *Terre Napoléon; a history of French explorations and projects in Australia*, London, 1910 (?), 295 pp.; and L. A. Triebel and J. C. Ball: *The French exploration of Australia, with special reference to Tasmania*, Hobart, Tasmania, 1957, 96 pp.

2. Jean Parmentier: "Discorso d' un gran capitano di mare francese . . . sopra le navigationi fatte alla terra nuova dell' Indie occidentali chiamata la Nuoua Francia . . . & sopra . . . & quella di Sumatra," in G. B. Romusio: . . . *Navigationi et Viaggi . . .*, vol. 3, pp. 423–434, Rome, 1556; Jean Parmentier: *Description nouvelle des merveilles de ce monde, en liste Taprobane aultrement dicte Samatra . . .*, copy in Americana Series of Photostats in Mass. Hist. Soc., no. 32, 96 leaves, Boston, 1920; Jean Parmentier: . . . *Le discours de la navigation de Jean et Raoul Parmentier de Diéppe. Voyage à*

Chapter 11

Sumatra en 1529. Description de l'isle de Sainct Domingo, Paris, 1883, 202 pp.; and Alice Guibon "Navigateurs et découvreurs français du XVIe siècle. A Sumatra sur les traces des Dieppois de 1529," *L'Illustration,* vol. 94, pp. 289–291, Paris, 1936.

3. Erik W. Dahlgren: *Voyages français . . . op. cit.* [see note 1], pp. 438–520.

4. Frank A. Golder: *Russian expansion on the Pacific, 1641–1850; an account of the earliest and later expeditions made by the Russians along the Pacific coast of Asia and North America; including some related expeditions to the Arctic regions,* Cleveland, 1914, 368 pp.

5. John N. L. Baker: · . . *A history of geographical discovery and exploration,* London, 1931, 543 pp.; and George A. Wood: *The discovery of Australia,* London, 1922, 541 pp.

6. Edgar Aubert de la Rue: *Deux ans aux îles de la Désolation, archipel de Kerguélen,* Paris, 1954, 316 pp.; René E. Bossière: *Notice sur les îles Kerguélen, possession française,* Paris, 1893, 31 pp.; Auguste Dupouy: . . . *Le breton Yves de Kerguélen,* Paris, 1929, 265 pp.; and Yves J. de Kerguélen-Trémarec: *Relation de deux voyages dans les mers Australes & des Indes, faits en 1771, 1772, 1773 & 1774. Par M. de Kerguélen, commandant les vaisseaux du Roi le Berrier, la Fortune, le Gros-Ventre, le Rolland, l'Oiseau & la Dauphine. Ou, Extrait du journal de sa navigation pour la découverte des terres Australes, . . . ,* Paris, 1782, 244 pp.

7. Charles de Brosses: "Australasia. Introductory observations," in J. Pinkerton (ed.): *A general collection . . . voyages and travels . . . ,* vol. 11, pp. 421–427, London, 1804–1814; Charles de Brosses: *Histoire des navigations aux Terres Australis . . . ,* Paris, 1756, 2 vols.; Charles de Brosses: *Terra Australis incognita: or, Voyages to the Terra australis, or Southern hemisphere, during the sixteenth, seventeenth, and eighteenth centuries,* Edinburgh-London, 1766–1768, 3 vols.; Charles de Brosses: *Vollständige geschichte der schiffarthen nach den noch gröstentheils unbekanten südlandern aus dem französischen des Herrn präsidenten de Brosse . . . ,* Halle, 1767, 668 pp.; Jean P. Faivre: *L'expansion française dan le Pacifique de 1800 à 1842,* Paris, 1953, 550 pp.; Yves Florenne: *Le président de Brosses,* Paris, 1964, 316 pp.; and Alan C. Taylor: . . . *Le president de Brosses et l'Australie . . . ,* Paris, 1937, 187 pp. In Jean P. Faivre is the following significant paragraph which translated into English reads: "Writing as a citizen and a geographer the President de Brosses thinks that, contrary to the commercial companies, the state, who is able to give up capital without an immediate profit, will set up an expedition made up of carefully selected sailors and competent leaders supported by a staff of scientists in order to initiate a complete expedition," p. 56.

8. Ricardo Rodolfo Caillet-Bois: . . . *Un capitulo de la historia de las Malvinas; Bougainville y la negociación franco-española,* Buenos Aires, 1940, 19 pp.; Denis Dederot: . . . *Supplément au Voyage de Bougainville,* Paris and Baltimore, 1935, 211 pp.; Jean Dorsenne: "La découverte de Tahiti. M. de Bougainville et ses compagnons (d'après des documents inédits)," *Revue de France,* vol. 8, pp. 619–641, Paris, 1928; Édouard L. Doublet: . . . *Le centenaire de Bougainville . . . ,* Bordeaux, 1913, 109 pp.; Vsevolod N. Evreino: *Za ubegainshchim gorizontoon,* Moskva, 1964, 213 pp.; Édouard Goepp and Émile L. Cordier: *Les grands hommes de la France. Navigateurs; . . . ,* Paris, 1873, 419 pp.; Charles G. M. B. de La Roncière: *Bougainville,* Paris, 1942, 251 pp.; Jean Lefranc: *Bougainville et ses compagnons,* Paris, 1929, 253 pp.; Jean-Étienne Martin: "Essai sur Bougainville, circumnavigator. La genèse de sa carrière maritime," *La Géographie,* vol. 52, pp. 321–345, Paris, 1929; Maurice Thiéry: *Bougainville, soldier and sailor,* London, 1932, 291 pp.; and "Bougainville, navigateur français-Relation," in Édouard T. Charton: *Voyageurs anciens et modernes,* vol. 4, pp. 286–350, Paris, 1857.

9. Louis A. Bougainville: *Podróz Bougainvillè a dookola swiata,* Warzawa, 1961, 202 pp.; Louis A. de Bougainville: *Reis rondom de weereldt, gedaen op bevel des Konings van Frankrijk in de jaren 1766 to 1769 met het fregat la Boudeuse en het fluitschip l'Etoile, door den heer Louis de Bougainville,* Te Dordrecht, 1772, 414 pp.; Louis A. de Bougainville: . . . *Viaje alrededor del mundo por la fragata del rey la "Boudeuse" y la fusta la "Estrella" en 1767, 1768, y 1769 . . . ,* Madrid, 1921, 2 vols.; Louis A. de Bougainville: . . . *Viaje alrededor del mundo por la fragata del rey la "Boudeuse" y la fusta la "Estrella" en 1767, 1768 y 1769,* Buenos Aires, 1943, 330 pp.; Louis A. de Bougainville: *Voyage autour du monde par la frégate du Roi la "Boudeuse" et la flûte l'Etoile en 1766, 1767, 1768 et 1769,* Paris, 1771, 417 pp.; Louis A. de Bougainville: *Voyage autour du monde, par la frégate du roi la Boudeuse, et la flûte l'Etoile; en 1766, 1767, 1768 & 1769,* Paris, 1772, 3 vols.; Louis A. de Bougainville: . . . *Voyage de Bougainville autour du monde pendant les années 1766, 1767, 1768 et 1769; préface et notes de P. Deslandres; . . . ,* Paris, 1924, 304 pp.; Louis A. de Bougainville: *A voyage round the world. Performed by order of His most Christian Majesty, in the years 1766, 1767, 1768 and 1769; translated from the French by John R. Forster,* London, 1772, 476 pp.; Louis A. de Bougainville: *Voyage autour du monde par la frégate la Boudeuse et la flûte L'Étoile, suivi du supplément de Diderot,* Paris, 1958, 377 pp.; M. de Fréville: *Journal d' un voyage autour du monde, en 1768, 1769, 1770, 1771; contenant les divers événemens du voyage, avec la relation des contrées nouvellement découvertes,* Paris, 1772, 362 pp.; Anonymous: *Supplément au voyage de M. de Bougainville; ou, journal d' un voyage autour du monde,*

388

fait par Mo. Banks et Solander, anglois, en 1768, 1769, 1770, 1771, Paris, 1772, 362 pp.; Anonymous: *Bougainville. Le Détroit de Magellan. Taiti*, Paris, 1894, 36 pp.; Anonymous: *Catalogue of the highly important papers of Louis Antoine de Bougainville, F. R. S. (1729–1811) . . . his voyage round the world . . .*, London, 1957, 45 pp. See especially John Dunmore: *French explorers in the Pacific . . .*, Oxford, 1965, 365 pp.

10. Alan C. Taylor: *op. cit.* [see note 7], pp. 96, 98.

11. Jean P. Faivre: *op. cit.* [see note 7], p. 66.

12. Jean F. M. de Surville: "Extrait du voyage de M. de Surville [à la Mer du Sud]," in Marion de F. Crozet: *Nouveau Voyage à la Mer du Sud*, pp. 251–290, Paris, 1783.

13. H. Ling Roth (trans.): *Crozet's voyage to Tasmania, New Zealand, the Ladrone Islands, and the Philippines in the years 1771–1772 . . .*, London, 1891, 148 pp.; and J. Crozet: *Nouveau Voyage à la mer du Sud, commencé sous les ordres de M. Marion. Cette Relation a été rédigée d' après les Plans & Journaux de M. de Crozet. On a joint à ce Voyage un Extrait de celui M. de Surville dans les mêmes Passages*, Paris, 1783.

14. Joannès M. M. H. Tramond and André Reussner: *. . . Éléments d' histoire maritime et coloniale contemporaine (1815–1914)*, Paris, 1924, 728 pp.

15. Edward W. Allen: "Jean François Galaup de Lapérouse: A checklist," *Calif. Hist. Soc., Quart.*, vol. 20, pp. 47–64, San Francisco, 1941; Johann R. Forster and C. L. Sprengel (trans.-eds.): *La Perousen's Entdeckungsreise in den Jahren 1785, 1786, 1787 und 1788*, Berlin, 1800, 2 vols.; Jean F. G. de Lapérouse: *Voyage de La Pérouse autour du monde, publié conformément au décret du 22 avril 1791, . . .*, Paris, 1796, 4 vols. and atlas; Jean F. G. de La Pérouse: *Voyage de La Pérouse autour du monde, publié conformément au décret du 22 avril 1791 et rédigé par M. L. A. Milet-Mureau*, Paris, 1797, 4 vols. and atlas; Jean F. G. de Lapérouse: *The voyage of La Pérouse round the world in the years 1785, 1786, 1787 and 1788, with nautical tables*, London, 1798, 2 vols.; Jean F. G. de Lapérouse: *La Perousen's Entdeckungsreise in den jahren 1785, 1786, 1787 und 1788*, Leipzig, 1799, 2 vols.; Jean F. G. de Lapérouse: *Charts and plates to La Pérouse's voyage*, London, 1799, 31 maps, 39 plates; Jean F. G. de Lapérouse: *Reize van de La Pérouse, in de jaaren 1785, 1786, 1787 en 1788*, Amsterdam, 1801–1804, 3 vols.; Jean F. G.de Lapérouse: *Viaggi di La Pérouse intorno al mundo*, Livorno, 1827, 3 vols.; Jean F. G. de Lapérouse: *Voyage de Lapérouse, rédigé d' après ses manuscrits originaux, suivi d' un appendice renfermant tout ce que l' on a découvert depuis le naufrage jusqu à nos jours, et enrichi de notes par M. de Lesseps . . .*, Paris, 1831, 436 pp.; Ernest Scott: *Lapérouse*, Sydney, 1913, 104 pp.; Anonymous: "La Pérouse, navigateur français. Relation . . . ," in Édouard T. Charton: *Voyageurs anciens et modernes*, vol. 4, pp. 439–496, Paris, 1857; Anonymous: ". . . Le voyage de Lapérouse sur les côtes de l'Alaska et de la Californie (1786) avec une introduction et des notes par Gilbert Chimard," *Hist. Doc. Inst. Français de Washington*, vol. 10, pp. 1–144, Baltimore, 1937; Anonymous: *Voyage de La Pérouse autour du monde, 1785–1788; . . .*, Paris, 1933.

16. Peter Dillon: *Narrative and successful result of a voyage in the South Seas, performed by order of the government of British India, to ascertain the actual fate of La Pérouse's expedition . . .*, London, 1829, 2 vols.; and Pierre Dillon: *Voyage aux îles de la mer du Sud, en 1827, et 1828 et relation de la découverte du sort de La Pérouse . . .*, Paris, 1830, 2 vols.

17. Charles P. C. de Fleurieu: *Voyage autour du monde, pendant les années 1790, 1791 et 1792, par Étienne Marchand . . .*, Paris, 1798–1800, 3 vols. and atlas; Étienne Marchand: *Die neueste reise um die welt in dem jahren 1790, 1791 und 1792; . . .*, Leipzig, 1802 (?), 2 vols.; Étienne Marchand: *A voyage round the world, 1790–92, preceded by an historical introduction and illustrated by charts, etc., translated from the French of C. P. Claret Fleurieu*, London, 1801, 2 vols.; and G. Saint-Yves: *Le voyage autour du monde du Capitaine É Marchand, 1790–92. La découverte de la partte septentrionale de l'Archipel des Marqueses*, Paris, 1897, 32 pp.

18. Antoine R. J. de Bruni d'Entrecasteaux: *Voyage de Dentrecasteaux, envoyé à la recherche de La Pérouse. Publié par ordre de Sa. Majesté l' empereur et roi, . . .*, Paris, 1808, 2 vols. and atlas; Jacques J. H. de La Billardière: *An account of a voyage in search of La Pérouse, undertaken by order of the Constituent Assembly of France, and performed in the years 1791, 1792, and 1793, in the Recherche and Espérance, ships of war, under the command of rear-admiral Bruni d'Entrecasteaux*, London, 1802, 2 vols.; Jacques J. H. de La Billardière: *Relation du voyage à la recherche de La Pérouse, fait par ordre de l'Assemblée constituante, pendant les années 1791, 1792 . . .*, Paris, 1799, 2 vols. and atlas; Jacques J. H. de Labillardière: *Relation du voyage à la recherche de La Pérouse . . .*, Paris, 1800, 2 vols. in 4; Jacques J. H. de Labillardière: *Voyage in search of La Pérouse, . . .*, London, 1800, 476 pp.

19. Jacques J. H. de Labillardière: "Mémoire sur deux espèces de 'Litchi' cultivées dans les Molluques (Euphoria ramboutan, E. ramboutanake)," *Société Philomathique de Paris, Bull.*, vol. 2, p. 161, Paris, 1801; Jacques J. H. de Labillardière: "Sur le Sagoutier des Moluques (Sagus gennina) et le Cocotier des Maldives (Borassus)" *Ibid.*, pp. 170–171; Jacques J. H. de Labillardière: Mémoire

sur deux espèces de 'Litchi' cultivées dans les Molluques (Euphoria ramboutan)" *Savans Étrangers Mém.*, vol. 1, pp. 469–477, Paris, 1806; Jacques J. H. de Labillardière: *Novae Hollandiae plantarum specimen . . .* , Paris, 1804–1806, 2 vols.; Jacques J. H. de Labillardière: *Sertum austro-caledonicum,* Parisüs, 1824–1825, 2 vols.; and Jacques J. H. de Labillardière: "Sur la force du lin de la Nouvelle-Zélande comparée à celle des filaments de l'aloèspitte, du chanvre, du lin, et de la soie," *Museum d' Histoire Naturelle, Annales,* vol. 2, pp. 474–484, Paris, 1803.

20. Captain Nicolas Baudin's explorations are very little known, especially among English-speaking peoples. For example, Peter H. Buck in his book "Explorers of the Pacific; European and American discoveries in Polynesian," *Bernice P. Bishop Mus. Spec. Publ.* 43, pp. 1–125, Honolulu, 1953, does not mention him, nor does Andrew Sharp in his book *The discovery of the Pacific Islands,* Oxford, 1960, 259 pp.

As far back as the last quarter of the nineteenth century, the famed novelist Jules Verne in his *. . . Les grands navigateurs du XVIIIe siècle,* Paris, 1880 (?), 464 pp., wrote that ". . . Although the results of Captain Nicolas Baudin's campaign have been plentiful, it seems that until now an ill fate has been attached to this expedition. Biographical dictionaries and accounts of voyages as well acted in collusion to speak of him as little as possible . . ." (p. 334). We should note the article by Ernest Scott: "Baudin's voyage of exploration to Australia," *English Hist. Rev.,* vol. 28, pp. 341–346, London, 1913.

The following are fundamental works relating to Baudin's voyage: Nicolas Baudin: "Lettre sur la Nouvelle Hollande" *Museum Histoire Naturelle, Annales,* vol. 2, pp. 415–422, Paris, 1803; René Bouvier and Édouard Maynial: *Une aventure dans les mers australes; l'expedition du commandant Baudin (1800–1803),* Paris, 1947, 231 pp.; François Péron: *Voyage de découverte aux terres australes exécuté . . . sur les corvettes le Géographe, le Naturaliste et le goëlette la Casuarina pendant les années 1800, 1801, 1802, 1803 et 1804 . . .* , Paris, 1807, 498 pp.; François Péron: *A voyage of discovery to the southern hemisphere, performed by order of the Emperor Napoleon, during the years 1801, 1802, 1803, and 1804. Prepared for the press by M. F. Péron, translated from the French,* London, 1809, 314 pp.; François Péron: "Historical relation of a voyage undertaken for the discovery of southern lands," in John Pinkerton: *A general collection of the best and most interesting voyages and travels,* vol. 11, pp. 739–952, London, 1808–1814; François Péron: *Entdeckungsreise nach Australien, unternommen auf Befehl Sr. Maj. des Kaisers von Frankreich und Königs von Italien mit dem Korvetten, der Geograph und der Naturalist . . . in den Jahren 1800 bis 1804,* Weimar, 1808–1819, 2 vols.; and Jules Verne: *. . . The great navigators of the eighteenth century,* London, 1880, 409 pp.; Jules Verne: *Histoire générale des grands voyages et des grands voyageurs,* Paris, 1878–1880, 3 vols.

21. "Au Citoyen Ministre de la Marine et des Colonies" and "Aux membres de l'Institut National," signed by Baudin, in *Archives de la Marine, Série* BB 4–995, pl. 5, Paris; and "Voyages de découvertes," in *Archives Nationales* 5, JJ, 35, 2–4, Service Hydrographique de la Marine.

22. Instructions to Baudin in "Mémoire pour servir d'instructions particulières au Cd. Baudin, capitaine des Vaisseaux de la République."

23. See especially François Péron: *Voyage de découvertes aux terres Australes, exécuté par ordre de Sa Majesté l'empereur et roi, sur les corvettes le Géographe, le Naturaliste et la goëlette le Casuarina, pendant les années 1800, 1801, 1802, 1803, et 1804 . . .* , Paris, 1807–1816, 2 vols. and atlas. Vol. 1 is by François Péron, vol. 2 is in collaboration with Louis de Freycinet, and the *Atlas de navigation* in 32 plates (1812) is by Louis de Freycinet; François Péron: *Voyage de découvertes aux terres Australes, . . . Rédigé par Péron, et continué par m. Louis de Freycinet,* Paris, 1824, 4 vols. in 2 and an atlas; and François Péron: *Voyage de découvertes aux terres australes, . . . Navigation et géographie . . .* , par M. Louis Freycinet, Paris, 1815, 576 pp.

24. Jean P. Faivre: *op. cit.* [note 7], pp. 174–179; Jean P. Faivre: "Voyage du contreamiral Hamelin aux Terres Australes, 1800–1803," *Revue d'Histoire des Colonies,* vol. 45 (158), pp. 5–28, Paris, 1958; Jean P. Faivre: *Le contre-amiral Hamelin et la Marine française,* Paris, 1962, 194 pp.; A. H. Chisholm (ed.): "Nicholas Baudin (1754–1803)," *Australian Encyclopedia,* vol. 1, pp. 461–462, Sydney, 1962; G. W. Stocking, Jr.: "French anthropology in 1800," *ISIS,* vol. 55, pp. 134–150, Baltimore, 1964; and René Bouvier and Édouard Maynial: *Une aventure dans les mers australes. L'expédition du commandant Baudin, 1800–1803,* Paris, 1947, 232 pp.

25. H. Prentout: *L'Île de France sous Decaen, 1803–1810; essai sur la politique coloniale du premier empire, et la rivalite de la France et de l'Angleterre dans les Indes Orientales,* Paris, 1901, 688 pp.

26. Camille de Rocquefeuil: *A voyage round the world, between the years 1816–1819,* London, 1823, 112 pp.; Camille de Rocquefeuil: *Journal d'un voyage autour du monde, pendant les années 1816, 1817, 1818 et 1819,* Paris, 1823, 2 vols. in 1; Camille de Rocquefeuil: *Reise um die welt in den jahreu 1816 bis 1819,* Jena, 1823, 396 pp.; Anonymous: *Camille de Roquefeuil in San Francisco,* Los Angeles, 1954, 83 pp.

27. Louis C. D. de Freycinet: *Voyage autour du monde, entrepris par ordre du roi . . . Exécuté sur*

les corvettes de S. M. l' Uranie, et la Physicienne, pendant les années 1817, 1818, 1819 et 1820 . . . , Paris, 1824–1844, 7 vols. and atlas; and Louis C. D. de Freycinet: "Zwei Berichte von der in den Jahren 1817 bis 1820 in wissenschaftlichen Zwecken angestalten See-Reise um die Welt," *Annalen der Physik,* vol. 70, pp. 54–103, Halle and Leipzig, 1822. Freycinet's wife Rose maintained a journal account of the voyage. This has been reproduced as: Rose M. P. D. de Freycinet: *Campagne de l' Uranie (1817–1820); journal de madame Rose de Saulces de Freycinet d'après le manuscrit original, accompagné de notes par Charles Duplomb,* Paris, 1927, 190 pp.; and Marnie M. Bassett: *Realms and islands; the world voyage of Rose de Freycinet in the corvette Uranie, 1718-1820, from her journal and letters and the reports of Louis de Saulces de Freycinet, capitaine de corvette,* London, 1962, 275 pp.

28. For examples of Freycinet's scientific contributions see his "Des effets de l'eau de mer distillée sur l'économie animal," *Annales de Chimie,* vol. 7, pp. 220–223, Paris, 1817; *Mémoire sur la géographie et la navigation de l' Ile de France,* Paris, 1811, 66 pp.; "Mémoire sur la distillation de l'eau de mer," *Annales de Chimie,* vol. 4, pp. 225–250, Paris, 1817; and "Tableau de la distribution géographique des Polypiers recueillis pendant son voyage autour du monde," *Annales des Sciences Naturelles,* vol. 14, pp. 250–252, Paris, 1828.

29. For Jacques É. V. Arago's accounts see his: *Narrative of a voyage round the world, in the Uramie and Physicienne corvettes, commanded by Captain Freycinet, during the years 1817, 1818, 1819, and 1820; or a scientific expedition undertaken by order of the French government. In a series of letters to a friend,* London, 1823, 297 pp. (?); *Promenade autour du monde pendant les années 1817, 1818, 1819 et 1820, sur les corvettes du roi l' Uranie et la Physicienne commandées par M. Freycinet,* Paris, 1822, 2 vols.; and *Souvenirs d'un avengle. Voyage autour du monde,* Paris, 1839–1840, 5 vols. Additional publications by Arago on exploration of the Pacific Basin are *Beide oceane. Eine reise nach Chile, Californien, Tahiti, den Marquesas—inseln, Brasilien, &c.,* Leipzig, 1854 (?), 206 pp.; and *Deux océans,* Paris, 1854, 2 vols.

30. For references to some of the scientific products of Freycinet's expedition see Charles Gaudichaud: *Voyage autour du monde entrepris par ordre du Roi, exécuté sur les corvettes de S. M. l' Uranie et la Physicianne, pendant les années 1817, 1818, 1819 et 1820, . . . par Louis de Freycinet,* Paris, 1826, 522 pp. and atlas; and Jean B. M. A. D. de La Roquette: *Notices historiques sur M M Henri et Louis de Freycinet, . . . Lues à la séance générale de la Société de Géographie du 15 décembre 1843,* Paris, 1843, 39 pp.

31. Louis I. Duperrey: *Voyage autour du monde, exécuté par ordre du roi, sur la corvette de Sa Majesté, La Coquille, pendant les années 1822, 1823, 1824 et 1825, . . . ,* Paris, 1825–1830, 6 vols. in 7 and atlas; and Louis I. Duperrey: *Voyage autour du monde sur . . . La Coquille, 1822–1825. Partie historique,* Paris, 1926, 202 pp. Dominique F. J. Arago published several accounts of the scientific results, as for example, "Rapport fait à l'Acad. des Sci. sur le voyage [de la Coquille] de découvertes, exécutée pendant les années 1822–1825, sous le commandement de M. Duperrey," *Connaissance des Temps . . . [for] 1828,* pp. 240–272, Paris, 1828; and "Extrait du Rapport sur le Voyage de découvertes exécuté sous le commandement de M. Duperrey," *Annales des Sciences Naturelles,* vol. 6, pp. 206–221, Paris, 1825.

32. Pierre-Adolphe Lesson: *Voyage autour du monde exécuté par ordre du Roi sur la corvette de S. M. la Coquille, pendant les années 1822, 1823, 1824 et 1825,* Paris, 1826–1830, 2 vols.; and Pierre-Adolphe Lesson: *Voyage autour du monde, entrepris par ordre du gouvernement sur la corvette la Coquille,* Paris, 1838–1839, 2 vols.

33. Renè-P. Lesson published a number of scientific articles among which are the following: "Coup d'oeil sur les îles océanniennes et le grand océan," *Annales des Sciences Naturelles,* vol. 5, pp. 172–188, Paris, 1825; "Distribution géographique de quelques oiseaux marins obsérvés dans le voyage autour du monde de la corvette La Coquille," *Annales des Sciences Naturelles,* vol. 6, pp. 88–103, Paris, 1825; "Indication de quelques Cétacés nouveaux obsérvés dans le voyage autour du monde de la corvette La Coquille," *Sciences Naturelles et de Géologie, Bull.,* vol. 7, pp. 373–375, Paris, 1826; *Notice historique sur l'île de Rotouma située dans le Grand Océan austral,* Paris, 1825, 47 pp.; and two articles with Prosper Garnot: "Mammifères nouveaux ou peu connus décrits et figurés dans l'Atlas Zoologique du voyage autour du monde de la corvette 'La Coquille,'" *Sciences Naturelles et de Géologie, Bull.,* vol. 8, pp. 95–96, Paris, 1826; and "Mémoire sur les Tasmaniens, sur les Alfourous, et sur les Australiens," *Annales des Sciences Naturelles,* vol. 10, pp. 149–162, Paris, 1827.

34. Pierre-Adolphe Lesson published a number of scientific articles relating to the Pacific Basin, of which the following are representative examples: "Mollusques recueillis dans la Mer du Sud," *Revue Zoologique,* vol. 5, pp. 210–214 and 234–238, Paris, 1842; "Mollusques recueillis dans la Mer du Sud et l'Océan Atlantique . . . ," *Revue Zoologique,* vol. 5, pp. 184–187, Paris, 1842; "Mollusques . . . recueillis dans la Mer du Sud," *Revue Zoologique,* vol. 5, pp. 141–144, Paris, 1842; "notes sur les oiseaux nouveaux ou peu connus rapportés de la Mer du Sud . . . ," *Revue Zoologique,* vol. 5, pp. 135–136 and 209–210, Paris, 1842; "Notes sur quelques coquilles marines rapportées de

la Mer du Sud . . . ," *Revue Zoologique*, vol. 5, pp. 102–104, Paris, 1842; and "Notes sur quelques mollusques rares ou nouveaux recueillis dans la Mer du Sud . . . ," *Actes de la Société Linnéenne*, vol. 12, pp. 203–210, Bordeaux, 1841.

35. See his: *Voyage médical autour du monde, exécuté sur la corvette du Roi la Coquille, commandée par M. L. I. Duperrey, pendant les années 1822, 1823, 1824, et 1825 . . . suivi d'un Mémoire sur les races humaines répandues dans l'Océanie, la Malaisie, et l'Australie*, Paris, 1829, 244 pp.; *Journal d'un voyage pittoresque autour du monde exécuté sur la corvette la Coquille les années 1822, 1823, 1824, 1825*, Paris, 1830, 192 pp.; and *Voyage autour du monde entrepris par ordre du gouvernement sur la corvette la Coquille, . . .*, Paris, 1838–1839, 2 vols.

36. The following are among the scientific publications by Louis I. Duperrey: "Extrait d'une lettre écrite par M. le Capitaine Duperrey, commandant l'expédition Française de découvertes, à M. de Freycinet, en date de Port Jackson, le 30 Janvier 1824," *Soc. Géogr., Bull.*, vol. 2, pp. 92–94, Paris, 1824; *Mémoire sur les opérations géographiques faites dans la campagne de la corvette de S. M. la Coquille, pendant les années 1822, 1823, 1824, et 1825*, Paris, 18??, 104 pp.; "Notice sur la configuration de l'équateur magnétique conclue des observations faites dans la campagne de la corvette La Coquille," *Annales de Chimie*, vol. 45, pp. 371–425, Paris, 1830; *Observations du pendule invariable, de l'inclinaison et de la déclinaison de l'aiguille aimantée, faites dans la campagne de la corvette . . . la Coquille, pendant les années 1822, 1823, 1824 et 1825*, Paris, 1827 (?), 32 pp.; "Rapport sur le voyage de M. Rochet d' Hericourt; partie relative du Magnétisme Terrestre," *Comptes Rendus*, vol. 22, pp. 800–806, Paris, 1846; "Réduction des observations de l'intensité du magnétisme terrestre faites durant le cours du voyage de l' Uranie," *Comptes Rendus*, vol. 19, pp. 445–452, Paris, 1844; and "Résumé des observations de l'inclinaison et de la déclinaison de l'aiguille aimantée, ..." *Annales de Chimie*, vol. 34, pp. 298–320, Paris, 1827.

37. For biographical sketches of Dumont d' Urville see: George Day: *Dumont d' Urville, 1798– 1842; voyages et aventures*, Paris, 1947, 123 pp.; A. Soudry: *. . . Dumont d'Urville, sa vie intime pendant son troisième voyage autour du monde*, Paris, 1886, 310 pp.; and Camille Vergniol: *. . . Dumont d'Urville*, Paris, 1930, 308 pp.

38. For Jules S. C. Dumont d'Urville's account of the voyage see his *Voyage de Dumont d'Ur- ville, capitaine de vaisseau autour du monde, à bord de l'Astrolabe (1826) . . .*, Paris, 1883, 274 pp.; *Voyage de la corvette l'Astrolabe exécuté par ordre du roi, pendant les années 1826–1827–1828–1829, . . .*, Paris, 1830–1834, 14 vols. in 13 and an atlas; and *Voyage pittoresque autour du monde; résumé général des voyages de découvertes . . . accompagné de cartes et de nombreuses gravures en taille—douce sur acier . . . dessinateur du voyage de l'Astrolabe*, Paris, 1834–1835, 2 vols.

39. For accounts of this search see Jules S. C. Dumont d'Urville: "L'Astrolabe à Vanikoro," *Soc. Géogr. Bull.*, vol. 12, pp. 249–267, Paris, 1829; and R. Descombe: "The search for 'La Boussole' at Vanikoro," *Pacific Islands Monthly*, vol. 30 (4), pp. 53–57, Sydney, 1959.

40. Pierre Dillon: *op. cit.* [note 16].

41. Achille de Kergariou: *. . . La mission de la Cybèle en Extrême—Orient, 1817–1818; journal de voyage du Capitaine A. de Kergariou*, Paris, 1914, 248 pp.

42. Jean P. Faivre: *op. cit.* [note 7], pp. 328–329.

43. Jacques A. Moerenhaut: *Voyage aux îles du Grand océan . . .*, Paris, 1837, 2 vols.; Jacques A. Moerenhaut: *Voyages aux îles du Grand Océan. Reproduction de l'édition principale de 1837*, Paris, 1959, 520 pp.; and Abraham P. Nasatir (trans. and ed.): *The inside story of the gold rush by Jacques A. Moerenhout . . . translated and edited from documents in the French archives, . . .*, San Francisco, Calif., 1935, 94 pp.

44. Abel A. Dupetit-Thouars: *Voyage autour du monde sur la frégate la Vénus pendant les années 1836–1839*, Paris, 1840–1846, 9 vols. and an atlas; Abel A. Dupetit-Thouars: *Voyage autour du monde sur la frégate la Vénus pendant les années 1836–1839*, Paris, 1840–1864, 11 vols. and an atlas; Abel A. Dupetit-Thouars: *Voyage autour du monde sur la frégate la Vénus pendant les années 1836– 1839 . . .*, Paris, 1840–1855, 10 vols. and an atlas; and Charles N. Rudkin (trans.) and Abel A. Dupetit-Thouars: *Voyage of the Vénus: sojourn in California*, Los Angles, 1956, 113 pp.

For notes and articles by or about Dupetit-Thouars see his *Prise de possession, au nom du roi des Français, . . . des îles Marquesas*, Paris, 1842, plano; *Notes succincte sur les services à la mer de Du Petit- Thouars*, Paris, 1854, 10 pp.; M. Guizot: *Rapport de l'amiral Dupetit-Thouars sur Tahiti, com- muniqué le 15 avril à la Chambre des Députés*, Paris, 1844, 24 pp.; and J. Turot: *M. Dupetit-Thouars dans la Polynésie, etc.*, Paris, 1844, n. p.

For references to the scientific work of the expedition see Dominique F. J. Arago: "Rapport fait à l'Académie sur les travaux scientifiques exécutés pendant le voyage de la frégate la Vénus, com- mandée par M. le Capitaine de vaisseau Aubert Du Petit-Thouars," *Annuaire du Bur. des Longitudes*,

1840, pp. 254–353, Paris, 1840; and "Rapport sur les résultats scientifiques du voyage autour du monde de la frégate La Vénus," *Comptes Rendus*, vol. 11, pp. 298–300, Paris, 1840.

45. Jean B. T. M. Cécille: *Campagne dans les mers de l' Inde et de la Chine, à bord de la frègate l' Érigone commandée en 1841, 1842 et 1843 et en 1843 et 1844 par M. Roy ... (Météorologie et magnétisme)*, Paris, 1847–1850, 4 vols.

In the Archives of the French Navy is an "Extrait du rapport adressé à Monsieur le Ministre de la Marine par M. Cécille, capitaine de vaisseau, commandant la corvette l'Héroine, envoyée dans l'hémisphère austral à la protection de la pêche à la baleine dans les années 1837, 1838, 1839 et 1840."

46. Preliminary and early accounts of the voyage by Jacques S. C. Dumont d' Urville that appeared in the *Bulletin de la Société de Géographie* are as follows: "Voyage autour du monde des frégates l'Astrolabe et la Zélée. Rapport sur les opérations de la campagne depuis le départ de Rio de Janeiro jusqu' à l'arrivée à Valparaiso," vol. 10, pp. 249–279, Paris, 1838; and "Note sur le voyage de découvertes au pôle austral et dans l'Océanie de l'Astrolabe et de la Zélée," vol. 7, pp. 281–286, Paris, 1837.

47. The following are fundamental reports of the voyage by or in the name of Dumont d'Urville: *Voyage au pole sud et dans l' Océanie sur les corvettes l' Astrolabe et le Zélée par ordre du roi pendant les années 1837, 1838, 1839, 1840, sous le commandement de M. J. Dumont d' Urville*, Paris, 1842–1854, 23 vols. and atlas; *Voyage au pôle Sud et dans l' Océanie sur les corvettes l' Astrolabe et la Zélée, exécuté par ordre du roi pendant les années 1837, 1838, 1839, 1840 ..., Observations chronométriques et théorie nouvelle de lever sous voiles*, Paris, 1843, 332 pp.; *Voyage autour du monde, publ. sous la direction du contre-amiral Dumont d' Urville*, Paris, 1853, 2 vols.; *Expédition au pôle austral et dans l' Océanie des corvettes de Sa Majesté l' Astrolabe et la Zélée ... Rapports ...*, Paris, m. d. 110 pp.

For a recent account of a part of the voyage see Olive Wright: *The voyage of the Astrolabe, 1840; an English rendering of the journals of Dumont d' Urville and his officers of the visit to New Zealand in 1840, ...*, Wellington, N. Z., 1955, 180 pp.

Chapter 12
GEOGRAPHICAL EXPLORATION BY THE BRITISH

1. The following are excellent references for a study of English exploration: Charles R. Beazley: "Exploration under Elizabeth, 1558–1603," *Roy. Hist. Soc., London, Trans., n.s.*, vol. 9, pp. 119–165, London, 1895; Charles R. D. Bethune (ed.): "The discoveries of the world ... Corrected, quoted, and published in England by Richard Hakluyt (1601)"; *Hakly. Soc. Works*, vol. 30, pp. 1–242, London, 1862; Irwin R. Blacker: *Hakluyt's voyages; the principal navigations, voyages, traffiques & discoveries of the English nation ... within the compasse of these 1600 yeares*, New York, 1965, 522 pp.; Mary Blewitt: *Surveys of the seas; a brief history of British hydrography*, London, 1957, 168 pp.; C. M. Bowen: "Elizabethan travel literature," *Blackwood's Mag.*, Oct. 1916, pp. 489–498, London, 1916; Henry S. Burrage (ed.): *... Early English and French voyages, chiefly from Hakluyt, 1534–1608*, New York, 1932, 451 pp.; John Campbell: *Lives of admirals and other eminent British seamen ... our discoveries, plantations, and commerce ...*, London, 1761, 4 vols.; Robert R. Cawley: "Milton and the literature of travel," *Princeton Studies in English*, no. 32, pp. 1–158, Princeton, N. J., 1951; Robert R. Cawley: "Sailors in the time of Elizabeth; a study in the character of the men who composed the English crews during the great age of discovery," *Princeton Alumni Weekly*, May 27, 1927, pp. 977–982, Princeton, N. J., 1927; Robert R. Cawley: *Unpathed waters; studies in the influence of the voyagers on Elizabethan literature*, Princeton, N. J., 1853, 508 pp.; Jean A. A. J. Jusserand: *English wayfaring life in the middle ages (XIVth century)*, New York, 1931, 464 pp.; William P. Ker: "The Elizabethan voyagers," in his *Collected Essays*, London, 1925, 2 vols.; Ida Lee: "The first sighting of Australia by the English," *Geogr. Journ.*, vol. 83, pp. 317–321, London, 1934, and in *Hydrographic Rev.*, vol. 2, pp. 242–246, Monaco, 1935; Christopher Lloyd: *Pacific horizons, the exploration of the Pacific before Captain Cook*, London, 1946, 188 pp.; Halford J. Mackinder: "Progress of geography in the field and in the study during the reign of His Majesty King George the Fifth," *Geogr. Journ.*, vol. 86, pp. 1–16, London, 1935; Richard H. Major (ed.): "Early voyages to Terra Australis, now called Australia: ... ," *Hakly. Soc. Works*, vol. 25, pp. 1–200, London, 1859; Clements R. Markham: "Review of British geographical work during the last

hundred years," *Roy. Geogr. Soc., Supplementary Papers*, vol. 3, pp. 147–199, London, 1893; Ida (Lee) Marriott: *The coming of the British to Australia, 1788 to 1829*, London, 1906, 350 pp.; James K. Merton: "Science, technology and society in seventeenth century England," *Osiris*, vol. 4 (2), pp. 360–632, Bruges, 1938; William P. Morrell: *Britain in the Pacific Islands*, Oxford, 1960, 450 pp.; William P. Morrell: *British overseas expansion and the history of the Commonwealth; a select bibliography*, London, 1961, 40 pp.; Hosea B. Morse: *The chronicles of the East India Company trading to China, 1635–1834*, Oxford, 1926–1929, 5 vols.; George P. B. Naish: "Hydrographic surveys under the later Stuarts," *Navigation, Journ.*, vol. 9, pp. 47–55, London, 1956; George B. Parks (ed.): ". . . Richard Hakluyt and the English voyages," *Amer. Geogr. Soc., Spec. Publ.*, vol. 10, pp. 1–289, New York, 1928; David B. Quinn: "Edward IV and exploration," *Mariner's Mirror*, vol. 21, pp. 275–284, Cambridge, Engl., 1935; David B. Quinn: "Some Spanish reactions to Elizabethan colonial enterprises," *Roy. Hist. Soc. London, Trans., Fifth Series*, vol. 1, pp. 1–23, London, 1951; Eva G. R. Taylor: "The English world makers of the seventeenth century and their influence on the earth sciences," *Geogr. Rev.*, vol. 38, pp. 104–112, New York, 1948; Eva G. R. Taylor (ed.): "The original writings and correspondence of the two Richard Hakluyts," *Hakly. Soc. Works, Series 2*, vols. 76–77, London, 1935; J. M. Ward: "British policy in the exploration of the South Pacific, 1669–1793," *Roy. Austr. Hist. Soc., Journ. and Proc.*, vol. 33, pp. 25–48, Sydney, 1947; Oliver M. W. Warner: *English maritime writing: Hakluyt to Cook*, London, 1958, 35 pp.; James A. Williamson: *The ocean in English history, . . .*, Oxford, 1941, 208 pp.; James A. Williamson: *Maritime enterprise, 1485–1558*, Oxford, 1913, 416 pp.; James A. Williamson: *A short history of British expansion . . .*, London, 1930, 2 vols.; Arnold Wright: *Early English adventures in the East*, London, 1914, 331 pp.; and Henry Yule (ed.): "Cathay and the way thither; . . .," *Hakly. Soc. Works*, vols. 36–37, London, 1866.

Perhaps the best single source of information on the history of geographical exploration by the British are the works issued by the Hakluyt Society (*Hakly. Soc. Works*), printed for the Hakluyt Society in London, vols. 1 (1847)–100 (1898) and the second series vols. 1 (1899) to date.

2. Eva G. R. Taylor: *Tudor geography, 1485–1583*, London, 1930, 290 pp., p. 74. See also: Henry R. F. Bourne: *English seamen under the Tudors*, London, 1868, 2 vols.; James A. Froude: *English seamen in the sixteenth century . . .*, New York, 1895, 228 pp.; Arthur D. Innes: *England under the Tudors*, London, 1905, 481 pp.; Boies Penrose: *Travel and discovery in the Renaissance, 1420–1620*, Cambridge, Engl., 1952, 369 pp.; Boies Penrose: *Tudor and early Stuart voyaging*, Wash., D. C., 1962, 35 pp.; Walter A. Raleigh: *The English voyages of the sixteenth century*, Glasgow, 1906, 204 pp.; Conyers Read (comp.): *Bibliography of British history, Tudor period, 1485–1603, . . .*, Oxford, 1959, 624 pp.; Eva G. R. Taylor: "Early empire-building projects in the Pacific Ocean, 1565–1585," *Hisp. Amer. Hist. Rev.*, vol. 19, pp. 296–306, New York, 1934; Eva G. R. Taylor: *The English debt to Portuguese nautical science in the sixteenth century*, Lisboa, 1938, 11 pp.; and Eva G. R. Taylor: *Late Tudor and early Stuart geography, 1583–1650; a sequel to Tudor geography, 1455–1583*, London, 1934, 322 pp.

3. Roger Barlow: *Geographia Barlow*, Royal MSS., 18, B. XXVIII, British Museum, cited in Eva G. R. Taylor: "Tudor . . ." *ibid.*, p. 45. See also Eva G. R. Taylor: "Roger Barlow: A new chapter in early Tudor geography," *Geogr. Journ.*, vol. 74, pp. 157–170, London, 1929; and Eva G. R. Taylor (ed.): "A brief summe of geographie, by Roger Barlow," *Hakly. Soc. Works, Series 2*, vol. 69, pp. 1–210, London, 1932.

4. John Rastell: "A new interlude! and a mery of the nature of the iiij. elements, . . . , 1519" (64 leaves), cited in Eva G. R. Taylor: "Tudor geography," *op. cit.* [note 2], p. 8. See also Robert G. C. Proctor: "John Rastell, 1516–1533," *Handlists of English Printers, 1501–1556*, pt. 2, pp. 1–5, London, 1895–1896; and John Rastell: *The pastime of people; or the chroniclers of divers realms; . . .*, London, 1811, 299 pp.

5. The southern unknown continent.

6. A conjectural strait between Asia and America, which was later discovered to exist and was named Bering Strait. For a brief history see: George E. Munn: *Origin of the Strait of Anian concept*, Phila., Pa., 1929, 36 pp.

7. Papal Bull, 1493, Pope Alexander VI. See Catholic Church, Pope, 1492–1503 (Alexander VI): *Alfonsus De Fonseca, meratione diuiuna archiepiscopus toletañ. Hispanierum primas . . .*, Madrid (?), 1530, 6 leaves; and *The earliest diplomatic documents in America; the papal bulls of 1493 and the treaty of Tordesillas reproduced and translated with historical introduction and explanatory notes by P. Gottschalk*, Berlin, n.d., 91 pp.; Henry Harrisse: *The diplomatic history of America: its first chapter, 1452–1493–1494*, London, 1897, 230 pp.; and George E. Nunn: *The diplomacy concerning the discovery of America*, Jenkintown, Pa., 1948, 28 pp.

8. The Treaty of Tordesillas, June 7, 1494 is discussed in the references in note 7.

9. For example, Humphrey Gilbert's *How Her Majesty May Annoy the King of Spain*, 1577.

10. In 1567 the Spanish broke an agreement with an English fleet, commanded by Hawkins, not to molest them while the English ships were being refitted in San Juan de Ulua (now Veracruz), Mexico. For references on Hawkins see especially Philip Gosse: *Sir John Hawkins*, London, 1930, 290 pp.; Clements R. Markham (ed.): "The Hawkins' voyages during the reigns of Henry VIII, Queen Elizabeth, and James I," *Hakly. Soc. Works*, vol. 57, pp. 1–453, London, 1878; Antonio Rumeu de Armas: *Los viajes de John Hawkins a América, 1562–1595*, Sevilla, 1947, 484 pp.; James A. Williamson: *Sir John Hawkins, the time and the man*, Oxford, 1927, 542 pp.

11. John Dee: *The great volume of famous and rich discoveries*, 1577, MS. For general works by and on John Dee see John Dee: *General and rare memorials pertayning to the Perfect Arte of Navigation: annexed to the Paradoxal Cumpas, in Playne: . . .*, London, 1577, 80 pp.; and Eva G. R. Taylor: "List of John Dee's geographical and related works," in her Tudor geography *op. cit.* [note 2], pp. 191–192.

12. First draft plan (Cotton MSS., Otho. E. VIII, British Mus.). The first draft plan was greatly extended later (Lansdowne MSS., no. 100, British Mus.).

13. Two of the numerous hypothetical place names indicated on many maps to be located on the northern coast of Terra Australis Incognita.

14. The San Juan treachery. For details see references cited in note 10.

15. Francis Drake: *The world encompassed by Sir Francis Drake*, London, 1628, 108 pp.; and Francis Drake: "The world encompassed by Sir Francis Drake, . . . ," *Hakly. Soc. Works*, vol. 16, pp. 1–295, London, 1854. For other references see Edward F. Benson: *Sir Francis Drake*, New York, 1927, 315 pp.; R. P. Bishop: "Drake's course in the North Pacific," *Brit. Col. Hist. Quart.*, vol. 3, pp. 151–182, Victoria, B.C., 1939; George Davidson: "Francis Drake on the northwest coast of America in the year 1579 . . . ," *Geogr. Soc. Pacific, Trans. and Proc.*, vol. 5 (2), pp. 1–114, San Francisco, 1908; Edward Heawood: "Cartographical records of Drake's voyage," *Geogr. Journ.*, vol. 70, pp. 479–481, London, 1927; Léon Lemmonier: "Sir Francis Drake," *La Grande Légende de la Mer*, vol. 20, pp. 1–256, Paris, 1932; Norman M. Penzer (ed.): *The world encompassed and analogous contemporary documents concerning Sir Francis Drake's circumnavigation of the world, . . .*, London, 1926, 235 pp.; John W. Robertson: *Francis Drake & other early explorers along the Pacific coast*, San Francisco, 1927, 290 pp.; Eva G. R. Taylor: "The missing draft project of Drake's voyage of 1577–1580," *Geogr. Journ.*, vol. 75, pp. 46–47, London, 1930; Eva G. R. Taylor: "More light on Drake, 1577–1580," *Mariner's Mirror*, vol. 16, pp. 134–148, London, 1930; Eva G. R. Taylor: "Francis Drake and the Pacific: two fragments," *Pac. Hist. Rev.*, vol. 1, pp. 360–369, Glendale, Calif., 1932; J. D. Upcott (ed.): *Three voyages of Drake, as recorded in contemporary accounts*, London, 1936, 302 pp.; Henry R. Wagner: *Sir Francis Drake's voyage around the world; its aims and achievements*, San Francisco, 1926, 543 pp.; and James A. Williamson: *The age of Drake*, London, 1960, 399 pp.

16. Humphrey Gilbert: *A discourse of a discouerie for a new passage to Cataia. Written by Sir Humfrey Gilbert, knight (with a general map, made onelye for the particuler declaration of this discovery)*, London, 1576, 60 pp. For additional references see R. P. Bishop: "Lessons of the Gilbert map," *Geogr. Journ.*, vol. 72, pp. 237–243, London, 1928; William G. Gosling: *The life of Sir Humphrey Gilbert, England's first empire builder*, London, 1911, 304 pp.; and David B. Quinn (ed.): "The voyages and colonising enterprises of Sir Humphrey Gilbert," *Hakly. Soc. Works*, Series 2, vols. 83–84, London, 1940.

17. John C. Beaglehole: *The exploration of the Pacific*, London, 1934, 410 pp., p. 74.

18. James A. Williamson: *Cook and the opening of the Pacific*, London, 1946, 251 pp., p. 20.

19. Julian Corbett: "III. Francis Drake," *Geogr. Journ.*, vol. 21, pp. 605–611, London, 1903. See also British Museum: *Sir Francis Drake's voyage round the world, 1577–1580; two contemporary maps*, London, 1927, 11 pp.; Julian S. Corbett: *Drake and the Tudor navy, with a history of the rise of England as a maritime power*, London, 1898, 2 vols.; Joseph W. Cove: *The silver circle*, London, 1963, 168 pp.; Zelia Nuttall (trans. and ed.): "New light on Drake; . . . ," *Hakly. Soc. Works*, Series 2, vol. 34, pp. 1–443, London, 1914; and Robert M. Christy: *The silver map of the world; a contemporary medallion commemorative of Drake's great voyage (1577–80) a geographical essay; . . .*, London, 1900, 71 pp.

20. C. R. Drinkwater Bethune (ed.): "The observations of Sir Richard Hawkins knt. in his voyage into the South sea in the year 1593. Reprinted from the edition of 1622," *Hakly. Soc. Works*, vol. 1, pp. 1–246, London, 1847.

21. Charles T. Beke (ed.): "A true description of three voyages by the north-east towards Cathay and China, undertaken by the Dutch in the years 1594, 1595, and 1596. By Gerrit de Veer. Published in Amsterdam in the year 1598 . . . ," *Hakly. Soc. Works*, vol. 13, pp. 1–291, London, 1853.

22. Clements R. Markham (ed.): "The voyages of Sir James Lancaster, kt., to the East Indies, with abstracts of journals of voyages to the East Indies, during the seventeenth century, preserved in the India office . . . ," *Hakly. Soc. Works*, vol. 56, pp. 1–314, London, 1877; and William Foster (ed.): "The voyages of Sir James Lancaster to Brazil and the East Indies, 1591–1603," *Hakly. Soc. Works, Series 2*, vol. 85, pp. 1–178, London, 1940.

23. George Birchwood and William Foster (eds.): *The register of letters, &c., of the Gouvernour and company of merchants of London trading into the East Indies, 1600–1619*, London, 1893, 530 pp.; George A. Ballard: "The arrival of the Dutch and British in the Indian Ocean," *Mariner's Mirror*, vol. 12, pp. 69–94, London, 1926; Charles R. Boxer: "The London East India company's first expedition," *Mariner's Mirror*, vol. 19, pp. 240–241, London, 1933; Robert R. Cawley: *The influence of the voyagers in non-dramatic English literature between 1550 and 1650*, . . . , a Ph.D. thesis, Harvard Univ., Cambridge, Mass., 1921; and Henry Stevens (ed.): *The dawn of British trade in the East Indies as recorded in the court minutes of the East India company 1599–1603*, London, 1886, 331 pp.

24. Bolton Corney (ed.): "The voyage of Sir Henry Middleton to Bantam and the Maluco Islands; being the second voyage set forth by the governor and company of merchants of London trading in the East Indies, 1604," *Hakly. Soc. Works*, vol. 19, pp. 1–132, London, 1856; and William Foster (ed.): "The voyage of Sir Henry Middleton to the Moluccas, 1604–1606," *Hakly. Soc. Works, Series 2*, vol. 88, pp. 1–209, London, 1943.

25. "Voyage du capitaine William Keeling à Bantam & à Banda, en 1607" in Antoine F. Prévost: *Histoire générale des voyages* . . . , vol. 2, pp. 89–135, La Haye, 1747; and William Keeling: "A iournall of the third voyage to the East India; set out by the company of the merchants trading in those parts," in Samuel Purchas: *Pilgrimes* . . . , vol. 1. (bk 3), pp. 188–205, London, 1625.

26. "Fifth voyage of the English East India company, in 1609, under the command of Captain David Middleton," in Robert Kerr (ed.): *A general history and collection of voyages and travels* . . . , vol. 8, pp. 343–360, Edinburgh, 1813.

27. "Sixth voyage of the English East India company, in 1610, under the command of Sir Henry Middleton. Journal of the preceding voyage, by Nicholas Downton, captain of the Peppercorn," in Robert Kerr (ed.): *A general history and collection of voyages and travels* . . . , vol. 8, pp. 361–436, Edinburgh, 1813.

28. "Sevende reys na Ost-Indien, op kosten van de Engelse Maalschappy; door Kapiteyn Antony Hippon . . . gedaan in het jaar 1611 . . . ," in Pieter van der Aa: *De aanmerkenswaardigste en alomberoemde zee-und landreizen*, vol. 6 (4), 24 columns, Leyden, 1727 (?).

29. Ernest M. Satow: "The voyage of Captain John Saris to Japan, 1613," *Hakly. Soc. Works, Series 2*, vol. 5, pp. 1–242, London, 1900; and Takanobu Otsuka: "The first voyage of the English [John Saris] to Japan," *The Toyo Bunko Publications, Ser. D.*, vol. 3, pp. 1–266, Tokyo, 1941.

30. For additional voyages see William Foster (ed.): "The voyage of Thomas Bent to the East Indies, 1612–1614," *Hakly. Soc. Works, Series 2*, vol. 75, pp. 1–316, London, 1934; William Foster (ed.): "The voyage of Nicholas Downton to the East Indies, 1614–1615, as recorded in contemporary narratives and letters," *Hakly. Soc. Works, Series 2*, vol. 82, pp. 1–224, London, 1939; William Foster (ed.): "The journal of John Jourdain, 1608–1617, describing his experiences in Arabia, India, and the Malay archipelago," *Hakly. Soc. Works, Series 2*, vol. 16, pp. 1–394, London, 1905; William H. Moreland (ed.): "Peter Floris, his voyage to the East Indies in the Globe, 1611–1615; the contemporary translation of his journal," *Hakly. Soc. Works, Series 2*, vol. 74, pp. 1–164, London, 1934; C. J. Purnell: "The log book of William Adams, 1614–1619, and related documents," *Japan Soc., Trans. and Proc.*, vol. 13 (2), pp. 156–302, Tokyo, 1914–1915; and Edward M. Thompson (ed.): "Diary of Richard Cocks, cape merchant in the English factory in Japan 1615–1622, with correspondence," *Hakly. Soc. Works*, vols. 66–67, London, 1883.

31. William H. Bonner: *Captain William Dampier*, Stanford, Calif., 1934, 234 pp.; H. P. Collins: "William Dampier, buccaneer and circumnavigator," *Geogr. Mag.*, vol. 25, pp. 444–453, London, 1953; B. M. H. Rogers: "Dampier's voyage of 1703," *Mariner's Mirror*, vol. 10, pp. 336–381, London, 1924; Joseph C. Shipman: "William Dampier, seaman-scientist," *Univ. Kans. Publications, Library Series*, no. 15, pp. 1–63, Lawrence, Kans., 1962; and Clennell Wilkinson: *Dampier; explorer and buccaneer*, New York, 1929, 257 pp.

32. See for example Alexandre O. Exquemelin: *Pirates de América* . . . , Buenos Aires, 1945, 390 pp.; Alexandre O. Exquemelin: *The buccaneers of America, a true account of the most remarkable assaults* . . . , London, 1911, 508 pp.; and Basil Ringrose: "The dangerous and bold adventures of Captains Sharp, Coxon, Sawkins, and others in the South Sea," in A. O. Oexmelin: *The history of buccaneers of America*, pp. 229–413, London, 1810.

33. William Dampier: *A new voyage round the world. Describing particularly, . . . the passage by

Terra del Fuego, the South sea coasts Chili, Peru, and Mexico … London 1698–1703 3 vols.; Normam M. Penzer (ed.): *A new voyage round the world, by William Dampier*, London, 1927, 376 pp.

34. William Dampier: *Voyages and discoveries, by William Dampier*, London, 1931, 311 pp.

35. Norman M. Penzer (ed.): *op. cit.* [note 33], p. 190.

36. *Ibid.*, p. 239.

37. *Ibid.*, p. 312.

38. *Ibid.*, p. 200.

39. *Ibid.*, pp. 255–256.

40. William Dampier: "An account of New Holland and the adjacent islands," in John Pinkerton (ed.): *A general collection of the best and most interesting voyages and travels* …, vol. 11, 464–497, London, 1812; John Masefield (ed.): *Dampier's voyages; … a voyage to New Holland, …*, Edinburgh, 1906, 2 vols.; and James A. Wilkinson (ed.): *A voyage to New Holland, by William Dampier*, London, 1939, 266 pp.

41. "A view of the General Coasting Trade-Winds in the Atlantick and Indian Oceans, and A View of the General and Coasting Trade-Winds in the great South Ocean," in Norman M. Penzer: *op. cit.* [note 33], facing p. 227.

42. British Admiralty, Hydrographic Department: *Professional Paper*, no. 13, (H 21182/45), London, 1950, p. 29.

43. G. E. Manwaring (ed.): … *A cruising voyage round the world [by] Captain Woodes Rogers* …, New York, 1928, 320 pp.; and Woodes Rogers: *A cruising voyage round the world: first to the South seas, thence to the East Indies … Begun in 1708, and finish'd in 1711*, London, 1712, 428 M 45 pp.

44. "The voyage of Captain [John] Clipperton round the world," in David Henry: *An historical account of all the voyages round the world*, vol. 2, pp. 91–126, London, 1774.

45. William G. Perrin (ed.): … *A voyage round the world, by Captain George Shelvocke*, London, 1928, 262 pp.; and George Shelvocke: *A voyage round the world by way of the great South Sea, perform'd in the years 1719, 20, 21, 22, in the Speedwell of London* …, London, 1726, 468 pp.

46. Amédée F. Frézier: … *Reise nach Süd-see, und denen küsten von Chili, Peru, und Brazilien …in den jahren 1740 bis 1744 von dem berühmten engl.-commandeur, Hrn. Georg Anson, …*, Hamburg, 1745, 640 pp.; Henry B. T. Somerville: *Commodore Anson's voyage into the South seas and around the world*, London, 1934, 317 pp.; and Richard Walter (comp.): *A voyage round the world, in the years 1740, 1, 2, 3, 4. By George Anson, …*, London, 1748, 417 pp.

47. Harry C. J. Luke: *Islands of the South Pacific*, London, 1962, 284 pp., p. 111; Harry C. J. Luke: *Britain and the South seas*, London-New York, 1945, 71 pp.

48. Thomas Astley: *A New general collection of voyages and travels: …*, London, 1745–1747, 4 vols.

49. Among Alexander Dalrymple's publications the following are of particular interest: *An account of the discoveries made in the south Pacific Ocean, previous to 1764. Part I …*, London, 1767, 103 pp.; *An historical collection of the several voyages and discoveries in the south Pacific Ocean*, London, 1770–1771, 2 vols.; *Memoir concerning the passages to and from China, June 1782*, London, 1787, 28 pp.; *Voyages dans la mer du Sud, par les Espagnols et les Hollandois*, Paris, 1774, 502 pp. For cartographic and pictorial records see his *Charts and views of the coasts of Africa, … China … including various plans of islands and harbors in the Atlantic, Indian and Pacific oceans*, London, 1765–1836, 8 pp. of MSS notes and 149 maps.

50. John Hawkesworth (comp.): *An account of the voyages undertaken by the order of His present Majesty for making discoveries in the Southern hemisphere, and successively performed by Commodore Byron, Captain Wallis, Captain Cartaret, and Captain Cook …*, London, 1773, 3 vols.; Robert E. Gallagher (ed.): "Byron's journal of his circumnavigation, 1764–1766," *Hakly. Soc. Works, Series 2*, vol. 122, pp. 1–230, Cambridge, 1964; and John Byron: *The narrative of the Honourable John Byron (Commodore in a late expedition round the world … 1740 … 1746)*, London, 1780, 264 pp.

51. John Hawkesworth (comp.): *ibid.*; Hugh Carrington (ed.): "The discovery of Tahiti; a journal of the second voyage of H. M. S. Dolphin round the world under the command of Captain Wallis, R.N., in the years 1766, 1767, and 1768, written by her master," *Hakly. Soc. Works, Series 2*, vol. 98, pp. 1–291, London, 1948; and Teuira Henry: "Wallis, the discoverer of Tahiti," *Polyn. Soc., Journ.*, vol. 13, pp. 122–125, Wellington, N. Z., 1904.

52. Jacobus A. Van der Chijs: "Philip Cartaret in Nederlandsch-Indie," *Tijdschrift voor Indische Taal-, Land- en Volkenkunde*, vol. 34, pp. 1–61, Leyden, 1891; Andrew Sharp: "Cartaret's course in Solomon waters," *Polyn. Soc., Journ.*, vol. 70 (4), p. 497, Wellington, N. Z., 1961; and especially the scholarly work by Helen Wallis (ed.): "Cartaret's voyage round the world, 1766–1769," *Hakly. Soc. Works, Series 2*, vols. 124–125, Cambridge, 1965.

53. St. George's Channel and Byron Strait.

54. There is a large body of literature about James Cook and his accomplishments. The following are a few representative examples: Otto Baschin: "James Cook: der grösste Entdeckungsreisende aller Zeiten," *Deutsche Rundschau*, vol. 218, pp. 135–141, Berlin, 1929; John C. Beaglehole: "On the character of Captain James Cook," *Geogr. Journ.*, vol. 122 (4), pp. 417–429, London, 1956; Léon Lemonnier: . . . *Le capitaine Cook et l' exploration de l'Océanie*, 1940, 250 pp.; J. Holland Rose: "Captain Cook and the founding of British power in the Pacific," *Geogr. Journ.*, vol. 73, pp. 102–110, London, 1929; Maurice Thiéry: *The life and voyages of Captain Cook*, London, 1929, 237 pp.; and Maurice Thiéry: *Captain Cook, navigator and discoverer*, New York, 1930, 265 pp.

For bibliographical references see Rolf Du Rietz: *Captain James Cook: A bibliography of literature printed in Sweden before 1819*, Upsala, 1960, 28 pp.; Maurice G. Holmes: *Captain James Cook, R. N., F.R.S., a bibliographical excursion*, London, 1952, 103 pp.; James Jackson: "James Cook, 27 Octobre [1728]–14 Février 1779; cartographie et bibliographie," *Société Géogr., Series 6*, vol. 17, pp. 481–538, Paris, 1879; and S. Roberts: "Captain Cook's voyages: A bibliography of the French translations, 1772–1800," *Journ. of Documentation*, vol. 3, pp. 160–176, London, 1947.

55. For the role of the Royal Society of London in supporting the expeditions and in publishing scientific results see especially Royal Society of London: *Philosophical Transactions*, vols. 55 (1771)–75 (1785). For example see "XLIII. Observations made, by appointment of the Royal Society, at King George's Island in the South Sea; by . . . Lieut. James Cook, of his Majesty's Ship the Endeavour," vol. 61, pp. 397–432, London, 1772. As to the Society's role in Cook's explorations we note for example that ". . . In 1771 the Council were actively engaged at the request of the Admiralty in drawing up instructions for the expedition of discovery which was to be dispatched under Captain Cook; . . . ," Henry Lyons and others (comp.): *The record of the Royal Society of London for the promotion of natural knowledge*, London, 1940, 578 pp., pp. 46–47, see also pp. 162 and 166.

56. For representative examples of his scientific abilities and accomplishments see Frank Dyson: "Captain Cook as an astronomer," *Geogr. Journ.*, vol. 73, pp. 117–122, London, 1929; H. P. Douglas: "Cook as an hydrographical surveyor," *Geogr. Journ.*, vol. 73, pp. 110–116, London, 1929; H. P. P. Herdman: "Some notes on sea ice observed by Captain James Cook, R. N., during his circumnavigation of Antarctica, 1772–1775," *Journ. Glaciology*, vol. 26, pp. 534–541, London 1959; Elmer D. Merrill: "The botany of Cook's voyages and its significance in relation to anthropology, biogeography, and history," *Chronica Botanica*, vol. 14 (5–6), pp. 163–383, Waltham, Mass., 1954; and Raleigh A. Skelton: "Captain James Cook as a hydrographer," *Mariner's Mirror*, vol. 40, pp. 92–119, London, 1954.

57. James Cook: "XXIV. An observation of an eclipse of the sun at the island of New-foundland, August 5, 1766, by Mr. James Cook, with the longitude of the place of observation deduced from it," *Philosophical Transactions . . . of the Royal Society of London*, vol. 57 (1), pp. 215–220, London, 1768.

58. For the Royal Society's interest in this event and in James Cook's expedition's role in this see *Philosophical Transactions of the Royal Society of London*, vols. 58 (1768)–61 (1771).

59. The best source of information is John C. Beaglehole's "The journals of Captain James Cook on his voyages of discovery. Vol. 1. The voyage of the Endeavour, 1768–1771," *Hakly. Soc. Works, Extra Series*, no. 34, 284 and 684 pp., Cambridge, 1955. In his remarkably complete research and careful scholarly editorial work the senior author had the able assistance of James A. Williamson, J. W. Davidson, and Raleigh A. Skelton. Four volumes and a portfolio have been programmed for publication. Volumes 1 and 2 and the portfolio have been published. Volume 3 in two parts was in the press in 1966. The excellent portfolio was edited by Raleigh A. Skelton as "The journals of Captain James Cook on his voyages of discovery . . . Charts and views, drawn by Cook and his officers and reproduced from the original manuscripts," *Hakly. Soc. Extra Series*, 8 pp. of text and 58 plates, Cambridge, 1955. Assembling and editing this large work is ably discussed by John C. Beaglehole in his "Some problems of editing Cook's journals," *Historical Studies, Australia and New Zealand*, vol. 8 (29), pp. 20–31, Melbourne, 1957.

For references to illustrative materials created during the voyages see especially Raleigh A. Skelton: "The graphic records," in John C. Beaglehole (ed.): *vol. 1, ibid.*, pp. cclxv–cclxxi and vol. 2 [note 62], pp. clviii–clxiv.

The number of publications about Captain Cook and his accomplishments is large. For recent bibliographic references see Edward G. Cox (comp.): "A reference guide to the literature of travel, vol. 2. The new world," *Univ. of Wash. Publ. Languages and Literature*, vol. 10, pp. 1–391, Seattle, 1938; and Sydney A. Spence (comp.): *Captain James Cook, R. N., 1728–1779; a bibliography of his voyages, to which is added other works relating to his life, conduct, and nautical achievements*, Mitcham, Engl., 1960, 50 pp.

For accounts of all voyages and general references thereto see especially James Cook: *Cook's voyages . . . 1764–1780*, London, 1773–1784, 8 vols. and atlas; James Cook: *A collection of voyages round the world . . .* , London, 1790, 6 vols.; James Cook: *The three voyages of Captain James Cook round the world*, London, 1821, 7 vols.; and A. Grenfell Price (ed.): *The explorations of Captain James Cook in the Pacific, as told by selections of his own journals, 1768–1779*, New York, 1958, 292 pp. Of special interest are William B. Clark: "A Franklin postscript to Captain Cook's voyages," *Amer. Philos. Soc. Proc.*, vol. 98, pp. 400–405, Philadelphia, Pa., 1954; F. W. Howay: "Some notes on Cook's and Vancouver's ships, 1776–80, 1791–95," *Wash. Hist. Quart.*, vol. 21, pp. 268–270, Seattle, 1930; and F. L. Parker and J. D. Somerville: "Cook's log and journal dates," *Roy. Geogr. Soc. Australasia, So. Austr. Br., Proc.*, vol. 47, pp. 97–113, Adelaide, 1946.

In addition to John C. Beaglehole's definitive work, above, the following references are of interest: John M. Gwyther: *Captain Cook and the South Pacific; the voyage of the "Endeavour," 1768–1771*, Boston, 1955, 269 pp.; Sydney Parkinson: *A journal of a voyage to the South seas, in His Majesty's ship, the Endeavour . . .* , London, 1773, 212 pp.; Lynette Roberts: *The Endeavour: Captain Cook's first voyage to Australia*, London, 1954, 280 pp.; Paula Wagner: *. . . James Cook's erste Entdeckungsreise in die Südsee (1768–1771) . . .* , Münster, 1934, 122 pp.; Gunnar Wallén: "Kapten Cooks första och andra resa i Stilla havet," *Jorden Runt*, vol. 20, pp. 105–122, 1948; and George A. Wood: *The voyage of the Endeavour*, Melbourne, Austr., 1944, 116 pp. Special subjects include Philip G. King: *Comments on Cook's log (H. M. S. Endeavour, 1770) with extracts, charts and sketches*, Sydney, Austr., 1892; and H. Alan Lloyd: "A link with Captain Cook and H.M.S. Endeavour," *Endeavour: . . .* , vol. 10, pp. 200–204, London, 1951.

60. Edouard T. Charton: "James Cook, navigateur anglais—Nouvelle Zélande—Nouvelle Galles," in his *Voyageurs Anciens et Modernes*, pp. 351–438, Paris, 1857; and A. H. and A. W. Reed (eds.): *Captain Cook in New Zealand . . .* , Wellington, N. Z., 1951, 261 pp.

61. J. W. Forsyth: "Cook's debt to Torres. Some notes on the history of the exploration and cartography of Torres Strait," an unpublished paper read to a group of Sydney historians in 1955. A copy of this paper has been deposited in the Mitchell Library in Sydney, Australia.

62. The definitive and most scholarly work on Cook's second voyage is John C. Beaglehole (ed.): "The journals of Captain James Cook on his voyages of discovery, vol. 2. The voyage of the Resolution and Adventure, 1772–1775," *Hakly. Soc., Extra Series*, vol. 35, pp. 170 + 1021, Cambridge, 1961. See also James Cook: *A voyage towards the South pole, and round the world . . . 1772, 1773, 1774, and 1775 . . .* , London, 1777, 2 vols.; and David Henry (ed.?): *Journal of the Resolution's voyage in 1772, 1773, 1774 and 1775. On discovery to the southern hemisphere . . .* , London, 1775, 328 pp.

63. The definitive work on Cook's third voyage should be John C. Beaglehole's forthcoming vol. 3 (in two parts) of his "The journals of Captain James Cook on his voyages of discovery . . ." being published by the Hakluyt Society in its *Extra Series*. The following published accounts are of value: James Cook: *A voyage to the Pacific Ocean . . . Performed under the direction of Captains Cook, Clarke, and Gore, . . . 1776, 1777, 1778, 1779, and 1780 . . .* , London, 1784, 3 vols.; William Ellis: *An authentic narrative of a voyage performed by Captain Cook . . . 1776–1780; . . .* , London, 1782, 2 vols.; John Ledyard: *A journal of Captain Cook's last voyage to the Pacific ocean, . . . 1776–1779 . . .* , Hartford, Conn., 1783, 208 pp.; James K. Mumford (ed.): *John Ledyard's journal of Captain Cook's last voyage*, Corvallis, Oregon, 1964, 264 pp.; and John Richman: *An authentic narrative of a voyage to the Pacific ocean, performed by Captain Cook, . . .* , Philadelphia, Pa., 1783, 2 vols. For a summary of ethnographic work accomplished on this voyage see Enrico H. Giglioli: "Appunti intorno ad una collezione etnografica fatta durante il terzo viaggio di Cook . . . ," *Archivio per l' Anthropologia e la Etnologia Firenze*, vol. 23, pp. 173–182, Florence, Italy, 1893.

64. Peter H. Buck: "Cook's discovery of the Hawaiian Islands," *Bernice P. Bishop, Mus. Rept. for 1944, Bull.* 186, pp. 26–44, Honolulu, 1945; Erik W. Dahlgren: ". . . Were the Hawaiian Islands visited by the Spaniards before their discovery by Captain Cook in 1778? . . . ," *Kungl. Svenska Vetensk. Handl.*, vol. 57 (4), pp. 1–220, Stockholm, 1917; John W. Coulter: "Great Britain in Hawaii: the Captain Cook monument," *Geogr. Journ.*, vol. 130 (2), pp. 256–261, London, 1964; and Henry Newbolt: "Captain James Cook and the Sandwich Islands," *Geogr. Journ.*, vol. 73, pp. 97–101, London, 1929.

65. N. Bianchi: *. . . Il capitano Cook alla ricerca del passaggio di Nord-Ouest . . .* , Torino, Italy, 1939, 299 pp.

66. For representative examples of the scientific work done by and biographies of the scientists see the following:

SIR JOSEPH BANKS: Agnes Arber: "Sir Joseph Banks and botany," *Chronica Botanica*, vol. 9 (2–3), pp. 94–106, Waltham, Mass., 1945; Joseph Banks and Daniel Solander: *Illustrations of Australian plants collected in 1770 during Captain Cook's voyage round the world in H. M. S. Endeavour . . .* ,

London, 1900–1905, 3 vols.; John C. Beaglehole (ed.): *The Endeavour journal of Joseph Banks, 1768–1771*, Sydney, 1962, 2 vols.; Joseph D. Hooker (ed.): *Journal of the Right Hon. Sir Joseph Banks . . . during Captain Cook's first voyage in H.M.S. Endeavour in 1768–71, . . .*, London, 1896, 466 pp.

GEORG FORSTER: George Forster: *A voyage round the world, in His Britannic Majesty's sloop, Resolution, commanded by Captain James Cook, during the years 1772, 3, 4, and 5*, London, 1777, 2 vols.; Georg Forster: *James Cook; die suche nach dem südland . . .*, Leipzig, 1922, 157 pp.; Georg Forster: *Werke; sämtliche Schriften, Tagebücher, Briefe*, Berlin, 1958–1963, 9 vols.;

JOHANN REINHOLD FORSTER: Johann R. Forster: *Observations made during a voyage round the world, a physical geography, natural history and ethic philosophy . . .*, London, 1778, 649 pp.; Johann R. Forster: *Histoire des découvertes et des voyages faits dans le Nord*, Paris, 1788, 2 vols.

SYDNEY PARKINSON: Sydney Parkinson: *A journal of a voyage to the South seas, in His Majesty's ship, the Endeavour. Faithfully transcribed from the papers of the late Sydney Parkinson, draughtsman to Joseph Banks, . . .*, London, 1773, 212 pp.; and Sydney Parkinson: "Die pflanzen der insel Outahitée, aus der Parkinsonischen reisebeschreibung gezogen, . . . ," *Naturforscher*, vol. 4, pp. 22–258, Halle, 1777.

ANDERS SPARRMAN: Owen Rutter (ed.): *A voyage round the world with Captain James Cook in H.M.S. Resolution, by Anders Sparrman*, London, 1944, 218 pp.; Jan G. K. Söderstrom: *. . . A. Sparrman's ethnographical collection from James Cook's 2nd expedition (1772–1775)*, Stockholm, 1939, 70 pp.; and Anders Sparrman: *Un compagnon suedois du capitaine James Cook au cours de son deuxième voyage*, Oslo, 1939, 91 pp.

WILLIAM BAYLY: *The original astronomical observations made in the course of a voyage to the Northern Pacific ocean, . . . In His Majesty's ships the Resolution and Discovery . . .*, London, 1782, 351 pp. g. *William Wales and William Bayly: The original astronomical observations, made in the course of a voyage towards the South Pole, . . . 1772–1775*, London, 1777, 385 pp.

67. For helpful references see J. N. L. Baker: *A history of geographical discovery and exploration*, London, 1948, 553 pp.; Edward G. Cox: ". . . A reference guide to the literature of travel, including voyages, geographical descriptions, adventures, shipwrecks and expeditions," *Univ. Wash. Publ. Language and Literature*, vols. 9–10, Seattle, Wash., 1935 and 1938; Edward Heawood: *A history of geographical discovery in the seventeenth and eighteenth centuries*, Cambridge, Engl., 1912, 475 pp.; Frederic W. Howay (ed.): "Letters concerning voyages of British vessels to the northwest coast of America, 1787–1809," *Oregon Hist. Quart.*, vol. 39, pp. 307–313, Portland, Ore., 1938; Lawrence C. Wroth: "The early cartography of the Pacific," *Bibl. Soc. Amer., Papers*, vol. 38 (2), pp. 87–268, New York, 1944; and references in note 1.

68. Georg Forster: *Geschichte der reisen, die seit Cook an der nordwest-und nordöst-küste von Amerika und in dem nordlichsten Amerika selbst von Meares, Dixon, Portlock, Coxe, Long . . .*, Berlin, 1791, 3 vols.; Nathaniel Portlock: *A voyage round the world; but more particularly to the northwest coast of America: performed in 1785, 1786, 1787, and 1788, in the King George and Queen Charlotte, Captains Portlock and Dixon*, London, 1789, 384 pp.

69. John Meares: *Voyages made in the years 1788 and 1789, from China to the north west coast of America. To which were prefixed, an introductory narrative of a voyage performed in 1786 . . .*, London, 1790, 372 pp.; and Frederic W. Howay (ed.): *The Dixon-Meares controversy . . .*, Toronto, 1929, 156 pp.

70. George Mortimer: *Observations and remarks made during a voyage to . . .*, Otaheite, Sandwich Islands, Owhyhee, the Fox Islands on the North West Coast of America . . .*, London, 1791, 71 pp.

71. James Barclay: *The voyages and travels of James Barclay containing many surprising adventures and interesting narratives*, London (?), 1778, 40 pp.

72. See for example William Combe (comp.): *A voyage to the south Atlantic and round Cape Horn into the Pacific Ocean, for the purpose of extending the spermaceti whale fisheries . . . from Capt. Colnett's notes*, London, 1798, 179 pp.; Frederic W. Howay (ed.): "The journal of Captain James Colnett aboard the Argonaut from April 26, 1789 to Nov. 3, 1791," *Publ. Champlain Soc.*, vol. 26, pp. 1–328, Toronto, 1940; Johan Hunter: *Johan Hunters resa til Nya Södra Wallis, åren 1787, följande; . . . af capit. Tench och King omkring jorden, åren 1790, 1791, 1792 . . .*, Stockholm, 1797, 283 pp.; George Keate: *An account of the Pelew Islands, situated in the western part of the Pacific Ocean. Composed from the journals and communications of Captain Henry Wilson . . .*, London, 1789, 256 pp.; Watkin Tench: *Narrative of the expedition to Botany bay; with an account of New South Wales, its productions, . . .*, London, 1789, 146 pp.; and John Trusler: *A descriptive account of the islands lately discovered in the South Seas . . .*, London, 1778, 311 pp.

73. C. H. Bertie: "Captain Arthur Phillip's first landing place in Botany Bay," *Roy. Austr. Hist. Soc., Journ. and Proc.*, vol. 38, pp. 107–126, Sydney, Austr., 1952; Arthur Phillip: *The voyage of*

Governor Phillip to Botany bay; with an account of the establishment of the colonies of Port Jackson and Norfolk island; . . ., London, 1789, 298 pp.; Owen Rutter (ed.): *The first fleet; the record of the foundation of Australia from its conception to the settlement at Sydney cove . . .*, London, 1937, 149 pp.; and John White: *Journal of a voyage to New South Wales, . . . 1787–1789*, London, 1790, 299 pp.

74. Thomas Gilbert: *Voyage from New South Wales to Canton, in the year 1788, with views of the islands discovered*, London, 1789, 85 pp.

75. See especially Edward Heawood: *op. cit.* [note 67], p. 309.

76. For accounts of the Bass and Flinders surveys see H. M. Cooper: *The unknown coast; being the explorations of Captain Matthew Flinders, R.N., along the shores of South Australia, 1802*, Adelaide, 1953, 173 pp.; Matthew Flinders: *A voyage to Terra Australis; undertaken for the purpose of completing the discovery of that vast country, and prosecuted in the years 1801, 1802, and 1803 . . .*, London, 1814, 2 vols. and atlas; Matthew Flinders: *Collection of charts and views of the coasts of Australia, together with 10 plates of botanical drawings*, London, 1814–1829, 30 illus.; J. D. Mack: "Matthew Flinders and the British Admiralty orders to H.M.S. Investigator," *Roy. Austr. Hist. Soc., Journ. and Proc.*, vol. 43, pp. 205–222, Sydney, Austr., 1957; George Mackaness (ed.): "Observations on the coasts of Van Dieman's Land, on Bass's Strait and its islands, . . . ," *Austr. Hist. Monogr.*, vol. 14, pp. 1–59, Sydney, 1946; Geoffrey Rawson (ed.): *Matthew Flinders' narrative of his voyage in the Schooner Francis 1798; . . .*, London, 1946, 100 pp.; Ernest Scott: *The life of Captain Matthew Flinders, R.N.*, Sydney, 1914, 492 pp.; and L. A. Whitington: *Matthew Flinders and Terra Australis*, Adelaide, 1951, 11 pp.

77. For William Bligh's accounts see his *A Narrative of the mutiny, on board His Majesty's Ship Bounty; . . .*, London, 1790, 88 pp.; and his *A voyage to the South Sea . . . in His Majesty's Ship the Bounty . . . including an account of the mutiny . . .*, London, 1792, 264 pp. For recent literature on this epic voyage see George C. Henderson: *The discoverers of the Fiji islands; Tasman, Cook, Bligh, Wilson, Bellingshausen*, London, 1933, 324 pp.; George Mackaness: "Captain William Bligh's discoveries and observations in Van Diemen's Land . . . ," *Austr. Hist. Monogr.*, vol. 8, pp. 1–51, Sydney, 1943; George Mackaness: *The life of Vice-Admiral William Bligh, R.N., F.R.S.*, Sydney, 1951, 573 pp.; James Morrison: *The journal of James Morrisson, boatswain's mate of the Bounty*, London, 1935, 242 pp.; Owen Rutter: *The log of the Bounty; . . .*, London, 1937, 2 vols.; Ernest Rhys (ed.): *A book of the Bounty by William Bligh and others*, London, 1938, 326 pp.

78. Edward Edwards: *Voyage of the H.M.S. Pandora dispatched to arrest the mutineers of the Bounty in the South Seas, 1790–91; being the narratives of Captain Edward Edwards, . . .*, London, 1915, 177 pp.

79. For information on geographical work of the London Missionary Society see especially John Campbell: *Maritime discovery and Christian missions, considered in their mutual relations*, London, 1840, 578 pp.; Richard Lovett: *The history of the London missionary society, 1796–1895*, London, 1899, 2 vols.; and Louis B. Wright: *Puritans in the South seas*, New York, 1936, 347 pp.

80. Bern Anderson: "The career of Captain George Vancouver," *U. S. Naval Inst. Proc.*, vol. 64 (427), pp. 1304–1311, Menasha, Wisc., 1938; Hardin Craig, Jr.: "Peter Puget: An active and zealous officer," *Mariner's Mirror*, vol. 38, pp. 34–52, Cambridge, Engl., 1952; F. V. Longstaff: "Captain George Vancouver, 1792–1942: A study in commemorative placenames," *Brit. Col. Hist. Quart.*, vol. 6, pp. 77–94, Vancouver, B. C., 1942; and Thomas Manly: "Vancouver's brig Chatham in the Columbia," *Oregon Hist. Quart.*, vol. 43 (4), pp. 318–327, Portland, Ore., 1942.

81. For Alexander Mackenzie's publications see his *Voyages from Montreal, on the river St. Lawrence, through the continent of North America, to the frozen and Pacific oceans; in the years 1789 and 1793 . . .*, London, 1802, 2 vols. in 1; and his *A narrative or journal of voyages and travels, through the north-west continent of America; in the years 1789 and 1793, by Mr. Maclauries*, London, 1802, 91 pp. For publications about Mackenzie see George Bryce: *. . . Mackenzie, Selkirk, Simpson; . . .*, New York and Toronto, 1926, 351 pp.; Milo M. Quaife: *. . . Alexander Mackenzie's voyage to the Pacific Ocean in 1793, . . .*, Chicago, 1931, 384 pp.; Walter N. Sage: ". . . Sir Alexander Mackenzie and his influence on the history of the North west," *Depts. Hist. and Political and Econ. Sci., Queen's Univ., Publ. no. 43*, pp. 1–18, Kingston, Ont., Canada; Walter Sheppe (ed.): *First man West; Alexander Mackenzie's journal of his voyage to the Pacific coast of Canada in 1793*, Berkeley, Calif., 1962, 366 pp.; and Humphrey H. Wrong: *Sir Alexander Mackenzie, explorer and fur-trader*, Toronto, 1927, 171 pp.

82. For the official account of George Vancouver's voyage see his *A voyage of discovery to the North Pacific Ocean, and round the world; in which the coast of north-west America, has been carefully examined and accurately surveyed; . . . in the years 1790, 1791, 1792, 1793, 1794, and 1795, . . .*, London, 1798, 3 vols. and atlas of sixteen plates; and his *A voyage of discovery to the North Pacific Ocean, and round the world; in which the coast of north-west America has been carefully examined and accurately*

surveyed . . . , London, 1801, 6 vols. For more recent accounts of the Vancouver expedition see Bern Anderson (ed.): "The Vancouver expedition: Peter Puget's journal of the exploration of Puget Sound, May 7–June 11, 1792," *Pacific Northwest Quart.*, vol. 30 (2), pp. 177–217, Seattle, Wash., 1939; J. Neilson Barry (ed.): "Broughton's reconnaissance of the San Juan Islands in 1792," *Wash. Hist. Quart.*, vol. 21, pp. 55–60, Seattle, Wash., 1930; Lalla R. Boone: *Captain George Vancouver on the Northwest Coast*, a Ph.D. thesis, Dept. of Hist., Univ. of Calif., Berkeley, Calif., 1939, 130 pp.; Erna Gunther: "Vancouver and the Indians of Puget Sound," *Pacific Northwest Quart.*, vol. 51 (1), pp. 1–12, Seattle, Wash., 1960; Edmond S. Meany (ed.): *A new Vancouver journal on the discovery of Puget Sound, by a member of the Chatham's crew*, Seattle, Wash., 1915, 43 pp.; Edmond S. Meany: *Vancouver's discovery of Puget sound; portraits and biographies of the men honored in the naming of geographic features of northwestern America*, New York, 1907, 344 pp.; and Marguerite E. Wilbur (ed.): *Vancouver in California, 1792–1794, the original account*, Los Angeles, 1953–1954, 2 vols. For biographical accounts of Vancouver see Bern Anderson: *Surveyor of the sea; the life and voyages of Captain George Vancouver*, Seattle, Wash., 1960, 274 pp.; and Roderick L. H. Haig-Brown: *Captain of the Discovery; the story of Captain George Vancouver*, Toronto, 1956, 181 pp.

83. For excellent background on Spanish exploration of this region see the following works by Henry R. Wagner: *The cartography of the northwest coast of America to the year 1800*, Berkeley, 1937, 2 vols.; "Some imaginary California geography," *Amer. Antiq. Soc., Proc., New Series*, vol. 36, pp. 83–129, Worcester, Mass., 1927; *Spanish explorations in the strait of Juan de Fuca*, Santa Ana, Calif., 1933, 323 pp.; and *Spanish voyages to the northwest coast of America*, San Francisco, 1929, 571 pp.

84. George F. Cotterill: *The climax of a world conquest; the story of Puget Sound, the modern Mediterranean of the Pacific*, Seattle, Wash., 1928, 226 pp.; Charles F. Newcombe: ". . . The first circumnavigation of Vancouver Island," *British Columbia. Provincial Archives Dept., Archives . . . Memoir*, no. 1, pp. 1–69, Victoria, B. C.; and Robert B. Whitebrook: "Vancouver's anchorages on Puget Sound," *Pacific Northwest Quart.*, vol. 44, pp. 115–124, Seattle, Wash., 1953.

85. Mary Blewitt: *Surveys of the seas; a brief history of British hydrography*, London, 1957, 168 pp.; John A. Edgell: *Sea surveys; Britain's contributions to hydrography*, London, 1965, 29 pp.; Great Britain, Hydrographic Office: *Charting the seas in peace and war; the story of the Hydrographic Department of the Admiralty over a hundred fifty years, 12th August 1795 to 12th August 1945*, London, 1947, 24 pp.; and Adrian H. W. Robinson: *Marine cartography in Britain: A history of the sea chart to 1855*, Leicester, Engl., 1962, 222 pp.

86. William Dampier: *op. cit.* [note 33].

87. Joseph Banks: *op. cit.* [note 66].

88. Robert Fitzroy: *op. cit.* [note 121]; and Charles R. Darwin: *op. cit.* [note 122].

89. See notes 134–142 for details.

90. Mountstuart Elphinstone: *The rise of the British power in the East*, . . . , London, 1887, 553 pp.; William P. Morrell: *Britain in the Pacific Islands*, Oxford, Engl., 1960, 454 pp.; and Guy H. Scholefield: *The Pacific, its past and future, and the policy of the great powers from the eighteenth century*, London, 1919, 346 pp.

91. See for example Edward Cox: "A reference guide to the literature of travel . . . ," *Univ. Wash. Publ. Language and Literature*, vol. 9, pp. 1–404, Seattle, Wash., 1935; and vol. 10, pp. 1–591, Seattle, Wash., 1938.

92. For example see Edward K. Chatterton: *Whalers and whaling*, New York, 1931, 251 pp.; William J. Dakin: *Whalemen adventures; the story of whaling in Australian waters and other southern seas related thereto, from the days of sails to modern times*, Sydney, 1934, 263 pp.

93. For example see William J. (ed.) and Sarah M. Smythe: *Ten months in the Fiji islands . . .*, Oxford, Engl., 1864, 282 pp.

94. For example see Frederick D. Bennett: *Narrative of a whaling voyage round the globe, from the year 1833 to 1836 . . .*, London, 1840, 2 vols.; Thomas B. Brassey: *The "Sunbeam," R. Y. S.; voyages and experiences in many waters*, . . . , London, 1918, 449 pp.; Annie (A.) Brassey: . . . *A voyage in the Sunbeam*, London, 1881, 64 pp.; John Coulter: *Adventures in the Pacific; . . .*, London, 1845, 290 pp.; John Coulter: *Adventures on the western coast of South America; . . .*, London, 1847, 2 vols.; Peter Dillon: *Narrative and successful result of a voyage in the South seas performed by order of the government of India, to ascertain the actual fate of La Pérouse's expedition . . .*, London, 1829, 2 vols.; Villiam Mariner: *An account of the natives of the Tonga Islands in the South Pacific Ocean . . .*, London, 1817, 2 vols.; John Morseby: *New Guinea & Polynesia. Discoveries & surveys in New Guinea and the D'Entrecasteaux Islands . . .*, London, 1876, 327 pp.; and John Turnbull: *A voyage round the world, in the years 1800, 1801, 1802, 1803, and 1804; . . .*, London, 1810, 364 pp.

95. For example see Kathleen E. P. Fitzpatrick (ed.): *Australian explorers; a selection from their writings; . . .*, London, 1958, 503 pp.; George Grimm: *The Australian explorers; . . . : being a narrative of discovery, from the landing of Captain Cook to the centennial year*, Melbourne and Sydney, 1888,

247 pp.; Robert L. Jack: *Northmost Australia; three centuries of exploration, discovery, and adventure in and around Cape York Peninsula*, . . . , London, 1921, 2 vols.; Ida L. Marriott: *Early explorers in Australia, from the log-books and journals* . . . , London, 1925, 651 pp.; John D. Rogers: . . . *Australasia*, Oxford, Engl., 1907, 2 vols. in 1, Ernest Scott (ed.): *Australian discovery* . . . , London, 1929, 2 vols.; Andrew Sharp: *The discovery of Australia*, Oxford, Engl., 1963, 338 pp.; A. S. White: "On the achievement of Scotsmen during the nineteenth century in the fields of geographical exploration and research," *Scottish Geogr. Mag.*, vol. 5, pp. 540–548 and 595–605, Edinburgh, 1889; C. H. Wright: *Conquering the continent; the story of the exploration and settlement of Australia*, Melbourne, 1960, 96 pp.; and Ian Wynd and Joyce Wood: *A map history of Australia*, Melbourne, 1963, 60 pp.

96. *Op. cit.* [note 76].

97. Geoffrey Rawson (ed.): *Matthew Flinders' narrative of his voyage in the schooner Francis, 1798; preceded and followed by notes on Flinders, Bass, the wreck of the Sydney Cove, &.*, London, 1946, 100 pp.

98. James Grant: *The narrative of a voyage of discovery, performed in His Majesty's vessel the Lady Nelson* . . . *in the years 1800, 1801, and 1802, to New South Wales*, London, 1803, 195 pp.

99. *Ibid.*

100. Lieutenant John Murray was appointed commander of the *Lady Nelson*, after sailing through Bass Strait for the first time. Subsequently Murray returned to this area to discover and to explore. See in Ida (Lee) Marriott: *Early explorers* . . . [note 1], pp. 114–115; Ernest Favenc: *The history of Australian exploration, 1788–1888*, Sydney, 1888, p. 53; and Andrew Sharp: *op. cit.* [note 95] pp. 229–232.

101. K. A. Austin: *The voyage of the Investigator, 1801–1803, Commander Matthew Flinders, R. N.*, Adelaide, 1964, 222 pp.; Harold M. Cooper: *The unknown coast; being the explorations of Captain Matthew Flinders, R. N., along the shores of South Australia*, 1802, Adelaide, 1953, 173 pp. and supplement, 93 pp., 1955; Matthew Flinders: "Observations on the coasts of Van Diemen's Land, on Bass's Strait and its islands, and on part of the coasts of New South Wales," *Australia Hist. Monogr.*, no. 14, pp. 1–59, Sydney, 1946; Matthew Flinders: *Collection of charts and views of the coasts of Australia, together with 10 plates of botanical drawings*, London, 1814–1829 ?, 16 charts and 14 plates of drawings; and T. M. Perry and Donald H. Simpson (eds.): *Drawings by William Westall, landscape artist on board H.M.S. Investigator during the circumnavigation of Australia by Captain Matthew Flinders, R. N., in 1801–1803*, London, 1962, 71 pp. For a biography of Flinders see Sidney J. Baker: *My own destroyer, a biography of Matthew Flinders, explorer and navigator*, Sydney, 1962, 146 pp.; and Ernest Scott: *The life of Captain Matthew Flinders, R. N.*, Sydney, 1914, 492 pp. For reference to Flinders' observations see Charles F. Beautemps-Beaupré: *An introduction to the practice of nautical surveying, and the construction of sea-charts; . . . and the Description of observations by which the longitude of places, on the coasts of Australia & have been settled; Captain Matthew Flinders*, London, 1823, 77 pp.

102. Matthew Flinders: *A voyage to Terra Australis; undertaken for the purpose of completing the discovery of that vast country, and prosecuted in the years 1801, 1802, and 1803* . . . , London, 1814, 2 vols. and an atlas. For examples of the scientific work by Flinders see his "Concerning the differences in the magnetic needle, on board the Investigator, arising from an alteration in the direction of the ship's head," *Roy. Soc. Philos. Trans.*, vol. 95, pp. 186–197, London, 1805; and "Observations upon the Marine barometer, made during the examination of the coasts of New Holland and New South Wales, in the years 1801, 1802, and 1803," *Roy. Soc. Philos. Trans.*, vol. 96, pp. 239–265, London, 1806.

103. The publications by Philip P. King include "Abstract from a meteorological journal kept at Port Stephens, New South Wales, during the years 1843, 4, 5, 6, and 1847," *Tasmanian Journ. of Natural Sci.*, vol. 3, pp. 465–468, Hobart, Tasmania, 1849; *Narrative of a survey of the intertropical and western coasts of Australia performed between the years 1818 and 1822* . . . *With an appendix, containing various subjects relating to hydrography and natural history*, London, 1827, 2 vols.; and "On the maritime geography of Australia," in Barron Field (ed.): *Geographical memoirs of New South Wales* . . . , London, 1825, 504 pp.

104. *Ibid.*

105. J. N. L. Baker: *A history of geographical discovery and exploration*, London, 1948, 553 pp., pp. 435–438. An excellent history of exploration of New Zealand and circumjacent areas is T. M. Hocken: "Some accounts of the earliest explorations in New Zealand, &c.," *Rept. Third Meeting Australasian Assoc. Adv. Sci., 1891*, pp. 254–270, Christchurch, N. Z., 1891. See also John R. Elder's "Discovery and exploration [of New Zealand]," in John H. Rose: *The Cambridge History of the British Empire, etc.*, vol. 7, London, 1929; *New Zealand, an outline history*, Oxford, Engl., 1928; and *The pioneer explorers of New Zealand*, London and Glasgow, 1929, 121 pp.

106. J. N. L. Baker: *ibid.*, p. 436; and T. M. Hocken: *ibid.*, pp. 257–258.

107. J. N. L. Baker: *ibid.*, p. 436; and T. M. Hocken: *ibid.*, p. 258.

108. Everard im Thurn and Leonard C. Wharton (eds.): "The journal of William Lockerby, sandalwood trader in the Fijian islands during the years, 1808–1809; . . . ," *Hakly. Soc., Works, Series 2,* vol. 52, pp. 1–250, London, 1925.

109. Ireland was captain of the British ship *Adhemar.* See in Andrew Sharp: *The discovery of the Pacific Islands,* Oxford, Engl., 1960, 259 pp., p. 219.

110. Patrickson was captain of the British ship *Good Hope.* See in Andrew Sharp: *ibid.*, pp. 199–200.

111. For references to the work of the London Missionary Society, see note 79.

112. Examples of this large source of information are George Bennett: *Gatherings of a naturalist in Australasia;* . . . , London, 1860, 456 pp.; George Bennett: *Wanderings in New South Wales, Batavia, Pedir coast, Singapore and China; being the journal of a naturalist in those countries, during 1832, 1833, and 1834,* London, 1834, 2 vols.; James Montgomery (comp.): *Journal of voyages and travels by Rev. Daniel Tyerman and George Bennett, esq. . . . between the years 1821 and 1829 . . . ,* London, 1831, 2 vols.; Thomas Williams and James Calvert: *Fiji and the Fijians,* New York, 1860, 551 pp.; William Ellis: *. . . Polynesian researches, during a residence of nearly eight years in the Society and Sandwich,* New York, 1833, 4 vols.; Sarah S. Farmer: *Tonga and the Friendly Islands; . . . ,* London, 1855, 427 pp.; William W. Gill: *Gems from the Coral Islands; . . . ,* London, 1856, 2 vols.; J. Inglis: *In the New Hebrides; . . . ,* London, 1887, 352 pp.; W. Lawry: *Friendly and Feejee islands; . . . ,* London, 1850, 303 pp.; George Turner: *Samoa, a hundred years ago and long before . . . ,* London, 1884, 395 pp.; and Thomas West: *Ten years in south-central Polynesia; . . . ,* London, 1865, 500 pp.

113. For references to the history and work of the Hydrographic Office of the British Admiralty see note 85.

114. Examples of this large source of information are John E. Erskine: *Journal of a cruise among the islands of the western Pacific, . . . in Her Majesty's ship Havannah,* London, 1853, 488 pp.; Thomas H. Hood: *Notes on a cruise in H.M.S. "Fawn," in the western Pacific in 1862,* Edinburgh, Scot., 1863; Julian Huxley (ed.): *T. H. Huxley's diary of the voyage of H. M. S. Rattlesnake,* London, 1935, 371 pp.; John Macgillivray: *Narrative of the voyage of H.M.S. Rattlesnake commanded by the late Captain Owen Stanley . . . during the years 1846–50 . . . ,* London, 1852, 2 vols.; Albert H. Markham: *The cruise of the "Rosario" amongst the New Hebrides and Santa Cruz Islands, . . . ,* London, 1873, 304 pp.; John Milner and Oswald W. Brierly: *The cruise of H.M.S. Galatea, . . . in 1867–1868,* London, 1869, 487 pp.; John Moresby: *New Guinea & Polynesia . . . a cruise . . . of H.M.S. Basilisk by Captain John Moresby, R. N.;* and Frederick Walpole: *Four years in the Pacific. In Her Majesty's ship "Collingwood." From 1844 to 1848 . . . ,* London, 1849, 2 vols.

115. George A. Byron: *Voyage of H.M.S. Blonde to the Sandwich islands in the years 1824–1825,* London, 1826, 260 pp.

116. Andrew Bloxam: "Diary of Andrew Bloxam, naturalist of the "Blonde" on her trip from England to the Hawaiian islands, 1824–25," *Bernice P. Bishop Mus., Spec. Publ.* no. 10, pp. 1–96, Honolulu, 1925.

117. For the publications by Frederick W. Beechey see his *Narrative of a voyage to the Pacific and Beering's strait, to cooperate with the polar expeditions: . . . in the years 1825, 26, 27, 28,* London, 1831, 2 vols.; and *A voyage of discovery towards the North pole performed in His Majesty's ships Dorothea and Trent, under the command of Captain David Buchan, R. N., 1818; to which is added, a summary of all the early attempts to reach the Pacific by way of the Pole,* London, 1843, 351 pp. For accounts by others see William F. Ainsworth: "Analysis of a narrative of a voyage to the Pacific and Beering's Strait . . . under the command of Capt. F. W. Beechey in 1825–8," *Geogr. Journ.,* vol. 1, pp. 193–222, London, 1833; Frederick W. Beechey: *An account of a visit to California, 1826–27,* San Francisco, 1941, 74 + 9 pp.; Robert Huish: *A narrative of the voyages and travels of Captain Beechey . . . to the Pacific and Behring's Straits; performed in the years 1825, 26, 27, and 28 . . . ,* London, 1836?, 704 pp.; and Robert Huish: *The North-west passage; a history of the most remarkable voyages made in search of the North-west passage from the earliest periods,* London, 1851, 418 pp. For examples of the scientific results see William J. Hooker: *The botany of Captain Beechey's voyage; . . . , 1825, 26, 27, and 28,* London, 1841, 485 pp.; and J. Richardson: *The zoology of Captain Beechey's voyage; . . . , 1825, 26, 27, and 28,* London, 1839. 186 pp. and 44 plates.

118. For an account of this attempt see William E. Parry: *Journal of a third voyage for the discovery of a northwest passage, from the Atlantic to the Pacific; performed in the years 1824–25 in His ᶜMajesty's ships Hecla and Fury, under the orders of Captain William Edward Parry . . . ,* London, 1826, 186 + 151 pp.

119. Beechey had learned while in Kamchatka that Parry had returned to England because he found it impossible to penetrate the heavy ice in the western portion of the Northwest Passage.

120. For Robert Fitzroy's account see his *Narrative of the surveying voyages of His Majesty's ships Adventure and Beagle, between the years 1826 and 1836, . . .*, London, 1839, 3 vols. For hydrographical works by Philip P. King that resulted from these and later surveys see his *Directions for the inner route from Sydney to Torres Strait, surveyed by P. P. King*, Sydney, 1847; *Instructions nautiques sur les côtes de la Patagonie . . . traduites de l'ouvrage anglais du capitaine P. P. King*, Paris, 1835, 247 pp.; and *Sailing directions for the coasts of eastern and western Patagonia . . . Being the result of a voyage performed in H. M. sloops Adventure and Beagle . . . between the years 1826 and 1830 . . .*, London, 1832, 155+ pp. Examples of King's published scientific observations are "Observations on the intensity of magnetism made during a voyage of survey of the southern extremity of South America," *Magazin for Naturvidenskaberne*, vol. 8, pp. 106–120, Christiania, Sweden, 1827; "On the animals of the Straits of Magellan," *Zoological Journ.*, vol. 3, pp. 422–432 and vol. 4, pp. 91–105, London, 1928; "Some observations upon the geography of the southern extremity of South America, . . .," *Roy. Geogr. Soc., Journ.*, vol. 1, pp. 155–174, London, 1832; and "Observations on oceanic birds, particularly those of the genus Diomedea, Linn.," *Zoological Soc., Proc.*, vol. 2, pp. 128–129, London, 1834.

121. For the best contemporary account of this voyage see Robert Fitzroy: *ibid.*, vols. 2, Appendix to vol. 2, and vol. 3. Vol. 2, entitled "Proceedings of the Second Expedition, 1831–1836, under command of Captain Robert Fitz-Roy, R.N.," was published in London in 1839 (694 pp.). Vol. 3, entitled "Journal and remarks, 1831–1836," published in London in 1839 (615 pp.), was written by Charles Darwin. For a brief statement on surveying methods see "Notes on surveying a wild coast," Appendix to vol. 2, pp. 202–208, and accompanying maps.

122. In the preface to his account of the voyage (*ibid.*) Charles Darwin notes ". . . that it was in consequence of a wish expressed by Captain Fitz Roy, of having some scientific person on board, . . . that I volunteered my services, which received, through the kindness of the hydrographer, Captain Beaufort, the sanction of the Lords of the Admiralty . . . ." For biographical information on Darwin see Charles R. Darwin: *The autobiography of Charles Darwin, . . .*, New York, 1929, 64 pp.; Francis Darwin (ed.): *The life and letters of Charles Darwin, including an autobiographical chapter*, New York, 1888, 2 vols.; Bern Dibner: *Darwin of the Beagle*, New York, 1964, 143 pp.; Geoffrey H. Wells: *Charles Darwin, a portrait*, New York, 1938, 359 pp.; and *Charles Darwin's works*, New York, n.d., 18 vols.

123. For example see his *The descent of man, and selection in relation to sex*, London, 1871, 2 vols.; and *On the origin of the species by means of natural selection, or the preservation of favoured races in the struggle for life*, London, 1859, 502 pp.

124. For several versions of this work see Nora Barlow (ed.): *Charles Darwin's diary of the voyage of H.M.S. "Beagle,"* Cambridge, Engl., 1934, 451 pp.; Charles R. Darwin: *A naturalist's voyage round the world in H.M.S. "Beagle,"* London, 1930, 530 pp.; Charles R. Darwin: *The voyage of the Beagle*, Garden City, N. Y., 1962, 524 pp.; and Millicent E. Selsam: *The voyage of the Beagle . . .*, New York, 1959, 327 pp.

125. Charles R. Darwin (ed.): *The zoology of the voyage of H.M.S. Beagle, under command of Captain Fitzroy, R. N., during the years 1832 to 1836 . . .*, London, 1839–43, 5 vols.

126. For examples of Charles R. Darwin's publications in this field see his "Geological notes made during a survey of the east and west coasts of South America in the years 1832, 1833, 1834, and 1835; . . .," *Geol. Soc., Proc.*, vol. 2, pp. 210–212, London, 1838; *Geological observations on coral reefs, volcanic islands, and on South America: . . .*, London, 1851, 1 vol.; *Journal of researches into the natural history and geology of the countries visited . . .*, New York, 1846, 2 vols.; "Observations of proofs of recent elevation on the coast of Chili, . . .," *Geol. Soc., Proc.*, vol. 2, pp. 446–449, London, 1838; and "On the connexion of certain volcanic phaenomena, and on the formation of mountain-chains and the effects of continental elevations"; *Geol. Soc., Trans.*, vol. 5, pp. 601–632, London, 1840.

127. For examples of Charles R. Darwin's publications in this field see his "The structure and distribution of coral reefs," *Geol. Soc., Journ.*, vol. 12, pp. 115–119, London, 1842; and *The structure and distribution of coral reefs, . . .*, London, 1874, 278 pp.

128. Edward Belcher: *Narrative of the voyage round the world, performed in Her Majesty's ship Sulphur, during the years 1836–1842, . . .*, London, 1843, 2 vols. For an account of the scientific results see Richard B. Hinds (ed.): *The zoology of the voyage of H.M.S. Sulphur, under command of Captain Sir Edward Belcher . . . during the years 1836–42*, London, 1844, 2 vols.

129. Edward Belcher: *ibid.* For examples of Belcher's scientific contributions see his *A treatise*

on nautical surveying: containing an outline of the duties of the nautical surveyor: . . . , London, 1835, 290 pp.; and *The sailor's word-book: an alphabetical digest of nautical terms, . . .* , London, 1867, 744 pp.

130. The accounts of this voyage by Berthold C. Seemann includes his *Narrative of the voyage of H.M.S. Herald during the years 1845–1851, under the command of Captain Henry Kellett . . .* , London, 1853, 2 vols.

131. Scientific publications by Seemann include his *The botany of the voyage of H.M.S. Herald under the command of Captain Henry Kellett . . . during the years 1845–51*, London, 1852–57, 483 pp.

132. Julius L. Brenchley: *Jottings during the cruise of H.M.S. Curaçoa among the South Sea Islands in 1865*, London, 1873, 487 pp. For a résumé of the work in natural history see pp. 353–474.

133. These pioneering activities are discussed in William B. Carpenter: "Preliminary report . . . of dredging operations in the seas to the north of the British Islands, . . . ," *Roy. Soc., Proc.*, vol. 17, pp. 168–200, London, 1869; William B. Carpenter and J. Given Jeffreys: "Report on deep-sea researches carried on during the months of July, August and September 1870, . . . ," *Roy. Soc., Proc.*, vol. 19, pp. 146–221, London, 1871; and Charles W. Thomson: "On dredgings and deep-sea soundings in the South Atlantic, . . . ," *Roy. Soc., Proc.*, vol. 22, pp. 423–428, London, 1873–74.

134. See Royal Society of London. Circumnavigation Committee: ". . . Report of the Circumnavigation Committee . . . relative to the scientific work of the proposed expedition of Her Britannic Majesty's ship 'Challenger' round the world," *Bur. Nav., Navy Scientific Papers*, no. 4, pp. 1–15, Wash., D. C., 1872. For the official publications of the expedition see Great Britain: Challenger Office: *Report on the scientific results of the voyage of H.M.S. Challenger during the years 1873–1876 . . .* , London, 1880–95, 40 vols. in 44. For this reference see vol. 1, "Narrative . . . ," p. 1.

135. For an excellent description of the scientific facilities aboard ship see Great Britain: *ibid.*, vol. 1, "Narrative . . . ," pp. 1–20. The civilian scientific staff of the *Challenger* included Charles Wyville Thomson, Director; J. Y. Buchanan, chemist; H. N. Moseley, naturalist; John Murray, naturalist; R. von Willemoes-Suhm, naturalist; and J. J. Wild, secretary and artist.

136. Great Britain: *ibid.*, p. 10.

137. In addition to the voluminous official report of the expedition noted above [note 135] the following general accounts give a good description of the track and operations: George G. Campbell: *Log letters from "The Challenger,"* London, 1876, 448 pp.; Thomas F. Gaskell: *Under the deep oceans; twentieth century voyages of discovery*, London, 1960, 239 pp.; George S. Ritchie: *Challenger, the life of a survey ship*, New York, 1958, 249 pp.; William J. J. Spry: *The cruise of Her Majesty's ship "Challenger" voyages over many seas, scenes in many lands*, London, 1877, 388 pp.; Herbert Swire: *The voyage of the Challenger; . . .* , London, 1938, 2 vols.; and John J. Wild: *At anchor; a narrative of experiences afloat and ashore during the voyage of H.M.S. "Challenger" from 1872–1876*, London & Belfast, 1878, 198 pp.

138. In addition to the voluminous official publication of forty volumes, scientists who accompanied the expedition and those who examined, described, and interpreted the results and the collections published their studies in a wide variety of scientific periodicals. Examples of these include the following: Albert C. L. G. Gunther: *Report on the shore fishes, deep-sea fishes, pelagic fishes collected by H.M.S. "Challenger,"* New York, 1963, 82 + 335 + 46 pp. and an atlas; Henry N. Moseley: *Notes by a naturalist. An account of observations made during the voyage of H.M.S. "Challenger" round the world in the years 1872–1876*, London, 1892, 540 pp.; Thomas H. Tizard: *Narrative of the cruise of H.M.S. Challenger with a general account of the scientific results of the expedition . . .* , Edinburgh, Scotl., 1885, 1 vol. in 2; and Rudolph von Willemoes-Suhm: "Von der Challenger—Expedition," *Zeitschr. Wissensch. Zool.*, vol. 24, pp. 9–23, 1874.

139. Great Britain: *op. cit.* [note 134]. See also Challenger Expedition, 1872–1876: *"Challenger" expedition. List of observing stations, printed for the use of the naturalists engaged in preparing the account of the voyage*, Edinburgh (?), 1877, 55 pp.

140. See especially Great Britain. Hydrographic Office: *. . . Report on ocean soundings and temperatures . . . obtained by H.M.S. Challenger during the years 1873–76*, London, 1874–76, 7 vols.; and John Murray: *A summary of the scientific results obtained at the sounding, dredging, and trawling stations of H.M.S. Challenger . . .* , Edinburgh, Scot., 1895, 1 vol. in 2 and 54 maps.

141. See especially John Y. Buchanan: ". . . Preliminary report . . . on chemical and geological work done on board H.M.S. 'Challenger,' " *Roy. Soc., Proc.*, vol. 24, pp. 593–623, London, 1876; and Auguste Daubrée: "Deep-sea deposits," *Smiths. Inst. Ann. Rept. 1893*, pp. 545–566, Wash., D. C., 1894.

142. For example see Henry N. Moseley: "On the colouring matters of various animals, and especially deep-sea forms dredged by H.M.S. Challenger," *Quart. Journ. Microsc. Sci.*, vol. 17, pp. 1–23, London, 1877; and John Murray: "Preliminary report on specimens of the sea bottoms obtained in the soundings, dredgings and trawlings of H.M.S. Challenger in the years 1873–75 . . . ," *Amer. Journ. Sci. Arts, Series 3*, vol. 12, pp. 255–270, New Haven, Conn., 1876.

Chapter 13

GEOGRAPHICAL EXPLORATION BY THE UNITED STATES

1. The best primary source of information about the activities of the United States in the Pacific Basin is the large volume of official records of agencies of the Federal government in the National Archives in Washington, D. C. The records that are especially pertinent are: *General Records of the United States Government* (Record Group 11); *Records of the Coast and Geodetic Survey* (Record Group 23); *Records of the United States Coast Guard* (Record Group 26); *Records of the Hydrographic Office* (Record Group 37); *Naval Records Collection of the Office of Naval Records and Library* (Record Group 45); *Records of the United States Senate* (Record Group 46); *General Records of the Department of the Navy* (Record Group 80); *Records of the Naval Observatory* (Record Group 78); *General Records of the Department of State* (Record Group 59); and *Records of the Office of the Secretary of War* (Record Group 107). Finding aids, such as *Preliminary Inventories*, *Special Lists*, guides, and descriptive catalogs have been prepared to cover selected portions of the records of these agencies.

There is material of value to the serious researcher in the Manuscript Division and in the Geography and Map Division of the Library of Congress in Washington, D. C.

Reference should also be made to the many series of Government publications, most important of which are the documents of the House of Representatives and of the Senate which are published in the so-called Congressional Serial set. See especially Laurence F. Schmeckebier and Roy B. Eastin: *Government publications and their use*, Wash., D. C., 1961, 476 pp.

GENERAL WORKS: S. Whittemore Boggs: "American contributions to geographical knowledge of the central Pacific," *Geogr. Rev.*, vol. 28 (2), pp. 177–192, New York, 1938; James M. Callahan: "American relations in the Pacific and the Far East, 1784–1900," *Johns Hopkins Univ. Studies Hist. and Polit. Sci.*, vol. 19, pp. 1–177, Baltimore, Md., 1901, see especially pp. 13–24; George F. Emmons (comp.): *The navy of the United States from the commencement, 1775–1853, with a brief history of each vessel's service and fate*, Wash., D. C., 1853, 208 pp.; Herman R. Friis: "United States scientific geographical exploration of the Pacific Basin, 1783–1899," *U. S. National Archives Publication*, no. 62–2, pp. 1–26, Wash., D. C., 1961; Gordon Greenwood: *Early American-Australian relations; from the arrival of the Spaniards in America to the close of 1830*, Melbourne, 1944, 184 pp.; Alfred L. Lomox: "Hawaii-Columbia river trade in early days," *Oregon Hist. Quart.*, vol. 43, pp. 328–338, Portland, Ore., 1942; Raymond A. Rydell: *Cape Horn to the Pacific; the rise and decline of an ocean highway*, Berkeley, Calif., 1952, 213 pp.; and Shunzo Sakamaki: ". . . Japan and the United States, 1790–1853," *Asiatic Soc. Japan, Trans.*, Series 2, vol. 18, pp. 1–204, Tokyo, 1939. For additional excellent references see in the following notes.

MARINE AND RELATED SOCIETIES AND MUSEUMS: There are in the United States, especially in New England, a number of exceptionally valuable depositories of records, personal papers, graphic materials, and museum specimens, which are helpful sources of information on the history of geographical exploration of the Pacific Basin, especially by non-government personnel. For an excellent list of these museums see in American Association of Museums: *Museums directory of the United States and Canada*, Wash., D. C., 1039 pp.

2. For a good bibliographical source see: James W. Snyder: "A bibliography for the early American China trade, 1784–1815," *Americana . . .*, vol. 34 (2), pp. 297–345, New York, 1940. For general works see: Harold W. Bradley: *The American frontier in Hawaii, the pioneers, 1789–1843*, Stanford, Calif., 1942, 488 pp.; Harold W. Bradley: "The Hawaiian Islands and the fur trade, 1785–1813," *Pacific Northwest Quart.*, vol. 30 (3), pp. 275–299, Seattle, Wash., 1939; Henri Cordier: ". . . Americains et Français a Canton au XVIIIe siècle," *Soc. Americanistes Journ.*, vol. 2, pp. 1–13, Paris, 1898; Foster Rhea Dulles: *The old China trade*, New York, 1930, 228 pp.; Ernest S. Dodge: *New England and the South Seas*, Cambridge, Mass., 1965, 216 pp.; Ernest S. Dodge: "Early American contacts in Polynesia and Fiji," *Amer. Philos. Soc., Proc.*, vol. 107 (2), pp. 102–106, Philadelphia, Pa., 1963; Agnes D. Hewes: *Two oceans to Canton; the story of the old China trade*, New York, 1944, 184 pp.; Lawrence H. Leder: "American trade to China, 1800–1802. Some statistical notes," *Amer. Nept.*, vol. 23 (2), pp. 212–218, Salem, Mass., 1963; Kenneth S. Latourette: ". . . Voyages of American ships to China, 1784–1844," *Connecticut Acad. Arts and Sci., Trans.*, vol. 28 (4), pp. 237–271, New Haven, Conn., 1927; Samuel E. Morison: "Boston traders in the Hawaiian Islands, 1789–1823," *Mass. Hist. Soc., Proc.*, vol. 54, pp. 9–47, Boston, 1922; Samuel E. Morison: *The maritime history of Massachusetts, 1783–1860*, Boston and New York, 1921, 400 pp.; James D. Phillips: *East India voyages of Salem vessels before 1800*, Salem, Mass. (?), 1943, 75 pp.; James D. Phillips: "The voyage of the *Margaret* in 1801, the first Salem voyage to Japan," *Amer. Antiq. Soc., Proc.*, vol. 54 (2), pp. 313–339, Worcester, Mass., 1945; Wallace P. Strauss: *Americans in Polynesia*,

1783–1842, East Lansing, Mich., 1964, 187 pp.; Wallace P. Strauss: *Early American interest and activity in Polynesia, 1783–1842*, New York, 1958, 328 pp., a Ph.D. thesis, Columbia University; James W. Snyder, Jr.: *American trade in Eastern seas; a brief survey of its early years, 1783–1815*, New York, 1938, 20 pp.; James W. Snyder, Jr.: "Spices, silks and teas—cargoes of the old China trade," *Americana*, vol. 36 (1), pp. 7–26, New York, 1942; Henry R. Wagner: "The first American vessel in California Monterey in 1796," *Early Calif. Travel Series*, vol. 22, pp. 1–33, Los Angeles, 1954; Evelyn M. Waugh: *The "Boston ships" in the Pacific, 1787–1840* ..., Berkeley, Calif., 1926, 131 pp., an M.A. thesis, University of California; William B. Weeden: "Early oriental commerce in Providence," *Mass. Hist. Soc., Third Series*, vol. 1, pp. 236–278, Boston, 1907; and William B. Weeden: *Economic and social history of New England, 1620–1789*, Boston and New York, 1891, 2 vols.

3. James Cook and James King: *A voyage to the Pacific Ocean; ... in the years 1776, 1777, 1778, 1779, and 1780* ..., London, 1784, 4 vols. On p. 245 of vol. 4 the authors note that "During the absence of our party from Macao, a brisk traffic had been carrying on with the Chinese for our sea-otter skins, the value of which had augmented every day. One of our sailors disposed of his stock, alone, for eight hundred dollars; and a few of the best skins, which were clean, and had been carefully preserved, produced a hundred and twenty dollars each. The total amount of the value, in goods and cash, that was obtained for the furs of both our vessels, we are confident was not less than two thousand pounds sterling; ...."

4. For biographical sketches of Ledyard and his geographical accomplishments see Sanford H. Bederman: "The ethnological contributions of John Ledyard," *Georgia State College, Atlanta School of Arts and Sciences, Research Papers*, no. 4, pp. 1–29, Atlanta, Ga., 1964; E. Dvoichenko-Markov: "John Ledyard and the Russians (Cook's third and last expedition)," *Russian Rev.*, vol. 2, pp. 211–222, New York, 1952; James K. Mumford: *John Ledyard; an American Marco Polo*, Portland, Ore., 1939, 308 pp.; Jared Sparks: *The life of John Ledyard, the American; comprising selections from his journals and correspondence*, Cambridge, Mass., 1829, 310 pp.; and Jared Sparks: *Memoirs of the life and travels of John Ledyard, from his journals and correspondence*, London, 1828, 428 pp.

Manuscript materials by and about Ledyard are in the New York Historical Society, New York City; the Massachusetts Historical Society, Boston; the New York Public Library, New York City; the Houghton Library, Harvard College Library, Cambridge, Mass.; Dartmouth College Library, Hanover, New Hampshire; and in the Thomas Jefferson Papers, in the Manuscript Division, Library of Congress, Wash., D. C. The most complete collection is with the Jared Sparks Papers in Houghton Library.

5. Helen Augur: *Passage to glory; John Ledyard's America*, New York, 1946, 310 pp., pp. 133–139. Ledyard hoped to be able to accompany the ship to the northwest coast where he would explore the coast before beginning an overland trek back to the east coast of the United States with a dog as his only companion.

6. For Ledyard's role see in Jared Sparks: *The Life* ... [note 4], p. 131. Ledyard notes his contacts with Robert Morris and says that "... But it is a fact, that the Honorable Robert Morris is disposed to give me a ship to go to the North Pacific Ocean. I have had two interviews with him at the Finance Office, and tomorrow I expect a conclusive one. ...." For information on the *Empress of China* and Robert Morris see William B. Clark: "Journal of the Ship Empress of China," *Amer. Nept.*, vol. 11, pp. 59–71 and 134–144, Salem, Mass., 1950; Clarence L. Ver Steeg: "Financing and outfitting the first United States ship to China," *Pacific Hist. Rev.*, vol. 22, pp. 1–12, Berkeley and Los Angeles, 1953; and Samuel W. Woodhouse: "The voyage of the Empress of China," *Penn. Mag. Hist.*, vol. 63, pp. 24–36, Philadelphia, Pa. 1939.

7. John Ledyard: *A journal of Captain Cook's last voyage to the Pacific ocean, and in quest of a northwest passage between Asia & America; performed in the years 1776, 1777, 1778, and 1779* ..., Hartford, Conn., 208 pp., pp. 166–167 and 200. For recent republication of this work see *American Classics*, no. 10, 208 pp., Chicago, Ill., 1963; and James K. Mumford (ed.): *Journal of Captain Cook's last voyage*, Corvallis, Ore., 1964, 264 pp.

8. Adele Ogden: "Russian sea-otter and seal hunting on the California coast, 1803–1841," *Calif. Hist. Quart.*, vol. 12, pp. 217–239, San Francisco, Calif., 1933.

9. [William Sturgis]: "Examination of the Russian claims to the northwest coast of America," *North Amer. Rev.*, vol. 15, p. 372, 1822; and William Sturgis: "... The northwest fur trade, and the Indians of the Oregon Country, 1788–1830," *Old South Leaflets, General Series*, vol. 9 (219), pp. 1–20, Boston, 1911 (?).

10. Frederick W. Howay: "... A list of trading vessels in maritime fur trade, 1785–1825," *Roy. Soc. Canada, Proc. and Trans., Series 3*, vols. 24–28, Ottawa, 1930–34.; see vol. 24, pp. 111–134.

11. Frederick W. Howay (ed.): "Voyages of the 'Columbia' to the northwest coast 1787–1790 and 1790–1793," *Mass. Hist. Soc., Colls.* vol. 79, pp. i—xxxiv and 1–518, Boston, 1941, pp. 113–116.

This volume, containing four journals and a remnant of the official logbook of the *Columbia* on the second voyage and numerous letters and miscellaneous papers relating to the voyages, is the most authoritative single source for these important voyages. Howay (pp. x–xi) suggests that the brig *Eleanor*, commanded by Captain Simon Metcalf, of New York may have been trading on the northwest coast while the *Columbia* and *Lady Washington* were en route. See also T. C. Elliott (comp.) : "Remnant of official log of the Columbia," *Oregon Hist Quart.*, vol. 22 (4), pp. 352–356, Portland, 1921.

For additional accounts of the *Columbia* and the *Lady Washington*, of exploration of the northwest coast, and of Gray and Kendrick see Carleton Beals: *Adventure of the western sea*, New York, 1956, 192 pp.; Hubert H. Bancroft: Chapters VIII–XI in his *Works*, vol. 27, pp. 239–377, San Francisco, Calif., 1886; Frederick W. Howay and Albert Matthews: "Some notes upon Captain Robert Gray (1755–1809), "*Wash. Hist. Soc.*, vol. 21, pp. 8–12, Seattle, Wash., 1930; Frederick W. Howay: "Voyages of Kendrick and Gray in 1787–90," *Oregon Hist. Quart.*, vol. 30, pp. 89–94, Portland, Ore., 1929; and Francis E. Smith: *Achievements and experiences of Captain Robert Gray, 1788 to 1792*, Tacoma, Wash., 1923, 16 pp.

12. The first British vessel to engage in the fur trade on the Northwest Coast arrived from China in 1785, and eight vessels were there in 1786. This activity is well summarized in Arthur G. Day: "The earliest explorers—traders of the Northwest Coast," *U. S. Naval Institute Proc.*, vol. 67 (466), pp. 1677–1683, Annapolis, Md., 1941. Day's summary is based on unpublished manuscripts in the personal papers of Sir Joseph Banks in the Sutro Branch of the California State Library in San Francisco, California. See also Frederick W. Howay: *op. cit.* [note 10]; and George V. Blue (ed.): "Vessels trading on the northwest coast of America, 1804–1814," *Wash. Hist. Quart.*, vol. 19, pp. 294–295, Seattle, Wash., 1928.

13. Captain Kendrick later sailed for China, arriving there in January 1790. His conduct has been criticized, for he sold the cargo of the *Lady Washington* and in a sham sale transferred the ownership of the vessel to his name. He made two additional voyages to the northwest coast of America without ever making a remittance to the Boston merchants. He was accidentally killed in Honolulu, December 12, 1792.

14. The principal source for the first voyage is the log kept by Robert Haswell, second officer on the *Lady Washington*. Frederick W. Howay: *op. cit.* [note 11], pp. 5–107.

15. *Ibid.*, p. 42. See for reference to the Strait of Juan de Fuca.

16. *Ibid.*, pp. 70 and 79, 73, and footnotes 1 and 2.

17. *Ibid.*, p. 98.

18. For John Hoskin's narative see *ibid.*, reference on p. 280. The original of *The narrative of a voyage to the north west coast of America and China on trade and discoveries by John Hoskins, performed in the ship Columbia Rediviva, 1790, 1791, 1792 & 1793*, 206 + 48 pp. is in the Library of the Massachusetts Historical Society, Boston.

19. John Boit's log is included in Frederick W. Howay (ed.): *op. cit.* [note 11], reference is to p. 393, note 2. See also Frederick W. Howay, T. C. Elliott and F. G. Young: "John Boit's log of the Columbia—1790–1793," *Oregon Hist. Quart.*, vol. 22 (4), pp. 257–351, Portland, Ore., 1921; Dorothy O. Johansen (ed.): *Voyage of the Columbia; around the world with John Boit, 1790–1793 ...*, Portland, Ore., 1960, 92 pp.; Edmond S. Meany (annot.): "New log of the Columbia by John Boit," *Wash. Hist. Quart.*, vol. 12, pp. 3–50, Seattle, Wash., 1921; and Edmond S. Meany (ed.): *A new log of the Columbia by John Boit, on the discovery of the Columbia river and Grays harbor*, Seattle, Wash., 1921, 48 pp.

20. Frederick W. Howay (ed.): *op. cit.* [note 11], p. 394.

21. "Remnant of the official log of the 'Columbia' " in Frederick W. Howay (ed.): *op. cit.* [note 11], p. 436.

22. *Re* Boit's log see Frederick W. Howay (ed.): *op. cit.* [note 11], reference is to pp. 396–397.

23. George Vancouver's *A voyage of discovery to the North Pacific ocean, and round the world; in which the coast of north-west America has been carefully examined and surveyed ...* , London, 1798, 3 vols. and an atlas, and especially his map of the coast from San Diego to Cook Inlet, Alaska, had a profound influence on generally acceptable geographical knowledge of the area and on geographic names of features delineated. For details of Vancouver's accomplishments see Chapter 12.

24. Frederick W. Howay and T. C. Elliott: "Vancouver's brig Chatham in the Columbia," *Oregon Hist. Quart.*, vol. 43, pp. 318–327, Portland, Ore., 1942; T. C. Elliott: "The log of the H.M.S. Chatham, *Oregon Hist. Quart.*, vol. 18 (4), pp. 231–243, Portland, Ore., 1917. See also Rufus C. Holman: *The exploration of the Columbia river by Lieutenant W. R. Broughton, October 1792, ...*, Longview, Wash., 1927 (?), 28 pp.; and George Vancouver: [note 23], vol. 1, pp. 419–422 and vol. 2, pp. 53–56. The sketch Gray gave to Vancouver apparently has been lost.

25. Joseph Ingraham: *Journal of the voyage of the Brigantine "Hope" from Boston to the N.W. coast*

of America, 1790 to 1792, an unpublished manuscript in four volumes in the Manuscript Division of the Library of Congress, Wash., D.C. See vol. 3, pp. 147–148 and vol. 4, pp. 208–209. For references to the voyage and the log (journal ?) see Frederick W. Howay: "The voyage of the Hope: 1790–1792," *Wash. Hist. Quart.*, vol. 11, pp. 3–28, Seattle, Wash., 1920; ". . . The log of the brig Hope called 'The Hope's track among the Sandwich islands, May 20—Oct. 12, 1791 . . .,'" *Hawaiian Hist. Soc. Reprints*, no. 3, pp. 1–36, Honolulu, n.d.; and Bjarne Kroepelien (ed.): *Le voyage d'Ingraham aux îles Marquises*, Oslo, Norway, 1937, 2 + 26 pp.

26. See note 1. A large number of abstract logs prepared under Maury's direction and supervision, especially in the 1840s and early 1850s are with the Records of the Weather Bureau (Record Group 27) in the National Archives. For an excellent discussion of these and related records see Louis J. Darter, Jr.: "Federal archives relating to Matthew Fontaine Maury," *Amer. Nept.*, vol. 1, pp. 149–158, Salem, Mass., 1941.

27. The ship was registered in the name of Madame Hayley of Boston, but it appears to have been Rotch's ship. See Edouard A. Stackpole: *The sea-hunters; the New England whalemen during two centuries, 1635–1835*, Philadelphia, 1953, 510 pp., p. 188.

28. Frederick W. Howay: "Captain Simon Metcalfe and the brig 'Eleanora', "*Wash. Hist. Quart.*, vol. 16, pp. 114–121, Seattle, Wash., 1925.

29. For an account of several such voyages see Edmund Fanning: *Voyages round the world; with selected sketches of voyages of the South seas, north and south Pacific oceans, China, etc.*, New York, 1833, 499 pp. Reprinted as Edmund Fanning: *Voyages & discoveries in the South seas, 1792–1832*, Salem, Mass., 1924, 335 pp. See also Edmund Fanning: *Voyages to the South seas, Indian and Pacific oceans, China Sea, North-West Coast, . . . with an account of new discoveries made in the southern hemisphere, between the years 1830–1837 . . .*, New York, 1838, 324 pp.

30. Alonzo H. Clark: "The Antarctic fur seal and sea-elephant industries," in George B. Goode (ed.): *The fisheries and fishery industries of the United States*, vol. 2, pp. 400–467, Wash., D. C., 1887, see especially p. 407.

31. Edmund Fanning: *op. cit.* [note 29, 1924 ed.], pp. 160–161 and 168. For an account of the number of ships see Amasa Delano: *A narrative of voyages and travels in the northern and southern hemispheres; comprising three voyages round the world*, Boston, 1817, 598 pp., p. 306.

32. For discussion of initial exploration and discovery see R. T. Gould: "The charting of the South Shetlands, 1819–28," *Mar. Mirr.*, vol. 27 (3), pp. 206–330, 1941; Adolphus W. Greely: "American discoverers of the Antarctic continent," *Nat. Geogr. Mag.*, vol. 23, pp. 298–312, Wash., D. C., 1912; Arthur Hinks: "Antarctica discovered: A reply," *Geogr. Rev.*, vol. 31, pp. 491–498, N. Y., 1941; Lawrence Martin: "An American discovered Antarctica," *Comptes Rendus du Congres International de Géographie, Amsterdam, 1938, Section IV, Géographie Historique*, vol. 2, pp. 215–218, Leiden, 1938; Lawrence Martin: "Antarctica discovered by a Connecticut Yankee Captain Nathaniel Brown Palmer," *Geogr. Rev.*, vol. 30 (4), pp. 529–552, N. Y., 1940; Lawrence Martin: "Early explorations and investigations in southern South America and adjacent Antarctic waters by mariners and scientists from the U. S. A.," *Eighth Amer. Sci. Congr., Wash., D. C., 1940, Proc.*, vol. 9, pp. 43–46, Wash., D. C., 1940.

33. Edouard A. Stockpole: "The voyage ot the Huron and the Huntress; the American sealers and the discovery of the continent of Antarctica," *Marine Hist. Assoc., Publ.*, no. 29, pp. 1–86, Mystic, Conn., 1955. The logbook of the *Huron* was discovered by Alexander D. Vietor, Map Curator, Yale University Library, New Haven, Connecticut. The logbook of the *Huntress* was discovered by Edouard A. Stackpole, Curator of the Marine Historical Association, Mystic, Connecticut. This brief volume is the most complete summary of American activity at the South Shetlands between 1820 and 1822.

34. *Ibid.*, p. 51.

35. *Ibid.*, p. 47.

36. *The New York Gazette & General Advertiser*, May 16, 1821, New York City. Dr. Samuel Latham Mitchill, physician, promoter of science, and United States senator from New York ". . . was able to exert a pronounced influence in the promotion of scientific inquiry and in the practical application of scientific principles to life." See biography in DumasMalone (ed.): *Dictionary of American Biography*, vol. 13, pp. 69–71, New York, 1934. For additional biography see C. R. Hall: *An American scientist—Samuel Latham Mitchill*, a Ph.D. thesis in the Columbia University, New York, 1933.

37. These reports are typical of several relating to specimens brought back and of sketch maps made by sealers and fur traders. Unfortunately, there was at that time in the United States no organization or agency which systematically gathered and recorded such data. Consequently their contemporary usefulness was limited, and most of the records and specimens have been lost. Several

logbooks and journals which record significant events have been preserved, but few maps remain.

38. Some confusion exists on this point. See Edouard A. Stackpole: *op. cit.* [note 27], pp. 147, 148, 152 and 157. Two expatriate Nantucket whaleships were dispatched from Dunkirk, France, in October 1790 for the Pacific via Cape Horn. Six Nantucket and one New Bedford whaleships were fitted out for the Pacific in 1791. Apparently the first of these to round the Horn was the *Beaver* of Nantucket, commanded by Captain Paul Worth, early in 1792. By then four American ships based at Dunkirk had entered the Pacific. The logbook of the whaleship *Rebecca*, which sailed from New Bedford under Captain Joseph Kersey in 1791, records thirty-nine whaleships in the Pacific in 1792. Of these twenty-one were from British ports, nine from Dunkirk, and nine from New England. Americans commanded sixteen of the ships.

39. For references to the history of American whaling especially in the Pacific Basin see H. W. Bradley: "Hawaii and the American penetration of the northern Pacific, 1800–1845," *Pacific Hist. Rev.*, vol. 12, pp. 277–286, Berkeley, Calif., 1943; Lloyd G. Churchward: "Notes on American whaling activities in Australian waters, 1800–1850," *Hist. Studies, Australia and New Zealand*, vol. 9, pp. 59–63, Melbourne, Nov., 1949; George F. Dow: "Whale ships and whaling, a pictorial history of whaling during three centuries, with an account of the whale fishery in colonial New England," *Marine Research Soc., Publ.*, no. 10, pp. 1–446, Salem, Mass., 1925; Thomas Dunbabin: "The first Salem vessel in Sydney and Fiji," *Amer. Nept.*, vol. 13 (4), pp. 275–281, Salem, Mass., 1953; Thomas Dunbabin: "New light on the earliest American voyages to Australia," *Amer Nept.*, vol. 10, pp. 52–64, Salem, Mass., 1950; James T. Jenkins: *A history of the whale fisheries, . . .*, London, 1921, 336 pp.; W. Levi: "The earliest relations between the U.S.A. and Australia," *Pacific Hist. Rev.*, vol. 12, pp. 351–361, Berkeley, Calif., 1943; John R. Spears: *The story of the New England whalers*, New York, 1908, 418 pp.; Edouard A. Stackpole: *op. cit.* [note 27]; Alexander Starbuck: *History of the American whale fishery from its earliest inception to the year 1876*, Waltham, Mass., 1878, 768 pp.; Walter S. Tower: "A history of the American whale fishery," *Univ. Penn. Publ. in Polit. Econ. and Public Law*, no. 20, pp. 1–145, Philadelphia, Pa., 1907.

For a considerable collection of typescript copies of newspaper and similar records of discovery, exploration, and trade in the Pacific Basin, especially during the period 1780–1860, see the Central Pacific Island Study, *General Records of the State Department* (Record Group 59) in the National Archives and in the Peabody Museum of Salem, Mass. For forthcoming publication of much of this information see Stanley S. Dodge: *American activities in the Central Pacific, 1790–1870*, to be published by the Gregg Press of Ridgewood, N. J., in eight volumes.

40. Edouard A. Stackpole: *op. cit.* [note 27], p. 274.

41. Letter from Matthew Fontaine Maury to Commodore Charles Morris, Chief, Bureau of Ordnance and Hydrography dated Naval Observatory, Wash., Dec. 3, 1851, in *Letters Sent by the Naval Observatory*, vol. 7, pp. 275–277, in the National Archives.

42. S. Whittemore Boggs: *op. cit.* [note 1, GENERAL WORKS], p. 177. This article is the most complete analysis to date of American contributions in this part of the Pacific.

43. *Ibid.*, p. 187.

44. For the story of official United States government participation see Allan B. Cole (ed.): "Captain David Porter's proposed expedition to the Pacific and Japan, 1815," *Pacific Hist. Rev.*, vol. 9 (1), pp. 61–65, Berkeley, Calif., 1940; C. M. Drury: "Early American contacts with the Japanese," *Pacific Northwest Quart.*, vol. 36, pp. 319–330, Seattle, Wash., 1945; Hiram Paulding: *Journal of the cruise of the United States schooner "Dolphin" among the islands of the Pacific . . .*, Carvil, N. Y., 1831, 258 pp.; Charles O. Paullin: "Early voyages of American vessels to the Orient," *U. S. Naval Inst., Proc.*, vol. 36 (2–4), pp. 707–716, Annapolis, Md., 1910; Charles O. Paullin: "Early voyages of American naval vessels to the Orient: Explorations, surveys and missions: 1838–1857," *U. S. Naval Inst., Proc.*, vol. 37, pp. 407–417, Annapolis, Md., 1911; David Porter: *A voyage in the South seas, in the years 1812, 1813, and 1814. With particular details of the Gallipagos and Washington islands*, London, 1823, 126 pp.; David Porter: *Journal of a cruise made to the Pacific ocean by David Porter . . . in the years 1812, 1813, and 1814, . . .*, New York, 1822, 2 vols.; Charles S. Stewart: *A visit to the South Seas, in the U. S. Ship Vincennes, during the years 1829 and 1830; . . .*, New York, 1831, 2 vols.; Edgar K. Thompson: "Journal of a passage through the Straits of Magellan in 1829," *Amer. Nept.*, vol. 23 (3), pp. 186–191, Salem, Mass., 1963; and F. M. Van Matter: "First time around [the world by the U.S.S. Vincennes]," *U. S. Naval Inst., Proc.*, vol. 73, pp. 317–325, Annapolis, Md., 1947.

For the official background and the reasons for sending navy ships into the Pacific Basin see the documents of the United States Senate and the House of Representatives as published in the Congressional Serial Set and as permanent official records in the National Archives.

45. For the manuscript journal accounts of Nathaniel Bowditch's voyages between Beverly,

Massachusetts and Sumatra, and Salem, Massachusetts and the Philippine Islands in the 1790s and other works by him see his papers in the Manuscript Room of the Boston Public Library. His *The new American practical navigator* . . . was printed by E. M. Blunt for W. R. Wilder in Newport, Rhode Island in 1802 and included 589 pp. A bibliography of Bowditch's publications and a catalogue of his personal collection may be found in Raymond C. Archibald: *A catalogue of a special exhibition . . . of Nathaniel Bowditch (1773–1838) . . . at Peabody Museum Salem, Mass.,* . . . *1937,* Portland, Me., 1937, 40 pp. For biographical works see Robert E. Berry: *Yankee stargazer; the life of Nathaniel Bowditch,* New York and London, 1941, 234 pp.; Alfred B. Stanford: *Navigator; the story of Nathaniel Bowditch,* New York, 1927, 308 pp.; and Paul E. Wylie: "Nathaniel Bowditch and his work," *Navigation,* . . . , vol. 3 (5), pp. 160–168, Los Angeles, Calif., 1952.

46. For references to this activity see Harold L. Burstyn: *At the sign of the quadrant; an account of the contributions to American hydrography made by Edmund March Blunt and his sons,* Mystic, Conn., 1957, 119 pp.; and Lawrence A. Carton: *The Blunts: Guardians of American shipping in the first half of the nineteenth century,* a manuscript in Princeton University Library, New York, 1940.

47. For a brief account of the United States Hydrographic Office and its predecessor agencies such as the Depot of Charts and Instruments see Gustavus A. Weber: *The Hydrographic Office: Its history, activities and organization,* Baltimore, Md., 1926, 112 pp.; see pp. 1–40 for a brief history.

48. "December 10, 1825," *Niles Weekly Register,* vol. 9 (743), pp. 233–240, Baltimore, Md., 1825.

49. "Report: The Committee on Naval Affairs, to which was referred a great number of memorials from citizens of various sections of the United States, praying aid from the Government, in fitting out vessels for an exploring expedition to the Pacific Sea," *House Rept., no. 209, 20th Congr., 1st Sess.,* March 25, 1828. See also Philip I. Mitterling: *America in the Antarctic to 1840,* Urbana, Ill., 1959, 201 pp., pp. 82–92; and Harley H. Bartlett: "The reports of the Wilkes Expedition, and the work of the specialists in science," *Amer. Philos. Soc., Proc.,* vol. 82 (5), pp. 601–705, Philadelphia, Pa., 1940, pp. 602–606.

50. "Pacific Ocean and South Seas. Letter from Secretary of the Navy, transmitting report of J. N. Reynolds in relation to islands, reefs, and shoals in the Pacific Ocean, etc., January 27, 1835, [original report dated september 24, 1828]," *House of Representatives, Doc. no. 105, 23rd Congr. 2nd Sess.,* Wash., D. C.

51. Harley H. Bartlett: *op. cit.* [note 49], pp. 606–607; and Philip L. Mitterling: *op. cit.* [note 49], pp. 93–96.

52. For a description of the cruise see the *Journal of the Schooner Penguin bound to Falkland Island* [sic] *& Cape Horn on sealing voyage in the year 1829, Alex S. Palmer, Master, Phineas Wilcox, Mate,* in Marine Miscellany, Manuscript Division, Library of Congress, Wash., D. C. A well-documented summary of this expedition is found in Philip I. Mitterling: *op. cit.* [note 49], pp. 97–100. The expedition is described in Edmund Fanning: [note 29, 1833 ed.], pp. 478–488.

53. James Eights gained belated international recognition in a presidential address delivered by W. T. Colman before the Linnean Society of London on May 24, 1937. It was entitled "James Eights, a pioneer Antarctic naturalist," and is published in *The Linnean Soc. London, Proc.,* 149th Session, pp. 171–184, London, 1936–1937. For additional biography of Eights see John M. Clarke: "The reincarnation of James Eights, Antarctic explorer," *Sci. Mon.,* vol. 2, pp. 189–202, New York, 1916.

54. For details see accounts in references in note 52.

55. Perhaps the most important are "Description of an Isopod crustacean from the Antarctic seas, with observations on the New South Shetlands," *Silliman's Journ.,* vol. 22, pp. 391–397, New Haven, Conn., 1856; "Description of a new animal belonging to the *Crustacea* discovered in the Antarctic seas," *Albany Inst., Trans.,* vol. 2, 331–334, Albany, N. Y., 1833–1852; and "Description of a new Crustaceous animal found on the shores of the South Shetland Islands with remarks on their natural history," *Albany Inst., Trans.,* vol. 2, pp. 53–69, Albany, 1833–1852.

56. For details see note 53.

57. Jeremiah N. Reynolds: *Voyage of the United States Frigate Potomac under the command of Commodore John Downs during the circumnavigation of the globe in the years 1831, 1832, 1833, and 1834* New York, 1835, 560 pp.; and Francis Warriner: *Cruise of the United States frigate Potomac round the world, during the years 1831–1834,* . . . , Boston, 1835, 366 pp. A short summary of this voyage based on official sources is included in Charles O. Paullin: *op. cit.* [note 44]. Part V of Paullin's article in the *U. S. Naval Inst., Proc.,* vol. 36 (3), pp. 455–463, includes a discussion of the voyage of the U.S.S. *Vincennes* around the world in 1826–1830, under command of Commander William B. Finch. These and other voyages described in this article seem to indicate that it was easier to promote a voyage "to show the flag" than it was for surveying.

58. *Ibid.* See also Jeremiah N. Reynolds: *Address on the subject of a surveying and exploring expedi-*

tion to the Pacific ocean and South seas. Delivered in the Hall of representatives on the evening of April 3, 1836 . . . , New York, 1836, 300 pp.

59. Edmund Fanning: *op. cit.* [note 29].

60. See for example Jeremiah N. Reynolds: *Exploring expedition. Correspondence between J. N. Reynolds and the Hon. Mahlon Dickerson, under the respective signatures of "Citizen" and "Friend to the navy," touching the South sea surveying and exploring expedition* . . . , New York, 1837–1838, 151 pp.

61. There is a good official record of these activities for the period 1828–1838 among the records of the House of Representatives and of the United States Senate in the National Archives, many of which memorials, reports, and bills have been published as Congressional documents in the so-called Congressional Serial Set.

62. An indispensable source of information on the publications by and pertaining to the Expedition is Daniel C. Haskell (comp.): "The United States Exploring Expedition, 1838–1848, and its publications, 1844–1874, a bibliography . . . ," *New York Public Library, Bull.*, no. 45, pp. 68–89, 507–532, and 821–858, and no. 46, pp. 103–150, New York, 1941–1942. Also published separately in 1942 in 188 pp.

63. An excellent, well-documented summary of the problems and controversies relating to the organization of the Expedition is given in Philip I. Mitterling: *op. cit.* [note 49], pp. 101–128. See also Harley H. Bartlett: "The reports of the Wilkes Expedition, and the work of the specialists in science," *Amer. Philos. Soc., Proc.*, vol. 82 (5), pp. 601–705, Philadelphia, Pa., 1940; Doris E. Borthwick: "Outfitting the United States Exploring Expedition: Lieutenant Charles Wilkes' European assignment, August-November, 1836," *Amer. Philos. Soc., Proc.*, vol. 109 (3), pp. 159–172, Philadelphia, Pa., 1965.; George S. Bryan: "The purpose, equipment and personnel of the Wilkes Expedition," *Amer. Philos. Soc., Proc.*, vol. 82 (5), pp. 551–560, Philadelphia, 1940; Louis N. Feipel: "The Wilkes Exploring Expedition; its progress through half a century, 1826–1876," *U. S. Naval Institute, Proc.*, vol. 40, pp. 1323–1350, Annapolis, Md., 1914; George W. Littlehales: "The Navy as a motor in geographical and commercial progress," *Amer. Geogr. Soc., Journ.*, vol. 31, pp. 123–149, New York, 1899, especially pp. 124–129; and W. Partick Strauss: "Preparing the Wilkes Expedition: A study in disorganization," *Pacific Hist. Rev.*, vol. 28, pp. 221–232, Seattle, Wash., 1959.

64. For biography see "Charles Wilkes, 1798–1877," *Amer. Acad. Arts Sci., Proc.*, vol. 12, pp. 323–325, Boston, 1877; Van Wyck Brooks: "Charles Wilkes," in his *Fenollosa and his circle, with other essays in biography*, New York, 1962, 321 pp.; Adolphus W. Greely: "Charles Wilkes, 1798–1877," in his . . . *Explorers and travellers*, New York, 1893, 373 pp., pp. 194–211; Daniel Henderson: *The hidden coasts, a biography of Admiral Charles Wilkes*, New York, 1933, 306 pp.; Jim D. Hill: "Charles Wilkes—turbulent scholar of the old navy," *U. S. Naval Inst., Proc.*, vol. 57, pp. 867–887, Annapolis, Md., 1931; Mary H. Krout: "Rear Admiral Charles Wilkes and his exploits," *U. S. Naval Institute, Proc.*, vol. 50, pp. 405–416, Annapolis, Md., 1924; and Felix Riesenberg: "Wilkes: America's Captain Cook," in his *The Pacific Ocean*, New York, 1940, 322 pp.; pp. 246–266.

65. George S. Bryan: *op. cit.* [note 63], pp. 554–555.

66. Edwin G. Conklin: "Connection of the American Philosophical Society with our first national exploring expedition," *Amer. Philos. Soc., Proc.*, vol. 82 (5), pp. 519–541, Philadelphia, Pa., 1940.

67. James A. G. Rehn: "Connection of the Academy of Natural Sciences of Philadelphia with our first national exploring expedition," *Amer. Philos. Soc., Proc.*, vol. 82 (5), pp. 543–549, Philadelphia, Pa., 1940.

68. Edwin G. Conklin: *op. cit.* [note 66], p. 519.

69. Harley H. Bartlett: *op. cit.* [note 63], especially pp. 627–705; George S. Bryan: *op. cit.* [note 63], pp. 557. For biographical sketches see John Barnhart: "Brackenridge and his book on ferns," *New York Bot. Garden Journ.*, vol. 20, 117–124, New York, 1919; W. H. Dall: "Joseph Pitty Couthouy, 1808–1864," *Biol. Soc. Wash., Proc.*, vol. 4, pp. 108–111, Wash., D. C., 1888; L. V. Pirsson: "James Dwight Dana, 1813–1895," *Nat'l Acad. Sci., Biogr. Memoirs*, vol. 9, pp. 41–92, Wash., D. C., 1919; A. Hunter Dupree: *Asa Gray, 1810–1888*, Cambridge, Mass., 1959, 505 pp.; Charles S. Sargent (comp.): *Scientific papers of Asa Gray*, Boston and New York, 1889, 2 vols.; "Horatio Hale, 1817–1896," *Pop. Sci. Monthly*, vol. 51, pp. 401–410, New York, 1897; Jessie Poesch: "Titian Ramsey Peale, 1799–1885, and his journals of the Wilkes expedition," *Am. Phil. Soc., Memoir*, Vol. 52, x, Philadelphia, Pa., 1961; For Charles Pickering, see Charles S. Sargent (comp.): *ibid.*, vol. 2, pp. 406–410; and John Harshberger: "Charles Pickering," in his *The botanists of Philadelphia and their work*, Philadelphia, Pa., 1899, 457 pp., see pp. 190–193.

70. George S. Bryan: *ibid.*, p. 558.

71. George S. Bryan: *ibid.*, p. 556.

72. The best single source on the variant editions and printings of the *Narrative* . . . is Daniel C. Haskell (comp.): *op. cit.* [note 62]. See for example Charles Wilkes: *Narrative of the United States Exploring Expedition. During the years 1838, 1839, 1840, 1841, 1842* . . . , Philadelphia, Pa., 1844, 5 vols. and an atlas. See also Max Meisel: "Wilkes United States Exploring Expedition," in his *A bibliography of American natural history*, vol. 2, pp. 650–673, Brooklyn, N. Y., 1924–1929.

73. An excellent summary of the scientific work and exploration accomplished in the Pacific Basin may be found in Mary E. Cooley: "The exploring expedition in the Pacific," *Amer. Philos. Soc., Proc.*, vol. 85 (5), pp. 707–720, Philadelphia, Pa., 1940. See also Harley H. Bartlett: *op. cit.* [note 63]; and George S. Bryan: *op. cit.* (note 63).

74. James C. Palmer: *Thulia: A tale of the Antarctic*, New York, 1843, 72 pp., pp. 65–72.

75. Charles Wilkes: *op. cit.* [note 72], vol. 1, pp. 149–156 and 405–414.

76. For an excellent account of the successful 1960 penetration of the Bellingshausen Sea and the mapping of the region, especially around Thurston Island, by the United States Navy see "Bellingshausen Sea Expedition," *U. S. Antarctic Projects Officer, Bull.*, vol. 1 (6), pp. 3–8, Wash., D. C., 1960.

77. The more vessels involved and the more boats on shore, the more rapidly a survey could be made. After a round of angles was taken one of the ships forming the base line was moved, as were the boats on shore. In this way an entire island would be circled. At such stations angles of the sun would also be made to determine the geographical position. For an excellent detailed description of the method see Charles Wilkes: *op. cit.* [note 72], vol. 1, pp. 429–432; and Mary E. Cooley: *op. cit.* [note 73], pp. 709–710.

78. For discussion of this accomplishment and the problems involved see especially William H. Hobbs: "Conditions of exceptional visibility within high latitudes, particularly as a result of superior mirage," *Assoc. Amer. Geogr., Annals*, vol. 27 (4), pp. 229–240, Lancaster, Pa., 1937; William H. Hobbs: "The discovery of Wilkes Land, Antarctica," *Amer. Philos. Soc., Proc.*, vol. 82 (5), pp. 561–582, Phila., Pa., 1940; William H. Hobbs: "Discovery of a sketch of Cape Hudson in the Antarctic," *Geogr. Rev.*, vol. 24 (1), pp. 115–117, New York, 1934; William H. Hobbs: "The eastern landfalls of Wilkes within the Australian Sector of the Antarctic," *Geogr. Journ.*, vol. 81, pp. 538–540, London, 1933; William H. Hobbs: "Visibility and the discovery of polar lands," *Geografiska Annaler*, vol. 14, pp. 217–222, Stockholm, 1933; William H. Hobbs: "Wilkes Land rediscovered," *Geogr. Rev.*, vol. 22 (4), pp. 632–655, New York, 1932; Douglas Mawson: "The B. A. N. Z. Antarctic Research Expedition, 1929–31," *Geogr. Journ.*, vol. 80 (2), pp. 101–131, London, 1932, see especially pp. 116–118 and 122; Douglas Mawson: "Wilkes' Antarctic landfalls," *Roy. Geogr. Soc. Austr., So. Austr. Br., Proc.*, vol. 34, pp. 69–113, Adelaide, Austr., 1934; Frank E. Ross: "The Antarctic explorations of Lieutenant Charles Wilkes," *Roy. Georg. Soc., So. Austr. Br., Sess. for 1932–33*, vol. 25, pp. 69–113, Adelaide, Austr., 1935; and "Wilkes' work fully endorsed, at last, by a British authority," *Amer. Geogr. Soc., Bull.*, vol. 8, pp. 523–525, New York, 1912.

79. From the beginning Wilkes' conception of an Antarctic continent and even his landfalls were challenged by James C. Ross in his *A voyage of discovery and research in the southern and Antarctic regions, during the years 1839–43*, London, 1847, 2 vols., see vol. 1, p. 275. Subsequent explorers who have sailed over his supposed eastern landfalls cast doubt on his western landfalls. That Wilkes should have erred so badly is surprising in view of the demonstrated accuracy of his work in the Pacific islands. Aerial photographs taken along the coast of Wilkes Land by the *United States Navy Operation High Jump (1946–1947)* and ground control obtained by the *United States Navy Operation Windmill (1947–1948)* enabled the United States Geological Survey to compile and to publish in 1956 its *Antarctic reconnaissance map* (scale of 1:5,000,000) in eight sheets. When this modern accurate controlled cartographic delineation of the coast of Wilkes Land is superimposed over Wilkes' "Chart of the Antarctic Continent" in the Atlas to accompany his *Narratives . . .* , *op. cit.* [note 72] it is immediately apparent that Wilkes' map conforms very closely to the actual conditions west of longitude 147° E. His errors were mostly in latitude rather than in longitude. This is significant and apparently is due to confusing atmospheric conditions that prevail in the Antarctic and make it difficult to judge distance.

Wilkes' eastern landfalls, which have been challenged most, have now been identified, with one exception, by the Australian scientists B. P. Lambert and Philip G. Law, as a result of their reconnaissance of the coast by ship and by aircraft in 1958 and 1959 from Cape Freshfield to Oates Coast. See B. P. Lambert and Philip G. Law: "A new map of the coastline of Oates Land and Eastern King George V Land," a paper read in the *Antarctic Symposium*, November 1959, in Buenos Aires, Argentina; and Kenneth J. Bertrand: "Wilkes' Antarctic discoveries now fully confirmed," *U. S. Antarctic Projects Officer, Bull.*, vol. 1 (6), pp. 19–22, Wash., D. C., 1960. Thus, after more than a century, all of Wilkes' Antarctic landfalls have been confirmed or reasonably identified.

80. For a copy see "Chart of the Antarctic Continent Shewing the Icy Barrier Attached to it.

Discovered by the U. S. Ex. Ex. Charles Wilkes. Esq., Commander 1840." In the National Archives.

81. Charles Wilkes: *Narrative* ..., *op. cit.* [note 72]. The itinerary and accomplishments are discussed in vol. 2, pp. 369–414.

82. Charles Wilkes: *op. cit.* [note 72], vol. 3, pp. 400–402.

83. *Ibid.*, the itinerary and accomplishments are discussed in vol. 4. For examples of the scientific work resulting from the surveys in the Hawaiian Islands see James D. Dana's "Historical account of the eruptions on Hawaii," *Amer. Journ. Sci. Arts, Series 2*, vol. 9, pp. 347–364, New Haven, Conn., 1850; "On Labradorite from the island of Maui, Hawaiian Group," *Amer. Journ. Sci. Arts, Series 2*, vol. 11, p. 121, New Haven, 1851; "On the volcanic eruptions of Hawaii," *Amer. Journ. Sci. Arts, Series 2*, vol. 10, pp. 235–244, New Haven, Conn., 1850; and "On the isolation of volcanic action in Hawaii or volcanoes no safety valves," *Amer. Assoc. Adv. Sci., Proc.*, vol. 2, pp. 95–100, Boston, 1850.

84. Charles Wilkes: *ibid.*, the itinerary and accomplishments are discussed in vol. 4, pp. 291–496, 522–530, and vol. 5, pp. 113–256. For examples of scientific publications see James D. Dana: "Notes on Upper California; ... From observations made during the cruise of the United States Exploring Expedition, ...," *Amer. Journ. Sci. Arts, Series 2*, vol. 7, pp. 247–264, New Haven, Conn., 1849; James D. Dana: "Observations on some points in the physical geography of Oregon and Upper California," *Amer. Journ. Sci. Arts, Series 2*, vol. 7, pp. 376–394, New Haven, Conn., 1849; John Torrey: "On the *Darlingtonia Californica*, a new pitcher-plant from northern California," *Smiths. Inst., Contr. to Knowledge*, vol. 6 (4), pp. 1–8, Wash., 1853.

85. Louis H. Bolander: "The Vincennes, world traveller of the old navy," *U. S. Naval Institute, Proc.*, vol. 62, pp. 825–831, Menasha, Wisc., 1936.

86. For a good summary of the accomplishments and the collections see Charles Wilkes: *Synopsis of the cruise of the U. S. Exploring Expedition, ...*, Wash., D. C., 1842, 56 pp. See pp. 41–50. See also Daniel C. Haskell: *op. cit.* [note 62].

87. Mary E. Cooley: *op. cit.* [note 73], p. 707.

88. *Ibid.*, p. 709.

89. Daniel C. Haskell: *op. cit.* [note 62], pp. 18–19. This definitive and exhaustive bibliography includes a detailed descriptive listing of all published editions of the publications of the Expedition. Publication of most of the individual volumes was limited to 100 copies, which makes them rare items. Haskell indicates the location of each copy known to him. See also Harley H. Bartlett: *op. cit.* [note 63], which is an excellent review of the individual volumes.

90. For an excellent scholarly publication on the accomplishments of one of the scientists see Jessie Poesch: "Titian Ramsay Peale, 1799–1885, and his journals of the Wilkes Expedition," *Amer. Philos. Soc., Mem.*, vol. 52, pp. 1–214, Philadelphia, Pa., 1961.

91. ... *Atlas of Charts, ... From the Surveys of the Expedition by authority of Congress*, vol. 1, 2 pp. and 55 numbered charts, Philadelphia, Pa., 1850, and vol. 2, 2 p., 51 numbered charts, Philadelphia, Pa., 1858. *Op. cit.* [note 80].

92. There are in the National Archives manuscript and annotated charts which appear to be a product of the Expedition. Reference should also be made to the copper and zinc plates and the woodcuts prepared for the official publication of the Expedition that are in the National Museum of the Smithsonian Institution in Washington.

93. Mary E. Cooley: *op. cit.* [note 73], p. 718.

94. For contemporary synopses and appraisals of the accomplishments of the Expedition see "The Exploring Expedition," *Southern Quart. Rev.*, vol. 8, pp. 1–69 and 265–298, Charleston, S. C., 1845; Jean B. Boit: "Narrative of the United States Exploring Expedition," *Journ. des Savants*, 1848, pp. 672–687 and 709–728 and 1849, pp. 65–83, Paris, 1848–1849; Anna Ella Carroll: "The first American exploring expedition," in her *The star of the west; or, National men and national measures*, New York, 1857, 561 pp., pp. 13–136; Charles H. Davis: "The United States Exploring Expedition," *North Amer. Rev.*, vol. 61, pp. 54–107, Boston, 1845; James D. Dana: "United States Exploring Expedition," *Amer. Journ. Sci. and Arts*, vol. 44, pp. 393–408, New Haven, Conn., 1843; Pierre Daussey: "Exposé des travaux de l'expédition américaine pendant les années 1838, 39, 40, 41 et 42, ...," *Soc. de Géogr., Bull.*, Serie 2, vol. 19, pp. 37–79, Paris, 1843; Cornelius C. Felton and Asa Gray: "Scientific results of the Exploring Expedition," *North Amer. Rev.*, vol. 63, pp. 211–236, Boston, 1846; and Titian Ramsay Peale: "The South-sea surveying and exploring expedition," *Amer. Hist. Record*, vol. 3, pp. 244–251 and 305–311, Philadelphia, Pa., 1874.

95. For an excellent bibliography of these products see Daniel C. Haskell (comp.): *op. cit.* [note 62]. See also Harley H. Bartlett: *op. cit.* [note 63]; George S. Bryan: *op. cit.* [note 63]; Frank S. Collins: "The botanical and other papers of the Wilkes Exploring Expedition," *Rhodora*, vol. 14 (160), pp. 57–68, Boston, 1912; Henry W. Fowler: "The fishes obtained by the Wilkes

Expedition, 1838–1842," *Amer. Philos. Soc., Proc.*, vol. 82 (5), pp. 733–800, Philadelphia, Pa., 1940; George B. Goode: "The beginnings of American science. The third century," *U. S. Smiths. Inst., Ann. Rept. for 1897*, Part 2, pp. 407–466, Wash., D. C., 1901; Asa Gray: "Scientific results of the Exploring Expedition," *North Amer. Rev.*, vol. 63, pp. 211–236, Boston, 1846; J. Edward Hoffmeister: "James Dwight Dana's studies of volcanoes of coral islands," *Amer. Philos. Soc., Proc.*, vol. 82 (5), pp. 721–732, Philadelphia, Pa., 1840; George P. Merrill: "Contributions to the history of American geology," *U. S. Nat'l Mus. Ann. Rept. for 1904*, pp. 189–733, Wash., D. C., 1906, esp. pp. 423–427; F. W. Reichelderfer: "The contributions of Wilkes to terrestrial magnetism, gravity and meteorology," *Amer. Philos. Soc., Proc.*, vol. 82 (5), pp. 583–600, Philadelphia, Pa., 1940; and Benjamin Silliman: "United States Exploring Expedition," *Amer. Journ. Sci. Arts*, vol. 44, pp. 393–408, New Haven, Conn., 1843.

The scientific members of the Expedition and others who subsequently examined, identified, and interpreted the specimens gathered and the observations reported published their results in the leading scientific periodicals of the day. The following are representative examples: Joseph P. Couthouy: "Remarks upon coral formations in the Pacific; . . . ," *Boston Soc. Nat. Hist., Journ.*, vol. 4 (1) pp. 66–105 and 137–162, Boston, 1843–1844; Horatio Hale: "Migrations in the Pacific Ocean, . . . ," *Amer. Journ. Sci. Arts, Series 2*, vol. 1, pp. 317–332, New Haven, Conn., 1846; James D. Dana: ". . . Conspectus of the Crustacea of the Exploring Expedition under Captain C. Wilkes, U.S.N.," *Amer. Journ. Sci. Arts, Series 2*, vol. 13, pp. 121–123 and vol. 14, pp. 116–125, New Haven, Conn., 1852; James D. Dana: "On an isothermal oceanic chart, illustrating the geographical distribution of marine animals," *Amer. Journ. Sci. Arts, Series 2*, vol. 16, pp. 153–167 and 314–327, New Haven, Conn., 1853; James D. Dana: "On changes of level in the Pacific Ocean," *Amer. Journ. Sci. Arts, Series 2*, vol. 15, pp. 157–175, New Haven, Conn., 1853; James D. Dana: "On denudation in the Pacific," *Amer. Journ. Sci. Arts, Series 2*, vol. 9, pp. 48–62, New Haven, Conn., 1850; Augustus A. Gould: *Otia conchalogica: Descriptions of shells and mollusks from 1839 to 1862*, Boston, 1862, 256 pp., see pp. 1–100 for discussion of shells obtained by the Exploring Expedition; Asa Gray: ". . . characters of two new genera of plants of the order Violaceae, discovered by the naturalists of the U. S. Exploring Expedition . . . ," *Amer. Acad. Arts Sci., Proc.*, vol. 2, pp. 323–325, Boston, 1852; Asa Gray: "Notes upon some Polynesian plants of the order Loganiaceae," *Amer. Acad. Arts Sci., Proc.*, vol. 4, pp. 319–324, Boston, 1859; Asa Gray: "Notes upon some Rubiaceae, collected in the U. S. South-Sea Exploring Expedition, under Capt. Wilkes, with characters of new species . . . ," *Amer. Acad. Arts Sci., Proc.*, vol. 4, pp. 33–50 and 306–318, Boston, 1859; Charles Pickering: . . . *The geographical distribution of animals and plants*, Boston, 1854, 168 + 44 pp.; and Charles Pickering: . . . *The races of man: and their geographical distribution*, Boston, 1848, 447 pp.

96. Harley H. Bartlett: *op. cit.* [note 63], p. 601.

97. For brief references to the role of the Wilkes Exploring Expedition's collections or "gatherings" forming ". . . the legal nucleus of the [National] museum . . ." see Leonard Carmichael: *Joseph Henry, 1797–1878, and his Smithsonian Institution*, New York, 1956, 28 pp.; Robert W. Gibbes: "The National Institute," *Southern Quart. Rev.*, vol. 8, pp. 379–406, Charleston, S. C., 1845; George B. Goode: "The genesis of the National Museum," *U. S. Nat. Mus., Report, 1890–1891*, pp. 273–380, Wash., D. C., 1892; George B. Goode (ed.): *The Smithsonian Institution, 1846–1896. The history of its first half century*, Wash., D. C., 1897, 856 pp.; Daniel C. Haskell: *op. cit.* [note 62]; Joel Roberts Poinsett: *Discourse, on the objects and importance of the National Institute for the Promotion of Science, established at Washington, 1840, delivered at the first anniversary . . .*, Wash., D. C., 1841, 52 pp.; Richard Rathbun: ". . . The Columbian Institute for the Promotion of Arts and Sciences; a Washington Society of 1816–1838, which established a museum and botanic garden under government patronage," *U. S. Nat'l Mus., Bull.* no. 101, pp. 1–85, Wash. D. C., 1917; Wilham J. Rhees: "The Smithsonian Institution: Documents relative to its origin and history," *Smiths. Inst. Colls.*, vol. 17, pp. 1–1013, Wash., D. C., 1879; and the excellent volume by Wilcomb E. Washburn (ed.): *The great design. Two lectures on the Smithson bequest by John Quincy Adams, . . .*, Wash., D. C. 1965, 95 pp.

98. George S. Bryan: *op. cit.* [note 63], p. 558.

99. For an excellent account and listing of most of these records see Daniel C. Haskell (comp.): "Manuscripts, arranged alphabetically by repository," *op. cit.* [note 62], pp. 129–139; and for certain of these in the National Archives see in the *Guide to the records in the National Archives*, Wash., D. C., 1948, 684 pp.

100. For an excellent definitive presentation of this very complex problem of publication, edition, and issue see Daniel C. Haskell (comp.): *op. cit.* [note 62], pp. 31–110.

101. George B. Goode: "The origin of the national scientific and educational institutions of the

United States," *Report of the U. S. Nat'l Mus. for the year ending June 30, 1897, Part II*, pp. 265–354, Wash. D. C., 1901, p. 311.

102. For bibliographies of Maury's publications see Ralph M. Brown: ". . . Bibliography of Commander Matthew Fontaine Maury, including a biographical sketch," *Virginia Polytechnic Inst.*, vol. 37 (12), pp. 1–46, Blacksburg, Va., 1944; and Adelaide R. Hasse (comp.): *A tentative bibliography of Matthew Fontaine Maury*, Library of Congress, Wash., D. C., 1917, 36 pp., an autographed typescript.
Certainly the best biography of Maury is by Frances L. Williams: *Matthew Fontaine Maury, scientist of the sea*, New Brunswick, N. J., 1963, 720 pp. This is a dependable scholarly publication that will long remain the fundamental published source.

103. See especially the logbook of the "U. S. Sloop of War *Falmouth*, Francis H. Gregory, Esq. Commander, 1831–33," in *Records of the Bureau of Naval Personnel* (Record Group 24) in the National Archives.

104. Matthew F. Maury: "On the navigation of Cape Horn," *Amer. Journ. Sci. and Arts*, vol. 26, pp. 54–63, New Haven, Conn., 1834.

105. Matthew F. Maury: *A new theoretical and practical treatise on navigation: . . .*, Philadelphia, Pa., 1836, 216 + 174 pp.

106. Matthew F. Maury: "Remarks on the Gulf Stream and currents of the sea," *Amer. Journ. Sci. and Arts*, vol. 47, pp. 161–181, New Haven, Conn., 1844. See also his article "Currents of the sea as connected with meteorology," *Assoc. Amer. Geol. & Naturalists, Proc.*, no. 5, May 14, 1844, Boston, Mass., 1844.

107. For details see the large volumes of copies of letters sent and of letters received that are among the Records of the Naval Observatory (Record Group 78) in the National Archives.

108. *Ibid.*

109. As Maury's work progressed it became apparent that data from a wider range of sources was necessary. Therefore a circular, dated December 16, 1842, was issued by Maury's superior, Commodore William M. Crane, Chief of the Bureau of Ordnance and Hydrography, inviting ship owners and masters to communicate to the Bureau ten catagories of hydrographical information. As a result, many letters and logbooks were received, and Maury had copyists make abstracts of hundreds of logbooks of commerical and whaling vessels many of which had been in the Pacific Basin. One of these copyists was Captain Daniel McKenzie of New Bedford, who abstracted scores of logbooks of New England whalers. Because whalers ranged far and wide over the oceans, often far from the tracks of merchant vessels, these abstracts provide invaluable data from areas that would otherwise have been blank.

110. *Ibid.* See also his "Blank charts on board public cruises," *Southern Literary Messenger*, vol. 9, pp. 458–461, Richmond, Va., 1843.

111. For the full story see especially the copies of letters sent and the letters received, *op. cit.* [note 107] and the cartographic *Records of the United States Hydrographic Office* (Record Group 37) in the National Archives for the official record set of these and related charts.
See also "Maury's wind and current charts. Drawn by Lieut. William B. Whiting, U.S.N.," *Hunt's Merchant's Mag.*, vol. 18, pp. 516–517, New York, 1848; Matthew F. Maury: *Explanations and sailing directions to accompany the Wind and current charts*, approved by Commodore Lewis Warrington, . . . , Wash. City, 1851, 315 pp. and twelve charts; Matthew F. Maury: *Maury's wind and current charts*, Wash. City, 1857, 8 pp. and twenty-four colored charts; and E. Tricault: . . . *Résumé de la partie physique et descriptive des Sailing Directions du Lieutenant Maury*, Paris, 1857, 208 pp.

112. See correspondence of the Naval Observatory (Record Group 78), *op. cit.* [note 107].

113. *Ibid.*

114. Among his many publications the following are especially helpful with reference to exploration: "Contributions of the Navy to science and commerce," *De Bow's Review . . .* vol. 5 (5–6), pp. 64–68, New Orleans, La., 1848; "Progress of geographical science," *Amer. Geogr. and Stat. Society*, vol. 1 (3), pp. 1–31, New York, 1854; and "Steam navigation to China," *Southern Literary Messenger*, vol. 14, pp. 246–254, Richmond, Va., 1848.

115. Matthew Fontaine Maury: *The physical geography of the sea*, New York, 1855, 274 pp. For an excellent scholarly discussion of this book see John Leighly's introduction, pp. i-xxx, to *The physical geography of the sea and its meteorology, by Matthew Fontaine Maury*. Edited by John Leighly, Harvard University Press, Cambridge, Mass., 1963, 30 pp. and 432 pp. and 10 plates.

116. *Ibid.*, see first paragraph of Maury's introduction.

117. For details on this subject see the letters received and copies of letters sent in the Records of the Naval Observatory (Record Group 78), and the Naval Records Collection of the Office of

Naval Records and Library (Record Group 45) in the National Archives. See also Herman R. Friis: "Matthew Fontaine Maury, Captain, U. S. Navy. American pioneer in polar research and progenitor of the International Geophysical Year program in the Antarctic, 1840–1860," *U. S. Antarctic Projects Officer, Bull.*, vol. 1 (6), pp. 23–29, Wash., D. C., 1960.

118. Harry Wexler, Morton J. Rubin, and J. E. Caskey (eds.): "Antarctic research: the Matthew Fontaine Maury memorial symposium; papers presented at the Tenth Pacific Science Congress of the Pacific Science Association, . . . ," *Nat'l Res. Council, Publ.*, no. 1036, pp. 1–228, Wash., D. C., 1962.

119. For details see Frances L. Williams: *op. cit.* [note 102].

120. See S. Whittemore Boggs: *op. cit.* [note 1]; and Edouard A. Stackpole: *op. cit.* [note 33].

121. For details see Letters received by the Secretary of the Navy from commanding officers of squadrons, 1841–86, East India Letters, 1841–1861, December 13, 1852—May 16, 1855, Commo. Matthew C. Perry, microfilm rolls M89–7 and M89–8 in *Naval Records Collection of the Office of Naval Records and Library* (Record Group 45) in the National Archives.

122. David Hunter Miller (ed.): *Treaties and other international acts of the United States of America*, vol. 4, pp. 559–662, Wash., D. C., 1934.

123. For references on the history of Japan during the nineteenth century, and especially the nature of the closed-door policy, see William G. Beasley (trans. and ed.): *Select documents on Japanese foreign policy, 1853–1868*, London and New York, 1955, 359 pp.; Herbert H. Gowen: *An outline history of Japan*, New York, 1939, 458 pp.; and Payson J. Treat: . . . *The early diplomatic relations between the United States and Japan, 1853–1865*, Baltimore, Md., 1917, 459 pp.

124. For references see Letters received by the Secretary of the Navy from commanding officers of squadrons, 1841–86, East India Letters, 1841–61, August 1, 1845—September 16, 1846, Commo. James Biddle, and February 12, 1848—June 19, 1850, Commo. David Geisinger, and March 1, 1849—February 7, 1851, Commo. Philip F. Voorhees, microfilm rolls M89–3 through M89–5, in *Naval Records Collection of the Office of Naval Records and Library* (Record Group 45), in the National Archives. Brief references to these incidents may be found in M. C. Perry and Francis L. Hawks: *Narrative of the expedition of an American squadron to the China seas and Japan, performed in the years 1852, 1853 and 1854, under the command of Commodore M. C. Perry, United States Navy*, . . . , New York, 1856, 624 pp., see pp. 60–62.

125. For biographical sketches of Matthew C. Perry see Villiam E. Griffis: *Matthew Calbraith Perry; a typical American naval officer*, Boston and New York, 1890, 459 pp.; Hyman Kublin: "Commodore Perry and the Bonin Islands," *U. S. Naval Institute, Proc.*, vol. 78 (3), pp. 283–291, Annapolis, Md., 1952; For primary sources see Records relating to officers, 1825–1936, in *Records of the Bureau of Naval Personnel* (Record Group 24), in the National Archives.

126. For an account of President Fillmore's role see William E. Griffis: "Millard Fillmore and his part in the opening of Japan," *Buffalo Hist. Soc. Publ.*, vol. 9, pp. 53–79, Buffalo, N. Y., 1906.

127. David H. Miller, *op. cit.* [note 122], vol. 6, pp. 439–666, Wash., D. C., 1942.

128. Sydney Wallach (ed.): *Narrative of the expedition of an American squadron to the China seas and Japan, under the command of Commodore M. C. Perry*, . . . , New York, 1952, 305 pp. See p. xvii.

129. M[atthew] C[albraith] Perry and Francis L. Hawks: . . . *Narrative of the expedition of an American squadron to the China seas and Japan performed in the years 1852, 1853 and 1854, under the command of Commodore M. C. Perry, United States Navy, by order of the government of the United States, compiled from the original notes and journal of Commodore Perry—his officers, at his request, and under supervision by Francis L. Hawks*, Wash., 1856, 3 vols. These volumes appeared as publications of the *U. S. 33rd Congress, 2nd Session, Senate Executive Doc. 79*, Serials 769, 770, and 771, and the House Executive Doc. 97, Serials 802, 803, and 804. See also in *Records of the United States Senate* (Record Group 46), *Records of the United States House of Representatives* (Record Group 233), *General Records of the United States Government* (Record Group 11), and *General Records of the Department of State* (Record Group 59) in the National Archives.

The quotation is from the official *Narrative* . . . [see above], vol. 2, p. 407.

130. In addition to the official publications cited in notes 124 and 129 the following are helpful references to this Expedition: Thomas Allen: *Japan, and the expedition thereto of the United States:* . . . , St. Louis, Mo., 1853, 34 pp.; Allan B. Cole (ed.): *With Perry in Japan; the diary of Edward Yorke McCauley*, Princeton, N. J., 1942, 124 pp.; Wilhelm Heine: *Reise um die erde nach Japan an bord der expeditions—escadre unter commodore M. C. Perry in den jahren 1853, 1854 und 1855*, . . . , Leipzig, 1856, 2 vols.; Aaron H. Palmer: *Documents and facts illustrating the origin of the mission to Japan, authorized by government of the United States, May 10, 1851;* . . . , Wash., 1857, 22 pp.; Matthew C. Perry: *A paper by Commodore M. C. Perry, U.S.N., read before the American geographical and statistical society . . . March 6th, 1856*, New York, 1886, 31 pp.; Arthur Walworth: *Black ships off*

Japan: The story of Commodore Perry's expedition, New York, 1946; F. W. Williams (ed.): "A journal of the Perry expedition to Japan (1853–1854) by S. Wells Williams," *Asiatic Soc. Japan, Trans.*, vol. 37, pp. 1–259, Tokyo, 1910; and Albrecht Wirth and Adolph Dirr: *Die Erschliessung Japans, Erinnerungen des Admirals Perry von der Fahrt der amerikanischen Flotte 1853/54*, Hamburg, 1910, 375 pp.

131. M. C. Perry and Francis L. Hawks: *op. cit.* [note 129], vol. 1, p. 238, 241, 267, 268 and 271. See also "A report of the Secretary of the navy, . . . relative to the naval expedition to Japan," *33rd Congress 2nd Session, Senate Executive Doc. no 34*, pp. 1–195, Wash., D. C. In the notes, p. 47, is the following interesting statement by Perry:

I had directed that a surveying boat, well manned and armed, from each ship of the squadron, should commence at daylight this morning, the 9th [July 1853], the survey of the harbor and bay of Uraga, and thinking it quite possible they might meet with some resistance, I instructed Lieutenant Silas Bent, in command of the surveying party, not to go beyond the range of our guns, and caused a look-out to be kept upon them, that assistance might be sent should they be attacked; but though they were followed by numbers of Japanese boats, they did not, on seeing our men well armed, venture to molest them.

132. *Ibid.*, p. 326.

133. *Ibid.*, pp. 282–283.

134. *Ibid.*, p. 283.

135. *Ibid.*, pp. 308–323.

136. *Ibid.*, pp. 324–342.

137. *Ibid.*, p. 340.

138. *Ibid.*, p. 365.

139. *Ibid.*, p. 393.

140. *Ibid.*, pp. 332 and 355.

141. *Ibid.*, p. 468.

142. *Ibid.*, p. 501.

143. For a published account see in *ibid.*, vols. 1–3. For manuscript materials see Record Groups 11, 24, 37, 45, 46, 59, and 233 in the National Archives.

144. "A report . . ." [note 131], p. 3.

145. *Ibid.*, p. 2.

146. For the manuscript compilations, field sheets, and other hydrographic information see *Records of United States Hydrographic Office* (Record Group 37) in the National Archives.

147. The charts included with the official published report are: "The Harbor of Hokodadi . . . 1854 (1:36, 456);" "Endermo Harbor . . . 1854 (1:5,086);" "Reconnaissance of the Gulf and survey of the Western Shore of the Bay of Yedo . . . 1853–54 (1:72,913);" "Simoda Harbor . . . 1854 (1:18,439);" "The Coffin Islands . . . 1854 (1:109,369);" "Western Shore of the Bay of Yedo . . . 1854 (1:72,913);" "Island of Lew Chew . . . 1853–54 (1:9,914);" "The Harbor of Napha, Lew Chew Id . . . 1853 (1:21,445);" "Deep Bay . . . Lew Chew Id . . . 1853–54 (1:40,507);" "Tubootch & Suco Harbors . . . 1854 (1:20,000);" "Shah Bay, Lew Chew I. . . . 1853 (1:9,914);" "Keelung Harbor, Formosa Island . . . 1854 (1:9,914);" "Chart of the world showing the track of the U. S. Frigates . . . , 1853–54; and a small scale "Chart of the Coast of China and of the Japanese Islands, . . . 1855." These may be found in volume 2 of Matthew C. Perry: *op. cit.* [note 129] and in some instances in a separate atlas folio. Reproductions of some of these charts on a reduced scale, and one of the Bonin Islands may be found in volume 1. For the manuscript originals see in Record Group 37 in the National Archives.

148. *Ibid.* [note 129], vol. 2, p. 213.

149. For biographical sketches see Asa Gray: "Francis Boott, 1792–1863," *Amer. Journ. Sci. Arts, Series 2*, vol. 37, pp. 288–292, New Haven, Conn., 1864; "James Carson Brevoort, 1818–1887," *New York Acad. Sci., Trans.*, vol. 7, pp. 78–80, New York, 1887–1888; W. A. Setchell: "Daniel Cady Eaton, 1834–1895," *Torrey Bot. Club, Bull.*, vol. 2 (7), pp. 341–351, New York, 1895; "Asa Gray," *op. cit.* [note 69]; Asa Gray: "Biographical notice of Wm. Henry Harvey, . . . ," *Smiths. Inst. Ann. Rept.*, 1867, pp. 131–134, Wash., 1867; Herman L. Fairchild: "John Clarkson Jay, 1808–1891," in his *History of the New York Acad. Sci.*, New York, 1887, 190 pp., pp. 89 and 100; Allan B. Cole (ed.): *A scientist with Perry in Japan, the journal of Dr. James Morrow*, Chapel Hill, N. C., 1947, 307 pp.; A. Hunter Dupree: "Science vs the military: Dr. James Morrow and the Perry expedition," *Pacific Hist. Rev.*, vol. 22, pp. 29–37, Berkeley and Los Angeles, 1953.

150. For representative examples see James C. Brevoort: *Notes on some figures of Japanese fish, taken from recent specimens, by the artists of the U. S. Japan expedition*, Wash., 1856, 36 pp. and 12 pl.; and George Jones: "Observations of the zodiacal light," *Astronomical Journ.*, vol. 4, pp. 94–95,

Chapter 13

Albany, N. Y., 1856; See also volume two of Matthew C. Perry: *Narrative . . .*, *op. cit.* [note 129].

151. See especially his *Reise um die erde nach Japan an bord der expeditions—escadre unter commodore M. C. Perry in den jahren 1853, 1854 und 1855, . . .*, Leipzig, 1856, 2 vols. and his *Graphic scenes in the Japan expedition*, New York, 1856, 2pp. and 10 pl.

152. Allan B. Cole (ed.): *Yankee surveyors in the Shogun's seas; records of the United States Surveying Expedition to the North Pacific Ocean, 1853–1856*, Princeton, N. J., 161 pp., reference is on p. 5. For the official record and background see in U. S. 32d Congress, 1st Session, in *Records of the United States House of Representatives* (Record Group 233) in the National Archives.

153. See, for example, the Letters Received and Letters Sent in the *Records of the Naval Observatory* (Record Group 78) in the National Archives.

154. Although the expedition was very important and performed its tasks most creditably, relatively little has been written about it and there has been no official report. There is a large amount of manuscript records of the Expedition in the National Archives. These include especially the textual and cartographic records which may be found in *Records of the Bureau of Ships* (Record Group 19); *Records of the Bureau of Naval Personnel* (Record Group 24); *Records of the Hydrographic Office* (Record Group 37); *Naval Records Collection of the Office of Naval Records and the Library* (Record Group 45); *Records of the United States Senate* (Record Group 46); *General Records of the Department of State* (Record Group 59); *Records of the Naval Observatory* (Record Group 78); and *Records of the United States House of Representatives* (Record Group 233).

155. For the manuscript letter sent see Letter from John P. Kennedy to Commodore Charles Morris, Chief of the Bureau of Ordnance and Hydrography, dated Navy Dept. Sept. 24, 1852, in Letters Received, *Records of the Office of the Naval Observatory* (Record Group 78) in the National Archives. An office copy of this letter is in Letters Received by the Bureau of Ordnance and Hydrography, from Secretary of the Navy, vol. 3, no. 12 in *Records of Office of Naval Records and Library* (Record Group 45) in the National Archives. A copy of Maury's reply dated October 14, 1852 is in Letters Received, pp. 226–232, in the *Records of the Naval Observatory* (Record Group 78).

156. Richard Rathbun: "Descriptive catalogue of the collection illustrating the scientific investigation of the sea and fresh waters," *United States Nat'l Mus., Bull.*, vol. 27, pp. 513–621, Wash., D. C. 1884, see p. 533. There is some uncertainty as to the extent to which the Expedition was supplied with maps authored by Philipp Franz von Siebold, long-time resident of Deshima in Japan and in the 1850s residing in the Netherlands. Von Siebold's maps were purchased by the United States government ostensibly for the Perry Expedition. See letter from M. C. Perry to Wm. A. Graham, Secy of the Navy, dated New York, April 16, 1852, Captains' Letters, vol. Jan.— June, 1852, Letter no. 82, 2 pp. ALS, in the *General Records of the Department of the Navy* (Record Group 80) and M. C Perry to Wm. A. Graham, Secy of the Navy, Dated Wash., March 23, 1852, Letter no. 62, 2 pp. ALS, *ibid*. According to one account, Von Siebold smuggled a copy of Ino Chukei's map of Nippon out of Japan and a copy or copies of it were available to the Perry and Ringgold-Rodgers expeditions. Chukei's map was engraved in 1823. For a reference to this information see Allan B. Cole (ed.): *op. cit.* [note 152], p. 6.

157. Richard Rathbun: *ibid*.

158. For brief biographies see William J. Heffernan: *Edward M. Kern [1823–63] the travels of an artist-explorer*, Bakersfield, Calif., 1953, 112 pp.; and C. W. Eliot: "Francis H. Storer," *Amer. Acad. Arts Sci., Proc.*, vol. 54, pp. 415–418, Boston, Mass., 1919.

159. For a brief biography see Charles L. Lewis: "Brooke, John Mercer (Dec. 18, 1826—Dec. 14, 1906)," *Dict. Amer. Biogr.*, vol. 3, pp. 69–70, New York, 1929.

160. For a brief biography see Allan Westcott: "Ringgold, Cadwalader (Aug. 20, 1802—Apr. 29, 1867)," *Dict. Amer. Biogr.*, vol. 15, pp. 617–618, New York, 1935. During the years 1849 and 1850 Ringgold was engaged in a major project of surveying the California coast, especially San Francisco Bay and the Sacramento River. A primary product of his survey was his publication in 1851 of *A series of charts, with sailing directions . . . to the Bay of San Francisco*, which went through five editions, and the related *Correspondence* to accompany maps and charts of California. A published record set of these charts and correspondence is in *Records of the Hydrographic Office* (Record Group 37) in the National Archives.

161. For published accounts of the Expedition see Allan B. Cole: "Ringgold-Rodgers-Brooke expedition to Japan and the North Pacific, 1853–1859," *Pacific Hist. Rev.*, vol. 16, pp. 152–162, Berkeley, Calif., 1947; Allan B. Cole: *. . . The dynamics of American expansion toward Japan, 1791–1860*, Abstract of his Ph.D. thesis, Univ. Chicago, 1940, 14 pp.; Allan B. Cole (ed.): *op. cit.* [note 152]; William Heine: *Die expedition in die seen von China, Japan und Ochotsk, unter commando von commodore Colin Ringgold und commodore John Rodgers, . . . 1853 bis 1856*, Leipzig, 1858–1859, 3

vols.; Joseph E. Nourse: *American explorations in the ice zones. The expeditions of De Haven, Kane, Rodgers, . . . Prepared chiefly from official sources*, Boston, 1884, 578 pp.; and Richard Rathbun: "The North Pacific Exploring Expedition," *op. cit.* [note 156], pp. 532–535.

162. The only detailed published source that is available as a reference to the route traveled and the work accomplished is Allan B. Cole: *Yankee surveyors . . .* , [note 152]. The official correspondence and reports comprising most of this publication have been used as the source for this brief discussion of the route and the accomplishments of the Expedition. In his letter of February 23, 1853 to Commander Ringgold Lieutenant Rodgers remarked:

We commenced a system of triangulation with three vessels measuring the base by sound and altitude of masts at the same time cutting in all conspicuous peaks, points, &c. by careful rounds of angles. We have thus secured the basis of an accurate chart and of plotting our work quickly and correctly, having the points published except as to names our chart will differ in essential points from the various charts published.

This would not have been worth the time of making it had the changes been of little importance. The additions have been vital. We have some 7 or 8 new shoals and several islands not down on any chart . . .".

See in Letterbook of Lieutenant Commanding John Rodgers, U. S. Exploring Expedition of North Pacific, March 19, 1853—Aug. 10, 1854, Letterbooks of U. S. Naval Officers at Sea, *Records of the Office of Naval Records and Library* (Record Group 45), in the National Archives.

163. *Ibid.*, pp. 23–25. For a biography of John Rodgers see Charles O. Paullin: "Rodgers, John (Aug. 8 1812—May 5, 1882)," *Dict. Amer. Biogr.*, vol. 16, pp. 77–78, New York, 1935.

164. Allan B. Cole: *Yankee surveyors . . .* , [note 152], pp. 10 and 27–28.

165. *Ibid.*, p. 12.

166. *Ibid.*, p. 13.

167. *Ibid.*, p. 14.

168. *Ibid.*, p. 14. The track of this detailed survey is shown on the manuscript chart "East Coast of Nippon, Empire of Japan, Shimoda to Hokodadi," in the *Records of the Hydrographic Office*. (Record Group 37) in the National Archives.

169. Allan B. Cole (ed.): *op. cit.* [note 152], pp. 14–15 and 18.

170. *Ibid.*, p. 18.

171. *Ibid.*, p. 18.

172. *Ibid.*, p. 18.

173. *Ibid.*, pp. 154–156 include a list of the charts.

174. *Ibid.*, pp. 52–53.

175. For this correspondence relating to work to be done on the charts and negotiations that were to be made with the lithographers, see especially Letters Sent by the Naval Observatory, vol. 13, in *Records of the Naval Observatory* (Record Group 78) in the National Archives. Additional correspondence is in KH North Pacific Exploring Expedition 0–1873, Subject File in the *Records of the Office of Naval Records and the Library*, (Record Group 45) in the National Archives.

176. These and related nautical charts are in *Records of the Hydrographic Office* (Record Group 37) in the National Archives.

177. For an example of the original work sheets pasted together and mounted on cloth and containing pencil and ink annotations relative to surveying and compilation and the correlation of ingredients of the map with Russian, English, and Dutch charts see "Reconnaissance of the Gotto Islands and Straits with the S. W. Coast of Kiusiu Japan by the U. S. Schooner Fenimore Cooper, . . . ," File 451.36, no. 18, Records of the Hydrographic Office (Record Group 37) in the National Archives.

178. For examples of the charts see in *Records of the Hydrographic Office* (Record Group 37) and for correspondence thereto see in the *Records of the Naval Observatory* (Record Group 78) in the National Archives.

179. Richard Rathbun: *op. cit.* [note 156], p. 533. William Stimpson in his letter of Dec. 1, 1856 to James Dwight Dana notes that "The whole number of [zoological] species collected in all departments is about 5300. The number of specimens may be stated approximately as 12,000," for which see in his letter published in *Amer. Journ. Sci. Arts*, Series 2, vol. 23, pp. 136–138, New Haven, Conn., 1857.

180. Richard Rathbun: *ibid.*, pp. 533–534.

181. William Stimpson: "Report on the crustacea (Brachyura and Anomura) collected by the North Pacific Exploring Expedition, 1853–1856," *Smiths. Misc. Coll.*, vol. 49 (no. 1717), pp. 1–240, Wash., D. C. This publication is profusely illustrated with sketches of the specimens, presumably by Stimpson.

182. Richard Rathbun: *op. cit.* [note 156], p. 533.

183. Ferdinand V. Hayden: "United States government surveys," *Amer. Journ. Sci. Arts*, Series 2, vol. 34, pp. 98–101, New Haven, Conn., 1862, see p. 98 for this quotation.

184. These publications included particularly the *Proceedings of the Academy of Natural Science of Philadelphia; Proceedings of the American Academy of Arts and Sciences*, Boston, Mass.; *Proceedings of the Boston Society of Natural History;* and the *American Journal of Science and Arts*, New Haven, Conn. Accounts of the progress and accomplishments of the expeditions of the 1850s and later may be found in the *Annual Reports of the Smithsonian Institution* and in the *Journal* and the *Bulletin of the American Geographical and Statistical Society.*

185. The following are representative examples. Alexander Agassiz: "Synopsis of the Echinoids collected by Dr. W. Stimpson on the North Pacific Exploring Expedition . . . ," *Acad. Nat. Sci., Phila., Proc.*, vol. 15, pp. 352–361, Philadelphia, Pa., 1863; Augustus A. Gould: "New species of shells brought home by the North Pacific Exploring Expedition . . . ," *Boston Soc. Nat. Hist., Proc.*, vol. 7, pp. 323–340, 382–389, and 400–409, Boston Mass., 1860; Asa Gray: "Diagnostic characters of new species of phaenogamous plants, collected in Japan by Charles Wright, botanist of the U. S. North Pacific Exploring Expedition . . . ," *Amer. Acad. Arts Sci., Memoirs*, vol. 6 (2), pp. 377–452, Boston, Mass., 1858; John Rodgers and Anton Schonborn: "On the avoidence of the violent portions of cyclones; with notices of a typhoon at the Bonin islands," *Amer. Journ. Sci. Arts, Proc.*, vol. 23, pp. 205–211, New Haven, Conn., 1857; William Stimpson: "On the crustacea and echinodermata of the Pacific shores of North America," *Bost. Journ. Nat. Hist.*, vol. 6, pp. 444–532, Boston, 1857; William Stimpson: *op. cit.* [note 179]; P. R. Uhler: "Hemiptera of the North Pacific Exploring Expedition . . . ," *Acad Nat. Sci., Phila., Proc.*, vol. 12, pp. 221–231, Philadelphia, Pa., 1860; and Addison E. Verrill: "Corals and polyps of the North Pacific exploring expedition, . . . ," *The Essex Institute, Proc.*, vol. 4, pp. 147–152, vol. 5, pp. 181–196, Salem, Mass., 1865–1866.

186. See a "Map of the territory of the United States from the Mississippi to the Pacific Ocean . . . Compiled from authorized explorations and other reliable data by Lieut. G. K. Warren, . . . in 1854, 5, 6, 7." In volume 11 of *Reports of Explorations and Surveys to Ascertain the Most Practicable and Economical Route for a Railroad . . .* , Wash., 1859. A copy, slightly reduced in scale, is in William H. Goetzmann: *Army exploration in the American West, 1803–1863*, New Haven, Conn., 1959, 509 pp., see esp. pp. 313–315. A good account of this subject is in Carl I. Wheat: "Mapping the American West, 1540–1857; a preliminary study," *Amer. Antiq. Soc., Proc.*, vol. 64, pp. 19–194, Worcester, Mass., 1954; and Carl I. Wheat: *Mapping the transmississippi West, 1540–1861*, San Francisco, 1957–1963, 5 vols. in 6. Examples of maps of the West are described in Herman R. Friis and Suzanne Pitzer: "Federal exploration of the American West before 1880," *Nat'l Archives Publ.*, no. 64–6, pp. 1–31, Wash., 1963.

187. The results of these surveys were published in *Reports of explorations and surveys to ascertain the most practical and economical route for a railroad . . .* , Wash., 1853–60, 12 vols. in 13.

188. *Ibid.*, see vols. 1, 6 and 7.

189. Cadwalader Ringgold: *A series of charts, with sailing directions, embracing surveys of the Farollones, entrance to the bay of San Francisco, . . .* , Wash., 1851, six charts and 44 pp.; and his *Correspondence to accompany maps and charts of California*, Wash., 1851 (?), 15 pp.

190. William H. Goetzmann: *op. cit.* [note 186]; and Carl I. Wheat: *op. cit.* [note 186]. For the official manuscript record of the maps, reports, journals, and notes of these explorations see in *Records of the Office of the Chief of Engineers* (Record Group 77) in the National Archives. For the official manuscript of the maps, charts, journals, reports, and related materials of the Coast Survey see *Records of the Coast and Geodetic Survey* (Record Group 23) in the National Archives.

191. For the official records see in the National Archives, especially Nathan Reingold (comp.): "Records of the Coast and Geodetic Survey," *National Archives Preliminary Inventory*, no. 105, pp. 1–83, Wash., D. C., 1958. The history of the Coast Survey is given in *Report on the history and progress of the American coast survey up to the year 1858; . . .* , n.p., 1858, 88 pp.; Elliott B. Roberts: "Coast and Geodetic Survey highlights of 150 years," *U. S. Naval Institute, Proc.*, vol. 83 (2), pp. 188–211, Annapolis, Md., 1957, see pp. 192–193; and A. Joseph Wraight and Elliott B. Roberts: *The Coast and Geodetic Survey, 1807–1957; 150 years of history*, Wash., D. C., 1957, 89 pp.

192. The official published reports for the period 1850–1860 are included in the U. S. Coast Survey: *Annual report of the superintendent of the Coast Survey showing the progress of that work during the year ending . . .* , Wash., 1852–1861, 11 vols. These annual reports give an excellent account of the operations of the field parties, publications, chart publication, and achievements generally. See also the "General Correspondence of Alexander Dallas Bache" in the *Records of the Coast and Geodetic Survey* (Record Group 23) in the National Archives. For references to publications of the Coast Survey see E. B. Hunt: "Report on an index of reference to memoirs and papers on subjects

related to the Coast Survey operations," *Annual report* . . . , *the year ending 1856*, pp. 325–330, Wash., 1857; E. L. Burchard (comp.): *List and catalogue of the publications issued by the U. S. Coast and Geodetic Survey, 1816–1902, reprinted with a supplement, 1903–1908*, Wash., D. C., 1908, 237 pp.; U. S. Coast Survey: . . . *Original topographical sheets registered in the archives of the U. S. Coast Survey from Jan. 1834 to July 1875 (Nos. 1–1378 inclusive)*, Wash., 1877, 26 pp.; and "Review of the operations and results of the United States Coast Survey," *Amer. Journ. Sci. Arts, Proc., Series 2*, vol. 25, pp. 75–83 and 249–258, New Haven, Conn., 1858. See also Carl I. Wheat: *The maps of the California gold region, 1848–1857, a bibliocartography of an important decade*, San Francisco, 1942, 152 pp.

193. See *Annual report* . . . , *ibid.*, for 1848 through 1852.

194. For a review of McArthur's accomplishments see Lewis A. McArthur: "The Pacific coast survey of 1849 and 1850," *Oregon Hist. Quart.*, vol. 16, pp. 246–274, Portland, Ore., 1915; and William P. McArthur: "Report accompanying a reconnaissance chart of the western coast of the United States from Monterey, California to the Columbia River, Oregon," *Annual report . . . for 1850*, pp. 119–122, Wash., 1851.

In Lewis A. McArthur, above, is a letter of instruction from Alexander D. Bache, Superintendent of the Coast Survey, to William P. McArthur, dated October 27, 1848, which notes that ". . . I have been directed by the Treasury Department to make arrangements for commencing the survey of the Western Coast of the United States . . ." Bache selected McArthur to lead this survey.

195. For references to the biography and scientific achievements of George Davidson see Leo O. Colbert: "Pioneer personalities in the Coast and Geodetic Survey," *Journ. Coast and Geodetic Survey*, no. 3, pp. 25–37, Wash., D. C., 1950; Oscar Lewis: *George Davidson, pioneer west coast scientist*, Berkeley, Calif., 1954, 146 pp.; Morgan B. Sherwood: "A pioneer scientist in the far north: George Davidson and the development of Alaska," *Pacific Northwest Quart.*, vol. 53 (2), pp. 77–80, Seattle, Wash., 1962; and Henry R. Wagner: "George Davidson, geographer of the northwest coast of America," *Calif. Hist. Soc., Quart.*, vol. 11 (4), pp. 299–320, San Francisco, 1932, an excellent summary of Davidson's geographical and cartographical work on the Pacific coast. For a good example of Davidson's scholarly interest in the history of exploration of the northwest coast see his "Voyages of discovery and exploration on the Northwest Coast of America from 1539 to 1603," *Annual report . . . U. S. Coast and Geodetic Survey for 1886*, Appendix 7, pp. 155–253, Wash., 1887; and his "Early voyages on the northwestern coast of America," *Nat'l Geogr. Mag.*, vol. 5, pp. 235–256, Wash., 1894. An excellent list of Davidson's publications is in Henry R. Wagner: *ibid.*, pp. 314–320.

196. See in *Annual report . . . Coast Survey . . . 1852*, Wash., 1853.

197. *Ibid.*

198. For a list of the charts completed prior to 1860 see in U. S. Coast Survey: *Catalogue of charts, 1875*, Wash., 1875, 28 pp., pp. 26–28.

199. Lieutenant James Alden was a competent hydrographer-surveyor and an artist. For examples of his work as an artist see in *Records of the Coast and Geodetic Survey* (Record Group 23) and in *Records of Boundary and Claims Commissions and Arbitrations* (Record Group 76) in the National Archives in Wash., D. C. For an account of a survey by James Alden see in Jean Hazeltine: "The discovery and cartographical recognition of Shoalwater Bay," *Oregon Hist. Quart.*, vol. 58, pp. 251–263, Portland, Ore., 1952. See also James B. Rhoads: "When the wild northern boundary stretched to the sea, a government artist recorded the rugged surveying job," *Amer. Heritage*, vol. 8 (4), pp. 14–17, New York, 1957. Reports on geographical subjects by James Alden are in the *Annual reports . . . U. S. Coast Survey*, for the 1850s.

200. For the permanent record of these charts see in *Records of the Coast and Geodetic Survey* (Record Group 23) in the National Archives.

201. In his *Annual report . . . for the year ending 1853*, Director Alexander Dallas Bache noted that "The hydrographic reconnaissance of the Western coast, so essential to commerce and navigation there, has been completed from San Francisco north, having been finished this summer . . . Reconnaissances and preliminary surveys have been made in a rapid way, and sketches have been published to meet the immediate wants of the country; accurate surveys and complete maps will in turn speedily take the place of these . . ." p. 6, Wash., 1854.

202. For an account of these activities see *Annual report . . . U. S. Coast Survey . . . 1854*, Wash., 1855, esp. pp. 76 and 85.

203. For excellent examples of the wide range of scientific subjects discussed in articles by specialists in the agency, especially those in the field on the Pacific coast, see in the *Annual reports . . . U. S. Coast Survey, . . .*, for the 1850s.

204. See in *Naval Records Collection of the Office of Naval Records and Library* (Record Group 45)

and *General Records of the Navy Department* (Record Group 80) in the National Archives in Wash., D. C. For published information about these voyages see especially *Annual reports of the Navy department . . . , 1822/23—1859/60*, Wash., 1823–1860; *Amer. Journ. Sci. Arts, Series 1*, vols. 39–50, 1840–1846 and *Series 2*, vols. 1–50, New Haven, Conn., 1846–1860; and the *Annual report of the Board of Regents of the Smithsonian Institution, 1846–1860*, Wash., 1847–1861, 13 vols.

205. Allan B. Cole: *op. cit.* [note 152], pp. 158–159. For original letter see in Secretary of the Navy, Confidential Letters, no. 3, Feb. 1, 1853—Oct. 17, 1857, in *General Records of the Navy Department* (Record Group 80) in the National Archives.

206. See in copies of letters sent in Letterbooks and in letters received in *Records of the Naval Observatory* (Record Group 78) in the National Archives.

207. For the manuscript account and profile see in *Records of the Hydrographic Office* (Record Group 37) in the National Archives.

208. For information about the status and method of operations of deep-sea sounding during this period see especially the following contemporary articles by W. P. Trowbridge: "On deep sea soundings," *Amer. Journ. Sci. Arts, Proc., Series 2*, vol. 26, pp. 157–177, New Haven, Conn., 1858; "On deep sea explorations," *Amer. Journ. Sci. Arts, Proc., Series 2*, vol. 26, pp. 386–391, New Haven, Conn., 1858; and "On a new sounding apparatus for deep-sea sounding," *Amer. Journ. Sci. Arts, Proc., Series 2*, vol. 28, pp. 1–8, New Haven, 1859.

209. For a brief account of the background see James M. Gilliss: *. . . Origin and operations of the U. S. Naval astronomical expedition*, Wash., D. C., 1856, 13 pp.

210. For the published report see James M. Gilliss: ". . . The U. S. Naval astronomical expedition to the southern hemisphere, during the years 1849, '50, '51, '52 . . . ," *United States 33d Congress, 1st Session, House Executive Doc.*, no. 121, parts 1–3, and 6, Wash., D. C., 1855–1856, Congressional Serial nos. 728, 729, 730, and 733. For a brief résumé of the accomplishments see "The U. S. Naval Astronomical Expedition to the Southern Hemisphere, during the years 1849–'52 . . . ," *Amer. Journ. Sci. Arts, Proc., Series 2*, vol. 21, pp. 147–148, New Haven, Conn. For a good biography of Gilliss see Benjamin A. Gould: "Memoir of James Melville Gilliss, 1811–1865," *Nat'l Acad. Sci., Biogr. Memoirs*, vol. 1, pp. 135–179, Wash., D. C., 1877. The manuscript records of this expedition are in the *Naval Records Collection of the Office of Naval Records and Library* (Record Group 45) and in the *Records of the Naval Observatory* (Record Group 78) in the National Archives.

211. Scientific results were published in the four-volume official report issued by the Congress of the United States in 1855–1856, *ibid*. Volumes 1 and 2 cover the general geographical observations and natural history.

212. For representative examples of the publications in addition to those in volume 2 see Charles Girard: "Abstract of a report to Lieut. James M. Gilliss, U. S. N., upon the reptiles collected during the U. S. N. Astronomical Expedition to Chili," *Acad. Nat. Sci., Philadelphia, Proc.*, vol. 7, pp. 226–227, Philadelphia, Pa., 1854; and Charles Girard: ". . . report to Lieut. Jas. M. Gilliss, U. S. N., upon the fishes . . . ," *Acad. Nat. Sci., Philadelphia, Proc.*, vol. 7, pp. 197–199, Philadelphia, 1854.

213. *Op. cit.* [note 210]. Volumes 3 and 6 cover astronomical, magnetical, and meteorological observations. See also James M. Gilliss: "A catalogue of 16,748 southern stars deduced by the U. S. Naval Observatory from the zone observations made at Santiago de Chile . . . ," *U. S. 54th Congress, 1st Session, House Doc.*, no. 219, Appendix 1, pp. 1–66 and 1–420, Wash., D. C., 1895, Congressional Serial no. 3424.

214. For official recognition of the "guano problem" in relation to discovery, exploration, and trade see for example *U. S. 31st Congr. 1st Sess., Senate Executive Documents*, no. 73, pp. 1–8, Wash., 1850; *U. S. 35th Congr. 1st Sess., House Reports*, no. 307, pp. 1–10, Wash., 1858; and *U. S. 35th Congr. 2d Sess., House Miscellaneous Documents*, no. 25, pp. 1–75, Wash., 1859. The American Guano Company in 1856 memorialized the Congress for ". . . recognition and protection of all guano islands discovered and settled by Americans, past, present, and future . . ." Quoted from *U. S. 34th Congr. 1st Sess., Senate Miscellaneous Documents*, no. 60, pp. 1–12, Wash., 1856.

215. Representatives of the American Guano Company of New York landed on Jarvis and Baker islands in 1857, taking the first shipment of guano. The Pacific Company operated on Johnston Island and the Phoenix Guano Company on Starbuck, McKean, Phoenix, and Enderby islands Lieutenant Brooke, while commanding the *Fenimore Cooper* investigating the steamship route across the Pacific, in 1859 visited some islands reported to contain guano. He confirmed the existence of deposits on French Frigate Shoal northwest of the Hawaiian Islands. For a good account of this activity and especially of the physical geography of the guano islands see J. D. Hague: "On phosphatic guano islands of the Pacific Ocean," *Amer. Journ. Sci. Arts, Series 2*, vol. 34, pp. 224–243, New Haven, Conn., 1862.

216. For the official records of these surveys see in *Records of the Hydrographic Office* (Record Group 37) in the National Archives.

217. *Ibid.*

218. See *Annual Report of the Secretary of the Smithsonian Institution, 1849–1860*, Wash., 1850–1861, 10 vols. This summary usually was prepared by the Assistant Secretary (Professor Spencer F. Baird) and included with his report which was attached to that of the Secretary, Joseph Henry.

219. The details as to specific accessions are included in the official records of the Smithsonian Institution that are in its Archives.

220. For summaries and frequent references to these expeditions and surveys see in The American Geographical Society of New York: *Journ.*, vols. 1–32, New York, 1859–1900; The Geographical Society of Philadelphia: *Bull.*, vols. 1–3, Philadelphia, Pa., 1893–1899; August H. Petermann and Others (eds.): *Petermanns Mitteilungen*, vols. 1–45, Gotha, Germany, 1855–1899; and the Royal Geographical Society, London: *Geogr. Mag.*, vols. 1–5, 1874–1878, *Journ.*, vols. 1–50, 1831–1881 and vols. 1–14, 1893–1899, and *Proc.*, vols. 1–22, 1855–1878. See especially: "The progress of marine geography," *Amer. Geogr. and Stat. Soc., Journ.*, vol. 2 (1), pp. 1–12, New York, 1860; Charles P. Daly: "The geographical work of the world for 1875, *Amer. Geogr. Soc., Journ.*, vol. 8, pp. 4–59, New York, 1876; and Daniel C. Gilman: "The last ten years of geographical work in this country," *Amer. Geogr. Soc., Journ.*, vol. 3, pp. 111–133, New York, 1873.

221. For a continuous official published discussion of these activities see U. S. Navy Department: *Annual reports of the Navy Department . . . 1860/61–1898/99*, Wash., D. C., 1861–1900. For the official records see *Records of the Hydrographic Office* (Record Group 37), *General Records of the Department of the Navy* (Record Group 80), and *Naval Records Collection of the Office of Naval Records and Library* (Record Group 45) in the National Archives in Wash., D. C. See also Gardner W. Allen: *List of articles from periodicals relating to the United States Navy*, Wash., D. C., 1916, 133 typed pages, manuscript in the Library of Congress, Wash., D. C.; Charles T. Harbeck (comp.): *A contribution to the bibliography of the history of the United States Navy*, Cambridge, Mass., 1906, 247 pp.; Robert E. Johnson: *Thence round Cape Horn; the story of United States Naval Forces on Pacific Station, 1818–1923*, Annapolis, 1963, 276 pp.; and Robert W. Neeser: *Statistical and chronological history of the United States Navy, 1775–1907*, New York, 1909, 2 vols.

222. The extent to which this was involved is shown by the recognition of source noted on each U. S. Hydrographic Office nautical chart. See the manuscript and published record set of these charts in *Records of the Hydrographic Office* (Record Group 37) in the National Archives.

223. For references on this history see Joe B. Cochran: "Hydro at 125," *U. S. Naval Institute, Proc.*, vol. 81, pp. 1361–1377, Annapolis, Md., 1955; Walter S. Hughes: *Founding and development of the U. S. Hydrographic Office*, Wash., 1887, 71 pp.; Thelma B. Player (comp.): *A selected bibliography on the U. S. Hydrographic Office*, Wash., 1887, 71 pp.; Thelma B. Player (comp.): *A selected bibliography on the U. S. Hydrographic Office*, Wash., 1958, 14 pp.; Gustavus A. Weber: *. . . The Hydrographic Office; its history, activities and organization*, Baltimore, Md., 1926, 112 pp.; and the following by the U. S. Hydrographic Office: *The Hydrographic Office; its founding, object, organization and fieldwork*, Wash., D. C., 1908, a typescript; "United States Navy Hydrographic Office," *U. S. Hydrographic Office Publ.* no. 15561, pp. 1–46, Wash., D. C., 1952; *History of the U. S. Navy Hydrographic Office*, Wash., D. C., 1953, 14 pp.; *125th anniversary, United States Navy Hydrographic Office, Dec. 6, 1830—Dec. 6, 1955*, Wash., D. C., 1955, 25 pp.

224. For a history of the accomplishments of this firm and of its large role in the creation of the Hydrographic Office see *op. cit.* [note 46].

225. The manuscript boat sheets, smooth sheets, and compilation drawings for and the published record set (including variant editions) of the cartographic products and the logbooks, journals, and a wide variety and large volume of related observations are in *Records of the Hydrographic Office* (Record Group 37) in the National Archives. For a brief description of these records see Walter W. Weinstein: "The records of the Hydrographic Office (Record Group 37)," *The National Archives Preliminary Inventory* no. 39, pp. 1–17, 1952.

226. John E. Pillsbury (comp.): "Reported dangers to navigation in the Pacific ocean, inclusive of the China and Japan seas, . . . ," *U. S. Hydrographic Office, Publ.*, no. 41, 2 vols., Wash., 1871–1879. For an earlier edition see William Reynolds (comp.): "A list of the reported dangers to navigation in the Pacific Ocean, whose positions are doubtful, or not found on the charts in general use," *U. S. Hydrographic Office, Publ.*, no. 3, pp. 1–191, Wash., 1866.

227. For the published record set of these and related maps see in *Records of the Hydrographic Office* (Record Group 37) in the National Archives.

228. See for example its *General Catalogue of mariners' and aviators' charts and books . . .*, Wash., D. C., 1871–1931, 28 vols.; and *Catalog of charts and plans issued to vessels of the United States Navy on the Pacific Station by the Hydrographic Office*, Wash., D. C., 1872–1933, 6 vols.

229. For a brief history see U. S. Hydrographic Office: *Surveys by the Hydrographic Office, . . . , from the survey of Georges Bank and shoal by Lieut. Charles Wilkes, U.S.N. in 1837 to July 1, 1924, with*

a brief history of several of the earlier surveying expeditions, Wash., D. C., 1924, 20 pp.; George W. Littlehales: "The Navy as a motor in geographical and commercial progress," *Amer. Geogr. Soc., Journ.*, vol. 31 (2), pp. 123–149, New York, 1899; George W. Littlehales: "Recent foreign surveys under the direction of the U. S. Hydrographic Office," *Amer. Geogr. Soc., Journ.*, vol. 29 (1), pp. 160–167, New York, 1897; and George W. Littlehales: "Recent advances in geographic knowledge accomplished by the United States Hydrographic Office at Washington," *Amer. Geogr. Soc., Journ.*, vol. 30, pp. 124–126, New York, 1898.

230. For the records of these and related surveys see in *Records of the Hydrographic Office* (Record Group 37) in the National Archives.

231. *Op. cit.* [notes 228 and 229].

232. George Dewey: "Remarks on the coast of Lower California and Mexico," *U. S. Hydrographic Office, Publ.*, no. 56, pp. 1–60, Wash., 1874.

233. For reference to these and other surveys see *op. cit.* [note 221].

234. There is a substantial literature on this subject. For a general contemporary review by a participant see Daniel Ammen: *American Isthmian canal routes*, Philadelphia, Pa., 1889, 33 pp.; and his "Interoceanic ship canal across the American isthmus. The proposed interoceanic ship canal between Greytown and Brito, . . . ," *Amer. Geogr. Soc., Journ.*, vol. 3, pp. 142–162, New York, 1878; W. I. Chambers: "Notes on the Nicaraguan ship canal," *U. S. Naval Institute, Proc.*, vol. 11, (35), pp. 807–814, Annapolis, 1885, Frederick Collins: "The Isthmus of Darien and the valley of the Atrato . . . ," *U. S. Naval Institute, Proc.*, vol. 1 (6), pp. 123–148, Annapolis, 1874; J. W. Miller: "The Nicaragua survey," *U. S. Naval Institute, Proc.*, and C. H. Stockton: "The American interoceanic canal," *U. S. Naval Institute, Proc.*, vol. 25 (92), pp. 753–797, Annapolis, 1899.

235. For an excellent brief résumé of this history and especially of extant official cartographic records see James B. Rhoads: "Cartographic records of the Panama Canal," *National Archives Preliminary Inventory*, no. 91, pp. 1–72, Wash., D. C., 1956.

236. Thomas O. Selfridge: *Reports of explorations and surveys to ascertain the practicability of a ship-canal between the Atlantic and Pacific Oceans by the way of the isthmus of Darien*, Wash., 1874, 268 pp. For a discussion of this subject see in his *Memoirs of Thomas Selfridge, Jr., rear admiral, U. S. N.*, New York, 1924, 288 pp.

237. U. S. Navy Department: ". . . Reports of explorations and surveys for the location of interoceanic ship-canals through the Isthmus of Panama and by the Valley of the River Napipi, by U. S. Naval expeditions, 1875," *U. S. 45th Congr., 3rd Sess., Senate Exec. Doc.*, no. 75, pp. 1–124, Wash., 1879.

238. U. S. Navy Department: ". . . Reports of explorations and surveys for the location of a ship-canal between the Atlantic and Pacific oceans, through Nicaragua, 1872–73 . . . ," *U. S. 43rd Congr., 1st Sess., Senate Exec. Doc.*, no. 57, pp. 1–143, Wash., 1874.

239. Nearly all of these records are in the National Archives, *op. cit.* [notes 225, 227, and 228].

240. *Op. cit.* [note 220]. See also "Oceanography and the Hydrographic Office," *Sea Frontiers*, vol. 3 (1), pp. 38–47, Coral Gables, Fla., 1957.

241. See for example George E. Belknap: "Concerning deep sea sounding," *Asiatic Soc. Japan, Trans.*, vol. 2, pp. 182–195, Yokohama, Japan, 1874; George E. Belknap: "The depths of the Pacific off the east coast of Japan, with a comparison of other oceanic depths," *Asiatic Soc. Japan, Trans.*, vol. 19 (1), pp. 1–15, Tokyo, 1891; Thomas F. Gaskell: *Under the deep oceans; twentieth century voyages of discovery*, London, 1960, 239 pp.; Theodore F. Jewell: "[Lecture upon] deep sea soundings," *U. S. Naval Institute, Papers*, vol. 4 (3), pp. 37–63, Annapolis, Md., 1877; and U. S. Engineer School: "The history and development of sounding . . . ," *U. S. A. Engineer School. Occas. Papers*, no. 73, pp. 1–92, Wash., D. C., 1941. For bibliographic references see Mary C. Grier (comp.): ". . . References on the physical oceanography of the western Pacific ocean . . . ," *U. S. Hydrographic Office, Publ.*, no. 238, pp. 1–174, Wash., D. C., 1946; Mary C. Grier (comp.): "Oceanography of the north Pacific ocean, Bering sea, and Bering strait; a contribution toward a bibliography," *Univ. of Wash., Libr. Series*, vol. 2, pp. 1–290, Seattle, 1941; and Giovanni Magrini and Others (eds.): *Bibliographia Oceanographica*, vols. 1–22, Venice, 1928–1954.

242. "Cable soundings in the Pacific [by the USS *Albatross* and USS *Thetis*]," *Geogr. Journ.*, vol. 1, p. 463, London, 1893; *Telegraphic cable between the United States and the Hawaiian Islands. Report of the results of the survey . . .*, Wash., 1892; and Zera L. Tanner: "Cable surveys from California to the Hawaiian Islands, 1891–1892," *Geogr. Soc. Pacific, Trans. and Proc.*, vol. 3, pp. 63–83, San Francisco, 1892.

243. This cruise of the *Tuscarora* was the first in which steel wire was used on a deep-sea sounding expedition. Thomson's invention had not been installed on the *Challenger* for use during that ship's renowned British exploration in 1872–1876, because it was considered untested, and earlier uses of steel wire for sounding had not been satisfactory. The *Tuscarora* was so equipped largely because

of the interest of Commodore Daniel C. Ammen, Chief of the Bureau of Navigation. He was confident that wire could be used successfully, thereby avoiding some of the difficulties in the use of hemp line. The sheer bulk of several thousand fathoms of hemp line was a serious problem aboard ship. Moreover, the figures obtained for deep soundings were considered unreliable because the great weight of 2000 or more fathoms of hemp line made it difficult, if not impossible, to determine when the lead touched bottom. See Daniel C. Ammen: "Report of the Chief of the Bureau of Navigation" in the *Annual Rept. Secy. Navy for 1873*, Wash., D. C., 1874, p. 78; Henry Cummings (comp.): *A synopsis of the cruise of the U. S. S. "Tuscarora" from the date of her commission to her arrival in San Francisco, Cal., Sept. 2d, 1874*, San Francisco, 1874, 61 pp.; George E. Belknap: "Deep-sea soundings in the North Pacific ocean, obtained in the United States Steamer Tuscarora," *U. S. Hydrographic Office, Publ.*, no. 54, pp. 1–54, Wash., 1874; and "Les grandes sondes de l'océan Pacifique nord," *Annales Hydrographiques, Series 1*, vol. 38, pp. 69–85, Paris, 1875. For the "Tracing of track chart of line of deep sea soundings from San Francisco Cal., to Honolulu, H. I., run by U. S. S. 'Tuscarora,' November 1874," manuscript map on cloth, see File 272.27.2 and for related profile see File 272.27-1 in *Records of the Hydrographic Office* (Record Group 37) in the National Archives.

244. For the cartographic and other scientific records see in the *Records of the Hydrographic Office* (Record Group 37) in the National Archives.

245. Albert S. Barker: *Deep-sea sounding. A brief account of the work done by the U. S. S. Enterprise in deep-sea sounding during 1883–1886*, New York, 1892, 133 pp.

246. James M. Flint: *A contribution to the oceanography of the Pacific; compiled from data collected by the United States steamer "Nero" while engaged in the survey of a route for a trans-Pacific cable*, Wash., 1905, 62 pp.

247. Thomas H. Streets: "A study of the Phronimidae of the North Pacific Surveying Expedition [1873–1874]," *U. S. National Mus., Proc.*, vol. 5, pp. 3–9, Wash., 1883.

248. Pierre L. Jouy: "Ornithological notes on collections made in Japan from June to December, 1882," *U. S. National Mus., Proc.*, vol. 6, pp. 273–318, Wash., 1884; and Thomas H. Streets: "Contributions to the natural history of the Hawaiian and Fanning Islands and Lower California, made in connection with the United States North Pacific Surveying Expedition, 1873–75," *U. S. National Mus., Bull.*, no. 7, pp. 1–172, Wash., 1877.

249. For references to the history of these activities see especially U. S. Coast Survey: *Annual report of the Superintendent of the Coast Survey showing the progress of the work for the fiscal year ending 1860/61—June 1877*, vols. 1–18, Wash., 1861–1880; and U. S. Coast and Geodetic Survey: *Report of the superintendent . . . 1878–1899*, vols. 1–22, Wash., 1881–1900. See also the official files of the Superintendent in the *Records of the Coast and Geodetic Survey* (Record Group 23) in the National Archives.

250. *The United States Coast and Geodetic Survey: products and functions*, Wash., D. C., 1957, 41 pp.; and . . . *The work of the Coast and Geodetic Survey*, Wash., 1905, 67 pp.

251. *Ibid.*, and the U. S. Coast and Geodetic Survey: *Annual reports . . . , op. cit.* [note 249]. See especially the "Appendices" and "Reports."

252. *Ibid.*

253. The best source of information on these publications by the U. S. Coast and Geodetic Survey are its *General index of professional and scientific papers contained in the United States Coast Survey reports from 1851 to 1870*, Wash., 1874, 17 pp.; *Catalogue of charts, coast pilots, and tide tables . . .*, vols. 1–14, Wash., 1866–1900; and "Bibliography. Descriptive catalogue of publications relating to the U. S. Coast and Geodetic Survey, 1807 to 1809," in its *Annual report . . . for 1891, Appendix no. 11*, pp. 365–478, Wash., 1892.

254. *Op. cit.* [note 199].

255. For an excellent series of maps of Alaska and vicinity for the period ca. 1790–1900 see "U. S. Alaskan Boundary, Convention of 1903. Alaskan Boundary Tribunal, Maps and Charts," in *Records of Boundary and Claims Commissions and Arbitrations* (Record Group 76) in the National Archives in Wash., D. C.

256. U. S. Coast and Geodetic Survey: *Annual report, op. cit.* [note 249].

257. For a brief history of the exploration of this area see William W. Woollen: *The inside passage to Alaska, 1792–1920, with an account of the North Pacific coast from Cape Mendocino to Cook inlet, from the accounts left by Vancouver and other early explorers, and from the author's journals of exploration and travel in that region*, Cleveland, Ohio, 1924, 2 vols.

258. For bibliographic references to exploration of Alaska see Katherine B. Judson: *Subject index to the history of the Pacific northwest and of Alaska as found in the United States government documents, . . . 1789–1881*, Olympia, Wash., 1913, 341 pp.; and James Wickersham: *. . . A bibliography of Alaskan literature, 1724–1924; . . .*, Cordova, Alaska, 1927, 635 pp. For a history of scientific exploration see

William H. Dall: *Scientific results of exploration of Alaska under the charge of W. H. Doll during the years 1865–1874*, Wash., 1876; James A. James: ". . . The first scientific exploration of Russian America and the purchase of Alaska," *Northwestern Univ. Studies Soc. Sci.*, no. 4, pp. 1–276, Evanston, Ill., 1942; and especially Morgan B. Sherwood: *Exploration of Alaska*, New Haven, Conn., 1965, 207 pp.

259. An excellent collection of reports of these explorations is in U. S. Congress. Senate: "Compilation of narratives of explorations in Alaska [1869–1899]," *U. S. 56th Congr., 1st. Sess., Senate Rept.*, no. 1023, pp. 3–856, Wash., D. C., 1900. See also Henry Allen: ". . . Report of an expedition to the Copper, Tananá, and Koyukuk rivers in the territory of Alaska, in the year 1883, . . . ," *U. S. 49th Congr. 2nd Sess., Senate Exec.* doc. 125, pp. 1–172, Wash., 1887; Edwin F. Glenn and William R. Abercrombie: . . . *Reports of explorations in the territory of Alaska, . . .*, 1898, Wash., 1899, 464 pp.; and Frederick Schwatka: ". . . Report of a military reconnaissance in Alaska made in 1883," *U. S. 48th Congr. 2nd Sess., Senate Exec.*, doc. 2, pp. 1–121, Wash., 1885.

260. For example see Lucien McS. Turner: "Contributions to the natural history of Alaska. Results of investigations made chiefly in the Yukon district and the Aleutian islands, conducted under the auspices of the Signal Service, U. S. Army, extending from May 1874 to August 1881," *U. S. Signal Office, Arctic Series of Publications*, no. 2, pp. 1–226, Wash., 1886.

261. For publications about the west coast of North America by the Geological Survey see its *Publications of the Geological Survey, 1879–1961*, Wash., D. C., 1961, 457 pp.; and . . . *Maps and descriptions of routes of exploration in Alaska in 1898, with special information concerning the territory*, Wash., D. C., 1899, 138 pp. and maps.

262. For the official records such as correspondence, logs, and scientific reports, especially of the *Albatross*, 1881–1900, see in the "General Records of the Bureau of Fisheries" in the *Records of the Fish and Wildlife Service* (Record Group 22) in the National Archives. See also G. Paul Goode: "The first decade of the United States Fish Commission; its plan of work and accomplished results, scientific and economical," *Rept. of the Commission of Fish and Fisheries, for the year 1800*, pp. 53–62, Wash., 1883; and *Report of the United States Commissioner of Fish and Fisheries . . . 1871–1900*, Wash., 1872–1901.

263. Joel W. Hedgepeth: "The United States Fish Commission steamer 'Albatross,' " *Amer. Neptune*, vol. 5, pp. 5–26, Salem, Mass., 1945.

264. For examples of the scientific publications on the results of these surveys see Richard Rathbun: "Summary of the fishery investigations conducted in the north Pacific Ocean and Bering Sea from July 1, 1888 to July 1, 1892, by the . . . Albatross," *U. S. Fish Commission, Bull.*, no. 13, pp. 127–201, Wash., 1894; and Zera L. Tanner: "Record of hydrographic sounding and dredging stations occupied by the steamer Albatross in 1886," *U. S. Fish Commission Bulletin for 1886*, pp. 277–285, Wash., 1887.

265. For example see Spencer F. Baird: "List of expeditions and other sources from which the specimens in the Government Museum have been mainly derived," *Annual report . . . 1867*, pp. 76–78, Wash., 1868.

266. See in *Annual report of the Board of Regents of the Smithsonian Institution, showing the operations, expenditures, and conditions of the institution for the year . . .* , Washington, 1861–1899. For serial publications of the Smithsonian see its *Bulletin of the United States National Museum*, vol. 1–49, Wash., 1875–1899; *Proceedings of the United States National Museum*, vol. 1–21, Wash., 1878–1899; *Smithsonian Contributions to Knowledge*, vol. 1–26, Wash., 1847–1899; *Smithsonian Miscellaneous Collections*, vol. 1–41, Wash., 1862–1899; and the *Contributions from the U. S. National Herbarium*, vol. 1–5, Wash., 1890–1899 (prior to 1903 this was a publication of the U. S. Department of Agriculture).

Chapter 14
GEOGRAPHICAL EXPLORATION IN THE TWENTIETH CENTURY

1. John A. Fleming: "The relation of earth physics to geographical progress," *U. S. Dept. State, Conferences Series*, no. 28, pp. 338–346, Wash., D. C., 1937. For general bibliographic sources see Thomas A. Bender, Jr. and Charles S. Vitale: *Selected bibliography of climatic maps of the western Pacific Ocean*, Wash., D. C., 1958, 28 pp.; Richard H. Fleming: "Review of the oceanography of the northern Pacific," *Wash. State Univ., Dept. Oceanography, Techn. Rept.*, no. 44, pp. 1–43, Seattle, Wash., 1955; Mary C. Grier (comp.): "Oceanography of the North Pacific Ocean, Bering Sea,

and Bering Strait: A contribution toward a bibliography," *Univ. Wash. Publ., Library Series*, vol. 2, pp. 1–290, Seattle, Wash., 1941; Mary C. Grier (comp.): ". . . References on the physical oceanography of the western Pacific Ocean " *U. S. Navy Dept., Hydrographic Off. Publ. 238*, pp. 1–174, Wash., D. C., 1946; Mark W. Pangborn, Jr.: "Bibliography of oceanographic publications," *U. S. Fed. Council Sci. and Techn., Interagency Comm. Oceanography*, ICO Pamphlet 9, pp. 1–23 Wash., D. C., 1963; Cuthbert M. Love: "Sources of oceanographic data for a portion of the North Pacific Ocean . . . Years: 1916–1954," *Wash. State Univ. Dept. Oceanography, Spec. Rept.*, no. 25, 21 pp., Seattle, Wash., 1956; John H. Roscoe: "Exploring Antarctica vicariously: a survey of recent literature," *Geogr. Rev.*, vol. 48 (3), pp. 406–427, New York, 1958; Richard D. Terry (comp.): "Bibliography of marine geology and oceanography, California coast," *Calif. Dept. Natural Resources, Div. Mines, Spec. Rept.*, 44, pp. 1–131, San Francisco, 1953; Esther E. Thompson (comp.): "Oceanography: a report bibliography (for 1953—Mar. 1963)," *U. S. Defense Doc. Center*, pp. 1–355, Arlington, Va., 1963; U. S. Joint Publications Research Service: "Soviet bibliography on oceanography," *Publ. no. 3438*, pp. 1–142, Wash., D. C., 1960; and particularly *Bibliographia oceanographica*, vol. 1–22, Venice, 1929–54.

There is a large and rapidly growing literature in the subject field. Among the many helpful recent references are Luis R. A. Capurro and others (comp.): "Oceanographic vessels of the world, . . . ," *Nat. Oceanographic Data Center, Publ. G-2* in NODC General Series, vol. 1, Wash., D. C., 1961; Richard Carrington: *A biography of the sea; the story of the world ocean, its animal and plant populations, and its influence on human history*, New York, 1961, 285 pp.; Robert C. Cowen: *Frontiers of the sea; the story of oceanographic exploration*, Garden City, N. Y., 1960, 307 pp.; Gifford C. Ewing: "Conference on the feasibility of conducting oceanographic explorations from aircraft, manned orbital and lunar laboratories, proceedings 24–28 August 1964, Woods Hole, Mass.," *Woods Hole, Mass., Oceanographic Inst., Ref.*, no. 65–10, pp. 1–469, Woods Hole, Mass., 1965; Charles J. Gravier: "Recent oceanographic researches," *Smiths. Inst. . . Ann. Rept., . . . 1914*, pp. 353–362, Wash., D. C., 1915; Muriel L. Guberlet: *Explorers of the sea; famous oceanographic expeditions*, New York, 1964, 226 pp.; Seabrook Hull: *The bountiful sea*, Englewood Cliffs, N. J., 1964, 340 pp.; Cuchlaine A. M. King: *Oceanography for geographers*, London, 1962, 337 pp.; Edward J. Long (ed.): *Ocean sciences*, Annapolis, Md., 1964, 304 pp.; Nat. Research Council, Comm. on Oceanography: "Economic benefits from oceadographic research, a special report," *Nat. Res. Council, Publ.* 1228, pp. 1–50, Wash., D. C., 1964; and Lionel A. Walford: *Living resources of the sea; opportunities for research and expansion*, New York, 1958, 321 pp.

2. W. S. Wooster: "Recent oceanographic exploration in the north and equatorial Pacific Ocean," *Eighth Pacific Sci. Congr. Manila, 1953, Proc.*, vol. 3, pp. 679–683, Quezon City, Philippines, 1957.

3. See John H. Paul: *The last cruise of the Carnegie*, Baltimore, 1932, 331 pp.

4. H. U. Sverdrup and others: ". . . Scientific results of cruise VII of the Carnegie during 1928–1929 under command of Captain J. P. Ault: "Observations and results in physical oceanography," *Carnegie Inst. Wash., Publ.* 545A, pp. 1–156, Wash., D. C., 1944, and *Publ.* 545B, pp. 1–315, Washington, 1945.

5. J. Lyman: "U. S. Navy contributions to the study of Pacific circulation," *Eighth Pacific Sci. Congr., Manila, 1953, Proc.*, vol. 3, pp. 609–612, Quezon City, 1957.

6. Uncertainty about the breadth of the current and the region to which previously given names applied made it necessary to consider the question of nomenclature in the light of the results of this survey and to draw a distinction between inshore and offshore components, consisting of (a) cool surface water close to the coast, termed the Peru Coastal Current; and, (b) the adjacent oceanic drift lying to the west, to which the suggested name Peru Oceanic Current was applied. Since both currents composed the eastern limb of the anticyclonic circulation of the eastern Pacific, and as no sharp boundary was found to exist between them, they were jointly referred to by the name Peru Current.

7. E. R. Gunther: "A report on oceanographical investigations in the Peru Coastal Current," *Discovery Reports*, vol. 13, pp. 107–276, Cambridge, Engl., 1936.

8. Public Information Division, U. S. Coast Guard Headquarters, Washington 1964, *Release* no. 59–64.

9. Clifford A. Barnes and T. G. Thompson: ". . . Physical and chemical investigations in Bering Sea and portions of the North Pacific Ocean," *Univ. Wash., Publ. Oceanography*, vol. 3 (2), pp. 35–79 and appendix pp. 1–164, Seattle, 1938.

10. U. S. Coast Guard: "Oceanographic cruise USCGC Northwind, Bering and Chukchi seas, July–Sept. 1962," *Oceanographic Rept.*, no. 1, CG 373–1, pp. 1–104, Washington 1964.

11. Koji Hidaka: ". . . Advancement in Pacific oceanography since 1920," *Tenth Pacific Sci. Congr. Honolulu, 1961, Proc.*, pp. 327–339, Honolulu, 1963.

12. D. Shoji and K. Suda: "On the variation of the Kuroshio near the Japan Islands," *Eighth Pacific Sci. Congr., Manila, 1953, Proc.*, vol. 3, pp. 619–636, Quezon City, Philippines, 1957.

13. Herbert W. Graham: "A contribution to the oceanography of the Sulu sea," *Seventh Pacific Sci. Congr., Auckland and Christchurch, N. Z., 1949, Proc.*, vol. 3, pp. 225–266, Wellington, 1952.

14. K. Wyrtki: "Physical oceanography of the southeast Asian waters," *NAGA Rept.*, vol. 2, pp. 1–195, La Jolla, Calif., 1961.

15. Koji Hidaka: *op. cit.* [note 11]. Australian and New Zealand fisheries and oceanographic investigations are reported in the *Australian Journal of Marine and Freshwater Research*, by the Commonwealth Scientific and Industrial Research Organization, Melbourne, 1950–65.

16. University of California, Scripps Institution of Oceanography: *Oceanic observations of the Pacific pre-1949 through 1955*, Berkeley, 1957–1963, 5 vols. Reference is to pp. 7–9 of the vol. for 1949; E. D. Stroup and T. S. Austin: "Review of the oceanographic programs of the Pacific Oceanic Fishery Investigations," *Amer. Geophysical Union, Trans.*, vol. 36 (5), pp. 881–884, Washington, 1955.

17. W. S. Wooster: *op. cit.* [note 2].

18. Townsend Cromwell, R. B. Montgomery, and E. D. Stroup: "Equatorial undercurrent in Pacific Ocean revealed by new methods," *Science*, vol. 119 (3097), pp. 648–649, Washington, 1954.

19. Thomas S. Austin: "Oceanography of the east central equatorial Pacific as observed during Expedition Eastropic," *U. S. Fish & Wildlife Service, Fishery Bull.*, 168, pp. 257–282, Washington, 1960.

20. NORPAC Committee: *Oceanic observations of the Pacific, 1955: The NORPAC data*, Berkeley and Tokyo, 1960.

21. NORPAC Committee: *Oceanic observations of the Pacific, 1955: The NORPAC Atlas*, Berkeley and Tokyo, 1960.

22. Robert L. Fisher (ed.): "Preliminary report on Expedition Downwind . . . IGY cruise to the southwest Pacific," *Nat. Acad. Sci., IGY General Rept. Series*, no. 2, pp. 1–58, Wash., D. C., 1958.

23. Luis R. A. Capurro (comp.): "Oceanographic observations in the intertropical region of the world ocean during IGY and IGC. Part IIb. Pacific Ocean," *Agric. Mech. Coll., Texas, IGY Oceanographic Rept.*, no. 3, pp. 1–298, College Station, Texas.

24. Science Council of Japan: *The results of the Japanese Oceanographic Project for the International Geophysical Year 1957/1958*, Ueno Park, Japan, 1960.

25. V. G. Kort: "Scientific research of 'Vityaz' during IGY," *Internat'l Hydrogr. Rev.*, vol. 37 (2), pp. 137–141, Monaco, 1960.

26. K. M. Sirotov: "The study of variations in conditions of the ocean and atmosphere," *Okeanologiya*, vol. 1 (5), pp. 922–924, Moscow, 1961. For English translation see in *Deep-Sea Research*, vol. 10 (5), pp. 648–649, Oxford, Engl. and New York, 1963.

27. William A. Herdman: *Founders of oceanography and their work, an introduction to the science of the sea*, New York, 1923, 340 pp.

28. Reginald Spink (trans.): *The Galathea deep sea expedition, 1950–1952, described by members of the crew*, London and New York, 1956, 296 pp.

29. G. E. R. Deacon: "The Discovery investigations in the Southern Ocean," *Amer. Geophysical Union, Trans.*, vol. 36 (5), pp. 877–880, Washington, 1955.

30. Peter J. Schmidt: "Scientific explorations in the western part of the North Pacific in 1932," *Fifth Pacific Sci. Congr., Victoria-Vancouver, 1933, Proc.*, vol. 1, pp. 611–617, Toronto, 1934.

31. Lev A. Zenkevich: *Biology of the seas of the U. S. S. R.*, New York and London, 1963, 955 pp.; pages 675–841 treat the Far Eastern seas of the USSR.

32. M. E. Vinogradov: "Quantitative distribution of deep-sea plankton in the western Pacific and its relation to deep-water circulation," *Deep-Sea Research*, vol. 8 (3–4), pp. 251–258, Oxford, Engl. and New York, 1962.

33. O. E. Sette: "Pacific Oceanic Fishery Investigations," *Copeia*, no. 1, pp. 84–85, Pittsburgh, 1949; Descriptive reports on mid-Pacific oceanography by the Pacific Oceanic Fishery Investigations are published by the U. S. Fish and Wildlife Service, in its publication series entitled *Special Scientific Reports—Fisheries*.

34. Joseph L. Reid, Jr.: "Oceanography of the northeastern Pacific Ocean during the last ten years," *Univ. Calif., Scripps Inst. Oceanography, Contr., New Series, 1960*, pp. 543–556, La Jolla, Calif., 1961.

35. A. J. Dodimead, F. Favorite, and T. Hirano: *Review of oceanography of the subarctic Pacific region*, published by the International North Pacific Fisheries Commission. This publication summarizes oceanographic investigations in the Bering Sea and in the western, central, and eastern subarctic regions of the Pacific prior to 1955 and contains a more complete summary of individual cruises after 1955.

36. Canadian work in the northeast Pacific Ocean is described in the *Manuscript report series* and the *Annual reports* of the Pacific Oceanographic Group, a section of the Biological Station at Nanaimo, B. C., both of which are published by the Fisheries Research Board of Canada.

37. Articles by Y. K. Chau, C. S. Wong, C. Y. Chu, and F. D. Ommanney in Hong Kong University, *Fisheries Jour.*, no. 3, Hong Kong, April, 1960.

38. Maxwell S. Doty: "Algal productivity of the tropical Pacific as determined by isotope tracer techniques," *Botany Dept., Univ. Hawaii*, was prepared for the Environmental Studies Branch, Division of Biology and Medicine, U. S. Atomic Energy Commission, under Contract AT-(04-3)-15.

39. H. W. Menard: *Marine geology of the Pacific*, New York, 1964, 271 pp., p. 1. See also J. N. Carruthers: "The deepest oceanic sounding," *Nature*, vol. 169, pp. 601–603, London, 1952; and I. Littman: *Deeps of the ocean; a brief history of the discovery of the deepest known places in oceans*, Washington, 1938, 25 pp.

40. Robert H. Randall, Jr.: *United States surveys in the Pacific, 1900–1960, presented at the Tenth Pacific Science Congress Symposium on highlights of the history of scientific geographical exploration in relation to the development of the Pacific map*, Washington, 1961, 31 pp.

41. Full independence of the Philippines was granted in 1946.

42. E. A. Deily: "The Coast and Geodetic Survey in the Philippine Islands," *U. S. Coast and Geodetic Survey, Journ.*, no. 7, pp. 4–12, Washington, 1957.

43. Robert H. Randall, Jr.: *op. cit.* [note 40].

44. H. W. Menard: *op. cit.* [note 39], p. 2.

45. Harold W. Murray: "Submarine mountains in the Gulf of Alaska," *Geol. Soc. Amer., Bull.*, vol. 52 (3), pp. 333–362, Washington, 1941.

46. Koji Hidaka: *op. cit.* [note 11].

47. Robert H. Randall, Jr.: *op. cit.* [note 40].

48. Thomas W. Vaughan and others: *International aspects of oceanography; oceanographic data and provisions for oceanographic results*, Washington, 1937, 225 pp. See the section on "Charting of the bottom of the oceans; sounded and unsounded areas."

49. Harry H. Hess: "Drowned ancient islands of the Pacific Basin," *Amer. Journ. Sci.*, vol. 244, pp. 772–791, New Haven, Conn., 1946.

50. Edwin L. Hamilton: "Sunken islands of the Mid-Pacific Mountains," *Geol. Soc. Amer., Memoir* 64, pp. 1–97, New York, 1956; R. S. Dietz, H. W. Menard, and E. L. Hamilton: "Echograms of the Mid-Pacific Expedition," *Deep-Sea Research*, vol. 1, (4), pp. 258–272, Oxford, Engl. and New York, 1954.

51. Rhodes W. Fairbridge and Harris B. Stewart, Jr.: "Alexa Bank, a drowned atoll on the Melanesian Border Plateau," *Deep-Sea Research*, vol. 7 (2), pp. 100–116, Oxford, Engl. and New York, 1960.

52. W. M. Gibson: "Submarine topography in the Gulf of Alaska," *Geol. Soc. Amer., Bull.*, vol. 71 (7), pp. 1087–1108, New York, 1960.

53. Henry W. Menard and Robert S. Dietz: "Submarine geology of the Gulf of Alaska," *Geol. Soc. Amer., Bull.*, vol. 62 (10), pp. 1263–1286, New York, 1951; Henry W. Menard: "Deformation of the northeastern Pacific basin and the west coast of North America," *Geol. Soc. Amer., Bull.*, vol. 66 (9), pp. 1149–1198, New York, 1955.

54. J. M. Zeigler, W. D. Athearn, and H. Small: "Profiles across the Peru-Chile Trench," *Deep-Sea Research*, vol. 4 (4), pp. 238–249, Oxford, Engl. and New York, 1957. See also Robert L. Fisher: "On the sounding of trenches," *Deep-Sea Research*, vol. 2, pp. 48–58, Oxford, Engl. and New York, 1954; and Robert L. Fisher and Roger Revelle: "The trenches of the Pacific," *Sci. Amer.*, vol. 193 (5), pp. 36–41, New York, 1955.

55. Robert L. Fisher: "Middle America Trench: Topography and structure," *Geol. Soc. Amer., Bull.*, vol. 72 (5), pp. 703–720, New York, 1961.

56. G. S. Ritchie: "Sounding profiles between Fiji, Christmas and Tahiti Islands," *Deep-Sea Research*, vol. 5 (2), pp. 162–168, Oxford, Engl. and New York, 1958.

57. Robert H. Randall, Jr.: *op. cit.* [note 40].

58. A. P. Lisitzin and A. V. Zhivago: "Marine geological work of the Soviet Antarctic Expedition, 1955–1957," *Deep-Sea Research*, vol. 6 (2), pp. 77–87, Oxford, Engl. and New York, 1960.

59. Roger R. Revelle: "Marine bottom samples collected in the Pacific Ocean by the *Carnegie* on its seventh cruise," *Carnegie Inst. Wash., Publ.* 556, Oceanography II (1), pp. 1–182, Washington, 1944.

60. Alexander Agassiz: "General sketch of the expedition of the 'Albatross,' from February to May, 1891," *Mus. Comparative Zoology, Bull.*, vol. 23, pp. 1–90, Cambridge, Mass., 1892–1893, p. 11.

61. Alexander Agassiz: "The islands and coral reefs of Fiji," *Mus. Comparative Zoology, Bull.*, vol. 33, pp. 1–167, Cambridge, Mass., 1899. See also G. S. Ritchie: *op. cit.* [note 56].

62. Alexander Agassiz and others: "Reports on the scientific results of the expedition to the tropical Pacific, in charge of Alexander Agassiz, by the U. S. Fish Commission steamer 'Albatross,' from August, 1899, to March, 1900, Commander Jefferson F. Moser, U.S.N., commanding," *Mus. Comparative Zoology, Memoirs*, vol. 26, pp. 1–343, Cambridge, Mass., 1902–1911. See also John Murray and G. V. Lee: "The depth and marine deposits of the Pacific," *Mus. Comparative Zoology, Memoirs*, vol. 38 (1), pp. 1–169, Cambridge, Mass., 1909.

63. Alexander Agassiz: "General report of the [Albatross] expedition [of October 1904–March 1905]," *Mus. Comparative Zoology, Memoirs*, vol. 33, pp. 1–73, Cambridge, Mass., 1906.

64. See discussion of Pacific cruises of non-magnetic research ship *Carnegie* in the section on Magnetic Field Measurements.

65. Roger R. Revelle: *op. cit.* [note 59].

66. C. S. Piggot: "Radium content of ocean-bottom sediments," *Carnegie Inst. Wash., Publ.* 556, Oceanography II (2), pp. 183–196, Washington, 1944.

67. E. Neaverson: "The sea-floor deposits, 1. General characters and distribution," *Discovery Reports*, vol. 9, pp. 295–349, Cambridge, Engl., 1934. See also Carl J. Shipek: "Photographic survey of sea floor on southwest slope of Eniwetok atoll," *Geol. Soc. Amer., Bull.*, vol. 73 (7), pp. 805–812, New York, 1962.

68. Philip H. Kuenen: "Collecting of the samples and some general aspects," *Snellius Expedition in the Eastern Part of the Netherlands East Indies, 1929–1930*, vol. 5 (3–1), pp. 1–46, Utrecht, 1943,

69. Bertil Kullenberg: "Deep-sea coring," *Reports of the Swedish Deep-Sea Expedition, 1947–1948*, vol. 4 (2), Göteborg, 1955.

70. S. Hanzawa: "Preliminary report on marine deposits from southwestern North Pacific Ocean," *Records of the Oceanographic Works*, vol. 1 (2), pp. 59–77, Tokyo, 1928.

71. Seiichi Skoji: "Study of deep-sea deposits of the southwestern part of the northern Pacific Ocean," *Tohoku Imperial Univ., Institute Geol. Paleontology, Contr.*, no. 29, Sendai, Japan. In Japanese with summary in English. For an English translation see United States Army Forces, Far East, Headquarters, Office of the Engineer, Engineer Intelligence Division: *Pacific Survey Repts.*, no. 150–60, Tokyo, 1956.

72. Hiroshio Niino and K. O. Emery: *Sediments of shallow portions of East China Sea and South China Sea*, Los Angeles, 1957, 58 pp.; Hirsoshi Niino: "Summary of the researches on the submarine configuration and bottom deposits of the neighbouring seas of Japan during 1939–1948," *Seventh Pacific Sci. Congr., Christchurch and Wellington, Proc.*, vol. 3, pp. 214–216, Wellington, 1952; F. Betz and H. H. Hess: "The floor of the North Pacific Ocean," *Geogr. Rev.*, vol. 32, pp. 99–116, New York, 1927; and B. P. Petetin: "The relief of the floor and the bottom deposits in the northwest Pacific," *UNESCO Symposium on Physical Oceanography, Proc.*, pp. 225–237, Tokyo, 1957; F. P. Shepard, Kenneth O. Emery, and H. R. Gould: "Distribution of sediments on east Asiatic Continental Shelf," *Allan Hancock Foundation, Publ., Occasional Paper*, no. 9, pp. 1–64, Los Angeles, 1949. This earlier work was primarily a compilation based on about 400,000 bottom notations on earlier Japanese, British, Dutch, and French charts but limited by differences in analysis and density of observations.

73. James G. Moore and Ronald K. Reed: "Pillow structures of submarine basalts east of Hawaii," *U. S. Geol. Survey, Prof. Paper* 475–B, pp. B153–B157, Washington, 1963.

74. R. Y. Morita and C. E. ZoBell: "Occurrence of bacteria in pelagic sediments collected during the Mid-Pacific Expedition," *Deep-Sea Research*, vol. 3 (1), pp. 66–73, Oxford, Engl. and New York, 1955.

75. H. Kuno, R. L. Fisher, and N. Nasu: "Rock fragments and pebbles dredged near Jimmu Seamount, northwestern Pacific," *Deep-Sea Research*, vol. 3 (2), pp. 126–133, Oxford, Engl., and New York, 1956.

76. R. Nayudu: "Volcanic ash deposits in the Gulf of Alaska and problems of correlation of deep-sea ash deposits," *Marine Geology*, vol. 1 (3), pp. 194–211, Amsterdam and New York, 1964.

77. A. P. Juze and E. Y. Koreneva: "On the paleogeography of the Sea of Okhotsk," *Acad. Sci. U.S.S.R., Bull., Geogr. Series*, no. 2, pp. 12–24, Moscow, 1959. In Russian. G. B. Udincev, I. G. Boishenko, V. F. Kanaev, and A. P. Lisitzin: "Geographical characteristics of the Sea of Bering. Topography and submarine deposits," *Institute of Oceanology, Trans.*, vol. 29, 1–188, Moscow, 1959.

78. Edward E. Horton and Others: "Preliminary drilling phase of Mohole Project," *Amer. Assoc. Petrol. Geol., Bull.*, vol. 45 (11), pp. 1789–1800, Tulsa, Okla., 1961. For a good general

account see Willard Bascom: *A hole in the bottom of the sea; the story of the Mohole project*, Garden City, N. Y., 1961, 352 pp.

79. Reference has been made to the unpublished official oceanographic cruise report of the U. S. Coast and Geodetic Survey Ship *Pioneer*, 1961, in the U. S. Coast and Geodetic Survey in Washington.

80. Alexander Agassiz: "The coral reefs of the tropical Pacific," *Mus. Comparative Zoology, Memoirs*, vol. 28, pp. 1–410, Cambridge, Mass., 1903.

81. C. M. Yonge: "Origin, organization and scope of the Expedition," *Great Barrier Reef Expedition, 1928–1929 Scientific Repts.*, vol. 1 (1), pp. 1–11, London, 1930–1940.

82. Philip H. Kuenen: "Geology of coral reefs," *The Snellius Expedition . . .* , vol. 5 (2), pp. 1–125, Utrecht, 1933.

83. Risaburo Tayama: "Coral reefs of the South Seas," *Japanese Hydrographic Office, Bull.*, vol. 11, Publ. no. 941, Tokyo, 1952.

84. Kenneth O. Emery, J. I. Tracey, Jr., and H. S. Ladd: "Geology of Bikini and nearby atolls," *U. S. Geol. Survey, Prof. Paper* 260–A, pp. 1–265, Washington, 1954.

85. Thomas B. Nolan and others: "Synopsis of geologic, hydrological, and topographic results . . . , Geological Survey research, 1962," *U. S. Geol. Survey, Prof. Paper* 450A, pp. A1–A257, Washington, 1964, p. A59.

86. F. R. Fosberg: "Northern Marshall Islands Expedition, 1951–1952, Narrative," *Atoll Research Bull.*, no. 38, pp. 1–37, Washington, 1955.

87. Investigations on coral reefs and atolls are reported in a series of publications entitled *Atoll Research Bulletin*, published by the Pacific Science Board of the Nat. Research Council, Washington. Between August 1951 (no. 1) and December 1965, 113 bulletins were published. *Bulletin* no. 100, pp. 11–16, includes a "List of Atoll Research Bulletins 1–100."; The *Pacific Science Board* of the Nat. Academy of Sciences—Nat. Research Council, Washington, was established in 1946 to aid American scientific investigations in the Pacific area, to advise governmental and other agencies on scientific matters pertaining to the Pacific, and to further international cooperation in the field of Pacific science. The work of the Board is described in the booklet *Ten years of Pacific Science Board field programs, 1947–1956*, Washington, 1957. For examples of the publications sponsored by the Board see especially *Atoll Research Bull.*, nos. 1–113, Washington, 1951–1955; *Coordinated Investigations of Micronesian Anthropology, 1947–1949 (CIMA), Final Repts.*, vols. 1–18, Cambridge, Mass., 1949–1951; *Scientific Investigations in the Ryukyu Islands (SIRI) Repts.*, nos. 1–8, Washington, 1952–1955; and Harold J. Coolidge (comp.): *Conservation in Micronesia; a report on two conferences held under the auspices of the Pacific Science Board, in Honolulu, T. H., and Washington, D. C., in April and May 1948*, Washington, 1948, 70 pp. For details of the activities of this important office in the Nat. Academy of Sciences—Nat. Research Council see the *Annual Reports of the Pacific Science Board*, 1947 to date.

88. A. Guilcher: "Present-time trends in the study of recent marine sediments and in marine physiography," *Marine Geology*, vol. 1 (1), p. 6, Amsterdam, 1964.

89. R. G. Mason: "Geophysical investigations of the sea floor," *Univ. Calif., Scripps Inst. Oceanography, Contr.*, New Series, 1960, pp. 623–644, La Jolla, Calif., 1961.

90. Henry H. Howe and L. Hurwitz: "Magnetic surveys," *U. S. Coast and Geod. Surv., Serial*, no. 718, pp. 1–21, Washington, 1956.

91. "Continuous magnetic work at fixed observatories was initiated by Gauss in 1832 at Göttingen to measure variations in declinations and horizontal intensity. With the assistance of Weber and Humboldt he aroused such interest that the survey was extended to magnetically unexplored regions through international cooperation soon after 1840, a number of observatories being established in widely separated parts of the world, and instruments for the precise determination of the three magnetic elements and their variations being designed." From John A. Fleming: "The distribution and need of additional magnetic observatories and secular-variation stations in the Pacific region," *Fifth Pacific Sci. Congr., Victoria-Vancouver, 1933, Proc.*, vol. 3, pp. 1675–1683, Toronto, 1934.

92. Annual or secular changes in the earth's magnetic field vary both in rate of change and region of occurrence. For this reason, magnetic charts must be prepared at frequent intervals and for a given date or period, referred to as an epoch. Most countries have agreed that isogonic charts showing declination shall be published at five-year intervals for epochs representing the years ending in "0" and "5," as for 1960.0, 1965.0, etc., and that charts for other elements shall be revised at ten-year intervals, as for 1955.0, 1965.0, etc.

93. Magnetic base stations on distant islands can be too far removed from foci of rapid secular

change to provide adequate data and stations on oceanic islands sometimes have the additional disadvantage of being subject to local magnetic disturbances which render the records difficult to interpret.

94. An. Belobrov: "Terrestrial magnetism" in *The Pacific—Russian Scientific Investigations*, pp. 92–94, Leningrad, 1926.

95. Sydney Chapman and Julius Bartels: *Geomagnetism*, Oxford, 1940, 2 vols.; see vol. 1, p. 67.

96. George W. Littlehales: "Forthcoming advances in the terrestrial magnetism of Antarctica," *Terrestrial Magn. and Atm. Electr., Journ.*, vol. 7, pp. 1–8, Baltimore, 1902.

97. Adolf Schmidt: "On the distribution of magnetic observatories over the globe," *Terrestrial Magn. and Atm. Electr., Journ.*, vol. 2, pp. 27–31, Cincinnati, 1897.

98. Editor: "3. Magnetic work in Japan," *Terrestrial Magn. and Atm. Electr., Journ.*, vol. 5, pp. 93–94, Baltimore, 1900.

99. C. Coleridge Farr: "The Christchurch magnetic observatory, New Zealand," *Terrestrial Magn. and Atm. Electr., Journ.*, vol. 8, pp. 9–10, Baltimore, 1903.

100. A. Nippoldt: "19. Magnetic observatory in Samoan Islands," *Terrestrial Magn. and Atm. Electr., Journ.*, vol. 6, p. 201, Baltimore, 1901.

101. E. R. Gunther: *op. cit.* [note 7].

102. Louis A. Bauer and John A. Fleming: "Appendix No. 5. The Magnetic observatories of the United States Coast and Geodetic Survey in operation on July 1, 1902," *Rept. Superintendent Coast and Geod. Surv. . . . June 30, 1902*, pp. 301–331, Washington, 1903.

103. Louis A. Bauer was appointed the first Director of the Department and was later succeeded by John A. Fleming. Both Bauer, who initiated the proposal for the Department, and Fleming were engaged in magnetic work with the U. S. Coast and Geodetic Survey prior to the establishment of the Department in 1904.

104. John A. Fleming: "Magnetic survey of the oceans," in Thomas W. Vaughan and others: *International aspects of oceanography; oceanographic data and provisions for oceanographic research*, pp. 50–56, Washington, 1937.

105. E. H. Vestine: "The survey of the geomagnetic field in space," *Amer. Geophysical Union, Trans.*, vol. 41 (1), pp. 4–21, Washington, 1960. (This reference is to p. 7 only.)

106. D. G. Knapp: "Arctic aspects of geomagnetism," *U. S. Navy Publ.*, no. OPNAV PO3–10, Washington, 1956.

107. Niels Arley: "Geomagnetic investigations" in Anton F. Bruun and others (eds.): *The Galathea Deep Sea Expedition, 1950–1952*, pp. 237–245, New York, 1956.

108. In addition to providing greater coverage in less time, aerial magnetic surveys, if flown at sufficient heights above the earth's surface, do not show the effects of the most localized magnetic disturbance. Hence, the magnetic picture from deeper magnetic horizons can be detected.

109. E. O. Schonstedt and H. R. Irons: "NOL vector airborne magnetometer type 2A," *Amer. Geophysical Union, Trans.*, vol. 36 (1), pp. 25–41, Washington, 1955.

110. H. D. Stockard and F. B. Woodcock: "A new magnetic survey aircraft for the United States Navy Hydrographic Office," *Int. Hydrogr. Rev.*, vol. 37 (2), pp. 117–122, Monaco, 1960.

111. U. S. Naval Oceanographic Office: "Geomagnetic survey information," *Brochure* no. 2, Washington, 1965.

112. Leroy R. Alldredge and others: "A magnetic profile around the world," *Geophysical Research, Journ.*, vol. 68 (12), pp. 3679–3692, Washington, 1963.

113. E. H. Vestine: *op. cit.* [note 105]. This reference is based on pp. 7–9 only.

114. E. C. Bullard and D. G. Mason: "The magnetic field over the oceans," in Maurice N. Hill (ed.): *The Sea . . .* , vol. 3, pp. 175–217, New York, 1963.

115. Donald G. Mason and Arthur D. Raff: "Magnetic survey off the west coast of North America, 32° N. Latitude to 42° N. Latitude," *Geol. Soc. Amer., Bull.*, 72 (8), pp. 1259–1265, New York, 1961; Arthur D. Raff and Donald D. Mason: "Magnetic survey off the west coast of North America, 40° N. Latitude to 52° N. Latitude," *Geol. Soc. Amer., Bull.*, vol. 72 (8), pp. 1267–1270, New York, 1961.

116. All towed magnetometer surveys refer to total magnetic field intensity, as there still is no means of making vector component measurements with a towed sensing head.

117. See especially the following *Technical Reports* of the U. S. Naval Oceanographic Office and its predecessor the U. S. Navy Hydrographic Office, Wash., D. C.: "Operation Deep Freeze 61, 1960–1961 marine geophysical investigations," TR-105, pp. 1–217, June 1962; "Operation Deep Freeze 62, 1961–1962, Marine geophysical investigations" TR-118, 1965; "A marine magnetic survey south of the Hawaiian Islands," TR-137, 1962; and "Marine magnetic surveys in the

northwest Pacific Ocean," TR-168, 1963; and *Informal Manuscript Report* "Marine magnetic profiles in the Pacific Ocean, 1961–1962," M-4-63, Washington, 1963.

118. M. M. Ivanov: "(The work of the nonmagnetic vessel Zarya in the Pacific ocean)," *Okeanologiya*, vol. 1 (5), pp. 920–922, Moscow, 1961. For an English translation see *Deep-Sea Research*, vol. 10 (5), pp. 645–647, Oxford, Engl. and New York, 1963.

119. James H. Nelson, Louis Hurwitz, and David G. Knapp: "Magnetism of the earth," *U. S. Coast and Geod. Surv., Publ.* no. 40–1, Washington, 1962.

120. Ernest H. Vestine: "Instruction manual on world magnetic survey," *Internat'l Assoc. Union Geod. Geophysics, Monogr.*, no. 11, pp. 1–11, Paris, 1961.

121. James P. Heppner: "The world magnetic survey," *Space Sci. Rev.*, vol. 2, pp. 315–354, Dordrecht, Netherlands, 1963.

122. The unit of measurement for gravity is the gal, so named in honor of Galileo. The milligal, or commonly used unit, is one thousandth of a gal, the microgal equals one millionth of a gal. One gal is exactly equal to an acceleration of one cm/sec^2.

123. Felix A. Vening-Meinesz: . . . *Gravity expeditions at sea, 1923–1930* . . . , Delft, 1932–1934, 2 vols. See vol. 1, *The expeditions, the computations and the results*. On a 1925 voyage of the Dutch submarine *K XI* from Holland to the Netherlands East Indies, gravity data were collected only to Alexandria, Egypt.

124. Felix A. Vening-Meinesz: *ibid.*, vol. 1.

125. Felix A. Vening-Meinesz: "The expeditions, the computations, and the results," . . . *Gravity measurements at sea, 1934–1939*, vol. 3, pp. 1–97, Delft, 1941.

126. M. Matuyama: "Measurements of gravity over the Nippon Trench on board the Imperial Japanese submarine RO-57, preliminary report," *Imperial Acad., Proc.*, vol. 10 (10), pp. 626–628, Tokyo, 1934. M. Matuyama: "Distribution of gravity of the Nippon Trench and related areas," *Imperial Acad., Proc.*, vol. 12 (4), pp. 93–95, Tokyo, 1936.

127. M. Talwani, J. L. Worzel, and Maurice Ewing: "Gravity anomalies and crustal section across the Tonga Trench," *Geophysical Research, Journ.*, vol. 66 (4), pp. 1265–1278, Washington, 1961.

128. G. J. Bruins (ed.): *Gravity expeditions, 1948–1958*, vol. 5, Delft, 1960.

129. Nearly every country engaged in precise gravity observations has its own base station whose value has been determined with special care relative to the absolute value at Potsdam, Germany. The absolute value of gravity at Potsdam has been determined by a long series of careful measurements over many years. See G. T. Rude and others: "Physics of the earth—II. The figure of the earth," *Nat. Research Council, Bull.*, no. 78, pp. 1–286, Washington, 1931.

130. G. P. Woollard: "World wide gravity measurements with a gravity meter," *Woods Hole Oceanographic Inst. Ref.*, no. 49–33, Woods Hole, Mass., 1949.

131. J. C. Harrison and others: "Gravity measurements in the northeastern Pacific Ocean," *Amer. Geophysical Union, Trans.*, vol. 38 (6), pp. 835–840, Washington, 1957.

132. An underwater gravity meter for use on the sea floor was also developed but its use was limited to relatively shallow depths.

133. The Lamont Geological Observatory, in cooperation with the United States Navy in the International Geophysical Year program, mounted a gravity meter on a gyro-stabilized platform aboard the U. S. S. *Compass Island*. For details see J. L. Worzel: "Continuous gravity measurements on a surface ship with the Graf Sea Gravimeter," *Geophysical Research, Journ.*, vol. 64 (9), pp. 1299–1315, Washington, 1959.; A. Brunel: "Gravity acceleration measurements at sea by gravity meters," *Int. Hydrogr. Rev.*, vol. 37 (2), pp. 153–159, Monaco, 1960.

134. J. C. Harrison: "Tests of the La Coste-Romberg surface-ship gravity meter I," *Geophysical Research, Journ.*, vol. 64 (11), pp. 1875–1881, Washington, 1959.

135. J. L. Worzel and J. C. Harrison: "Gravity at sea," in Maurice N. Hill (ed.): *The Sea* . . . , vol. 3, pp. 134–174, New York, 1963.

136. Information provided by the U. S. Naval Oceanographic Office, Washington.

137. Hyman Orlin: *Gravity meter observations aboard a surface vessel and their geodetic applications*, Washington, 1962, 141 pp. F. R. Gossett: "Geodetic operations in the United States and in other areas through international cooperation," *U. S. Coast and Geod. Surv., Publ.*, 60–3, Washington, 1963.

138. J. L. Worzel and J. C. Harrison: *op. cit.* [note 135], pp. 148–150.

139. Frederick E. Romberg: "Exploration geophysics: A review," *Geol. Soc. Amer., Bull.*, vol. 72 (6), pp. 882–932, New York, 1961.

140. R. M. Field: "Report of the committee on geophysical and geological study of ocean basins," *Amer. Geophysical Union, Trans.*, vol. 14, p. 13, Washington, 1933.

141. R. M. Field: "Report of special committee on geophysical and geological study of oceanic basins," *Amer. Geophysical Union, Trans.*, vol. 17, pp. 8–9, Washington, 1936.

142. Maurice Ewing, G. P. Woollard, A. C. Vine, and J. L. Worzel: "Recent results in submarine geophysics." *Geol. Soc. Amer., Bull.*, vol. 57 (10), pp. 909–934, New York, 1946.

143. J. I. Ewing: "Elementary theory of seismic refraction and seismic reflection measurements," in Maurice N. Hill (ed.): *The Sea . . .*, vol. 3, pp. 3–19, New York, 1963.; G. G. Shor, Jr.: "Refraction and reflection techniques and procedure," in Maurice N. Hill (ed.): *The Sea . . .*, vol. 3, pp. 20–38, New York, 1963.

144. Waloddi Weibull: "Sound explorations," *Report of the Swedish Deep-Sea Expedition, 1947–1948*, vol. 4 (1), pp. 1–31, Göteborg, Sweden, 1955.

145. The uss *EPCE(R) 857* and rv *Horizon* were used on the Mid-Pacific Expedition and the rv *Horizon* and rv *Spencer F. Baird* on the Capricorn Expedition. The leader of both expeditions was Dr. Roger R. Revelle, Director of Scripps Institution of Oceanography at that time. R. W. Raitt: "Seismic-refraction studies of the Pacific Ocean Basin." *Geol. Soc. Amer., Bull.*, vol. 67 (12), pp. 1623–1640, New York, 1956.

146. Russell W. Raitt: "Seismic-refraction studies of Bikini and Kwajalein atolls and Sylvania Guyot," *U. S. Geol. Survey, Prof. Paper* 260-K, pp. 507–526, Washington, 1954.

147. R. W. Raitt, Robert L. Fisher, and R. G. Mason: "Tonga Trench," *Geol. Soc. Amer. Spec. Paper* 62, pp. 237–254, New York, 1955.

148. Maurice N. Hill: "Single-ship seismic refraction shooting," in his *The Sea . . .*, vol. 3, pp. 39–46, New York, 1963.

149. T. F. Gaskell, M. N. Hill, and J. C. Swallow: "Seismic measurements made by H.M.S. *Challenger* in the Atlantic, Pacific, and Indian oceans and in the Mediterranean Sea, 1950–53," *Philosophical Trans. Royal Soc., London, Sereies A*, no. 988, vol. 251, pp. 23–83, London, 1958.

150. George G. Shor, Jr., and Robert L. Fisher: "Middle America Trench: Seismic-refraction studies," *Geol. Soc. Amer., Bull.*, vol. 72 (5), pp. 721–730, New York, 1961.

151. George G. Shor, Jr.: "Reflexion studies in the eastern equatorial Pacific," *Deep-Sea Research*, vol. 5 (4), pp. 283–289, Oxford, Engl. and New York, 1959.

152. George G. Shor, Jr.: "Seismic refraction studies off the coast of Alaska: 1956–1957," *Seismological Soc. Amer., Bull.*, vol. 52 (1), pp. 37–57, Baltimore, 1962.

153. George G. Shor, Jr.: "Crustal structure of the Hawaiian Ridge near Gardner Pinnacles," *Seismological Soc. Amer., Bull.*, vol. 50, pp. 563–574, Baltimore, 1960.

154. Robert L. Fisher (ed.): *op. cit.* [note 22].

155. Thomas B. Nolan and others: "Geological Survey research, 1963," *U. S. Geol. Survey, Prof. Paper* 475A, pp. A1–A300, Washington, 1963, p. A134.

156. J. B. Hersey: "Continuous reflection profiling," in Maurice N. Hill (ed.): *The Sea . . .*, vol. 3, pp. 47–72, New York, 1963.

157. D. G. Moore: "Acoustic-reflection studies of the continental shelf and slope off Southern California," *Geol. Soc. Amer., Bull.*, vol. 71 (8), pp. 1121–1136, New York, 1960.

158. U. S. Dept. Commerce, Environmental Science Services Administration, Coast and Geodetic Survey: "Cruise narrative and scientific results," *International Indian Ocean Expedition, USC & GS Ship Pioneer—1964*, vol. 1, pp. 1–140, Washington, 1966. See especially Gilbert Corwin and Joshua I. Tracey, Jr.: "Marine geological investigations near the Palau Islands and Guam, Mariana Islands," pp. 81–90.

159. The vela uniform program is under the direction of the Vela Uniform Branch, Advanced Research Projects Agency, U. S. Department of Defense, Washington.

160. William A. Schneider, Patrick J. Farrell, and Ross E. Brannian: "Collection and analysis of Pacific ocean—bottom seismic data," *Geophysics*, vol. 29 (5), pp. 745–771, Tulas, Okla., 1964.

161. E. C. Bullard, A. E. Maxwell, and Roger Revelle: "Heat flow through the deep sea floor," in H. E. Landsberg (ed.): *Advances in Geophysics*, vol. 3, pp. 153–181, London, 1956. The first estimation of oceanic heat flow by measurements consisted of two probes in sediments of the central and western Pacific Ocean during the 1947 Swedish Deep-Sea Expedition of the *Albatross*. See Hans Pettersson: "Exploring the bed of the ocean," *Nature*, vol. 164 (4168), pp. 468–470, London, 1949.

162. W. H. K. Lee: "Heat flow data analysis," *Reviews of Geophysics*, vol. 1 (3), pp. 449–479, Richmond, Va., 1963.

163. E. C. Bullard and others: *op. cit.* [note 161], p. 166.

164. The following are references to publications reflecting these and related measurements: Richard P. Von Herzen: "Heat-flow values from the southeastern Pacific," *Nature*, vol. 183 (4665), pp. 882–883, London, 1959; Richard P. Von Herzen: "Geothermal heat flow in gulfs of California and Aden," *Science*, vol. 140 (no. 3572), pp. 1207–1208, Washington, 1963; R. P. Von Herzen and

S. Uyeda: "Heat flow through the eastern Pacific Ocean floor," *Geophysical Research, Journ.*, vol. 68 (14), pp. 1429–4250, Washington, 1963; S. Uyeda and others: "Heat-flow measurements over the Japan Trench," *Geophysical Research, Journ.*, vol. 67 (3), pp. 1186–1188, Washington, 1962; M. Yasui, K. Horai, Saburo Ueyda, and H. Akamatsu: "[Heat flow measurements in the western Pacific during JEDS-5 and other cruises in 1962 aboard M/S Ryofu-Maru]," *Oceanographical Mag.*, vol. 14 (2), pp. 147–156, 1963; T. D. Foster: Heat-flow measurements in the northeast Pacific and Bering Sea," *Geophysical Research, Journ.*, vol. 67 (7), pp. 2991–2993, Washington, 1962; Marcus G. Langseth, Paul J. Grim, and Maurice Ewing: "Heat-flow measurements in the east Pacific Ocean," *Geophysical Research, Journ.*, vol. 70 (2), pp. 367–380, Washington, 1965.

165. Richard P. Von Herzen and A. E. Maxwell: "Measurements of heat flow at the preliminary Mohole site off Mexico," *Geophysical Research, Journ.*, vol. 69 (4), pp. 741–748, Wash., D. C., 1964.

166. W. J. Hutchinson: "The growth of the vessel weather service of the Northeast Pacific Ocean," *Monthly Weather Rev.*, vol. 57 (8), pp. 334–336, Washington.

167. G. C. Whiting: "Ships' weather observations, Part 2, cooperative observations program development," *Mariner's Weather Log*, vol. 2 (2) and vol. 2 (6), Washington, 1958.

168. U. S. Navy, Chief of Naval Operations: "North Pacific Ocean," *Marine Climatic Atlas of the World*, vol. 2, *NAVAER 50-10-529*, Washington, 1956.; U. S. Navy, Chief of Naval Operations: "South Pacific Ocean," *Marine Climatic Atlas of the World*, vol. 5, *NAVAER 50-10-532*, Washington, 1959; U. S. Weather Bureau: *Atlas of climatic charts of the oceans*, Washington, 1938. This is an earlier atlas of climatological significance covering the Pacific Ocean region in part.

169. H. C. Summer: "New marine climatological exchange program adopted by WMO [World Meteorological Organization]," *Mariner's Weather Log*, vol. 7 (6), pp. 197–199, Washington, 1963.

170. Most of the exploring expeditions include with their published reports one or more maps based on field surveys. The principal expeditions may include with their published results an atlas or folio of maps. The published and unpublished scientific results generally are used by map and chart-mapping agencies in the compilation of topographic and hydrographic maps.

171. For an excellent reference to maps of the Pacific Basin in the twentieth century prior to World War II see Clifford H. MacFadden: *A bibliography of Pacific area maps*, San Francisco, 1941, 107 pp. The following are catalogs and indexes to nautical charts and maps of the Pacific Basin published by the principal concerned nations: Canadian Hydrographic Service: *Catalogue of Canadian Hydrographic Service nautical charts* . . . , Ottawa, 1955, 47 pp.; Deutsches Hydrographisches Institut, Hamburg: *Verzeichnis der nautischen karten und bücher, 1963*, Hamburg, 1963, 102 pp.; Hydrographer of the [British] Navy: *Catalogue of Admiralty charts and other hydrographic publications, 1966*, London, 1966, 144 pp.; Hydrographic Branch: *New Zealand chart catalogue and index* . . . , Wellington, 1962, 30 pp.; Hydrographic Service, Royal Australian Navy: *Catalogue and index of Australian charts*, Sydney, 1962, 46 pp.; Lands and Survey Department, New Zealand: *Catalogue of maps*, Wellington, 1959–1965, in four sections; Maritime Safety Board, Japan: *Catalogue of charts and publications with aeronautical charts and publications*, Tokyo, 1960, 49 pp.; Service Hydrographique de la Marine: *Catalogue des cartes et ouvrages qui composent l'hydrographie française*, Paris, 1960–1962, 242+32 pp.; U. S. Coast and Geodetic Survey: *Nautical chart catalog of the Pacific Coast, Guam, and Samoa Island*, Washington, 1966, and *Catalog of Aeronautical charts and related publications*, Washington, 1966; U. S. Aeronautical Chart and Information Center: *USAF catalog of aeronautical charts and flight information publications*, St. Louis, Mo., 1964, variously paged by sections; U. S. Naval Oceanographic Office: *Catalog of nautical charts and publications*, Washington, 1964–1965, including "Introduction Part I," 1964, 14 pp. "Introduction Part 2" 1965, 47 pp.; "Region I Canada, . . . ," 1965, 10 pp.; "Region 2 Central and South America and Antarctica," 1965, 23 pp.; "Region 7 Australia and Indonesia," 1964, 13 pp.; "Region 8 Oceania," 1964, 11 pp.; and "Region 9 East Asia," 1965, 18 pp.; and U.S.S.R. Glavnoye Upravleniye Geodesi i Kartografi: *Karty i atlay katalog*, Moskva, 1957, 199 pp.

172. See *Rel' ef dna Tikhogo Okeana* (Submarine relief of the Pacific Ocean), Moskva, 1964. Compiled in the Institut of Oceanology, Academy of Sciences, USSR and GUGK, scale 1:10,000,000. In six sheets and multi-colored. Three insets include: 1. Routes of research expeditions, 2. Individual depths used for the compilation of the map, and 3. Routes of research ships which were operated during the IGY, 1957–1959. Examples of other sea-floor mapping projects at the Institut of Oceanology include the preparation of bottom sediment charts for the Pacific Ocean showing the distribution of iron and manganese; of nickel, copper, and cobalt; of planktonic and benthonic Foraminifera; and of radiolaria, pteropods, and coccoliths; as reported by Robert S. Dietz in his *Soviet Oceanography 1964: A Trip Report*, U. S. Dept. Commerce, Washington, April 1965, reprinted September 1965.

173. Attention should also be drawn to the important current publication by the U. S. Environmental Science Services Administration, Coast and Geodetic Survey, *Bathymetry of the Aleutian Arc*,

Alaska, Washington, 1966, which includes a series of six charts at a scale of 1:400,000 showing topography of the islands at a contour interval of 300 feet and bathymetry of the sea floor at an interval of 50 fathoms. See Chart no. 15,254 [*Bathymetric map of*] *the World*, Washington, 1961, compiled in the U. S. Naval Oceanographic Office, scale 1:12,233,000 at the equator. In twelve multi-colored sheets. Sheets (sections) 5, 6, 9, 10, and 11 pertain to and include the Pacific Basin.

174. R. S. Quackenbush, Jr., Arthur C. Lundahl, and E. Monsour: "Development of photo interpretation," in *Manual of Photographic Interpretation*, pp. 1–18, Washington, 1960.

175. For a good brief review of this subject and a discussion of the variant forms of maps and of the importance of aerial photography and recent satellite (SECOR) data in map-making see Robert C. Miller: "Mapping in the Pacific," *Amer. Congr. Surveying and Mapping, Journ.*, vol. 23 (4), pp. 551–561, Washington, 1963.

176. W. D. Lambert, Frank Schlesinger, and E. W. Brown: "The variation of latitude," *Nat. Research Council, Bull.*, no. 78, pp. 245–277, Washington, 1931, p. 250.

177. General historical accounts of geodetic operations are reported in the publication series of the U. S. Coast and Geodetic Survey entitled *Geodetic operations in the United States and in other areas through international cooperation*, Washington, 1900–to date.

178. Information about Pacific occultation, Hiran, and SECOR operations was provided by the Department of the Army, Office of the Chief of Engineers. For additional information about the use of artificial Earth satellites for making geodetic surveys over long distances (such as the SECOR system) see Frank L. Culley: "Electronic trispheration—a method by three-dimensional geodesy," *Amer. Geophysical Union, Trans.*, vol. 47 (1), pp. 223–229, Washington, 1966. See also the brief mention in Robert C. Miller: *op. cit.* [note 175], p. 560.

179. This summary of Pacific Loran coverage was provided by the Aids to Navigation Division of the Coast Guard Headquarters, U. S. Treasury Department, Washington, in 1965.

Chapter 15

THE INTELLECTUAL ASSUMPTIONS AND CONSEQUENCES OF GEOGRAPHICAL EXPLORATION IN THE PACIFIC

1. Wilcomb E. Washburn: "Japan on early European maps," *Pacific Hist. Rev.*, vol. 21 (3), pp. 221–236, Berkeley, Calif., 1952, p. 232.

2. *Ibid.*, pp. 221–236. For a discussion of the meaning of some of the terms used in the Age of Discovery, see Wilcomb E. Washburn: "The meaning of 'discovery' in the fifteenth and sixteenth centuries," *Amer. Hist. Rev.*, vol. 68 (1), pp. 1–21, Washington, 1962.

3. John C. Beaglehole: *The exploration of the Pacific*, London, 1947, 410 pp., p. 45; and Otis W. Freeman (ed.): *Geography of the Pacific*, New York, 1951, 573 pp., p. 64.

4. John B. Brebner: *The explorers of North America, 1492–1806*, New York, 1933, 502 pp., pp. 28–31.

5. For comments on the role of the Moslems in relation to Western expansion into Asia and the Pacific, see George F. Hourani: *Arab seafaring in the Indian Ocean in ancient and early medieval times*, Princeton, N. J., 1951, 131 pp., and the discussion of "Early Progress in the East" in Chapter 2 of the present volume, by Norman J. W. Thrower. See also John K. Wright: ". . . The geographical lore of the time of the crusades; a study in the history of medieval science and tradition in western Europe," *Amer. Geogr. Soc., Res. Ser.*, no. 15, pp. 1–563, New York, 1925, and an unabridged and corrected republication in 1965 by Dover Publications, Inc., Chapter III, "The contribution of the Moslems," pp. 77–87. See also Donald F. Lach: *Asia in the making of Europe*, Chicago, 1965, 2 vols., vol. 1, *The century of discovery*, 492 pp., *passim*. Lach's important work was not available during the initial period of preparation of this paper, though it has been used in the process of revising it. See also George Masselman: *The cradle of colonialism*, New Haven, Conn., 1963, 534 pp., *passim*; Kalidas Nag: *Discovery of Asia*, Calcutta, 1957, 789 pp., pp. 58–59, and the several works of Charles R. Boxer and Réné Grousset.

6. George Sansom: *The Western world and Japan, a study in the interaction of European and Asiatic cultures*, New York, 1950, 504 pp., pp. 74–75; Charles R. Boxer: *Race relations in the Portuguese colonial empire, 1415–1825*, Oxford, 1963, 136 pp.

7. Donald F. Lach: *op. cit.* [note 5] vol. 1, pp. 318–319.

8. Louis J. Gallagher (trans.): *China in the sixteenth century: the journals of Matthew Ricci,*

1583–1610; . . . , New York, 1953, 616 pp., especially p. xx of translator's preface; and Vincent Cronin: *The wise man from the West*, London, 1955, 300 pp., especially pp. 117 and 176–177.

9. J. S. Cummins (ed.): "The travels and controversies of Friar Navarrete, 1618–1686," *Hakly Soc. Works, Second Series*, vols. 118–119, Cambridge, 1962, vol. 118, p. 15.

10. *Ibid.*, vol. 118, pp. xxix, xxxii, and xxxiv.

11. George B. Sansom: *op. cit.* [note 6] pp. 110–113.

12. The pertinent lectures of Vitoria, prima professor of theology at the University of Salamanca who died in 1546, are translated and printed in James B. Scott: *The Spanish origin of international law. vol. 1. Francisco de Vitoria and his law of nations*, Oxford, 1934. I do not agree with some of the interpretations placed upon Vitoria's work and would qualify considerably the praise that has been extended to it.

13. John C. Beaglehole: *op. cit.* [note 3] pp. 169–194; and John C. Beaglehole: "The place of Tasman's voyage in history" in *Able Janszoon Tasman & the discovery of New Zealand*, Wellington, 1942, 66 pp.

14. George B. Sansom: *op. cit.* [note 6] *passim;* Charles R. Boxer: *The Christian century in Japan, 1549–1650*, Berkeley, Calif., 1951, 535 pp.; and his *Jan Compagnie in Japan, 1600–1850; an essay on the cultural, artistic and scientific influence exercised by the Hollanders in Japan from the seventeenth to the nineteenth centuries*, the Hague, 1950, 198 pp.

15. Quoted in John A. Harrison: *Japan's northern frontier; a preliminary study in colonization and expansion, with special reference to the relations of Japan and Russia*, Gainesville, Fla., 1953, 202 pp., p. 150.

16. *Ibid.*, pp. 11–28. See also George A. Lensen: *The Russian push toward Japan* . . . , Princeton, 1959.

17. Samuel E. Morison (ed.): *William Bradford: Of Plymouth Plantation*, New York, 1959, p. 79n., and map on p. 91. The misconception, based in part on Verrazano's optimistic reports of the close proximity of the Pacific to the Atlantic, is graphically portrayed in the Virginia Farrer Map of Virginia, published in London in 1651 (see Plate 38).

18. Francis Parkman: *LaSalle and the discovery of the great West*, Boston, 1898, 483 pp., p. 4.

19. *Ibid., p. 29.*

20. Earlier and later French editions of the polar map of Buache omit the traced route from Portugal to Japan. It was published in David Henry (ed.): *An historical account of all the voyages round the world, performed by English navigators;* . . . , London, 1773–1774, 4 vols.

21. Henry R. Wagner: *The cartography of the northwest coast of America to the year 1800*, Berkeley, 1937, 2 vols., vol. 1, pp. 53, 57, 113–114, and *passim;* Lawrence C. Wroth: "The early cartography of the Pacific," *Bibliographical Soc. Amer., Papers*, vol. 38 (2), pp. 87–268, New York, 1944, p. 155, and *passim;* George E. Nunn: *Origin of the Strait of Anian concept*, Philadelphia, 1929, 36 pp. The uncertainties surrounding the geography of the region prior to Bering's discoveries are evident in Engelbert Kaempfer: *The history of Japan, together with a description of the kingdom of Siam, 1690–1692*, Glasgow, 1906, 3 vols, vol. 1, pp. 106–112.

22. Tryggvi J. Oleson: *Early voyages and northern approaches, 1000–1632*, Toronto, 1963, 211 pp., pp. 121 and 147. See also Wilcomb E. Washburn: *op. cit.* [note 2].

23. Betty J. Meggers, Clifford Evans, and Emilio Estrada: *Early formative period of coastal Ecuador: the Valdivia and Machalilla phases*, Smithsonian Contributions to Anthropology, vol. I, 234 pp. and 196 plates. Smithsonian Institution, Washington, 1965.

24. John H. Parry: *The age of reconnaissance*, Cleveland, 1963, 364 pp.; Part I for developments in the period 1450–1650. The assumption that the scientific exploration of the Pacific in the eighteenth century overcame narrow nationalist motives is challenged by A. Hunter Dupree: "Nationalism and science, Sir Joseph Banks and the wars with France," in David H. Pinkney (ed.): *A festschrift for Frederick B. Artz*, pp. 37–51, Durham, N. C., 1964, who concludes (p. 42) that if ". . . *Terra Australis* had materialized as another North America, a great war for empire would doubtless have been fought over it." See also John Dunmore: *French explorers in the Pacific* . . . , Oxford, 1965, 365 pp.

25. Michel E. de Montaigne: "Of coaches (*ca.* 1585–1588)" in *Complete works: essays, travel journal, letters, trans.* by Donald M. Frame, Stanford, 1957, 1093 pp., Book III, Chapter 6, especially pp. 693–695; and Jean-Jacques Rousseau: *Discourse upon the origin and foundation of the inequality among mankind, 1755*, published in London in the English translation in 1761, especially pp. 114–118 and note, pp. 252–256.

26. Bernard W. Smith: *European vision and the South Pacific, 1768–1850; a study in the history of art and ideas*, Oxford, 1960, 287 pp., p. 15; and John C. Beaglehole (ed.): *The journals of Captain James Cook on his voyages of discovery* . . . , vol. 1, *The voyage of the 'Endeavour,' 1768–1771*, Cambridge, 1955, and vol. II, *The voyage of the 'Resolution' and 'Adventure' 1772–1775*, Cambridge, 1961. The

promised vol. IV will contain a series of essays on particular aspects of Cook's life and achievement and on the scientific results of the voyages.

27. Bernard W. Smith: *ibid.*, p. 6.

28. *Ibid.*,Preface, pp. 4–5.

29. William Hodges: *Travels in India, during the years 1780, 1781, 1782 and 1783*, London, 1793, 157 pp., see Ch. IV, "Dissertation on the Hindoo, Moorish, and Gothic Architecture," pp. 59–77. Hodges is perceptively discussed by Bernard W. Smith: *op. cit.* [note 26] pp. 54 and 67–69.

30. Quoted in Bernard W. Smith: *ibid.*, pp. 151–152.

31. *Ibid.*, pp. 155 and 235.

32. Gilles Boucher de La Richarderie: *Bibliothèque universelle des voyages ...*, Paris, 1808, 6 vols., introduction p. v.

33. Percy G. Adams: *Travelers and travel liars, 1660–1880*, Berkeley, 1962, 292 pp., p. 224.

34. William H. Bonner: *Captain William Dampier, buccaneer—author, . . . some account of a modest buccaneer and of English travel literature in the early eighteenth century*, Stanford, 1934, 234 pp., pp. 1–2.

35. John N. L. Baker: *The history of geography; papers*, New York, 1963, 266 pp., especially chapter X, "The geography of Daniel Defoe," and chapter XI, "Geography in the essays of Elia;" and Christopher Lloyd: *Pacific horizons, the exploration of the Pacific before Captain Cook*, London, 1946, 188 pp., pp. 105–118.

36. Worthington C. Ford: *The isle of Pines, 1668; an essay in bibliography*, Boston, 1920, 116 pp.

37. Philip C. Ritterbush: *Overtures to biology; the speculations of eighteenth-century naturalists*, New Haven, 1964, 287 pp., p. 62.

38. An excellent review of the historical and anthropological literature concerning the island peoples of the Pacific is contained in William P. Morrell: *Britain in the Pacific Islands*, Oxford, 1960, 454 pp., pp. 1–11. A discussion of the anthropological questions raised by the discoveries and a guide to further literature is available in A. Irving Hallowell: "The history of anthropology as an anthropological problem," *History of Behavoiral Sciences, Journ.*, vol. 1, pp. 24–38, Jan. 1965.

INDEX

A

Abe-no-Hirafu, 97
Abreu, Antonio de, 145
Abstract logs (M. F. Maury), 56
Academy Atlas (Russian), 178–180
Academy of Sciences (U.S.S.R.), 200
Acapulco Trench Expedition, 314, 315
Accidental movement of Pacific peoples, 70
Actaeon (ship), 254
Adventure (ship), 253, 258
Adzes, 70, 83
Aerial photographic surveys, 317
Afrikaansche Galei (ship), 165
Aguja de marear, Spanish mariner's compass, 111
Aids in exploration, 317–320
Ainu, 97, 99, 326
A. I. Voyeikov (ship), 296
Alaska
  reached by Pushkarev, 182
  Russian-American Company exploration of, 198
  Tebenkov's atlas of, 199
Aleutian Islands
  discovery by Vitus Bering, 180
  map of, by P. Zaikov, 183–184
  promyshlenniki cruises to, 183
Alexeev, Fedot, 170
Allen, Joseph, 262
Almost barrier reef, 8
Altura, 27
Alvarado, Fernando de, 122
Alvarado, Pedro de, 127
Alvares, Jorges, first Portuguese to China, 149
American Geographical Society of New York, 278
  role in exploration, 291
American Guano Company, 286
American Philosophical Society, its role in Wilkes' expedition, 265
American whalers, in the Pacific, 107, 261, 262
America (ship), 198
Amerinds, contacts with Polynesians, 86
Amsterdam (ship), 160, 161
Amur River, explored by Mamiya Rinzo, 102, 103
Amurskiy Liman, survey by G. I. Nevelsky, 197, 198
Ancestral migration routes, 60, 61
Andagoya, Pascual de, 123
Andesite Line, 3, 4
Angelis, Girolamo de, S. J.
  first European traveler in Ezo, 97
  map and report, 97
Annawan (ship), 263, 264
Anson, George, 237

Antarctica
  exploration urged by M. F. Maury, 273
  Wilkes' exploration of, 265, 268
Antarctic continent
  Cook's voyage to, 241
  discovery, 196–197
    by John Davis, 261
    by Bellinsgausen and Lazarev, 195–196
  exploration by Dumont d'Urville, 219–220
  exploration urged by M. F. Maury, 273
  Wilkes' chart of, 268
Antarctic Peninsula, cruise of *Hero* to, 261
Antarctic seas, visited by Polynesians, 64
Antiquera, Juan, 142
Antipodes, 41
Antiscorbutics, Spanish work on, 144
Antoikoi, 41
Anville, Jean B. B. d', map of North Pacific, 100
Aotearoa, isolation of, 83–84
Apron reef, 8
Arabs
  astonomy of, 23
  early trade with Canton, 145
  geography of, 23
  in New Guinea, 62
  to Australia, 61
  voyages of, 25
Arab geographers, 26
Arab voyages to China, 22
Aranzazú (ship), 141
Arago, Jacques Étienne V., 214, 215
Arai, Hakuseki
  description of Ryukyu, 106
  geography of northern Japan, 100
  first geography of Ezo, 99
Arellano, Alonso de, 129, 130
Arend (ship), 165
Aristarchus of Samos, proposed heliocentric theory, 21
Aristotle, encyclopedic works, 19
Arnhem (ship), 158
Arnhem Landers
  geographical knowledge of, 61
Arriola, Andrés de, 131
Arrowsmith, Aaron, 190
Arteaga, Ignacio, 140
Arte de navegar . . . , by Pedro de Medina, 28
Asia, northeastern
  maps, 175
  surveys by Ivan F. Kruzenshtern, 187
Astrolabe, 25, 31
  navigational instrument, 21
  Spanish use of, 111
Astronomical circle, 209
Astronomical observations, 20, 53, 196, 197
Astronomical systems, of Micronesians, 67, 73

Kruzenshtern, Ivan F., 186–190
  atlas by, 187
  doubted insularity of Sakhalin, 102
  exploration of northwestern Pacific, 186, 178
  his *Atlas de l'océan Pacifique*, 190
  published account of voyage, 186, 187, 190
  scientific observations, 187, 190
  surveys of Japan, 186, 187
  track of voyage, 188–189
  voyage of 1803–1806, 186–190
Kuril Islands, exploration of, 99, 101, 102, 108, 178, 179
Kuroshio (current), 108

L

Labillardière, Jacques Julien de, 208
  study of Tongans, 208
La Boudeuse (ship), 202
La Boussole (ship), 206, 207
La Casuarina (ship), 213
Lachlan (ship), 301
La Cosa, Juan de, map of Asia, 46
Ladrillero, Juan, 127
Lady Washington (ship), 257, 258
La Favorita (ship), 140
Lamont Geological Observatory, 311, 315
Lángara y Huarte, Cayetano de, 139
La Pérouse, Jean F. de Galaup de, 186, 187, 206
  and insularity of Sakhalin, 102
  search for, by D'Entrecasteaux, 207
  site of his wreck, 218
  track of voyage, 206–207
La Princesa (ship), 132, 140
La Recherche (ship), 208
Lasso, Bartolomeu, his sea charts, 50
L'Astrolabe (ship), 206, 215, 219
Lateen sail
  in Europe, 26
  in Mediterranean, 23
  use by Arabs, 23
  use by Polynesians, 23
Lateral drift, in voyaging, 66
Latitude
  accuracy of measurement, 48
  determination, 32
  error in Spanish measurement, 111
  Spanish observations at sea, 111, 144
Latitude sailing, 67
Laugerie, Forgeais de, 201
Lazarev, M. P., 194–197
La Zélée (ship), 219
Lead sheathing of ships, by Spaniards, 144
Ledyard, John, 256, 257
Leeuwin (ship), 160
Legazpi, Miguel López de, 47, 129–131
Le Géographe (ship), 209
Le Maire, Isaac, 155
Le Maire, Jacob, 138
  route in Pacific, 163
  search for Terra Australis, 156
  voyage, 51, 155–157

Le Maire Strait, 156
Le Naturaliste (ship), 209
Lenz, E., 191–193
Le Solide (ship), 207
L'Espérance (ship), 208
Lesson, Pierre-Adolphe, 215
Lesueur, Charles-Alexandre, 214
L'Étoile, 202
Levashov, M. D., 183
Lewis and Clark Expedition, 259
Lexington (ship), 275
Leza, Gaspar González de, 137
L'Héroine (ship), 219
Liefde (ship), 166
Limmen (ship), 163
Línea meridiana, a Spanish primary meridian, 112
Linschoten, Jan Huyghen van
  his *Itinerario*, 50, 166
  in Portuguese Indies, 50
  quoted, 157, 168
  sailing routes, 150
Linschoten Vereeniging, 151
L'Isle Joseph Nicolas de, 180
Lisyanski, Y. F., 186–190
  explorations in North Pacific, 190
  publication of his book and atlas, 190
  scientific observations of, 190
Log, 32
  mechanical form, 37
  Spanish *corredera*, 111
  Spanish use of, 110
Lok, Michael, prints map of Drake's voyage, 232
London Missionary Society, 248, 252
Longitude
  Board of, 34–36
  determination, 30, 33, 144, 160
  determination by Galileo, 33
  determination unresolved, 32
  errors on maps, 48
  finding at sea, 30, 40
  lack of accuracy, 111, 175
  precise determination, 112
Los Reyes (ship), 132, 133
Los Tres Reyes Magos (ship), 136
Low islands, 7–10
Loyolo, Ignatius, 324
Lozier, Bouvet de, 201
Lull, Edward P., 289
Lunar distances, Spanish measurement of, 111
Lunar tables, of Tobias Mayer, 36
Lütke, Fedor P.
  atlas of Bering Sea, 194
  atlas of Caroline Islands, 194
  discovers western part of equatorial counter-current, 194
  expedition discussed, 193–194
  track of expedition, Fig. 29
Lyceum of Natural History of New York, receives collections of specimens, 264

M